The American Imagination at Work

THE AMERICAN

IMAGINATION AT WORK

Tall Tales and Folk Tales

Edited by BEN C · CLOUGH

Police Court judge to voluble drunk: Is this true?

Drunk: Well, judge, it's kinda true.

NEW YORK:

ALFRED · A · KNOPF

1947

A WORD OF THANKS

It is impossible to thank all the people who have aided in the choice (or rejection) of material for this book. Many friends, over a period of years, have unknowingly helped the editor by their response to the telling or reading of some of these tales.

Special thanks are due to the editorial staff of Alfred A. Knopf, Inc., particularly to Milton A. Rugoff, who conceived the general idea of this collection, to Wilson Follett, who suggested that I should edit it, and to Bernard Smith.

Invaluable help has been given by the staff members of the John Hay Library at Brown University, the Providence Athenaeum, the John Carter Brown Library (Providence), and the Providence Public Library. I have also profited by research at the Boston Public Library, the New York Public Library, and the Widener Library at Harvard University, in all of which institutions I received courteous and intelligent assistance.

I am greatly indebted for information and encouragement to Samuel Hopkins Adams, Henry Beston, Esther W. Bates, Edith R. Blanchard, Ruth C. Coombs, Fred F. Flanagan, Beatrice Herford (Mrs. Sydney W. Hayward), Henry B. Van Hoesen, I. J. Kapstein, Susan Bacon Keith, Robert W. Kenny, Susanna A. Matteson, Elizabeth Riley, Charles Alexander Robinson, Jr., Winfield T. Scott, Randall Stewart, and Lawrence C. Wroth.

Ben C. Clough

CONTENTS

vii

Contents

Contents

Contents

INTRODUCTION

THIS BOOK tells of strange things that have happened, and strange peo
ple that have flourished, and only slightly stranger ones that have been
invented and described and embroidered upon in these United States.
It is perforce selective rather than inclusive. It omits not only Mexico
and Canada, but also many a twice- or thrice-told tale—perhaps your
favorite. Here, at all events, is the great American story-teller, with
generous samples of the great American story, true, false, and (often to
excellent effect) on the border-line between fact and fancy. Where versions vary, and they usually do, the one here selected is, in my judgment, best. But what is "best"? Veracity is, in story-telling, somewhat
beside the point; diction is not the sole touchstone, certainly, nor is
arrangement. I have preferred among variants that version in which
the teller was most thoroughly identified with the tale, seemed most
fully to believe it, or let himself go with most abandon. This criterion
admits, of course, both the naïve and the sophisticated; it also admits
stories in which these extremes meet. They confront each other starkly
at the end of Mark Twain's Jumping Frog story,[1] as follows:

" 'Well, thish-yer Smiley had a yaller one-eyed cow that didn't have
no tail, only just a short stump like a bannaner, and—'

"However, lacking both time and inclination, I did not wait to hear
about the afflicted cow, but took my leave."

Simon Wheeler, the speaker, is naïvely garrulous, and Mark Twain,
the interlocutor, is sophisticated—that is, he is an artist, and the point
of view that he displays in such a phrase as "the afflicted cow" would
be offensively supercilious were it not that every word of the story
shows a sympathetic delight in Wheeler's simplicity. Here, of course, is
a paradox, and lesser artists than Mark Twain often spoil a narrative
by giving away their consciousness of superiority, or by writing "down"
(with exaggerated dialect), or writing "up" for the sake of supposed
elegance. (Fortunately, at the present time folklore collectors are aware
of both these dangers and try to stand between the original narrator
and the new audience as little as possible.)

These yarns are arranged by types. There are history and pseudo-
history, "special providences" and Satanic powers, witches and ghosts,

---

[1] Mark Twain: *Sketches New and Old* (New York: Harper & Brothers; Author's
National Edition; copyright 1903 by Samuel L. Clemens), p. 32.

strange inventions and queer critters, oral tradition, transplanted book-lore, and artistic fantasy; danger and daring, and lies about these, real adventures and pipe dreams, explorers, mystery, murder, and myth; eccentrics and bad men. Nor is the literary tale wholly excluded, for the sailor who saw the sea-serpent and the writer who concocts weird goings-on in his study are of imagination all compact. Preference has naturally been given to the homely, folksy, and colloquial, but we may note in passing that even this particular flavor has been achieved (or preserved) often enough by a reporter with literary skill. The Jumping Frog story is sheer American folk-stuff, but Mark Twain's version of it [1] is sheer art; and Uncle Remus, though the offspring of Joel Chandler Harris, is not to be shrugged aside as a laboratory product.

Whether the narrators were artists or "just folks," America is and always has been a land of magnificent stories, both true and false. The early North American carved out his own destiny and at the same time created his own folklore. To him nothing, or little, seemed impossible. In later days the wild frontier produced the mighty boaster, and bold men begot bold myths. From the genuine Daniel Boones and Davy Crocketts of yesterday are descended, partly by oral legend, but more fully and variously by ephemeral journal, anecdotal almanac, and didactic pseudo-biography (such as Weems's *Life of Washington*), the mythical Boones and Crocketts that came to typify our frontier. Of vaguer ancestry but similar transmission are the John Henrys and Paul Bunyans of our day, who appeal in the same way to a primitive love of boast and brag, of the stupendous and the impossible. Today, too, the journalist, the folklorist, and the literary fabulist do more than their share not merely in keeping the myths alive, but in amplifying them indefinitely. Thus, though we are told, no doubt truly, of how the loggers relate Bunyan's exploits, examples of such narrative are strangely elusive, retreating like mirages before the would-be collector; at the same time, the "literary feller" multiplies tale upon tale of the mighty Paul, who thus becomes localized, generalized, exaggerated (if possible), and even served up for the nursery.

While the Bunyans are getting themselves into books, there are some signs of a reverse process, in virtue of which Tin Pan Alley contributes to the repertoire of the ballad-singing mountaineer, jokes old and new

---

[1] He did not invent the plot. See "Private History of the Jumping Frog Story," in *How to Tell a Story, and Other Essays* (New York: Harper & Brothers; Author's National Edition), pp. 121–2. He says: "I heard the story told by a man who was not telling it to his hearers as a thing new to them . . . none of the party was aware that a first-rate story had been told in a first-rate way." The essay goes on to marvel at the resemblances between the story and a Greek tale, but about this Mark Twain was mistaken. A Cambridge professor, A. C. Sidgwick, had paraphrased the American yarn to make an exercise for a textbook of Greek prose composition, and Mark Twain rather understandably failed to recognize his own Jim Smiley as the "Bœotian" of the textbook.

find their way from stage and radio into the popular legend from which a few of them originally came, and the fanciful, if synthetic product of Hollywood scenarists is adopted without much change by weavers of local lore. In the words of J. H. Plenn, a lively chronicler of Texas character,[1] "Al Capone and Legs Diamond and Baby Face are getting all mixed up with Sam Bass and Wild Bill Hickok and John Wesley Hardin and Jesse James. . . . Any day now it may be revealed that Donald Duck rode the Pony Express." American myths are manufactured in many workshops, with interchangeable parts, and free from restricting patents.

But why did Americans become the tellers *par excellence* of tall tales? It was partly, no doubt, because the New World was from the beginning a land of marvels, and its early explorers were little disposed to minimize these. Thorwald, the son of Eric the Red, was fatally wounded, in the year 1000, by a Uniped, or One-footer.[2] This was in Nova Scotia. Five centuries later Columbus learned from the Indians of Haiti that "far away" there were men with only one eye and others with dogs' noses, who were cannibals.[3] The explorers saw, in part, what they expected to see, and in this way and others the myths of the Old World tended to find their way into the New. What the Indians contributed in the way of wonders was almost negligible in comparison to what came from preconception and imagination.

Even the Puritan settlers of New England, whom unobservant writers have termed unimaginative, took a turn at myth-making, though it was pious credulousness rather than free play of fancy that led such men as Cotton Mather to chronicle wonder-working demons and two-headed snakes; of course it was mania, or little better, that led to the execution of the Salem "witches," but the records of the witchcraft trials abound in sheer folklore.

On the whole, the love of the marvelous in early New England had a pietistic core (or veneer, some would say), and found a sublimated expression in accounts of special providences—in the work, especially, of Increase Mather and of Edward Johnson. The latter worthy, when he had told of how Indians beheaded the heretical Anne Hutchinson, adds calmly: [4] "Yet was not this the first loud speaking hand of God against them" (that is, Anne's followers). Men like Edward Johnson

---

[1] J. H. Plenn: *Saddle in the Sky* (Indianapolis: Bobbs-Merrill Co.: 1940), p. 87.

[2] According to "The Saga of Eric the Red," *The Northmen, Columbus and Cabot* (Original Narratives of Early American History; New York: Charles Scribner's Sons; 1906), p. 40.

[3] Professor E. G. Bourne thinks Columbus got this impression from what the natives said because "of his strong preconceptions based on his reading of the book of Sir John Mandeville." Ibid., p. 138.

[4] *Wonderworking Providence of Sion's Savior in New England*, Book II, Chapter xii. Edited by J. J. Jameson (New York: Charles Scribner's Sons; 1910), p. 187.

did little enough to encourage plain, sober truthtelling. Their religiose yarns are unrecognized cousins of the tall tale, and gave birth, before the seventeenth century was over, to such delusions as appear in the story of *Lithobolia,* here reprinted from the London edition of 1678.

The eighteenth century was in this country, as elsewhere, an age of "enlightenment," or, to speak more plainly, of skepticism; it is this period that provides the fewest native tall stories, though there are some.[1] But the gift for romance was only dormant, and in the seventies and eighties the American Revolution gave birth to innumerable legends of daring, chiefly based on fact, but transcending the facts more and more as time went on. Crystallized in form in nineteenth-century schoolbooks and elsewhere, these were eventually bound to be attacked by iconoclastic critics. Of one collection of such tales (Lippard's *The Legends of the American Revolution,* Philadelphia, 1876), a recent critic [2] remarks that it consists of "wholly unreliable, but quite readable anecdotes which once were accepted as authentic fact." Yet sober history of the period gives ample record of brutal marauders and bold heroes, hairbreadth escapes, clever spies (some of them women), hapless prisoners, and consummate traitors. It must be confessed, however, that few contemporary chroniclers were as temperate as George Washington, who in 1780,[3] writing to Samuel Huntington of an unsuccessful attack by "Mad Anthony" Wayne on Bull's Ferry, concluded: "I have been thus particular lest the account of this affair should have reached Philadelphia much exaggerated, as is commonly the case upon such occasions." In a somewhat similar vein Thucydides had expressed a fear that "the absence of romance" might detract from the interest of his history. Wars, however, breed myths, and it is futile to hope that these can wholly be eliminated. Nor would the story-lover desire them to be.

In nineteenth-century America the war with the wilderness produced, perhaps, more marvelous tales than the War of 1812, the Civil War, and the Spanish-American War put together. The epic of exploration proceeded apace, and new folk-heroes arose. When Daniel Boone died in 1820, David Crockett was a man of thirty-four, and Kit Carson a boy of eleven. Crockett and Carson and their editors and imitators were articulate, and their contribution to America's chronicle is not

---

[1] Walter Blair: *Native American Humor* (New York: American Book Company; 1937), p. 6, mentions as notably exceptional for this period "Franklin's tales about prodigious American sheep and leaping whales, and some passages in the writings of Rev. Samuel Andrew Peters." One of Peters's fabrications will be found in this collection.

[2] Harry Emerson Wildes: *The Delaware* (New York: Farrar & Rinehart; 1940), p. 375.

[3] Bicentennial Commission Edition, *Writings of George Washington* (Washington: U. S. Government Printing Office; 1937), Vol. XIX, p. 262.

lost. But a thousand tales, told by a thousand campfires, must be un-known, for no Mark Twain was there to appropriate a rough jewel for polishing, no member of a Folklore Society sat by with notebook in hand. The stories were told and perished. A tantalizing passage in the *Recollections* of that estimable missionary Timothy Flint gives a glimpse of life on the Mississippi in the second decade of the nine-teenth century. It is worth transcribing here: [1]

I am sure it would seem tiresome repetition, if I were to attempt the detail of our pleasures, our "moving incidents," our "hairbreadth escapes," for we had them; and more than all, of our gratified curiosity. The most retired regions of Hindostan, or central Africa, could not have more keenly excited the sense of novelty and freshness. Every stopping-place opened upon us its little world of wonders. I had, as you know, travelled in the northern parts of the United States, and had seen the Indians of Canada and New York. But the Indians that we now saw, though perfectly resembling the former, in form and countenance, had, on closer examination, an untamed savageness of countenance, a panther-like expression, utterly unlike the tame and subdued countenance of the northern Indians. At first view, my family contemplated the Shawnee Indians too much as objects of terror, to receive much pleasure from the spectacle. But wild deer, frequently seen swimming the river, or scouring the bluffs above us, not only gratified curiosity, but gave us strong impressions of the character of the country we were visiting. When at night, after having surmounted the difficulties and dangers of the day, and after the point had been carefully considered, which of the hands had laboured most, been most efficient, or shown most courage and coolness, which had been most willing to swim on shore with the cordelle in his teeth, in short, which one had excelled in the points of a boatman's excellence,—and these points of precedence were often no easy matters to settle,—when mutual congratula-tions had passed round, that we had performed a good and a safe day's jour-ney, after they had had their rations, they would throw themselves at the foot of a tree. They then begin in turn to relate their adventures. Some of them had been to the upper world on the Missouri, a thousand leagues from the point we now occupied. Others had been above the falls of St. Anthony. Another had been in the Spanish country, through which he had penetrated by the almost interminable courses of the Arkansas and Red River. It will need no stretch of imagination to believe, that such trips, in such regions, among Indians and bears, and that non-descript race of men, Canadian and Spanish hunters, men in whose veins, perhaps, the blood of three races is mixed, must be fruitful in adventure. It would be incredible to any one who had not seen such men, and had full opportunities to become acquainted with their character, the hardihood and endurance of which they are capable. A hunt of months at the foot of the Rocky Mountains, at an immense distance from civilized man, without bread or salt, in constant dread of the Indians and white bears,—such is the lonely sojourn in the pathless deserts, in which these men patiently pursue their trapping, and contract a dexterity, a capacity to avail themselves of circumstances to circumvent the Indians and the game, an unshrinking spirit to suffer, almost beyond humanity. When one was wearied with his tale, another was instantly ready to renew the theme. Some-

---

[1] Timothy Flint: *Recollections of the Last Ten Years* (Boston: Cummings, Hilliard & Co.; 1826), pp. 93–4.

times we had details of their dusky loves; that no feature of romance might be wanting. These stories, told by boatmen stretched at the foot of a tree, just below which was the boat, and the wave of the Mississippi, and interlarded with the jargon of their peculiar phrase, or perhaps interrupted by the droll comment, or the incredulous questioning of the rest, had often to me no small degree of interest; and tricked out in the dress of modern description, would have made very tolerable romance.

The modern folklorist would be horrified at Flint's notion of improving the backwoodsman's language,[1] yet that sort of improvement was practiced justifiably, because subtly and skillfully, by such writers as Mark Twain and Joel Chandler Harris. Furthermore, although one of the most judicious critics in this field has rightly said [2] that Harris's Uncle Remus stories "are perhaps more properly literature than folklore," it is also true that Harris's version [3] of (for example) the tar-baby story seems right, just as Uncle Remus seems right. Nothing, of course, succeeds like success. "En he didn't hatter wait long, nudder" may or may not check with a scientific phonetic transcription of a known Negro dialect. Uncle Remus's talk sounds right, and that is enough.

There are, of course, many ways in which a story may (or may not) sound right. Kit Carson, in all his letters, appears phlegmatic, though he tells of thrilling Indian fights, but that is his style, and it sounds right; Ethan Allen sounds bombastic, but that is right for him.[4] Mark Twain declared [5] that he used seven different dialects in *Huckleberry Finn,* and "not in a haphazard fashion, or by guesswork." This explanation, he added, was made because "without it many readers would suppose that all these characters were trying to talk alike and not succeeding." Elsewhere [6] he speaks with some bitterness of the miners' dialect in Bret Harte's stories, "a dialect which no man

---

[1] Flint himself, judging by the words "tricked out" and "modern," seems to have realized that "improvement" could be overdone.

[2] B. A. Botkin: *A Treasury of American Folklore* (New York: Crown Publishers; 1944), p. 652.

[3] This word is used precisely. Aurelio M. Espinosa considers that he has identified two hundred and sixty-seven versions of this plot, which he thinks comes from India (not Africa). See *Journal of American Folklore,* Vol. LVI, pp. 31–7 (January-March, 1943).

[4] Right for him if he really said: "In the name of the Great Jehovah and of the Continental Congress." He says he did. Oral tradition has it, however, that his language was less polite. John Pell (*Ethan Allen;* Boston: Houghton Mifflin Co.; 1929; p. 85) thinks that Allen "shouted some such phrase as 'Come out of there, you damned old rat!'" and then, his authority being challenged, cried "In the name of the Great Jehovah and the Continental Congress!" Stewart Holbrook (*Ethan Allen;* New York: Macmillan Co.; 1940; p. 12) has it that Ethan said: "Come out of there, you sons of British bitches!" and later used the more dignified phrase. None of these three phrases, in the opinion of his biographers, sounds unlike Allen.

[5] Explanatory foreword to *Huckleberry Finn* (all editions).

[6] *Mark Twain in Eruption,* edited by Bernard De Voto (New York: Harper & Brothers; 1940), p. 263.

in heaven or earth had ever used until Harte invented it. With Harte it died." Yet the reading public dearly loved Harte's miners. The truth is that both Mark Twain and Bret Harte knew the miners thoroughly and liked them thoroughly, and though one wrote bluntly, the other sentimentally, this liking came out and carried over to their readers.

For the American story-audience, fortunately, is not hypercritical. The good reader, or listener, will gladly suspend disbelief if he can. The dialect may be wrong, the plot unlikely, the incidents impossible; no matter, if the narrative gift is there. As a matter of fact, a little impossibility has never seemed amiss in American narratives. It is likely that from the days of the *Mayflower's* adventurous trip to those of the hardly credible atomic bomb our romantic history has predisposed us toward fantastic fictions. This is true in folk-say and in book-say, nor does the fantasy diminish as the decades, the centuries, pass. Look upon Paul Bunyan and Pecos Bill; if anything, they even outdo the mighty men of earlier legend. Zora Hurston is no unworthy successor to Uncle Remus, nor need James Thurber defer to any earlier master of the grave magnificent lie. On a lower level, our weather stories, hunting stories, fish stories, impossible yarns, and sheer hoaxes go on. They go on at a lower level, yes, but they go on forever. The great American liar, as you will find him in these pages, is of no era, and of all; he is immortal.

BOOK I

AMERICAN BACKGROUND
AND AMERICAN MYTH

BOOK I

AMERICAN BACKGROUND

AND AMERICAN MYTH

AMERICAN BACKGROUND AND

AMERICAN MYTH: *Marvels, terrors, and travails of history, semihistory, and pseudo-history. The historian and the raconteur*

WHEN America was young, it was particularly hard for its settlers to see facts simply. Everything in England's new colonies was strange and new, even the weather. Everything, that is, except God and Satan. The early New Englanders knew them well and feared them almost equally. God-fearing and devil-fearing, they were otherwise credulous, and they found plenty to astound and alarm them; found plenty and imagined more. If our sober historians have erred through prejudice and through reliance on hearsay (as we shall presently see that they have), men like Captain John Smith and Cotton Mather, who certainly thought themselves historians, erred through sheer love of the marvelous, and the written tradition that they handed down was full of the wonderful, the terrible, and the exaggerated. These men cultivated the will to believe, and not in the religious sense only.

Oral tradition, from Maine to Mexico, from Florida to California, was to be wilder still. And rightly; our fireside talkers, for three centuries and more, have but half-heartedly pretended to be historians; they may say "I knew the man," or "You can see the very spot today," but this is only a gesture. They may strike a didactic or moral note, but that, though not necessarily insincere, is a gesture also—a bit of protective coloring, sometimes, under whose cover one may develop an edifying lie. Our story-tellers are prose-poets, though without much real message beyond the desire to entertain. Emancipated from fact, they do not scruple to make a good story a little better. In this, of course, they are eternally right.

Sober fact occupies but a secondary place in a collection such as this one, but in order to remind the reader at the outset that the line between history and fiction is tenuous and easily crossed, I have first of all pieced together an old and strange story in which serious American history is inextricably interwoven with the mischievous and sometimes ribald invention of American story-tellers and story-lovers, concocted and gaped at as they stood on the street-corners, sat in the taverns, or gathered at churches or town meetings or about the hearths of New England in 1802.

To this barely credible but quite accurate yarn of a corpse and a beaver hat have been added two pieces of sober historical writing that point the same moral. The first is by Charles Francis Adams (1835–1915), the historian, and traces the steps by which an incident in early American colonial history (1623) found its way, sadly altered, into English satirical poetry. The second, by Professor Allan Nevins, tells how Charles Francis Adams the diplomat (father of the historian) blundered by relying on circumstantial evidence, and drives a further lesson home by showing how this Adams's father—namely, President John Quincy Adams—because of certain prepossessions, proved unable to write accurately of Thomas Jefferson.

Such are some of the difficulties in the way of telling a straight factual narrative. The great American story-tellers have not let this worry them too much.

In America we often say: "What are the facts?" and "Let's look at the record." But the recorder's pen was often dipped in distilled prejudice. Our public men are for better (the "build-up") or for worse (the whispering campaign) subjected to this manifestation of original sin as they take their way into American history and simultaneously (if their characters be naturally picturesque) into American mythology.

As witness of all this (if any were needed) I here present a tale of a corpse and a beaver hat, nearly a century and a half after the event, from Rhode Island fact and fiction of the very beginning of the nineteenth century. Its mythology was enlarged by men on street-corners and grossly and merrily embroidered by the scurrilous press of that place and period; it has not deserved its present oblivion. I have followed its tantalizing trail through newspapers of 1802, through local histories, and through sundry historical tracts, but my chief reliance has been upon a rare pamphlet in my possession entitled: *"Report of the*

*Case John Dorrance against Arthur Fenner . . . carefully compiled
from NOTES correctly taken by several Gentlemen who were present
during the whole Course of the Trial. . . . Providence . . . Bennett
Wheeler . . . 1802."* Who were these anonymous Gentlemen? I cannot
say, but I am persuaded that John Dorrance and Bennett Wheeler were
chief among them.

The *United States Chronicle* for 1802 and the *Impartial Observer* for
the same year, both of Providence, have supplied me, as I strove to reconstruct the story, with many fragmentary tid-bits of wanton misinfor-
mation and richly ingenious malice. These were partisan journals, and
if a more partial paper than the *Impartial Observer* ever existed, I have
not seen it.

The corpse and the beaver hat

Five months after the death of George Washington, and ten years
after Rhode Island reluctantly entered the Federal Union, the two
capitals of that little state (Providence and Newport) were agog at a
story that, in view of the narrator and the persons of the narrative, was
tall indeed. Dr. Pardon Bowen, a leading physician of Providence, need-
ing a corpse for dissection, had obtained one from another leading citizen, Judge John Dorrance, and in return had bestowed upon the judge
a beaver hat. But the body had been stolen from a grave, it had been
most indecently handled, and some of the people who were privy to the
affair had been bribed to keep their mouths shut. This was the story;
the teller, Arthur Fenner, had been elected Governor of Rhode Island
in 1790 and annually thereafter, and was destined to continue in office
until 1805. He was impulsive, profane, shrewd, and enormously popular. He not only told the story of the corpse and the hat to all his friends,
but carried in his pocket a written copy, which he showed upon any
occasion or none to all who would read it, especially to members of the
Rhode Island legislature. One of these, Dr. Ezekiel Comstock, said that
he did not care to read the paper, and in fact never did so. If others were
as incurious, there is no record of the fact. Did Dr. Comstock doubt the
story? And what, anyhow, were the facts?

On the 11th or 12th of February in the year 1799 a homeless and destitute man wandered into the town of Scituate in Rhode Island. His
name and history are not known, and never will be, nor do we know
what residents of Scituate he met, if any. It was cold, and the ground
was covered with snow. Did he ask for shelter anywhere? This, too, we
cannot know, but we do know that somehow he procured a rope and

5

hanged himself. There were, naturally, no mourners, but the town officials bestirred themselves to the point of having a grave dug. One Gideon Austin dug the grave, and in it the corpse reposed briefly. Soon
after the burial two more strangers arrived in Scituate. They asked to
see the body, saying that they had heard of the suicide, and thought the
victim might be a missing acquaintance of theirs. The body was dug up
"immediately" at the order of accommodating town officials, but the
two strangers were apparently not satisfied. They said it was not the
person they were looking for, and took their departure; we hear no
more of them. The body was again buried.

At the second burial, which took place on the same day as the first,
a Saturday, a young man was observed looking on with some interest.
It was whispered that he came from Providence, some nine or ten
miles away. It is likely that he did, and that he was a medical student.
On the following day, a Sunday, two things are known to have happened. Some young medical students in Providence proposed to one
another the securing of the corpse, of which they had heard, for dissection. Later that day someone opened the unregarded grave in
Scituate; at least, on Monday it was seen to be empty, and sleigh-
tracks led away from it through the snow. Some citizens, suspicious
and indignant, according to their own account, and certainly curious,
followed these tracks all the way to Providence; they led into the yard
of a Dr. Dyer. Now, Dr. Dyer and his friend Dr. Pardon Bowen taught
anatomy to a number of young men, in a large room near Dr. Bowen's
known as the "Theatre," by which we may understand laboratory-
and-lecture room.

Here the story becomes clearer for a time. The body was in fact dissected by Dr. Pardon Bowen in the presence of the students, and
presumably the dissection was accompanied by explanatory discussion. This occupied several nights. In the meantime, however, a group
of Scituate citizens, including the amateur detectives who had followed
the sleigh-tracks, decided that something ought to be done. The more
they discussed the matter, the more it seemed to them that this something should be the payment—to them—of an indemnity. They felt
that they represented the conscience of Scituate, but they said (unfortunately without strict accuracy) that they represented the town.
They went to Providence. (Some of the party had already been there,
following the sleigh-tracks, and had even communicated their discovery to the Governor of the state.) In Providence they sought Judge
Dorrance, who was known to be Dr. Bowen's attorney. He was not at
home, and the self-appointed committee now went to Dr. Bowen. He
was also out, but next day they returned (from Scituate) and saw both
Judge Dorrance and Dr. Bowen. The latter gave them a short lecture
on the scientific value of dissection, but this being very ill received,

he asked them what they wanted. To this they had a ready answer; they thought the town should be "satisfied." Dr. Bowen had no difficulty in grasping their meaning, but thought it well that a further conference should take place at Hoyle's tavern, a more or less convivial resort at some distance from the doctor's house and "shop."

In this conference the men from Scituate finally decided that forty dollars, plus an agreement to see the body properly buried, would meet the demands of justice. Dr. Bowen agreed, and a remarkable paper was drawn up. (It is full of "Know all men" and "Whereas" and "persons unknown," but the editor's legal friends look blank when he asks them to name it. Perhaps it should be called a guarantee; certainly it is a receipt.) Five of the Scituate men signed their names to this paper, and the sixth made his mark, "the twentieth day of February, A.D. 1799." Although Dr. Bowen and Judge Dorrance did *not* sign this legal curiosity, it guarantees (just how?) that they, Bowen and Dorrance, will see that the "abovesd" body is buried "Deacently."

Dr. Bowen felt that Judge Dorrance had better define the term "Deacently"; the judge did so, and the good doctor turned over the next procedure to some of his students, who cannot at any point in this history be said to have been wanting in zeal. They knew themselves to be involved in an awkward business, and they were at pains to procure a coffin, which the admiring joiner later declared was "worth more than two dollars." Two dollars or no, this third burial of the unfortunate stranger was not very effective, for, considering that the letter of the contract had been fulfilled, the students returned that night (without Dr. Bowen's knowledge, needless to say) and dug him up again. They later said that they had a right to do this, as the body had been purchased of "the mob that came from Scituate, at such an extravagant price." This price, they said, was sixty or seventy dollars; the story was growing.

The corpse, though frozen, was by now in poor condition, but it was further dissected. The bones were removed, and the entrails; a certain Dr. Cleveland articulated the bones into a skeleton; later he moved away from Providence and took his skeleton with him. (What became of it? It may be extant, for all that anyone can say to the contrary.) Whether a fourth burial took place, or could take place, it is not now possible to say. The entrails were buried under the floor of a shop; and Dr. Cleveland does not appear to have been communicative about the antecedents of his skeleton. But the deceased was to haunt all concerned. Gossip, led by the Governor, who was already declaring that the man had never been buried, now spread throughout Rhode Island and into Connecticut.

Thus much for the corpse; what of the beaver hat? That is another story, almost.

7

Three years before the unfortunate stranger strayed into Scituate, Dr. Pardon Bowen, whose health was not then of the best, planned a trip to Europe. In 1797 he was actually about to embark when he was stricken with yellow fever, then prevalent in Providence. His chances of recovery not seeming very good, he sent for Judge Dorrance to make his will. At this time the epidemic had produced a degree of panic, and nobody was any too willing to visit a patient, but Judge Dorrance was courageous; he sat beside the patient, made notes, and drew up a will. Dr. Bowen recovered, but he never forgot the incident, and often consulted Judge Dorrance thereafter on legal matters. The two gentlemen were of similar political opinions and became close friends. One thing bothered the doctor; the judge would never accept a fee. Finally, feeling inspired, he asked if the judge would accept a beaver hat as a gift. He would indeed (for this was a stylish article at that time, worth ten or fifteen dollars). Accordingly Dr. Bowen gave an order for a hat to Benjamin Randall, a hatter. More than a year elapsed before the hat was finished, for, said Randall, he had to wait for some furs "from the northward." The date when the hat was ordered and that when it was delivered are not known; Dr. Bowen did not, he said, charge his mind with it, and the hatter was embarrassed because of his own delay. It seems very likely that it was during the intervening year that the stranger died and was three (or four) times buried.

The hat, when delivered, was doubtless a fine one. The judge, who had been president of the Providence Town Council since 1794, proceeded to wear it to a meeting of that body early in April (1800). It was at about this time that one John Beverly picked a quarrel with Judge Dorrance, in which he muttered something about a beaver hat. Said the judge:

"What hat?"

"The one on your head for aught I know, and for further particulars you may apply to the town of Scituate."

This the judge did not appear to understand, and probably he was really a little puzzled. He must have known in a general way what Beverly was driving at. He must have known, too, that the Governor of the state was telling all his friends and many strangers that Dr. Bowen had swapped a beaver hat to the judge for a corpse. Indeed, in the election of 1801, when Dorrance was candidate for election as judge in the court of common pleas (for Rhode Island judges were then elective), he became conscious that the Governor's story was telling against him. He was elected, but he felt that he had lost votes. He determined to sue the Governor for slander.

Why all the ado? The corpse was dead enough, the Scituate men had been paid off (and some called it blackmail), nobody was really shocked that anatomy teachers should engage in dissection, and nobody thought Judge Dorrance and Dr. Bowen other than honorable men. Again, why all the ado?

The concealed mainspring of these events was known to everybody in 1801, and it was purely political. Rhode Island had now belonged to the union for a decade, but the Federalist Party and the stronger anti-Federalist one were still functioning. Old animosities remained, and new issues had developed It was Federalist business against anti-Federalist agriculture, for one thing, and there were others. Dr. Bowen and Judge Dorrance were outstanding Federalists, and the leader of the anti-Federalists was Governor Fenner. Any stick will do to beat a political opponent, and the Governor was using a tale of a corpse and a hat. He was also using a newspaper, which he privately owned, though the ownership must have been an open secret. This was the *Impartial Observer,* although the rival paper, the *United States Chronicle,* used regularly to refer to it as "the Republican Mud-Machine." Governor Fenner's paper in return called the *Chronicle* the "Little Wheelbarrow," in allusion to the fact that its editor, Bennett Wheeler, was a small man. He was an influential Federalist, none the less, and his next-door neighbor, Judge Dorrance, doubtless gave him advice and support.

With this background, then, there opened in December of 1801 the slander trial of Dorrance vs. Fenner. Sensible people must have expected it to be a farce, and a farce it was, but played mostly with straight countenances. Everybody who could crowded into the courthouse. All the best people were there, many of them involved in the case. One of Dorrance's three lawyers, James Burrill, Jr., was later to become Chief Justice of Rhode Island, and one of Fenner's, David Howell, was the first professor of Brown University (then Rhode Island College). The presiding judge, Daniel Owen, had also presided, a decade earlier, at the convention that adopted the Federal Constitution for Rhode Island. He was not well educated, especially not in legal terminology, and he seems to have been an obvious partisan or the Governor; yet he had some shrewdness, and it should be remembered that the only record of his remarks in this trial was made by a hostile reporter.

The report of the trial begins formally enough with several pages of jargon. For instance, "that he the said John Dorrance, meaning the Plaintiff had received from said Pardon Bowen a beaver hat, in payment for the aforesaid dead body, sold to the said Pardon Bowen as aforesaid by the said John Dorrance, meaning the Plaintiff, and that said John Dorrance, meaning the Plaintiff, had the impudence to wear

9

the aforesaid hat on his, meaning the Plaintiff's head while he, meaning the Plaintiff, officiated as moderator," and so on. But this solemn (or possibly mock-solemn) machinery broke down when the witnesses began to speak. That was not right away, for many jurymen were challenged. James Hammon, accused of prejudice, admitted that he had said that he thought neither party ought to receive very heavy damages. For this moderate-sounding opinion he was at once thrown off the jury. Another juror was dismissed because Judge Pain (from the bench!) observed that "he believed that the grandmother of Mr. Aldrich was sister to the mother of the governor's wife." (It turned out that Judge Pain was mistaken, but that did Mr. Aldrich no good.) Very soon a vital question was asked of a witness:

"Did you ever hear the story of Judge Dorrance's selling the dead body for a Beaver-hat?"

The plaintiff's counsel here objected, for this was hearsay. The presiding judge finally said: "It is the opinion of the Court that the witness go on and tell all he knows." After this happy but unconventional decision anything was in order. It appeared that one of the judges on the bench had been the coroner at Scituate; he stepped down and was called as witness. The defendant, Governor Fenner, when a question of fact arose, told the court that *he* wished to have every fact brought out. He then rose and, apparently without anybody's objecting, delivered a brief oratorical address, saying "he wished the multitude of spectators who crowded the galleries and floor of the house would hearken to this his public declaration . . . he solemnly submitted the case to their candor, their judgment, and their feelings." Lawyer Howell denounced Judge Dorrance for not being a native Rhode Islander. "Is he one of the Browns, the Angells, the Arnolds, the Olneys, or one of the respectable descendants of good old Roger Williams?" Worse, said Howell, he was a man "of whom the State does not contain the bones of a single illustrious ancestor!" This was pretty cool, seeing that Howell himself was an immigrant from New Jersey, a mere Princeton man; but he evidently knew what he was about. The appeal to Rhode Island local pride and anti-Federalist prejudice was irresistible. The outcome, a foregone conclusion, was to be a decision for Fenner, but in the meantime the court must consider certain subsidiary issues. Was the corpse at the time of its third burial decently covered? The evidence was not conclusive on this point. One witness said: "It had no shirt on, and to the best of my recollection no cover at all." This sounds as if it might be true.

It appeared that Randall, the hatter, had been the first to say that a corpse was swapped for a hat. But Randall was not a wholly satisfactory witness. He had made a formal deposition in the case, but the plaintiff's counsel bethought themselves to ask: "Was Randall sober at that time?"

To this the answer was: "We took his first deposition in an evening. He was then very much in liquor; and the next day we took his deposition over again."

Resolved Smith, a witness, had only one bit of light to shed; it was this: he testified that he never heard the Governor direct Randall to misstate any fact in court. (It looks as if someone had asked a leading question.)

It was somewhat unfortunately brought out that the Governor had remarked: "There are two or three damned whore's-birds whom I intend to pay for the ill treatment I have received from them, and amongst the rest, your Judge Dorrance." But even this did not keep the jury from deciding: "We find for the defendant his cost." This not seeming clear, the presiding judge said: "Write the verdict in the common manner. I don't know what else to say." The counsel were not satisfied.

The judge then said: "The juriers ought to be dismissed, because they've been shut up so long, and haven't had no refreshment, that they can't stand it any longer. The Court can do about the verdict, I guess."

One more surprising diversion was in store for the lucky audience, for when the clerk asked the formal question: "Gentlemen of the Jury, is this your decision?" several jurors rose and declared that it was not their decision at all. There must have been some consternation, but the Chief Justice was not at a loss this time. He told the protesting jurors that they were dismissed and must immediately retire. Mr. Burrill, for the plaintiff, also protested, as well he might. The Chief Justice replied: "Speak louder, Mr. Burrill, I'm some deaf, an' 'tis like I've not heard all 'ts been said. The Court has a mind to do what's right."

The plaintiff's counsel here drew up a paper of remonstrance and gave it to the court, who said: "I'll put the paper in my pocket until the Court can see about it. Ye ha'nt no objection I spose to that, ha' ye? Heh?"

But the verdict was put on record; the protesting paper was never seen again. Dorrance was soundly beaten; the anti-Federalists were in power. Dorrance expressed a desire to have the matter submitted to Massachusetts or Connecticut judges, but Governor Fenner would not, of course, accede. He could not, for the story was too well known and state feeling too strong. When the Rhode Island legislature settled one of the sporadic political squabbles about the date of Thanksgiving Day by refusing to appoint any such day for 1801, the *Hartford Courant* burst into poetry, and with its poem this strange composite of American history and local myth may close:

> Rhode Island too, with virtuous soul
> Hath puked and purged the commonweal,
> Whitewashed old Fenner's smoky coat
> And proved him not guilty by a vote;
> By numbers borne Judge Dorrance down
> And warned Thanksgiving out of town.

The Wessagusset hanging[1]

The natives . . . on their side, had good grounds of complaint. Wretchedly poor, even for New England Indians, they had nothing but a few furs, and hardly food wherewith to sustain life. Yet they had been outraged, and they were still robbed. They had complained to the Plymouth people, but their wrongs were unredressed. Under these circumstances the Indians showed in their conduct a self-restraint and respect for persons which, had the position been reversed, would assuredly have been looked for in vain among Europeans. When pilferers were caught in the very act of stealing the hidden seed-corn, instead of inflicting punishment themselves on the spot, the Massachusetts brought the wrongdoers to the plantation, and delivered them up to be dealt with by their own people. But whippings and confinement could not hold in restraint thieves who were starving. Again the hidden stores were broken into, and again with angry threats the malefactor was brought back to the block-house. Thoroughly frightened now, the settlers told the savages to take their prisoner and to deal with him as they saw fit. This they refused to do, insisting that the settlers should punish their own thieves. His companions, thereupon took the culprit out, and, in full sight of those he had robbed, hanged him before their stockade.

This was that famous Wessagusset[2] hanging, which passed into literature as a jest, and then, received back into history as a traditional fact, was long used as a gibe and reproach against New England. It happened in this wise:—Thomas Morton, who . . . came out with young Weston in the Charity in June and returned to England in her with him in October, published, some fifteen years later, an account of his experiences in New England. Though he did not, it would appear,

---

[1] From Charles Francis Adams: *Three Episodes of Massachusetts History* (Boston: Houghton Mifflin Co.; 1893), Vol. I, pp. 78–83.
[2] In 1623. Wessagusset = Weymouth.

care to dwell upon his connection with Weston's abortive enterprise, for the obvious reason that he was then . . . a hanger-on of those with whom the very name of Weston was a scandal, he could hardly fail at times incidentally to refer to it. Of this particular episode of the hanging he gave the following characteristic account:—

"One amongst the rest, an able bodied man that ranged the woodes to see what it would afford, lighted by accident on an Indian barne, and from thence did take a cappe full of corne; the salvage owner of it, finding by the foote some English had been there, came to the Plantation and made complaint after this manner.

"The cheife Commander of the Company one this occasion called a Parliament of all his people, but those that were sicke and ill at ease. And wisely now they must consult upon this huge complaint, that a privy knife or string of beades would well enough have qualified, and Edward Johnson was a speciall judge of this businesse; the fact was there in repetition; construction made that it was fellony, and by the Lawes of England punished with death, and this in execution must be put for an example, and likewise to appease the Salvage; when straight wayes one arose, mooved as it were with some compassion, and said hee could not well gaine say the former sentence, yet hee had conceaved within the compasse of his braine an Embrion, that was of speciall consequence to be delivered and cherished; hee said that it would most aptly serve to pacifie the Salvages complaint, and save the life of one that might, (if neede should be,) stand them in some good steede, being younge and strong, fit for resistance against an enemy, which might come unexpected for any thinge they knew. The Oration made was liked of every one, and hee intreated to proceede to shew the meanes how this may be performed: says hee, you all agree that one must die, and one shall die; this younge mans cloathes we will take off, and put upon one that is old and impotent, a sickly person that cannot escape death, such is the disease one him confirmed that die hee must; put the younge mans cloathes on this man, and let the sick person be hanged in the others steede: Amen says one, and so sayes many more.

"And this had like to have prooved their finall sentence, and, being there confirmed by Act of Parliament to after ages for a precedent. But that one, with a ravenus voyce, begunne to croake and bellow for revenge, and put by that conclusive motion, alledging such deceipts might be a meanes hereafter to exasperate the mindes of the complaining Salvages, and that by his death the Salvages should see their zeale to Justice; and therefore hee should die: this was concluded: yet neverthelesse a scruple did represent itself unto their mindes, which was,—how they should doe to get the mans good wil? This was indeede a speciall obstacle: for without that, they all agreed, it would be danger-

13

ous for any man to attempt the execution of it, lest mischiefe should befall them every man; he was a person that in his wrath did seeme to be a second Sampson, able to beate out their braines with the jaw-bone of an Asse: therefore they called the man, and by perswation got him fast bound in jest; and then hanged him up hard by in good earnest, who with a weapon, and at liberty, would have put all those wise judges of this Parliament to a pittiful *non plus* (as it hath beene credibly reported), and made the chiefe Judge of them all buckell to him."

Thirty years after the publication of the "New England Canaan," when its author had long been dead and the book itself was forgotten, Butler's famous satire of "Hudibras" appeared. In speaking of this work Hallam has remarked, in his "Literary History of Europe," that the inexhaustible wit of the author "is supplied from every source of reading and observation. But these sources are often so unknown to the reader that the wit loses its effect through the obscurity of its allusions." The truth of this criticism was strikingly illustrated in the present instance. Either the author of "Hudibras" had at some time in the course of his reading come across the "New England Canaan," or he had met Thomas Morton and heard him tell the story, which, as a highly utilitarian suggestion of vicarious atonement, appealed to Butler's sense of humor and thereafter lingered in his memory. More-over, while in 1664 the Puritans of New England were fair game, whatever Samuel Butler found was his; and so, making, as a thing of course, those improvements of fact which literary exigencies de-manded, the incident, as finally transmuted by his wit, appeared in the following form in what long continued to be one of the most popular and generally read of English books:

> "Our Brethren of New England use
> Choice malefactors to excuse,
> And hang the Guiltless in their stead,
> Of whom the Churches have less need;
> As lately't happened: In a town
> There liv'd a Cobler, and but one,
> That out of Doctrine could cut Use,
> And mend men's lives as well as shoes.
> This precious Brother having slain,
> In times of peace, an Indian,
> (Not out of malice, but mere zeal,
> Because he was an Infidel),
> The mighty Tottipottymoy
> Sent to our Elders an envoy,
> Complaining sorely of the breach
> Of league held forth by Brother Patch,
> Against the articles in force
> Between both churches, his and ours,
> For which he craved the Saints to render

Into his hands, or hang th' offender;
But they maturely having weighed
They had no more but him o' th' trade,
(A man that served them in a double
Capacity, to teach and cobble),
Resolv'd to spare him; yet to do
The Indian Hoghan Moghan [1] too
Impartial justice, in his stead did
Hang an old Weaver that was bed-rid."

But the real humor of the thing was yet to come. The actual hanging took place in 1623. When, nearly half a century later, its memory was thus accidentally revived, the Cavalier reaction was at its height; and everything which tended to make the Puritans and Puritanism either odious or contemptible, was eagerly laid hold of. They had become the target for ribald jesting,—the standing butt of the day. The New England provinces also, and Massachusetts in particular, were known chiefly as the place of refuge of the chosen people;—there alone did they retain a sure ascendency. Morton's absurd fiction, as improved and embellished by Butler, was accordingly not only laughed over as a good jest forever, but, gradually passing into a tradition, it seems at last to have even assumed its place as one of those historical incidents, vaguely but currently accepted as facts, which periodically reappear in spite of every effort to put an end to them. Such were, and are, the famous Blue Laws of Connecticut; and, again, that limitation which prevented lords of the manor in feudal times from killing more than two serfs, after the hunt, for foot-warming purposes; or, finally (a yet more familiar example in later history), that dramatic sinking of the Vengeur, which not even Carlyle's exposure has sufficed to exorcise.

---

[1] Chief.

Even Adamses err [1]

American historical literature presents a singularly striking instance of a blunder, committed through reliance upon circumstantial evidence alone, by one who was both a practiced scholar and a highly experienced man of the world. Charles Francis Adams, Civil War minister to England, and the biographer of his grandfather John Adams, published soon after the Civil War (1873) a brochure

---

[1] Reprinted from *The Gateway to History*, by Allan Nevins, copyright, 1938, by D. C. Heath and Company, by permission of D. Appleton-Century Company, Inc., pp. 191–6.

on William H. Seward. He made therein the rash assertion that the success of Lincoln's Administration was traceable primarily to the keenness and wisdom of Seward. For this statement he marshalled a variety of circumstantial evidence. Lincoln was uneducated, Seward a graduate of Union College, deeply read and widely travelled. Lincoln possessed little experience of public office when chosen President, having been merely an inconspicuous Congressman for two years; Seward's public experience had begun with his election as Governor of New York, and in 1861 included twelve years of leadership in the Senate. Lincoln had been reared in a frontier State, Seward trained in the richest and most populous part of the nation. Lincoln had never taken that determined stand on questions of the day which Seward had long taken and which had led him in 1850 to refer to "a higher law than the Constitution." Lincoln had made Seward his Secretary of State, obviously meaning to lean heavily upon him—to make him Prime Minister. Lincoln had been given the benefit of Seward's advice at every step, consulting him not only in the Cabinet but in frequent private meetings. It was clear, declared Adams, that the enduring work of the administration had been done by Seward.

"It is the duty of history," he wrote, "in dealing with all human events, to do strict justice in discriminating between persons, and by no means to award to one honors that clearly belong to another. I must then affirm, without hesitation, that in the history of our government, no experiment so rash has ever been made as that of elevating to the head of affairs a man with so little previous preparation for his task as Mr. Lincoln. . . . Mr. Lincoln could not fail soon to perceive that whatever estimate he might put on his own natural judgment, he had to deal with a superior in native intellectual power, in extent of acquirement, in breadth of philosophic experience, and in the force of moral discipline. On the other hand, Mr. Seward could not have been long blind to the deficiencies of his chief in these respects." In brief, all the circumstances rendered it inevitable that Seward should lead, Lincoln follow. Mr. Adams pointed to circumstantial evidence that he had done so. Seward wished the emancipation of the slaves treated cautiously; and emancipation was effected at just the time and in just the way that Seward would have wished it done. Seward wished the Administration to defy the more radical and impetuous leaders of Congress; and Lincoln had defied Thaddeus Stevens and Zachariah Chandler. The evidence seemed overwhelming.

But one blow at the weakest point of that circumstantial evidence which is founded on the mere outward aspect of affairs, and it comes toppling down. So it was with Adams's impressive array of arguments. Gideon Welles, Secretary of the Navy under Lincoln, stepped forward with a small volume called *Lincoln and Seward* which proved con-

clusively that Lincoln had always been master of his Administration—
that he had led and others had followed. By direct evidence drawn
from his own unpublished diary, and buttressed by other data, he
showed that as between the two groups in his Cabinet, the radicals
headed by Chase and the moderates by Seward, Lincoln had acted
with masterly independence. He proved that all of the President's
decisive acts had been stamped with his own sagacity. Sixteen years
later Nicolay and Hay, in their ten-volume life of Lincoln based on
the Lincoln papers, demonstrated just how fatal any reliance on
Seward would have been. They staggered the admirers of the great
New Yorker by showing that on April 1, 1861, he had proposed that
the United States should provoke a war with France and Spain as a
means of reuniting the American people, suggesting that he be permitted to carry out this and other policies. They showed how
magnanimously Lincoln, while rejecting this folly and putting Seward
into his proper place, had suppressed all public notice of this proposal,
and how quickly he had brought Seward to recognize his superior
wisdom and firmness. Later research has revealed so much evidence of
Lincoln's complete control of his Administration, including at times
the State Department, that it seems almost incredible that C. F. Adams
should ever have made his reckless statements. His circumstantial
evidence was worthless.

The most difficult form of evidence to test is that given by the single
witness, who may be affected by a hundred forms of personal bias,
self-interest, or party, national, or other feeling. The varieties and
complexities of bias are almost endless, and they are frequently com-
patible with the utmost sincerity. Of course the simpler types of
prejudice are easy to detect—but how seldom we meet the simpler
types! The primary rule, in historical study as in the courts, is to
cross-examine the witness in an effort to ascertain how many varieties
of bias he expresses, and to what degree; for it is a safe rule that
everyone has some bias, conscious or unconscious. Suppose, for example, the student of Jefferson turns to the well-known passage in
John Quincy Adams's *Memoirs* in which that shrewd observer expresses his conclusions upon the Virginian:

"Washington, January 11, 1831.—I read about fifty pages of the first
volume of Jefferson's *Memoirs*. (J. Q. A. means the *Anas*.) He states
that he began his autobiography on the 6th of January, 1831. . . . He
tells nothing but what redounds to his own credit. He is like the
French lady who told her sister she did not know how it happened,
'but I am the only person in the world who is always right.' Jefferson,
by his own narrative, is always in the right. That is not uncommon to
writers of their own lives. Dr. Franklin was more candid. Mr. Jefferson
names the teachers from whom he learnt Greek, Latin, and French,

and speaks gratefully of William Small, a Scotchman, professor of mathematics at William and Mary College, who became attached to him and probably fixed the destinies of his life. . . . Loose morals necessarily followed. If not an absolute atheist, he had no belief in a future existence. All his ideas of obligation or retribution were bounded by the present life. His duties to his neighbor were under no stronger guarantee than the laws of the land and the opinions of the world. The tendency of this condition upon a mind of great compass and powerful resources is to produce insincerity and duplicity, which were his besetting sins through life. . . . (From 1790 to 1809) all the good and all the evil parts of his character were brought into action. His ardent passion for liberty and the rights of man; his patriotism; the depth and compass of his understanding; . . . the perpetual watchfulness of public opinion, and the pliability of principle and temper with which he accommodated it to his own designs and opinions:—all these were in ceaseless operation during these twenty years; and with them were combined a rare mixture of infidel philosophy and epicurean morals, of burning ambition and of stoical self-control, of deep duplicity and of generous sensibility, between which two qualities and a treacherous and inventive memory, his conduct toward his rivals and opponents appears one tissue of inconsistency. His treatment of Washington, of Knox, of my father, of Hamilton, of Bayard, who made him President of the United States, and lastly of me, is marked with features of perfidy worthy of Tiberius Caesar or Louis XI of France. This double-dealing character was often imputed to him during his life and was sometimes exposed. His letter to Mazzei and the agonizing efforts which he afterwards made to explain it away; his most insidious attack upon my father with his never-ceasing professions of respect and affection for his person and character; and his letter to Giles concerning me, in which there is scarcely a single word of truth—indicate a memory so pandering to the will that in deceiving others he seems to have begun by deceiving himself."

Here we find Jefferson accused by one who knew him well of loose morals; of being a freethinker, irreligious and probably atheistic; of having no principle; and of displaying utter selfishness in trying to gratify an inordinate ambition. We find him accused of duplicity, of treachery to superiors and friends, and of deliberate falsehood. It is a staggering indictment, drawn by a statesman famous for both astuteness and probity. But if we summon Adams for cross-examination, what do we find? We learn that he is now sixty-three, with a memory not always accurate. We learn that Jefferson defeated his father for the presidency, and that this event terminated J. Q. Adams's service as Minister to Prussia, a comfortable post—for John Adams recalled him, in order not to embarrass Jefferson. We learn that during Jefferson's Administration Adams was a political independent, distrusted by both parties, and frequently piqued because neither was friendly toward him. We learn that as a Massachusetts man he was constitutionally incapable of liking Virginians. As he mentioned religion, by a little inquiry we find that he is one of the devoutest of Congregationalists, distrusting Episcopalianism and detesting Deism; and that his ideas of what constitutes irreligion are narrow and dogmatic. As he mentions morals, a little inquiry elicits the fact that he regards card-playing, horse-racing, and any waste of time on mere amusement as immoral. And finally we learn that a multitude of witnesses will testify that Adams, however great and good, was the most censorious and cantankerous of mortals, whose diary has been called "a graveyard of slaughtered reputations."

When two of the judges who condemned Charles I fled to Massachusetts (at the accession of Charles II), a good many tall tales grew up concerning their sojourn, and it is hardly possible now to distinguish truth from myth. The two stories following are taken from Barber's *Massachusetts,* but Barber took the first from Stiles's *History of the Judges* and the second from Hoyt's *Indian Wars.* (He makes acknowledgment.) The first story deals with the pursuit of the judges by commissioners from England; the second, with the Indian attack upon Hadley, Massachusetts, in 1676. These tales may be true; the historian who omitted them would surely be overconscientious. Overconscientious, according to Professor Dobie,[1] are the historians who would erase the line drawn at the Alamo.

The historian without conscience is fortunately rare. The Reverend Samuel Peters was such a one, however. Born in Connecticut in 1735, he became a Tory, and so unhappy was his pastoral lot thereafter that he spent the Revolutionary period in England. His *General History of Connecticut,* published in London in 1781, pays off some old scores. Perhaps the story of the frog army had some slight foundation, but it is told to make the Connecticut folk look silly, and it does.

As for Skipper Ireson's ride—well, Whittier was a poet!

Goffe, Whalley, or the devil[2]

At or about the time the pursuers came to New Haven, and perhaps a little before, to prepare the minds of the people for their reception, the Rev. Mr. Davenport preached publicly from this text: ISAIAH XVI. 3, 4.—"Take counsel, execute judgment, make thy shadow as the night in the midst of the noonday; hide the outcasts, betray not him that wandereth. Let mine outcasts dwell with thee, Moab; be thou a covert to them from the face of the spoiler." This, doubtless, had its effect, and put the whole town upon their guard, and united the people in caution and concealment.

---

[1] "The Line That Travis Drew," below.

[2] From John Warner Barber: *Historical Collections of Every Town in Massachusetts* (Worcester: Dorr, Howland & Co.; 1839), p. 324.

To show the dexterity of the judges at fencing, the following story is told: That while at Boston, there appeared a fencing-master, who, on a stage erected for the purpose, walked it for several days, challenging and defying any one to play with him at swords; at length one of the judges, disguised in a rustic dress, holding in one hand a cheese, wrapped in a napkin, for a shield, with a broomstick, whose mop he had besmeared with dirty puddle water as he passed along—thus equipped, he mounted the stage. The fencing-master railed at him for his impudence, asked him what business he had there, and bid him begone. The judge stood his ground, upon which the gladiator made a pass at him with his sword, to drive him off—a rencounter ensued—the judge received the sword into the cheese, and held it until he drew the mop of the broom gently over his mouth, and gave the gentleman a pair of whiskers. He made another pass, and plunging his sword a second time, it was caught and held in the cheese, until the judge had rubbed the broom all over his face. Upon this, the gentleman let fall his small sword, and took up the broad sword. The judge then said, "Stop, sir; hitherto I have only played with you, and not attempted to harm you; but if you come at me now with the broad sword, know that I will certainly take your life." The firmness with which he spoke struck the master, who, desisting, exclaimed, "Who can you be? You must be either Goffe, Whalley, or the devil; for there was no other man in England that could beat me."

The angel of Hadley[1]

In the preceding night, they approached the town, laid an ambuscade at the southern extremity, and advanced the main body towards the other, and at day-light the attack was commenced with great spirit; but the English, turning out, received them at the palisades. The Indians gained possession of a house at the north end of the street, and fired a barn, but were in a short time driven back with loss. The attack was renewed on other points, and the Indians, though warmly opposed, appeared determined on carrying the place; but a discharge of a piece of ordnance checked their fury, and their ambuscade failing of their object, which was to attack the people who might be driven from the village, they drew off. Major Talcott, at Northampton, hearing the attack, hurried on, passed the river, and, joining the Hadley forces, precipitated the Indians into the woods. Only two or three men were lost by the English; the enemy's was not ascertained.

[1] Ibid., p. 325.

. . . When the people were in great consternation, and rallying to oppose the Indians, a man of venerable aspect, differing from the inhabitants in his apparel, appeared, and, assuming command, arrayed them in the best manner for defence, evincing much knowledge of military tactics, and by his advice and example continued to animate the men throughout the attack. When the Indians drew off, the stranger disappeared, and nothing further was heard of him. Who the deliverer was, none could inform or conjecture, but by supposing, as was common at that day, that Hadley had been saved by its guardian angel. It will be recollected that at this time the two judges, Whalley and Goffe, were secreted in the village, at the house of the Rev. Mr. Russell. The supposed angel, then, was no other than Gen. Goffe, who, seeing the village in imminent danger, put all at risk, left his concealment, mixed with the inhabitants, and animated them to a vigorous defence. Whalley, being then superannuated, probably remained in his secluded chamber.

Frog army [1]

At Windham] strangers are very much terrified at the hideous noise made on summer evenings by the vast number of frogs in the brooks and ponds. There are about thirty different voices among them, some of which resemble the bellowing of a bull. The owls and whippoorwills complete the rough concert, which may be heard several miles. Persons accustomed to such serenades are not disturbed by them at their proper stations; but one night in July, 1758, the frogs of an artificial pond, three miles square, and about five from Windham, finding the water dried up, left the place in a body, and marched, or rather hopped, towards Winnomantic River. They were under the necessity of taking the road and going through the town, which they entered about midnight. The bull-frogs were the leaders, and the pipers followed without number. They filled the road, forty yards wide, for four miles in length, and were for several hours in passing though the town unusually clamorous.

The inhabitants were equally perplexed and frightened: some expected to find an army of French and Indians; others feared an earthquake, and dissolution of nature. The consternation was universal. Old and young, male and female, fled naked from their beds, with worse shriekings than those of the frogs. The event was fatal to several

[1] From Rev. Samuel Peters: *General History of Connecticut* (London, 1871); reprinted, New York: D. Appleton & Co.; 1877), pp. 129–31.

22

women. The men, after a flight of half a mile, in which they met with many broken shins, finding no enemies in pursuit of them, made a hault, and summoned resolution enough to venture back to their wives and children, when they distinctly heard from the enemy's camp these words: Wight, Hilderkin, Dier, Tete. This last, they thought, meant treaty, and, plucking up their courage, they sent a triumvirate to capitulate with the supposed French and Indians. These the men approached in their shirts, and begged to speak with the general; but, it being dark and no answer given, they were sorely agitated for some time betwixt hope and fear: at length, however, they discovered that the dreaded inimical army was an army of thirsty frogs going to the river for a little water.

The line that Travis drew[1]

I n 1873 the *Texas Almanac* published W. P. Zuber's narrative, "An Escape from the Alamo," to which was appended a statement from his mother verifying the account. It sets forth how a man named Rose appeared at the Zuber home in Grimes County some days after the fall of the Alamo. He was in a pitiable plight physically, starved, his legs full of thorns, his wallet clotted with blood. The Zubers were good Samaritans to him. He told them how in the Alamo on the night of March 3, 1836, Travis had made a remarkable speech to his men; how at the end of it he had drawn a line across the dirt floor with his sword, and invited all who would stay, fight, and die to cross over; how all went over, Bowie being carried on his cot, except Rose himself; how he climbed the wall, threw his wallet on the ground, where it soaked up Mexican blood, and how he then got through the cordon of Mexicans and made his way east afoot.

Up to the year 1873, the chronicles of Texas contained no mention of an escape from the Alamo, though the name of Rose had been set down, both in print and in stone, as one of the men who died in the Alamo. Up to this date also, the chronicles of Texas contained no intimation of the speech made by Travis or of the line drawn by his sword. The personal experiences of Rose on his fear-hounded walk across a wide land either uninhabited or now deserted by families who had joined in the Runaway Scrape still makes good reading—a kind of parallel to John C. Duval's *Early Times in Texas*—the story of his escape from Goliad. But this part of the Zuber—or Rose—narra-

---

[1] J. Frank Dobie in *In the Shadow of History*, Texas Folk-lore Society Publications, No. XV (Austin: Texas Folk-lore Society: 1939), pp. 9–16.

tive is minor compared to the speech of Travis, the drawing of the line, and the crossing of the men to his side, four of them bearing the cot on which the shrunken lion Jim Bowie lay.

Here was indeed something new, dramatic and vital to inflame the imagination of the Texas people—a people who, though towers may rise higher than the Tower of Babel to mark the San Jacinto Battlefield and though monuments commemorating events and personalities of history may sprinkle the roadsides from Red River to the Rio Grande, cherish the Alamo as they cherish no other spot either in Texas or in the world beyond. The story seized not only the popular mind; it seized the imagination of story-tellers, poets and historians.

In the very year it was published, Sidney Lanier, a visitor in San Antonio, wrote for the *Southern Magazine,* an essay on "San Antonio de Bexar," which was later included in his *Retrospects and Prospects* and then popularized over Texas by inclusion in William Corner's *San Antonio de Bexar,* 1890, which remains the best history of that city to have been published. Writing on the fall of the Alamo, Lanier comes to Travis's speech and gesture with these words: "On the 3rd of March a single man, Moses Rose, escapes from the fort. His account of that day must entitle it to consecration as one of the most pathetic days of time."

In 1874 or 1875, hard upon the appearance of the Zuber narrative and the refinement that Lanier gave it, Morphis repeated the story in his *History of Texas.* But Thrall's history, which appeared in 1879, gave it only scant mention, along with a slur upon its validity.

The medium that gave the story its widest vogue was Mrs. Anna J. Hardwicke (Mrs. Percy V.) Pennypacker's *History of Texas for Schools.* No publisher would take the book, and she and her husband issued it themselves, the first edition appearing in 1888. During the next twenty-five years, it went into six editions and "several hundred thousand copies were sold, chiefly for use in Texas schools."

To quote from the 1888 edition of this work, which for a quarter of a century gave the school children and also teachers attending the state normals their chief education in Texas history: "On March 4 (sic), the Mexicans kept up a terrible cannonade. Just before sunset, this suddenly ceased, and Santa Anna ordered his men to withdraw some distance from the Alamo. The weary Texans, who, for ten days and nights, had toiled like giants, sank down to snatch a few moments' rest. Travis seemed to know that this was the lull before the last fury of storm that was to destroy them all; he ordered his men to parade in single file. Then followed one of the grandest scenes history records. In a voice trembling with emotion, Travis told his men that death was inevitable, and showed that he had detained them thus long, hoping for reinforcements.

"When Travis had finished, the silence of the grave reigned over all. Drawing his sword, he drew a line in front of his men and cried: 'Those who wish to die like heroes and patriots come over to me.' There was no hesitation. In a few minutes every soldier, save one, had crossed. Even the wounded dragged themselves across the fatal mark. Colonel Bowie was too ill to leave his couch, but he was not to be deterred by this. 'Lads,' he said, 'I can't get over to you, but won't some of you be kind enough to lift my cot on the other side of the line?' In an instant it was done."

In the revised edition of 1895 of the Pennypacker history (and also in the editions of 1898 and 1900) the story of Rose and of the Travis speech was included with extensions, Zuber at the invitation of the author adding many details. Scholars from the first had taken exception to the narrative, generally dismissing rather than discussing it. In Volume 5, (1901–1902) of the *Quarterly* of the Texas State Historical Association Zuber made three contributions in defense of the story; in Volume 6 he made another.

In 1903 Garrison's history appeared—without allusion to Rose or Travis's speech. Doctor George P. Garrison, Professor of History in the University of Texas, became the critic for Mrs. Pennypacker. The very much revised edition of her history that appeared in 1908 omitted, as if it had never appeared, the tale that Zuber ascribed to Rose. In 1913 the Pennypacker history, which had been used so long that some of the men and women who studied it in school saw their own children using it, was supplanted by *A School History of Texas,* by Barker, Potts, and Ramsdell. This kept its place in Texas schools until displaced in 1932 by Clarence A. Wharton's *Lone Star State,* now in use. I wonder if leaving out all reference to Rose and the Travis speech in this book cost Clarence Wharton a twinge.

On page 120 of the first edition of the Barker, Potts, and Ramsdell history, under the caption, in black letters, "Some Old Errors," the Rose narrative is bowed out. As Eugene C. Barker has remarked, "Until scientific scholars correct history, it is an illusion, and after they write it, it remains an illusion."

The latest study—the most searching that has ever been made—of the battle of the Alamo and the lives of participants, the treatise by Amelia Williams, sums up the matter by saying: "Historians have been divided in their opinion concerning this story, the most careful students have discredited it. At best they consider it a legend, plausible perhaps, but almost certainly the creation of a vivid imagination."

But what makes history, whether authenticated or legendary, live is that part of it that appeals to the imagination. Amid many imagination-rousing facts connected with the siege and fall of the Alamo—the superlatively moving letter written by Travis; the picture of

Crockett playing his fiddle to cheer the boys up; Bowie on his cot with pistols and Bowie knife; Bonham dashing back from liberty to die with his comrades; the final charge of Santa Anna's men to the strains of the death-announcing *deguello;* the extermination of a hundred and eighty-odd Texans at the hands of an army numbering perhaps five thousand, of whom more than fifteen hundred were killed before the last free man in the walls of the old mission went down; the one sentence entitled to immortality that Texas can claim: "Thermopylae had her message of defeat, the Alamo had none"—amid these and other facts no circumstance has appealed more to popular imagination than the story of how Travis drew the line and invited individuals of the little group to choose between life and immortality. Rose in choosing life got something of the other also, doomed like Carlyle's Doctor Guillotin to wander "a disconsolate ghost on the wrong side of Styx and Lethe."

I was sixteen or seventeen years old when for the first time I went to San Antonio and entered the Alamo, though I had lived all my life not much over a hundred miles away. As I walked through the low door with my father and mother and came into the darkling light of the ancient fortress—ancient for Texas, and a fortress and not a church for Texans—I looked first for the place where Travis drew the line. I never enter the Alamo now but that I think of the line.

It is a line that nor all the piety nor wit of research will ever blot out. It is a Grand Canyon cut into the bedrock of human emotions and heroical impulses. It may be expurgated from histories, but it can no more be expunged from popular imagination than the damned spots on Lady Macbeth's hands. Teachers of children dramatize it in school rooms; orators on holidays silver it and gild it; the tellers of historical anecdotes—and there are many of them in Texas—sitting around hotel lobbies speculate on it and say, "Well, we'll believe it whether it's true or not."

Could Rose, with his "broken English," no matter how good his memory, have transmitted the Travis speech as we have it from Zuber, who wrote it down thirty-five years after Rose had given it to Zuber's parents, who in turn repeated it to him? Zuber frankly said that he was transmitting only approximation. But it was the kind of speech that the inward-burning Travis might have made, the Travis who wrote "I shall never surrender or retreat," "I am determined to sustain myself as long as possible and die like a soldier," and whose rubric was "Victory or Death." And for Travis to have drawn the line would have been entirely natural, the more natural because of the fact that in both history and fiction Rubicon lines have repeatedly been drawn for fateful crossings. Because an act has precedent is no reason for denying it. History is sprinkled with momentous sentences spoken by military

26

men at crucial hours. These men about to die in the Alamo must have been conscious of doing a fine and brave thing. Travis certainly thought that he was acting a part that the light of centuries to come would illumine. To have imagination is no reflection on integrity. A magnificent gesture does not abnegate sincerity. Not everything orally transmitted is *mere* legend; there is traditional history as well as traditional folk-lore.

For hundreds of thousands of Texans and others who could not cite a single authenticated word spoken in the Alamo or a single authenticated act performed by a single man of the besieged group—for these hundreds of thousands of human beings the gesture and the challenge made by William Barrett Travis are a living reality—almost the only personal reality of the Alamo. In a book of reminiscences written by an old cowpuncher of Montana I came only yesterday upon this passage: "The Alamo had fallen. Brave Bob Travis, that drew the dead line with his sword, lay cold in death at the gate." In the "chronicles of wasted time" Travis's dead line belongs as inherently to Texas as William Tell's apple belongs to Switzerland, or as dying Sir Philip Sidney's generosity in refusing a drink of water so that a wounded soldier whose "necessity was greater" might sup it, belongs to England.

For this noble and moving tradition I would register a feeling of gratitude to Louis, or Moses, Rose—a character that from Zuber's narrative and R. B. Blake's study, following this, emerges strangely vivid, even while shrinking and striking back in this, to him, always foreign and bullying world.

Yet it is the thing created and not the creator that the world remembers. Nothing could make a creator happier. Rose has been forgotten, will continue to be forgotten. That line that Travis drew cuts out and off everything else. To illustrate the forgetting and the remembering, too, I will quote from a book dealing with San Antonio, written by an informed newspaper man thirty years ago.

"In the Chapel, sick almost unto death, Bowie lay on a cot, prone and unable to rise. Travis with his sword drew a line across the space in front of where his forces had been assembled. . . . He said: 'All who wish to leave, stand in their places. All who wish to remain and fight to the end cross over this line and come to me.' All but one crossed over to him. Bowie had his cot lifted and brought over. Rose was the only man who did not cross the line. . . . During the night Crockett lifted Rose up and helped him out of one of the windows. Rose was never heard of after. Probably he perished miserably, butchered before he had gone many yards from the shadow of the structure in which his comrades remained. No one knows his fate, or, if so, it has never been told."

But nobody forgets the line. It is drawn too deep and straight.

Reading the documented historians, you'd think nothing could be so unless it happened. I think Travis made the speech. He certainly made it according to something that the historians might well use—in proper place—to the advantage of truth. In *My Ireland* Lord Dunsany found it necessary to quote a fictional character in order to reveal a historical truth. I want to quote Lord Dunsany himself: "I look, in fact, as much for Ireland in the Irish mind as I do in the Irish fields. Much may pass over a field and leave no trace, but what wonderful tracks we may see where a fancy has passed over the mind."

Skipper Ireson's ride [1]

Marbleheaders don't like to talk about it; and you'll find it difficult to induce an old native to pilot you to the poor old skipper's home in the queer corner of Oakum Bay. They feel that Whittier did their town and their townspeople a great unkindness, which he would never have done had he sought fact instead of accepting tradition for the basis of his verse. The "Chant of Flood Oirson," as it has been called, was current in the town years before Whittier wrote, and ran in this wise:

> "Old Flood Oirson for his hord hort,
> Was tor'd and further'd and coried in a cort,
> A becos he left five men on a wrack
> Was tor'd and further'd all over his back!"

The true story was first published some twenty years ago by the late Rev. Charles T. Brooks, minister and poet, in a newspaper, by way of introduction to his verses, *A Plea for Flood Ireson,* written as an offset to Whittier's poem.

The incident occurred in the spring of 1808. Ireson was the skipper of the schooner Betsy of Marblehead. On her homeward voyage from the West Indies she sighted a wreck when passing Cape Cod. It being dark at the time, and the sea running high, she was unable to render immediate assistance; so the skipper, before going below, ordered the watch to "lay by" the wreck till daylight. But this order was disobeyed, and the Betsy was speeded on her course abandoning the sinking ship. Meanwhile another vessel, a Provincetown whaleboat, rescued her captain with part of his crew, and they reaching shore before the Betsy, report of her conduct preceded her in port. When she arrived a crowd, gathered on the wharf, called her crew to account; but they protested

---

[1] From Edwin M. Bacon: *Historical Pilgrimages in New England* (New York, Boston, Chicago: Silver, Burdett & Co.; 1898) pp. 210–12.

that the skipper would not allow them to go to the wreck's relief. Thereupon the mob seized Ireson, put him into an old dory, and dragged him through the streets toward Salem, intending to take him to Beverly, where he belonged, and humiliate him before his neighbors. But when nearing Salem, a number of its citizens, having heard of the affair, met the procession in the road and compelled it to turn about. Meanwhile, the bottom of the old dory had fallen out, and the victim had been shifted to a cart. On the way back, the mob encountered a party of indignant Marblehead citizens, who gave poor Ireson their protection, and he was borne to his home without further molestation. When he got down from the cart he remarked simply, "I thank you for my ride, gentlemen, but you'll live to regret it!"

As for the part which the women of Marblehead took in the affair, Mr. Brooks said: "A few old fishwives may have thrown their feather beds out of the window; but as to the story of the men's giving their victim over to the tender mercies of the women, and of their punching him with marlin-spikes to make him sing the rhymed history of his disgrace—to me, who have been familiar with the tradition of the occurrence from childhood, this ornamentation of the story seems clearly a sailor's yarn." The public of Marblehead, he added, were from the first on the side of their much respected townsman. His crew were an unruly and dissolute set, more likely to have prevented their captain from going on upon an errand of mercy than he was to have hindered them; and the form of government on a Marblehead fishing-smack was then a pretty unlimited democracy.

Poor Ireson sailed another voyage as skipper, the following year, but never after. Later in life he followed dory-fishing in the bay, and used to peddle his catch in a hand-cart through the streets. Although the best townspeople soon after the affair became entirely satisfied that he had suffered unjustly, and treated him with respect, his life was wrecked; and he drifted aimlessly till his death, only a year or two before the appearance of Whittier's ballad. His name was Benjamin Ireson; "Flood," not "Floyd," as Whittier gives it, being a nickname.

3. ORAL TRADITION: THE TELLERS
AND THE TALES

Oral tradition is not, as some romanticists seem to think it, a semi-automatic phenomenon; on the contrary, it is for the most part a process directed by experts. These may be, and often are, men and women of rustic background, but they are nearly always skillful practitioners; their greatest skill is apt to be an assumed simplicity, for they are quite well aware that "art conceals art." They expand in the sunshine of an appreciative audience,[1] and their art must have skilled listeners if it is to bloom richly and fully. Mark Twain was, of course, a genius at the drawing-out process. Many of today's listeners have developed their own simple roles admirably, and what a collector like Herbert Halpert, or Richard M. Dorson, or George Loveridge tells us about artists-in-narrative and their art is well worth knowing. Hence in the next group of stories a few of the reporters' comments on the story-tellers have been added.

Usually the tellers are conservative and prefer a single version; they are likely to say (with or without a sly look): "That's the way it happened." Youthful audiences and unsophisticated ones undoubtedly prefer telling by rote, but a first-rate story-teller is almost certain to experiment with slight alterations until he finds the shape, tone, and phrasing that best suit him and his audience. No better account of this process exists than Mark Twain's.[2] Of course any story-teller worth listening to will alter, and even improvise at times, and he will usually be quite bare-faced about it. (Ballad-singers are an exception; they usually revere their traditional texts, but in any case the bonds of rhyme and tune will not let them stray very far.) The American story-teller usually lets his audience understand that he is lying, but he hints this gracefully, and his mockery never becomes obtrusive enough to scuttle the yarn itself.

Such typically humorous detachment is well illustrated in the narrative manner of Thomas Newell, an A.A.F. soldier (in 1944) from Mississippi.[3] Newell said of his story of the enormous alligator: [4] "I don't know where I heard it," but he said at another time that he had in-

---

[1] (And dry up when no sympathy makes itself manifest.)

[2] P. 37, below.

[3] As told by Lieutenant Herbert Halpert. *Southern Folklore Quarterly*, Vol. VIII, pp. 110–12 (June 1944).

[4] P. 31, below.

vented it.[1] The old story of "the wonderful hunt"[2] he told in three forms, and his reporter (Herbert Halpert) has preserved the date of each telling; he has also preserved Newell's delightful comment: "I believe I like it best the last way I told it."

The enormous 'gator[3]

There was a guy he kept losin' his hogs and cattle. That was in No'th Ca'lina. He couldn't figger out where they were goin'. He checked his pasture fence and couldn't find any holes where they went out. Also checked around the woods on the outside. Never could find any of them.

So one day he happened to go down by the pond—found a 'gator. So he killed this 'gator, cut him open, found one hog that he'd just swallowed. Searched on further and found his oxens that had been lost over a year. They was fat and purty. Found them feeding on two acres of burnt woods that the alligator had swallowed.

The wonderful hunt[4]
(As told October 10, 1943.)

This guy was out huntin' and he had only one shell. So he looked —he sees a turkey settin' on a limb. So he starts to take his aim to shoot the turkey, he sees there's a deer standin' on the ground beneath the limb and before he gets to shoot he heard a racket down near his feet and it's a rattlesnake—he finds a rattlesnake there. So he don't know what to do. He thinks if he shoots the turkey the rattlesnake'll bite him and the deer'll run off. So he eventually decides to shoot the turkey and take a chance on the snake bitin' him and the deer gettin' away. So he shoots the turkey and part of the load went in the limb, knocked it off. It fell on the deer and killed him. And the lock fell off his gun and killed the rattlesnake. That's how lucky he was—and his name didn't happen to be Tom Newell.

---

[1] *Southern Folklore Quarterly*, Vol. VIII, p. 110 (June 1944).
[2] See also pp. 628–33 of this book.
[3] From *Southern Folklore Quarterly*, Vol. VIII, p. 110 (June 1944).
[4] Ibid., p. 111.

The wonderful hunt[1]

(As told November 21, 1943.)

This guy was huntin' and the gun he used was one of these muzzle loaders—you have to put your powder in, then your wad in, and then your shot. All right. He had plenty of powder, and he only had enough lead to load one time. So he looked and he could see a turkey settin' up on a limb. So he loaded his gun with this last load; then he looked back—beneath the limb stood a deer. Heard a racket down under his feet—was a rattlesnake. So he was settin' near a stream and he finally decided to shoot the turkey and take chances on the rattlesnake bitin'. So he was kinda nervous when he drew his gun. He shot a little too low. Part of his load went into the turkey, the other part went in the limb. The limb fell on the deer and killed him, ramrod fell out of the gun killed the rattlesnake. The gun kicked him backwards into the stream and when he came up he had his shirt tail full of fish. So he carried home deer, turkey, and fish.

The wonderful hunt[2]

(As told November 21, 1943.)

Some tells it that quails was on the limb and the bullet—he shot a rifle—the bullet splits the limb—and the line of quails settin' on the limb, and their toes falls down in the split and it closes up on them before they get away. The bullet goes on through and kills the deer; the barrel of the gun busted. One piece went one way, and one the other, and killed the turkey on each side of him, and the ramrod drops down and kills the rattlesnake—and the gun kicks him back in the water and he comes up with his shirt-tail full of fish.

The next group of stories is the product of a Yankee narrator, one "Slick" MacQuoid, of Wilton, Maine. The stories were garnered in 1942 by Richard M. Dorson.[3] Mr. Dorson, who has done much to re-

---

[1] Ibid., p. 112.

[2] Ibid. Variant forms of this story are innumerable, and it is found in most parts of the United States. Richard M. Dorson quotes six versions, and lists many others in *New England Quarterly*, Vol. XVI, 253–9 (June 1943).

[3] They are taken from *Southern Folklore Quarterly*, Vol. VIII, pp. 279–83.

mind folklorists of the wealth of folk tales in Yankeeland, past and present,[1] describes Mr. MacQuoid felicitously as one of those "gifted amateurs" who "amass, hoard, and distribute floating story." Mac-Quoid did not require prompting, and would talk readily to strangers. Some of his tales are familiar and conventional (for example, "Killing and cleaning a deer with one shot"),[2] but many are improvisations. When he is not improvising, he prefers (unlike Thomas Newell) to stick to a fixed phrasing that has become his favorite. His stories are told as true, but since "he customarily assigns the hero-role to some present listener," we may hardly suppose that he expects them to be taken literally.

Old John Soule[3]

Old John Soule is the Wilton "character"—eighty-five years old, and weighing about a pound for each year. Because of his slightness he always carries a hoe on his shoulder, to weight him down to earth. One time, however, he was working on a roof when a strong breeze lifted him off and he floated right up in the air; I had to throw a rope thirty-five feet long to get him down.

One time going into town for a banquet, John got all duded up—stove-pipe hat, tails, duster. Just as he was turning off the black onto a dirt road, a car came along and scared the horse; it reared and pitched John right into the ditch. He climbed out hopping mad, frothing and tearing at his stove-pipe hat, which had jammed right over his ears. He struggled so hard that he lifted himself right off the ground.

Killing and cleaning a deer with one shot[4]

Best shot I ever knew was George Parker, who used to guide up around Moosehead. George and I spotted a deer in the woods one day, some 250 yards away; George said he'd get him from there.

---

[1] See, for instance, *Jonathan Draws the Long Bow* (Cambridge: Harvard University Press; 1946).

[2] Obviously related to "The wonderful hunt" (pp. 31–2, above), and to what I call the hardiest American perennial yarn (pp. 628–33, below).

[3] From *Southern Folklore Quarterly*, Vol. VIII, p. 280 (December 1944).

[4] Ibid., p. 281.

But after George had made his shot, the deer reared up and leaped off; I felt so badly I didn't tell George he had missed him clean. We went to pick up his track, and found that deer dead all right, and cleaned as well. George had hit him right in the brisket, and jumping up after he had been hit, he landed on a windfall with his innards hanging out, and his hind legs kicked them out clean. A piece of his liver shot off and killed a partridge.

The partridge and the sweater[1]

D id you ever hear how Mardi Bass right here shot the partridge? Well, last fall Mardi was coming along that same road from Seboomook to Caucomgomoc when she spied a partridge and took a shot at him. She didn't kill him, but she knocked all the feathers off him. When Mardi got home she felt so badly about it she sat right down and knitted that partridge a sweater, and put it on him, and let him go. This spring Mardi saw that partridge with five little partridges behind, all wearing little sweaters. And one of them had the prettiest little feather-necked ruff you ever saw.

The fish and the frying-pan[2]

T his actually happened to a fisherman up at Moosehead. He had caught a five-pound trout, and was going to fry it for supper. While it was cooking over the fire, he turned away for a minute to get a plate, and when he looked around, the fish had flopped off with the frying pan, by gorry. Next spring that fisherman caught the same fish, with the frying pan on his tail, and the next five fish he caught all had little frying pans on their tails.

[1] Ibid., p. 281.
  This story and the next one, with their burlesque of the notion of inheritance of acquired characteristics, appear in countless forms. One of the fullest and best versions is that told by Owen Wister's Virginian, and quoted later in this book.
[2] From *Southern Folklore Quarterly*, Vol. VIII, p. 281 (December 1944).

The snake, the frog, and the liquor[1]

Earl Sawyer here can tell you about a real surprising thing that happened to us on a fishing trip. It was up at Lake Mooselockmeguntic, and the general law had been taken off bait so we could use anything—worms, smelt or anything. But we only had flies, so we looked around for a frog, and saw a black snake swimming carrying one half-devoured in its mouth. We netted the snake, and pried the frog out of its jaws, and cut it up for bait. The snake kept following us with its jaws open the way they had been when carrying the frog; Earl felt sorry for it and poured a little liquor down its throat. Well, we had pretty good luck with the frog bait and in about an hour it was all gone. Earl said, "Lord, I wish we had another frog," and began looking around for one, when he felt a tugging at his trouser leg— and there was that snake back with another frog.

623051

"You take off ten pounds . . ."[2]

Two fishermen met at the Parker House in Boston and started to talk about their luck. One said he had caught a twenty pound salmon in Mooselockmeguntic. The other said that the year before he had been out night fishing and the lantern fell out of the boat. A couple of months later he was trolling and felt a heavy tug at the line, and pulled up the lantern—still lit. "Come now, you don't expect me to believe that," said the first fisherman. "All right," answered the other, "You take off ten pounds and I'll put out the light!"

The unsuccessful minister[3]

Everyone else in the lake was having good luck—not the minister. He kept trolling without landing a thing; people passed by, asked him how he was doing—nothing doing. Finally some one sug-

---

[1] Ibid., p. 282.
[2] Ibid., p. 282.
[3] Ibid., p. 282.

gested he spit on his worm. Still no luck. Then the party advised him to give his worm some liquor, and poured some into the minister's hands. He gave it to the worm, and in a minute felt a terrible tug— he reeled in and found that worm had wrapped itself around a two and one-half pound trout.

Those army mules[1]

M y father bought up a couple of army mules after the last war to work on the farm. Those mules were too cussed lazy to do any work, but my brother Jimmy and I made up our minds we'd teach them. We put green glasses on 'em and fed 'em shavings, but still they wouldn't work. Then one morning we led 'em out and hitched 'em head on to the plow, and showed them a big sign nailed up on the plow—"Work." It took the hired man five gallons of oil to keep the plow point from heating, those mules tore over the ground so fast. They plowed 165 acres that day; we hauled water for three days to cool the ground. The hired man planted corn. After he had planted three acres he looked around to see how he was doing. The ground was still so hot that when the corn came up it popped; the old man thought it was snowing and froze to death.

Outracing a boat[2]

I n the old days we used to wear "reacher" skates—long iceskates that reached way over the foot, were clamped to the heel and strapped to the sole. One day I raced a boat on the St. John's from Woodstock to Frederickton on my skates, and beat it by an hour and a quarter. I'd have done better, only I fell in some air holes and would have drowned if I hadn't had presence of mind to swim to shore and get some logs to help me climb out.

---

[1] Ibid., p. 283.
[2] Ibid., p. 283.

Fancy log-rolling[1]

Georg Bass was pretty good at log-rolling, so I told him he ought to go into the championships at Lake Marancook. He went down and got into the finals against the champion, Eberhard. They started at noon; by four o'clock George had worn out the spikes on the arch of his boot and couldn't clench the log; I went back to Wilton and got him another pair of driving boots from the Bass Company. Well, George held on till well after supper, but about nine o'clock he gave out—he'd worn his end of the log all away, he turned so much faster than Eberhard.

Telling a story[2]

One of the readings which I used was a part of an extravagant chapter in dialect from *Roughing It* which I entitled "His Grandfather's Old Ram." After I had memorized it it began to undergo changes on the platform and it continued to edit and revise itself, night after night, until by and by, from dreading to begin on it before an audience I came to like it and enjoy it. I never knew how considerable the changes had been when I finished the season's work; I never knew until ten or eleven years later, when I took up that book in a parlor in New York one night to read that chapter to a dozen friends of the two sexes who had asked for it. It *wouldn't read*—that is, it wouldn't read aloud. I struggled along with it for five minutes and then gave it up and said I should have to tell the tale as best I might from memory. It turned out that my memory was equal to the emergency; it reproduced the platform form of the story pretty faithfully, after that interval of years. I still remember that form of it, I think, and I wish to recite it here, so that the reader may compare it with the story as told in *Roughing It,* if he pleases, and note how different the spoken version is from the written and printed version.

The idea of the tale is to exhibit certain bad effects of a good

---

[1] Ibid., p. 283.

[2] From *Mark Twain in Eruption, Hitherto unpublished pages about men and events,* by Mark Twain; edited, and with an introduction, by Bernard De Voto—Copyright, 1940, by The Mark Twain Company—(New York and London: Harper & Brothers; 1940), pp. 217-23.

memory: the sort of memory which is too good, which remembers everything and forgets nothing, which has no sense of proportion and can't
tell an important event from an unimportant one but preserves them
all, states them all, and thus retards the progress of a narrative, at the
same time making a tangled, inextricable confusion of it and intolerably wearisome to the listener. The historian of "His Grandfather's Old Ram" had that kind of a memory. He often tried to communicate that history to his comrades, the other surface miners, but he
could never complete it because his memory defeated his every attempt
to march a straight course; it persistently threw remembered details in
his way that had nothing to do with the tale; these unrelated details
would interest him and sidetrack him; if he came across a name or a
family or any other thing that had nothing to do with his tale, he
would diverge from his course to tell about the person who owned
that name or explain all about that family—with the result that as he
plodded on he always got further and further from his grandfather's
memorable adventure with the ram, and finally went to sleep before he
got to the end of the story, and so did his comrades. Once he did manage to approach so nearly to the end, apparently, that the boys were
filled with an eager hope; they believed that at last they were going
to find out all about the grandfather's adventure and what it was that
had happened. After the usual preliminaries, the historian said:

"Well, as I was a-sayin', he bought that old ram from a feller up in
Siskiyou County and fetched him home and turned him loose in the
medder, and next morning he went down to have a look at him, and
accident'ly dropped a ten-cent piece in the grass and stooped down—
so—and was a-fumblin' around in the grass to git it, and the ram he
was a-standin' up the slope taking notice; but my grandfather wasn't
taking notice, because he had his back to the ram and was int'rested
about the dime. Well, there he was, as I was a-sayin', down at the foot
of the slope a-bendin' over—so—fumblin' in the grass, and the ram
he was up there at the top of the slope, and Smith—Smith was
a-standin' there—no, not jest there, a little further away—fifteen foot
perhaps—well, my grandfather was a-stoopin' way down—so—and the
ram was up there observing, you know, and Smith he . . . (musing)
. . . the ram he bent his head down, so . . . Smith of Calaveras . . .
no, no it couldn't ben Smith of Calaveras—I remember now that he—
b'George it was Smith of Tulare County—course it was, I remember
it now perfectly plain.

"Well, Smith he stood just there, and my grandfather he stood just
here, you know, and he was a-bendin' down just so, fumblin' in the
grass, and when the old ram see him in that attitude he took it fur an
invitation—and here he come! down the slope thirty mile an hour
and his eye full of business. You see my grandfather's back being to

him, and him stooping down like that, of course he—why sho! it *warn't* Smith of Tulare at all, it was Smith of Sacramento—my goodness, how did I ever come to get them Smiths mixed like that—why, Smith of Tulare was jest a nobody, but Smith of Sacramento—why the Smiths of Sacramento come of the best Southern blood in the United States; there warn't ever any better blood south of the line than the Sacramento Smiths. Why look here, one of them married a Whitaker! I reckon that gives you an idea of the kind of society the Sacramento Smiths could 'sociate around in; there ain't no better blood than that Whitaker blood; I reckon anybody'll tell you that.

"Look at Mariar Whitaker—there was a girl for you! Little? Why yes, she was little, but what of that? Look at the heart of her—had a heart like a bullock—just as good and sweet and lovely and generous as the day is long; if she had a thing and you wanted it, you could have it—have it and welcome; why Mariar Whitaker couldn't have a thing and another person need it and not get it—get it and welcome. She had a glass eye, and she used to lend it to Flora Ann Baxter that hadn't any, to receive company with; well, she was pretty large, and it didn't fit; it was a number seven, and she was excavated for a fourteen, and so that eye wouldn't lay still; every time she winked it would turn over. It was a beautiful eye and set her off admirable, because it was a lovely pale blue on the front side—the side you look out of—and it was gilded on the back side; didn't match the other eye, which was one of them browny-yellery eyes and tranquil and quiet, you know, the way that kind of eyes are; but that warn't any matter—they worked together all right and plenty picturesque. When Flora Ann winked, that blue and gilt eye would whirl over, and the other one stand still, and as soon as she begun to get excited that hand-made eye would give a whirl and then go on a-whirlin' and a-whirlin' faster and faster, and a-flashin' first blue and then yaller and then blue and then yaller, and when it got to whizzing and flashing like that, the oldest man in the world couldn't keep up with the expression on that side of her face. Flora Ann Baxter married a Hogadorn. I reckon that lets you understand what kind of blood she was—old Maryland Eastern Shore blood; not a better family in the United States than the Hogadorns.

"Sally—that's Sally Hogadorn—Sally married a missionary, and they went off carrying the good news to the cannibals out in one of them way-off islands round the world in the middle of the ocean somers, and they et her; et him too, which was irregular; it warn't the custom to eat the missionary, but only the family, and when they see what they had done they was dreadful sorry about it, and when the relatives sent down there to fetch away the things they said so—said so right out—said they was sorry, and 'pologized, and said it shouldn't happen again; said 'twas an accident.

39

"Accident! now that's foolishness; there ain't no such thing as an accident; there ain't nothing happens in the world but what's ordered just so by a wiser Power than us, and it's always fur a good purpose; we don't know what the good purpose was, sometimes—and it was the same with the families that was short a missionary and his wife. But that ain't no matter, and it ain't any of our business; all that concerns us is that it was a special providence and it had a good intention. No, sir, there ain't no such thing as an accident. Whenever a thing happens that you think is an accident you make up your mind it ain't no accident at all—it's a special providence.

"You look at my Uncle Lem—what do you say to that? That's all I ask you—you just look at my Uncle Lem and talk to me about accidents! It was like this: one day my Uncle Lem and his dog was downtown, and he was a-leanin' up against a scaffolding—sick, or drunk, or somethin'—and there was an Irishman with a hod of bricks up the ladder along about the third story, and his foot slipped and down he come, bricks and all, and hit a stranger fair and square and knocked the everlasting aspirations out of him; he was ready for the coroner in two minutes. Now then people said it was an accident.

"Accident! there warn't no accident about it; 'twas a special providence, and had a mysterious, noble intention back of it. The idea was to save that Irishman. If the stranger hadn't been there that Irishman would have been killed. The people said 'special providence—sho! the dog was there—why didn't the Irishman fall on the dog? Why warn't the dog app'inted?' Fer a mighty good reason—the dog would 'a' seen him a-coming; you can't depend on no dog to carry out a special providence. You couldn't hit a dog with an Irishman because—lemme see, what was that dog's name . . . (musing) . . . oh, yes, Jasper—and a mighty good dog too; he wa'n't no common dog, he wa'n't no mongrel; he was a composite. A composite dog is a dog that's made up of all the valuable qualities that's in the dog breed—kind of a syndicate; and a mongrel is made up of the riffraff that's left over. That Jasper was one of the most wonderful dogs you ever see. Uncle Lem got him of the Wheelers. I reckon you've heard of the Wheelers; ain't no better blood south of the line than the Wheelers.

"Well, one day Wheeler was a-meditating and dreaming around in the carpet factory and the machinery made a snatch at him and first you know he was a-meandering all over that factory, from the garret to the cellar, and everywhere, at such another gait as—why, you couldn't even see him; you could only hear him whiz when he went by. Well, you know a person can't go through an experience like that and arrive back home the way he was when he went. No, Wheeler got wove up into thirty-nine yards of best three-ply carpeting. The widder was sorry, she was uncommon sorry, and loved him and done the best she

40

could fur him in the circumstances, which was unusual. She took the whole piece—thirty-nine yards—and she wanted to give him proper and honorable burial, but she couldn't bear to roll him up; she took and spread him out full length, and said she wouldn't have it any other way. She wanted to buy a tunnel for him but there wasn't any tunnel for sale, so she boxed him in a beautiful box and stood it on the hill on a pedestal twenty-one foot high, and so it was monument and grave together, and economical—sixty foot high—you could see it from everywhere—and she painted on it 'To the loving memory of thirty-nine yards best three-ply carpeting containing the mortal remainders of Millington G. Wheeler go thou and do likewise.' "

At this point the historian's voice began to wobble and his eyelids to droop with weariness, and he fell asleep; and so from that day to this we are still in ignorance; we don't know whether the old grandfather ever got the ten-cent piece out of the grass; we haven't any idea what it was that happened, or whether anything happened at all.

The Barton sisters tell of Lorenzo Dow[1]

Miss Sadie is known as a teller of stories. Miss Jennie, while marketing only that morning, had been approached by a woman she hadn't seen in 50 years, and the woman had said, "How is Sadie? Does she still tell stories?" Many of them Miss Sadie had from her aunt and from her grandmother.

"I will tell you the story of Lorenzo Dow," Miss Sadie said, settling herself in her chair. "The scene is somewhere in Rhode Island and the time is a long time ago. Lorenzo Dow was a minister, a circuit preacher, I guess you'd call him. He went around all over the country. I remember reading about him as a child, and I have heard my grandmother say she heard him. My grandmother was born in 1812.

"He was going through the country, this Lorenzo Dow, preaching where he was in the habit of having meetings. He would tell the people, as he went around, that he'd be at a certain meeting house at a certain time.

"There was deep snow on the ground at the time and the roads hadn't been very well broken out, so it was hard to notify many people and hard for them to get there. However, he preached, and after he had preached, the people gathered around to talk as usual. He detected some embarrassment among them but he didn't know the reason.

---

[1] From "The Barton Sisters," by G. Y. Loveridge, *Providence Sunday Journal*, April 2, 1944.

Finally the deacon said, 'Now, Elder Dow, I don't know where you are going to stay tonight. All the children are down with measles at my house.' And the minister's wife was sick, with a new addition to the family.

"Standing at one side was a young woman comfortably dressed. She stepped up diffidently and said that Elder Dow could stay at her house. The others didn't know what to say. They . . ."

"They were kinda sorta somehow," Miss Jennie commented.

"He thought he could stand to go home with Mary Magdalen (that was what they called her, for she was in the habit of entertaining)," Miss Sadie continued. "Her husband was a hard drinker. The people didn't know what else to do, so they let Elder Dow go home with Mary Magdalen. She made a hasty pudding, and they had hasty pudding and milk for supper.

"In the great-room, or gret-room, which was what they called the living-room in those days, the fire was all laid in the fireplace, and Mary lighted it with a coal that she carried in the tongs from the kitchen. In the gretroom was the spare bed, with curtains around it, standing beside the fireplace. There was also a spinning-wheel beside the fireplace, and on the other side was a linen-wheel. After the room warmed up . . ."

"You've forgotten the barrel," Miss Jennie interrupted.

"Oh, yes. Beside the fireplace there was a barrel of tow. Tow is the waste from flax, you know, and they put that in a barrel. Elder Dow got into bed and was warm and comfortable, sleepy, and he began thinking that Mary's husband would probably come home drunk. He was just going to sleep when he heard somebody come and knock and call, 'Mary.'

" 'Well,' he thought, 'he can't be very drunk tonight.'

"The man came in and Elder Dow heard them talking. Then a door squeaked, closed, and he was just dropping off when he heard somebody else coming singing, cursing, and swearing up the road. That was John, her husband. He came to the door, and shook it good and hard and called Mary Magdalen.

"Then the door between the gretroom and the kitchen opened and somebody rushed in, went to the barrel of tow beside the chimney, scattered the tow all over, got into the barrel, and pulled the tow in after him."

Miss Hannie said, "A man couldn't get in a tow barrel."

"Maybe he was a little man," Miss Sadie said.

"Maybe it was a sugar barrel," Miss Jennie put in, smiling and going on with her knitting.

"Well, anyway," Miss Sadie said, "he got into it and covered himself with the tow. Mary's husband called, 'Mary!'

" 'Hush!' Mary said, 'Don't make a noise. Lorenzo Dow is sleeping in the gretroom.'

" 'Lorenzo Dow the preacher?'

" 'Yes.'

" 'I've got to see Lorenzo Dow.'

"She tried to keep him from the gretroom, but he said, 'I must see Lorenzo Dow, for they say he can raise the devil, I want to see him do it.'

"Mary couldn't keep him back. He pulled the curtain of the bed aside and said, 'Are you Lorenzo Dow?'

" 'Yes.'

" 'Can you raise the devil?'

" 'I can try.'

" 'If you do, I promise that I will leave off drinking and become a Christian man and live as I should.'

"So Lorenzo Dow put one foot out. It was cold, and he drew on his woolen stockings and pulled on his pants. Mary stood anxious. Lorenzo said, 'Well, you know the devil is supposed to live where it is hot. The devil has to do with fire. I'll have to raise him with fire.' So he shook up the fire."

" 'He didn't shake the fire,' Miss Jennie said. "They didn't shake fires in those days. He stirred it up with the tongs.'

"He stirred up the fire in the fireplace," Miss Sadie said imperturbably, "with the tongs, and took three coals in the shovel. He walked over and dropped the coals into the barrel of tow.

"The tow flamed up. The devil jumped up with bits of tow flaming on him, rushed to the kitchen, and went blazing down the road."

She paused.

"As far as I know John reformed, and he and Mary Magdalen lived together happily," she said.

Adirondack anecdotes[1]

One morning last summer I went to see Mr. Samuel Beardsley, one of the last living stage drivers in Essex County who drove a four-horse team. Mr. Beardsley, who was "Sammy" to the whole community for over eighty years, was a big man, scarcely stooped at all, though he walked with a cane. Most of the day he spent in his favorite rocker, with his pipe-stand close at hand. As he talked about the old

---

[1] From Edith E. Cutting: *Lore of an Adirondack County* (Ithaca: Cornell University Press; 1944), pp. 22-7.

days, his voice was deep and rumbling, and he had a way of chuckling to himself before he reached the point of a story. I had planned to stay an hour or two, but lunch-time came before I realized it, and it must have been after two o'clock before I left. I promised to come back, but when I do, Mr. Beardsley will not be there.

Although he loved good horses, and had driven everywhere in every kind of weather, the trip he talked most about was between Lake Placid and Saranac. Driving a four-horse stagecoach, he made only two trips a week between the two towns. The roads were bad—muddy in spring, dusty and rough in summer, and drifted in winter. The road by the Cascade Lakes is one that old-timers still talk about. The north side had high rock walls, and there was a drop of fifteen or twenty feet from the south side to the lake, which was very deep. The worst of the situation was that the road there was very narrow, in fact, Mr. Beardsley said, that if he met another wagon, in order to pass he had to take the curtain-buttons off the stage! In the winter the road was plowed only wide enough for one vehicle. If two met, one of them —and it wouldn't be the stage—had to back up to a "turning-out place," made for that purpose at intervals in the banks of snow.

One of the worst trips he ever made over that road was in a buggy, not in the stage. That day he had been hired to take a passenger through, as no stage was scheduled till the next day. The fog was so thick that he couldn't see the horse, but as long as the buggy kept going, he figured the horse was still there. He certainly had the worst of that trip, for the fog kept the passenger from seeing how dangerous the road was, and the horse was blind anyway!

Most of the time, though, Mr. Beardsley talked about people he had known. Driving stage was his business, and therefore thoroughly familiar and unexciting. On the other hand, people were always doing funny things.

One day Will and Alfred was over to Wadhams Falls. They wasn't drinkin' men, but they thought they'd go into the tavern and have a drink. When they got their glasses full, Will says, "Well, here's to you,—a good man, a good husband, a good father, a good Christian, a good neighbor."

Alfred picked up his glass and said, "Will, I wish I could say the same about you."

"Well, you could, if you'd lie like hell, the way I did."

Another story he told was about two of his neighbors.

Henry was neat, always. Jim was a hard worker, but he never looked put together. One morning Henry went down to Jim's to get some straw, and Jim wasn't up yet. Finally Jim came out of the bedroom, half-dressed, and his suspenders still hangin' down. Well, when he come out, he says to his wife, "Mary, what shall I do towards gettin' breakfast?" (She was kinda feeble, so he used to make a big show of helpin' her.) Quick as a flash Henry spoke up, "Gol, man, put yourself to soak!"

44

Although most stories about peddlers involve murder and robbery, Mr. Beardsley told a different type of one about a peddler who used to sell tea and coffee through the county.

> Ted would start singin' his wares out to the road, and by the time he got to the house, he would have told you all he had to sell. The day he went to get married, he had had quite a few drinks, and he was feelin' perty happy, you know; so when the minister got to the part of the ceremony where he says, "Join hands," Ted said, "Yeah, join hands and circle to the left."

While Mr. Beardsley rested, his daughter took me to see the cellar-hole where used to stand the house of Joe Call, the Lewis Giant. Joe was the subject of many tales. He was about six feet tall, thickset, and supposed to be double-jointed. A mill-wright and lumberman by trade, he was noted as a wrestler, and many stories were told of his strength. "Strong as Joe Call" was a common comparison at one time, and no wonder, according to the stories. "Sammy" Beardsley was too young to remember Joe, although he had heard his father talk of their powerful neighbor.

> I remember my father tellin' how he went over there with my grandfather one morning, and Joe wasn't up. He was awful lazy. Well, Grandfather called out to him, "Time to get up, Joe."
> He answered, "Oh, you'll live longer if you don't get up too early."
> Grandfather reached out, pulled back the bedclothes, picked up a barrel-stave, and hit Joe a crack. Joe jumped out of the bed with one bound, picked Grandfather up by the ankles, and dumped him head first into a sugar-barrel that was standing there.

A taller, more generally known tale is told by Mr. Alec Couthey of Essex.

> At one time Joe was asked for direction to a neighbor's house. Without a word, he lifted one of his oxen by the tail, straightened his arm out, and pointed up the road.

One which Mr. Beardsley would have appreciated is told by Mr. George Cutting.

> During the winter a certain man in the community had plowed out the toad with his team. Since he had plowed it, he was determined that, if he met anyone, it would be the other fellow who turned out into the drifts to go by. It wasn't long before he did meet someone. When the other man asked him to turn out, he yelled back, "I plowed this road, and I'm not goin' to turn out for no man." The other man climbed out of his sleigh, pushed the first man's horses into the drifts, turned the cutter over, climbed back into his own cutter and drove on. That was Joe Call.

Mr. Beardsley said he wasn't much on tall tales, but then he proceeded to tell me quite casually about a bear some of his friends had found frozen to death. They hauled it into camp, and when it thawed out, they had to shoot fast, or it would have got away after all!

45

Wherever a group of men spent the evening together, whether they were stage-drivers meeting at terminal points or lumberjacks perched along the deacon's bench, stories abounded. As practically all of the men were from farms, many of the stories were of their experiences during haying season. One that my father tells shows the feeling between Vermont and New York.

When Charlie and Wally were young, they got jobs on a farm in Vermont durin' the hayin' season. At the height of the hayin' there, the men always worked till eight or nine o'clock at night and then dragged their hand-rakes all the way to the barn to gather scatt'rin's of hay, but the first night, the two men from Lewis started for the barn with their rakes over their shoulders. The man they worked for shouted at 'em, "Here in Vermont we drag our rakes."

Wally shouted back, "We folks from York State ain't so damn lazy but what we can carry ours."

Apparently Wally had an answer for every occasion, for Mr. George Smart, of Elizabethtown, tells another story about him.

The fellow Wally worked for that summer was a hustler. He would throw a tumble of hay onto the wagon, start runnin' for the next tumble, and prick the horses with his fork as he went by, to make sure they started fast enough. Wally was up on the load, and one time when the boss pricked the horses, he was 'way at the back. O' course, when the horses jumped, he tumbles off the end. The boss yelled back at him, "What you doin' down here?"

And Wally yelled right back at him, "I'm down after more hay."

The men weren't the only ones who could tell a good story. Mrs. Edna Beahan, of Keene Valley, likes the story of a man who owned a big field of hay along the Raquette River.

John had the hay all cocked ready to draw in when a thunderstorm broke. He was afraid the river would come up and carry off the hay, so he hitched up his team and started for the field. He got there just in time to see the hay floatin' down the river. Well, he up with his fork and threw that into the hay and yelled, "If the Lord wants that hay, he'll want a fork to handle it with!"

Summer experiences sometimes grew a little tall in the telling, however, according to my grandfather.

One farm I worked on, they never got through hayin' till snow flies. They'd rake the hay up into a win'row and leave it there till it froze. Then they'd hitch the team onto one end and haul it to the barn.

As an evening progressed, the stories were apt to grow taller and taller. One of Uncle Kell's favorites is about Bill Young.

When Bill Young was a kid, he was goin' into the woods after the cows one night. He had a pocket full of stones, throwin' 'em at one thing 'n' another along the way. All of a sudden he come face to face with a big black bear. She was comin' right at him with her mouth open. Well, sir, he up with one of those stones and let 'er have it right in the mouth. She turned tail quicker'n a wink, but before she could run away, he threw another rock at 'er. That one went right in her back side 'n' struck fire on the first one 'n' burned the bear up in front of his eyes.

Another story is also similar to those told by the Baron Munchausen in a collection of tales published in the eighteenth century. The story itself is tall enough, but the fact that it has been retold for so many years and under such different circumstances seems even taller.

An old fellow I used to know was out huntin' when he saw a fox runnin' right at 'im. He up with his gun and fired right into the fox's mouth. It turned the fox wrong side out so he was runnin' away from the man. He was so surprised, the fox had time to get away 'fore he could shoot again.

At least, that is the way Uncle Jack tells it.

John Darling[1]

In 1934 Miss Mildred Tyler, of a family long domiciled in Sullivan County, brought me a cycle of tales about a certain John Darling, of whom she knew few biographical facts except that he died a long time ago, yet in the memory of some now living; that he had a farm on the banks of Sand Pond, that he probably had rafted on the Delaware, and that he certainly was the champion liar of her county. In order to recover more of the legend, I broadcast in February, 1935, some stories of which I shall proceed to give samples.

"You know, boys," John would say, "you know I never shave nor have my hair cut oftener than once a year. Yessir, every May I figure on going down to the barber in Roscoe and getting my whiskers cut off. 'Taint worth while to go oftener than that. Well, last spring I went down, and when the barber cut off my beard, I decided to take it home. Seemed as if there was quite a bit of weight to it; so I took it along, and my old woman poured a little water on it and put it on the stove; and darned if she didn't get seven gallons of maple syrup out of them whiskers! You see, boys, we'd had an extra lot of pancakes that winter.

"I remember a colder winter, though. One day it was so cold that the fire in my chimley wouldn't draw, and the smoke kept coming into the room. Well, I couldn't stand that; so finally I figured a way to get the smoke up. I whittled a paddle out of a piece of wood, and I

---

[1] From Harold W. Thompson: *Body, Boots and Britches,* Copyright, 1939, by Harold W. Thompson, published by J. B. Lippincott Co., pp. 131-4.

fastened it onto the end of a bit of rope. I hung the rope over a nail, and then I stuck the paddle into the fireplace under the smoke. I sat down by the fire and began to pull the rope, like ringing a bell. The paddle kept jerking up and down every time I pulled the rope, and pushed the smoke up the chimley. Well, I sat there a spell, working the paddle and singing songs. (You know, boys, I was born with a clarion lung.) Pretty soon I noticed that the paddle wasn't working so good. It was getting awful heavy and hard to lift, and the smoke seemed harder to push up. Finally I went outside and looked at the chimley. The weather was so cold that the smoke I had paddled had frozen as it came out, and had made a solid column ninety-six feet in the air. Yessir,—that was a real pretty sight all the rest of the winter; and in the spring, when the smoke began to melt, coming out of the air I heard the songs I had sung while I was paddling.

"I remember another day when it was pretty cold. That was when I had that old tomcat that I was so fond of. Well, my old woman, she used to set the jug of pancake-batter behind the stove so it would get light. One day, the cat got into the pancakes, and the old woman took a notion that they was spoilt. She seemed to be pretty mad, and she grabbed a dipperful of boiling water off the stove and went after the cat. I didn't want to see him hurt just for liking pancakes; so I opened the door, and he run for it. Just as he flopped through the door, the old woman let loose with her boiling water. Well, sir, it was so cold that day that the water froze the minute it left the dipper, and when it hit the cat on the head, it was such a heavy chunk of ice that it killed him.

"Speaking of pancakes and syrup—I worked out in California for a man who had some of them tremendous big sugar-bushes. They boiled down so much sap, that the man had to have big pans that weighed one ton each. About that time, mosquitoes out in California used to be pretty brisk, and they was big too. My boss told me that if I ever heard a sort of thundering sound coming from the sky, I'd better hide quick, because it wouldn't do no good to run.

"Well, I was out in the woods working one day when I heard a sort of *roar, roar, roar* up in the sky that made me look for a place to hide. There wasn't any place except under the big sap-pan, laying bottom-side up on the ground; so I picked up one corner of it and jumped under. Less than a minute later, there was a *crash;* a swarm of mosquitoes had hit that pan so hard that they drove their bills into it. There was some big stones on the ground under the pan where I was; so I picked up a stone and went around clinching all the bills of those mosquitoes onto the inside of the pan. The next thing I knew, they begun to clap their wings and make a sound like as if a big storm was coming. Then the sap-pan begun to lift up slow. It riz up graceful from the ground and over the tree-tops, and the last thing I saw of that sap-pan, it looked no bigger'n a base-ball, on the way to China.

"Did I ever have any pets after the old Tom was killed? Well, I got kind of attached to an old sow once, though she caused me some trouble by always snooping around under the barn and getting into the feed-box. One day when I caught her at her tricks, I grabbed up a broom-stick and hit her on the back. I guess I hit harder than I meant to, and it seemed like I broke her back—I never know my own stren'th. Anyway, she couldn't use her hind legs, and I thought for a while I might have to kill her. But I managed to build a nice two-wheeled truck for her to pull around under her hind-quarters. One day I missed this particular sow and finally decided that she had gone off somewhere to die. But a few months later, up in our grove of oaks I found her, grunting around, picking up acorns, and as nice and friendly as could be. There was thirteen little pigs running around beside her under the trees, and every one of them had a nice little two-wheeled truck under his hind-quarters."

Ali Baba in New York State[1]

T his story was transacted in Europe. Ali Baby was a poor boy. He had only a span of mules for a team. And with them he drawed wood to the village for a living—kinda. His brother Nelson was rich and lived in the village and felt smarter than Ali Baby and shunned him. But Ali made his living by drawing wood just the same.

In the neighborhood there was what they called "forty thieves." People's horses and cattle and other things they carried away, nobody knew where. One day Ali went to the woods to get more wood. He left his team at the bottom of a hill and traveled up farther. While he was going along, he heard a noise that made him think he had better hide himself. So he clum to the top of a tree and hid in the branches. Close to the tree was a lot of rocks. And pretty soon the men making the noise Ali had heard, come along. They happened to be some of the thieves, so Ali sot very still out of sight in the top of the tree. When the thieves got close they clum off their horses right near him settin' up there in the tree. And one of them said to a big rock: "Open seesame, open seesame." And the rock opened and they all went in carrying bags of something off from their horses. When they come out they said: "Shut up, seesame, shut up seesame." And the rock shut itself up. Then they got on their horses and went off.

[1] From Emelyn Elizabeth Gardner: *Folklore from the Schoharie Hills, New York* (Ann Arbor: University of Michigan Press; 1937), pp. 140–3.

When they had got out of sight, Ali clum down and thought he'd try the sign. So he said to the rock: "Open seesame, open seesame." And the rock opened for him just the same as it had for the thieves. He went in and found legs, arms, bodies, heads and other pieces, and lots of money. He loaded himself with all the money he could carry and started out. When he got out, he said: "Shut up seesame, shut up seesame." And the rock done what he told it to. Then he went home with wood covering up his money. But when he got home he couldn't count the money, there was so much of it, so he thought he'd measure it.

His wife went over to Nelson's and borrowed a measure, but she didn't tell Nelson's folks what Ali was going to measure. Next day Ali went again to the den of thieves and got lots more gold and silver. When he got home with the treasure, his wife again had to go over to Nelson's for the measure. Nelson's wife wanted to know so bad what they measured that she played a trick on 'em. She put grass in the bottom of the measuring cup. So when Ali's wife returned the measure, some money was left in the grass because they had turned the cup bottomside up and never once thought of looking inside to see whether any of the money stuck. When Nelson's wife shook out the money caught in the grass, she made Ali tell her where he got money because he had always been terrible poor up to then. So he told her all about it, and she told her husband.

Then Nelson went to the rock and said: "Open seesame, open seesame." It worked all right, and he got inside. But when he wanted out, he forgot the right words and said: "Open rye, open rye." And of course the rock didn't open.

Pretty soon the thieves came with more gold and silver, and found him, and killed him, and cut his body up in pieces. When Nelson didn't come home, his wife went and told Ali that his brother had gone to the cave to get some money for them, and that she was afraid that something had happened to him. Ali went to see, and when he got in the cave, there was his brother all drawn and quartered. He gathered up the pieces and drug 'em down to the village to Nelson's house because he didn't know what else to do with 'em.

When he had thought quite a spell, he told Nelson's wife he'd go get the shoemaker and blindfold him so he wouldn't know where he had been, and have him sew the body together. Then they'd hold a funeral, he told her, just as though nothing had happened except Nelson had died.

So Ali went for the shoemaker and blindfolded him, then took him to Nelson's house. He blindfolded him so the shoemaker wouldn't know whose house he was in, and tell. The shoemaker sewed the pieces of the body together as Ali told him to, though he thought it was awful queer what had happened to the body. When he had finished, Ali blindfolded him again and took him back home. Next morning Ali gave out that Nelson was dead and that they'd hold a funeral such and such a time.

When the thieves went to the cave and found money gone and Nelson's body missing, they knew that they'd have to hunt the man who knew how to get into the cave and out again. They knew that he had druv to the village from the wheel tracks he had left. The king of the thieves went to a witch woman and got her to point out the house where Ali had took the corpse. Then for fear the king would forget or make a mistake, she went and put a number on the gatepost of Ali Baby's house or Nelson's house, so when the thieves come along they would know the right house. You see, Ali and his wife had moved right in with Nelson's widow as soon as the funeral was over.

Now it happened Ali Baby had a smart niece who always wanted to help her uncle. So when she saw a number on her uncle's gatepost she suspicioned something right off and started out and put the same number on all the gateposts in the neighborhood. When the thieves come along with their king, they didn't find out any more than they knew before because there was the same number on almost all the gateposts in the village.

Then the king of the thieves went to the witch woman again and this time asked her to put blood on the gatepost of the house he ought to search. And she did what he asked. But the niece, who was on the look-out for something more, saw the blood and marked lots of other gateposts the same way, so the thieves couldn't be sure of the right house.

All this time the king had suspicion on Ali Baby. But he went all the same to the witch woman again. This time she told him to take two trunks and put a man in each of them. Then she told him to ask Ali Baby if he could set the trunks in his house until he got ready to call for 'em. The witch woman said after Ali's folks had gone to bed and to sleep, the men could climb out of the trunks and kill the whole lot. The king tried it and the trick worked all right until the niece, who had been out when the king left the trunks, got home. Right away when they told her about the trunks, she smelt a rat. After the rest went to bed, she tiptoed over to one of the trunks so careful that the man who was in it, when he heard her, thought it was the king come to let 'em out. So he whispered: "Are they all to bed?"

Then the niece knew for certain there was trouble. And she went and told her uncle. He got his gun and shot into the trunks until the men in them was all shot full of holes. Then he threw the trunks out in front of another house near by.

Next, the king fetched some tin cans with men inside. He pretended they had oil in and that he wanted to leave them in Ali Baby's yard until next day. The niece knew that there was some mischief about it. So she peeked in several and saw the men all unbeknownst to them. Then she went and got a kettle and put into it ashes and grease and some water and boiled it all up until it made a strong lye. When it was boiling hot, she threw the stuff into one can, then into all the others and scalded all the thieves to death. Of course no one knew that all the other fellows were scalded to death, but they were all scalded except the head boss who wasn't in a can, but who was going to give the signal for the rest to climb out and kill the family. By and by he came and found that he had nobody to help him but dead men. But he didn't give up. He just put on airs and pretended that he was a king from way off. But the niece knew better. She knew he was the worst robber of all.

The king, when he saw that all his men were dead, said he wanted to give a party, and the girl might invite anybody she wanted. When they got to dancing and playing at the party, her Uncle Baby wanted her to dance before the king swinging a dagger as she knew how to do. So she did what her uncle wanted and made a great display. She swung the dagger in front of first one and then another. When she came to the king, she let him have it full in the stomach, and he fell over dead. At first the uncle was as mad as he could be. But the girl said: "Don't you take on; he was going to kill us." With that she showed her uncle a dagger that the king had hid under his coat where he could get it easy when he wanted it. Then Ali Baby gave his niece a fortune because she had saved his life and destroyed all the thieves. After that I came away and left them.

NOTE. It seems probable that this story is not actually very far removed from some printed version of the original. Many good yarns (including some of Grimm's) are told by people who, if pressed, will admit that they have read them somewhere. The hard fact is that a great deal of what recent American scholarship has too readily called "oral tradition" is more oral than traditional. See also p. 684 of the present volume.

4. WRITTEN TRADITION: DRESSING THE STORY UP

Word-of-mouth narration is rarely stilted in any country or age, but a written story is apt to become more conventional, a printed one even more so. It is not strange that in a country settled by Englishmen an artificial and Addisonian elegance should too often have been thought a necessary part of narrative-writing. This convention obtained widely in America well into the nineteenth century, as did the desire for religious edification in fictional form. Even men of action wrote with labored artifice, and preachers like Mason L. Weems found morals everywhere. Yet Weems was a good lively story-teller (they little know of Weems who only the cherry-tree story [1] know); his pamphlets sold extremely well, and his success inspired an infinite amount of hack writing. None of his imitators could report everyday talk as well as Weems, nor get as much out of a simple anecdote.

The next four selections show four American writers of very varying gifts spicing their stories for lovers of sensation; the stories themselves vary greatly in their essential drama. Parson Weems, in 1805 or thereabouts, "wrote up" a particularly banal murder, but from the first phrase of his title-page (the whole of which is given below) he baited his pamphlet adroitly—or at least effectively. (It cost twenty-five cents, and sold tremendously.)

The story poor Ann Saunders had to tell in 1826 was too gruesome to need any adornment; she has overlaid but not smothered it with a genuine if incongruous piety. Putnam's fight with the wolf also deserved the plainest language, but got (in 1834) something rather different. Finally, the humble anecdote of General Marion's simple fare was related by an anonymous hack writer of 1847 in a pompously abstract style that nearly killed it. Weems had told it much better back in 1824, but by mid-century he was considered old-fashioned and even crude. (He had quoted many an oath, and had printed, though with apologetic dashes, the phrase "son of a b-tch.") The books that his successors offered to the young American of the forties were indeed discreetly worded, but they were also starched stiff.

---

[1] The story of young Washington and his hatchet has never been proved false.

God's revenge against murder

The modern reader of "God's revenge against murder" is likely to ask: "Where does God's revenge come in?" Weems would perhaps reply that the speed with which this particular murderer was caught and punished was providential; he does imply this. But the real answer to the question is: "Only on the title-page." There the phrase occupied a place of honor, but an elaborate metaphor was also employed to catch the reader's eye and mind. Thus it ran:

GOD'S
REVENGE AGAINST MURDER
OR
THE DROWN'D WIFE
A TRAGEDY
AS LATELY PERFORMED, WITH UNBOUNDED APPLAUSE
(OF THE DEVIL AND HIS COURT)
BY NED FINDLEY, ESQUIRE,
ONE OF THE
GRAND COMPANY OF TRAGEDIANS
IN THE SERVICE OF THE
BLACK PRINCE
Who was so highly gratified with Ned's performance that he instantly
provided him Rooms in one of his own *Palaces;* created him a
Knight of the most ignoble order of the Halter, clapped
bracelets on his wrists, and an ornament round his neck;
and in a few days promoted him to the ridge pole
of the gallows at Edgefield Court-House,
South Carolina

BY M. L. WEEMS

Most readers who read this title-page must have gone further. They found an odd alternation of flowery sermonizing with realistic everyday language, for though Weems talks like a preacher, his characters do not. He says parenthetically to the victim, Mrs. Findley: "Poor afflicted sister! thy sorrows will soon be ended!" but she, as her husband knocks her overboard, cries: "O my husband! my husband! don't kill me! for God's sake what have I done?"

Weems seems to have been quite conscious that he was leading, so far as literary style was concerned, a double life. Having told us how Polly Findley struggled in the water "till choked by the *bubbling, blood-stained* wave, her cries were silenced forever!" he apostrophizes her unkind father; this leads to a digression upon the inhumanity of Europeans (though Polly's father was an American), and a eulogy of American penitentiaries (where Americans snatch a criminal from madness and restore him to wisdom and happiness), and a dissertation upon cruel stepmothers (for Polly had one). After three pages of this, Weems resumes his other manner, with the words: "Let us now go back to the wretched Findley, whom we left murdering his wife." Findley is apprehended and hanged in the next two pages, saying to the sheriff: "For God's sake give me something to raise my spirits, for indeed I am very low." The something is a half-pint of brandy, and when he has tossed it off, Findley is hanged. The language now changes to Weems's other key; "his trembling spirit forsook her wretched companion, to meet the presence of a *blood-avenging God!*" This phrase and the one on the title-page are all that we read of God's revenge. It is unlikely that any purchasers of the little tract complained, and it is readable even today.

Ann Saunders's bitter cup

One of the most startling narratives ever penned in America was the work of one Ann Saunders, whose story was published as written by herself in 1827. The printer was Z. S. Crossman, the place was Providence, R. I., and the title: *Narrative of the Shipwreck and Sufferings of Miss Ann Saunders.* In that title was no exaggeration whatsoever.

Ann Saunders, a half-orphan of English birth, set out from New Brunswick for Liverpool on the ship *Frances Mary* on January 18, 1826. She was twenty-four years old, was acting as companion to a Mrs. Kendall, and was in love with and in fact engaged to James Frier, the ship's cook, whom she had known in England. Early in February the *Frances Mary* ran into very bad weather, and on the 5th she was hove to in a violent storm; the whole stern was stove in, and the hold and cabin filled with water. She did not sink, but most of the provisions were lost. The storm continued violent for most of six days. At the end of this time, Ann records: "All on board were reduced to the most deplorable state imaginable! our miserable bodies were gradually perishing, and the disconsolate spirits of the poor sailors (who were probably like too many of their seafaring brethren, strangers to prayer) overpowered by the horrible prospects of starving without any appearance of relief! as for myself . . . my spirits were probably more buoyed up by the reflection that the greatest afflictions which we meet with, are often productive of the greatest blessings, and that they are the means which a merciful Creator often makes use of to bring souls to the knowledge of Jesus. . . . We had now arrived at an awful crisis—our provisions were all consumed, and hunger and thirst began to select their victims!—on the twelfth, James Clarke, a seaman, died of no other complaint (as was judged) than the weakness caused by famine; whose body, after reading prayers, was committed to the deep—and on the twenty-second, John Wilson, another seaman, fell a victim to starvation!—as the calls of hunger had now become too importunate to be resisted, it is a fact, although shocking to relate, that we were reduced to the awful extremity to attempt to support our feeble bodies a while longer by subsisting on the dead body of the deceased—it was cut into slices, then washed in salt water, and after being exposed to and dried a little in the sun, was apportioned to each of the miserable survivors, who partook of it as a sweet morsel—from this revolting food I abstained for twenty-four hours, when I too was compelled by hunger to follow their example! . . . to such an awful extremity, I can assure my christian readers, was I and my wretched companions now reduced! . . . On the twenty-third, J. Moore, another seaman, died, whose body was committed to the deep after taking therefrom the liver and heart, which was reserved for our subsistence—and in the course of twelve days after . . . the following persons fell victims to fatigue and hunger, to wit, Henry Davis and John Jones, cabin boys, James Frier, cook, Alexander Kelly, Daniel Jones, John Hutchinson, and John Jones, seamen . . . some of them expired raving mad, crying out lamentably for water."

Miss Saunders naturally felt most keenly the death of the cook, James Frier, for she was engaged to him. "It was partly by his solicitations," she records, "that I had been induced to comply with the wishes of Mrs. Kendall, to accompany her on this unfortunate voyage." She appeals with particular fervor to "christian female readers" to judge "what must have been my feelings to see a youth for whom I had formed an indissoluble attachment . . . expiring before my eyes . . . and myself at the same moment so far reduced by hunger and thirst as to be driven to the horrid alternative to preserve my own life (O God of Heaven! the lamentable fact is known to thee, and why should I attempt to conceal it from the world?) to plead my claim to the greater portion of his precious blood, as it oozed half congealed from the wound inflicted upon his lifeless body!!! Oh, this was a bitter cup indeed! but it was God's will that it should not pass me—and God's will must be done. O, it was a chastening rod, that has been the means I trust of weaning me forever from all the vain enjoyments of this frail world; and of fixing my hopes and trust in the merits of Jesus."

For some reason—she believed it was the result of prayer—Ann Saunders remained stronger than the other victims, and she tells us that while all the rest were unable "to detach from the lifeless bodies of their unfortunate companions that food which was now nature's only support, the Almighty, in mercy to me, endowed me with" not only the strength to exhort them continually in prayer, but also to prepare their food, "for which purpose I constantly carried about with me a knife, with which I daily detached and presented each with a proportionable quantity." Two days before they were rescued, Ann's patroness, Mrs. Kendall, ate the brains of a deceased seaman (Ann's phrasing) and declared that "it was the most delicious thing she ever tasted!" Ann was touched by the fact that this seaman had been three times wrecked before, but "providentially" saved.

Twenty-one days after the first cannibalistic meal, Ann gathered the other five survivors on the quarter-deck and delivered a very special prayer for them. The spirit of God (she says) was in her soul. A voice whispered to her: "Thy prayers are heard, fear not, I am with thee." And sure enough, the next day they were picked up by His Majesty's ship *Blonde*. The mate remarked to Ann, observing certain slices that she had spread on the deck: "You have yet, I perceive, fresh meat!" but his horror "can be better conceived than described when he was informed" that these slices were of human flesh.

Here Ann might have ended, but she had further lessons to draw. The men whose bodies were eaten had during the voyage been guilty of "impiously blaspheming," and many of them were "no doubt addicted to those vices peculiar to too great a portion of that class of people." As for those who survived, they had had, Ann thought, a most instructive experience. "It was good for us that we were afflicted." There are twelve more pages of pious exhortation in this piteous little pamphlet, but they soar away from the shipwreck into a theology that would not interest many readers today.[1]

Mansion of horror[2]

The first years on a new farm, are not however exempt from disasters and disappointments, which can only be remedied by stubborn and patient industry. Our farmer, sufficiently occupied in building a house and barn, felling woods, making fences, sowing grain, planting orchards, and taking care of his stock, had to encounter,

---

[1] Although Ann Saunders's narrative is here grouped with other pieces that show a disposition to adorn a tale, it might well have been placed with those stories which I have headed: "Special providences and strange deliverances," pp. 116ff.

[2] From Col. David Humphreys: *The Life & Heroic Exploits of Israel Putnam* (New York: E. Strong; 1834), pp. 8–12.

in turn, the calamities occasioned by drought in summer, blast in harvest, loss of cattle in winter, and the desolation of his sheep-fold by wolves. In one night he had seventy fine sheep and goats killed, besides many lambs and kids wounded. This havock was committed by a she wolf, which, with her annual whelps, had for several years infested the vicinity. The young were commonly destroyed by the vigilance of the hunters, but the old one was too sagacious to come within reach of gun-shot; on being closely pursued she would generally fly to the western woods, and return the next winter with another litter of whelps.

This wolf at length became such an intolerable nuisance, that Mr. Putnam entered into a combination with five of his neighbours, to hunt alternately until they could destroy her. Two by rotation, were to be constantly in pursuit. It was known that, having lost the toes from one foot, by a steel trap, she made one track shorter than the other. By this vestige, the pursuers recognized, in a light snow, the route of this pernicious animal. Having followed her to Connecticut river, and found she had turned back in a direct course towards Pomfret, they immediately returned, and by ten o'clock the next morning the bloodhounds had driven her into a den, about three miles distant from the house of Mr. Putnam. The people soon collected with dogs, guns, straw, fire and sulphur, to attack the common enemy. With this apparatus several unsuccessful efforts were made to force her from the den. The hounds came back badly wounded, and refused to return. The smoke of blazing straw had no effect; nor did the fumes of burnt brimstone, with which the cavern was filled, compel her to quit the retirement. Wearied with such fruitless attempts, which had brought the time to ten o'clock at night, Mr. Putnam tried once more to make his dog enter, but in vain; he proposed to his negro man to go down into the cavern and shoot the wolf: the negro declined the hazardous service. Then it was that the master, angry at the disappointment, and declaring that he was ashamed to have a coward in his family, resolved to destroy the ferocious beast, lest she should escape through some unknown fissure of the rock. His neighbours strongly remonstrated against the perilous enterprise: but he, knowing that wild animals were intimidated by fire, and having provided several strips of birch-bark, the only combustible material which he could obtain, that would afford light in this deep and darksome cave, prepared for his descent. Having, accordingly, divested himself of his coat and waistcoat, and having a long rope fastened round his legs, by which he might be pulled back, at a concerted signal, he entered head foremost, with the blazing torch in his hand.

The aperture of the den, on the east side of a very high ledge of rocks, is about two feet square; from thence it descends obliquely fifteen feet, then running horizontally about ten more, it ascends gradually sixteen feet towards its termination. The sides of this subterraneous cavity are composed of smooth and solid rocks, which seem to have been divided from each other by some former earthquake. The top and bottom are also of stone, and the entrance, in winter, being covered with ice, is exceedingly slippery. It is in no place high enough for a man to raise himself upright, nor in any part more than three feet in width.

Having groped his way to the horizontal part of the den, the most terrifying darkness appeared in front of the dim circle of light afforded by his torch. It was silent as the house of death. None but monsters of the desert had ever before explored this solitary mansion of horror. Cautiously proceeding onward, he came to the ascent, which he slowly mounted on his hands and knees until he discovered the glaring eyeballs of the wolf, who was sitting at the extremity of the cavern. Startled at the sight of fire, she gnashed her teeth, and gave a sullen growl. As soon as he had made the necessary discovery, he kicked the rope as a signal for pulling him out. The people, at the mouth of the den, who had listened with painful anxiety, hearing the growling of the wolf, and supposing their friend to be in the most imminent danger, drew him forth with such celerity that his shirt was stripped over his head and his skin severely lacerated. After he had adjusted his clothes, and loaded his gun with nine buckshot, holding a torch in one hand and the musket in the other, he descended the second time. When he drew nearer than before, the wolf, assuming a still more fierce and terrible appearance, howling, rolling her eyes, snapping her teeth, and dropping her head between her legs, was evidently in the attitude and on the point of springing at him. At the critical instant he levelled and fired at her head. Stunned with the shock, and suffocated with the smoke, he immediately found himself drawn out of the cave. But having refreshed himself, and permitted the smoke to dissipate, he went down the third time. Once more he came in sight of the wolf, who appearing very passive, he applied the torch to her nose, and perceiving her dead, he took hold of her ears, and then kicking the rope, the people above, with no small exultation, dragged them both out together.

Marion's dinner-party[1]

It was at the encampment on Snow's Island that the famous potato dinner took place. The account of this is one of the most pleasant legends of the Revolution, and has been celebrated throughout the land in song and story. It forms the subject of one of our most agreeable national pictures, the production of the pencil of John H. White, of Charleston. It has been circulated in various forms as an engraving, being first published by the Art Union, and never fails to please. The story is, that a British officer arrived at Marion's[2] encampment with a flag of truce, to negotiate an exchange of prisoners. His business finished, he was about to depart, when Marion pressed him to remain and share his dinner. The guest looked round, and perceived a fire, but no tokens of anything in the way of a banquet. Curiosity, or politeness, or both motives, induced him to accept the invitation; and Marion then directed one of the men to serve the repast.

The plate on which the American general's dinner was served was a clean piece of bark, and the viands themselves, which the man proceeded to unearth from among the glowing ashes, were tolerably simple, being neither more nor less than sweet potatoes, baked to a nicety. The General ate heartily, pressing his guest to follow his example. The stranger was at once awed and surprised at what he had seen, and forgave the dinner in the pleasure he received at being the guest of a soldier so renowned as Francis Marion; but a soldier without any of the factitious and extrinsic circumstances which usually accompany military dignity. As our readers are already aware, there was nothing commanding or noble in the presence of Marion; and his men looked like anything but an encampment of soldiers. The whole scene was decidedly unmilitary, so far as ornament and parade are concerned; but there was a look of determination in the swarthy faces of the men who passed and repassed, and an air of self-denial in the hard fare to which these soldiers of liberty submitted, which were far more formidable than any mere military pomp.

His politeness could not, however, prevent the officer from inquiring whether this frugal mode of living was Marion's usual fare. The General informed him that on that day, having a guest, he regarded himself as fortunate in having rather a better dinner than usual. The

---

[1] From *Life of General Marion* [Anon.] (Philadelphia: Lindsay & Blackiston; 1847), pp. 148–50.

[2] Francis Marion (1732–95) was known as the Swamp Fox for his exploits against the British.

conversation continued till the Briton was apprised that Marion's pay was no better than his rations; and the story goes on to say that, on his return to the British garrison, the officer was so much impressed with what he had heard and seen, and so convinced of the impossibility of overcoming soldiers who fought thus upon principle, and for the pure love of liberty, that he decided to throw up his commission. He returned to England, satisfied that the struggle, if not a vain, was an unjust one; and that those who fought so valiantly for independence deserved it. Whether in all its details this be strictly true or not, it is certain that the successful issue of the Revolution was as much due to the resolution and endurance of the patriots as to their active courage. The latter could only occasionally be called into exercise; the former was necessary every day. It was a long struggle, and harder in its resistance against want and suffering, than its battles with the enemy.

5. WITCHCRAFT AND OTHER SATANIC MISCHIEF

The belief in witchcraft came to New England from old England, of course, but it found in the New World an intellectual climate unfortunately all too congenial. Nowadays it is easy to look back with horror on the delusion that afflicted Salem Village [1] in the late seventeenth century, but it must be remembered that the age and place were swayed by theology, not to say theocracy, and not by reason. The Bible seemed to sanction a belief in witches. If the clergy had doubts, they were timid about expressing them, though there were some honorable exceptions. In any case, the universality of the superstition among common folk overwhelmed any possible skepticism. The "witnesses" who testified against the accused at Salem undoubtedly were moved by hysteria and by malice, but they were also moved by a fear so genuine that modern students, poring over the testimony, have found themselves oppressed with a strange sense of evil powers abroad. In the atmosphere of the witchcraft trials good things of day begin to droop and drowse. The "afflicted," as they were called, were among the greatest liars of American history—greatest and most sinister. It must be admitted that part of their appeal was to those, whether judges, clergy, or simple folk, who liked to hear a wondrous tale well told.

But though Satan visited Harvard, as we shall see, in the seventeenth century, he and his train of witches and wizards, ghosts and goblins, seem to have been little heard of in the eighteenth, that skeptical century. Early in the nineteenth they returned, much altered, reduced, in fact, to throwing stones. This Lithobolia, as one of the chief victims learnedly called it, was convincing enough to those who saw, heard, and felt the stones, but the modern reader is bound to suspect mere mischief, probably achieved by boys.

More impressive are some tales told today in remote and unworldly corners of this country. To such regions devils and witches have retreated, where people can understand them, partly believe in them, and more than half fear them. Such a story is "Sop Doll"; it contains elements familiar in European folk tale, and the virtue is by no means gone out of them.

By the middle of the nineteenth century Satan's kingdom had sadly

---

[1] Now Danvers, Massachusetts.

contracted. In Sam Slick's story of Barney Oxman, for instance, it will be seen that the devil is no more than a hoax, whose victim, furthermore, is painted as hopelessly simple. One twentieth-century writer made amends to the slighted demon; this was Stephen Vincent Benét, who in *The Devil and Daniel Webster* supplied enough old-fashioned brimstone to make a suitably awesome effect. In a story so well told as this the old terrors (otherwise relegated to the backwoods or the nursery) return with some force. Hence its great popularity; most members of the story-audience are rightly like children in their expectations. They hope always that a good artist will come along and make their blood run cold.

As for the Jersey Devil, he is as elusive as the will-o'-the-wisp. Henry Charlton Beck's quest for him, however, as will be seen, was not un-rewarding.

Satan at Harvard[1]

The story of one student prank was handed down for two centuries in Dunster family tradition. The President was at Concord visiting his kinsman Simon Willard, when a messenger came post-haste to say that he was urgently wanted at Cambridge, for the scholars had literally raised the Devil! The role of exorcist was a new one for Dunster, but he was quite equal to the emergency. Hastening back to Cambridge, he found the College in a turmoil. Some of the scholars had tried a bit of black magic, and it had succeeded only too well; old Nick, impersonated no doubt by some practical joker,[2] had materialized, and the young boys were thoroughly frightened. The President solemnly emptied his horn of gunpowder in the Yard, laid a train, touched it off with a live coal, and literally "threw the Devil out of Harvard College!"

---

[1] Reprinted by permission of the publishers from Samuel Eliot Morison—*Harvard College in the Seventeenth Century*—Volume I, p. 119. Cambridge, Mass.: Harvard University Press, 1936.

[2] Cf. the story of Barney Oxman, pp. 81–4, below.

Martha Carrier[1]

The Trial of Martha Carrier, at the Court of Oyer and Terminer, held by adjournment at Salem, August 2, 1692

Martha Carrier was Indicted for the bewitching certain Persons, according to the Form usual in such Cases, pleading *Not Guilty* to her Indictment; there were first brought in a considerable number of the bewitched Persons; who not only made the Court sensible of an horrid Witchcraft committed upon them, but also deposed, That it was *Martha Carrier,* or her Shape, that grievously tormented them, by Biting, Pricking, Pinching, and Choaking of them. It was further deposed, That while this *Carrier* was on her Examination, before the Magistrates, the Poor People were so tortured that every one expected their Death upon the very spot, but that upon the binding of *Carrier* they were eased. Moreover the Look of *Carrier* then laid the Afflicted People for dead; and her Touch, if her Eye at the same time were off them, raised them again: Which Things were also now seen upon her Tryal. And it was testified, That upon the mention of some having their Necks twisted almost round, by the Shape of this *Carrier,* she replyed, *It's no matter though their necks had been twisted quite off.*

II. Before the Tryal of this Prisoner, several of her own children had frankly and fully confessed, not only that they were Witches themselves, but that this their Mother had made them so. This Confession they made with great Shews of Repentance, and with much Demonstration of Truth. They related Place, Time, Occasion; they gave an Account of Journeys, Meetings, and Mischiefs by them performed, and were very credible in what they said. Nevertheless, this evidence was not produced against the Prisoner at the Bar, inasmuch as there was other Evidence enough to proceed upon.

III. *Benjamin Abbot* gave his Testimony, That last March was a twelvemonth, this *Carrier* was very angry with him, upon laying out some land, near her Husband's: Her Expressions in this Anger were, *That she would stick as close to* Abbot *as the Bark stuck to the Tree; and that he should repent of it afore seven years came to an end, so as* Doctor Prescot *should never cure him.* These Words were heard by

---

[1] From *"The Wonders of the Invisible World, Being an account of the tryals of several witches lately executed in New-England.* By Cotton Mather, D.D. To which is added *A farther account of the tryals of the New-England witches* By Increase Mather, D.D., President of Harvard College. London: John Russell Smith, Soho Square, 1862." Pp. 154-9.

others besides Abbot himself; who also heard her say, *She would hold his Nose as close to the Grindstone as ever it was held since his Name was* Abbot. Presently after this, he was taken with a Swelling in his Foot, and then with a Pain in his Side, and exceedingly tormented. It bred into a Sore, which was lanced by Doctor *Prescot,* and several Gallons of Corruption ran out of it. For six Weeks it continued very bad, and then another Sore bred in the Groin, which was also launced by Doctor *Prescot.* Another Sore then bred in his Groin, which was likewise cut, and put him to very great Misery: he was brought unto Death's Door, and so remained untill *Carrier* was taken, and carried away by the Constable, from which very day he began to mend, and so grew better every Day, and is well ever since.

Sarah Abbot also, his Wife, testified, That her Husband was not only all this while Afflicted in his Body, but also that strange, extraordinary and unaccountable calamities befel his Cattel; their Death being such as they could guess at no Natural Reason for.

IV. Allin Toothaker, testify'd, That *Richard,* the son of *Martha Carrier,* having some difference with him, pull'd him down by the Hair of the Head. When he Rose again, he was going to strike at *Richard Carrier;* but fell down flat on his Back to the ground, and had not power to stir hand or foot, until he told *Carrier* he yielded; and then he saw the shape of *Martha Carrier,* go off his breast.

This Toothaker, had received a wound in the Wars; and he now testify'd, that *Martha Carrier* told him, *He should never be Cured.* Just afore the Apprehending of *Carrier,* he could thrust a knitting Needle into his wound, four inches deep; but presently after her being seized, he was throughly healed.

He further testify'd, that when *Carrier* and he sometimes were at variance, she would clap her hands at him, and say, *He should get nothing by it;* whereupon he several times lost his Cattle, by strange Deaths, whereof no natural causes could be given.

V. *John Rogger* also testify'd, That upon the threatning words of this malicious *Carrier,* his Cattle would be strangely bewitched; as was more particularly then described.

VI. *Samuel Preston* testify'd, that about two years ago, having some difference with *Martha Carrier,* he lost a Cow in a strange Preternatural unusual manner; and about a month after this, the said *Carrier,* having again some difference with him, she told him; *He had lately lost a Cow, and it should not be long before he lost another;* which accordingly came to pass; for he had a thriving and well-kept Cow, which without any known cause quickly fell down and dy'd.

VII. *Phebe Chandler* testify'd, that about a Fortnight before the apprehension of *Martha Carrier,* on a Lordsday, while the Psalm was singing in the Church, this *Carrier* then took her by the shoulder and shaking her, asked her, *where she lived*: she made her no Answer, although as *Carrier*, who lived next door to her Fathers House, could not in reason but know who she was. Quickly after this, as she was at several times crossing the Fields, she heard a voice, that she took to be *Martha Carriers,* and it seem'd as if it was over her head. The voice told her, *she should within two or three days be poisoned.* Accordingly, within such a little time, one half of her right hand, became greatly swollen, and very painful; as also a part of her Face: whereof she can give no account how it came. It continued very bad for some dayes; and several times since, she has had a great pain in her breast; and been so seized on her leggs, that she has hardly been able to go. She added, that lately, going well[1] to the House of God, *Richard,* the son of *Martha Carrier,* look'd very earnestly upon her, and immediately her hand, which had formerly been poisoned, as is abovesaid, began to pain her greatly, and she had a strange Burning at her stomach; but was then struck deaf, so that she could not hear any of the prayer, or singing, till the two or three last words of the Psalm.

VIII. One *Foster,* who confessed her own share in the Witchcraft for which the Prisoner stood indicted, affirm'd, that she had seen the prisoner at some of their *Witch-meetings,* and that it was this *Carrier,* who perswaded her to be a Witch. She confessed, that the Devil carry'd them on a pole, to a Witch-meeting; but the pole broke, and she hanging about *Carriers* neck, they both fell down, and she then received an hurt by the Fall, whereof she was not at this very time recovered.

IX. One *Lacy,* who likewise confessed her share in this Witchcraft, now testify'd, that she and the prisoner were once bodily present at a *Witch-meeting, in Salem Village;* and that she knew the prisoner to be a Witch, and to have been at a Diabolical sacrament, and that the prisoner was the undoing of her, and of her Children, by enticing them into a snare of the Devil.

X. Another *Lacy,* who also confessed her share in this Witchcraft, now testify'd, that the prisoner was at the *Witch-meeting,* in Salem Village, where they had Bread and Wine Administred unto them.

XI. In the time of this prisoner's Trial, one Susanna Sheldon, in open Court, had her hands Unaccountably ty'd together with a wheelband,[2] so fast that without cutting, it could not be loosed: it was done by a *Spectre;* and the Sufferer affirm'd, it was the *Prisoners.*

NOTE: Martha Carrier was convicted, and was executed August 19, 1692. In all, nineteen innocent persons were executed in this terrible year. The tide of opinion then turned. There were witchcraft trials the following year, but no convictions.

---

[1] I.e., in good health.
[2] A pulley-cord.

Sop doll![1]

Said one time Jack started out to hunt him a job of work. He pulled out and traveled on till he got to another settle-ment, ran across a feller told him there was a man there wanted to hire some work done. So he told Jack where the man's house was at, and Jack went over there; stopped by the gate and hollered, "Hello!"

The man came out, asked Jack what did he want. So Jack told him.

The man told Jack to come on in; asked him what his name was. Says, "Well, Jack, I've got a mill on a watercourse down the road a piece, but I got no time to run it. I've hired several men to grind down there, but the very first night somethin' has always killed 'em. Looked like it was some kind of pizen. Now I thought I'd tell ye, Jack, so you'd know all about it 'fore ye took the job."

"Well," says Jack, "if you don't care, we might walk down there and look that mill over."

So they went on down to the mill. Hit was a old log house with a fireplace and ever'thing fixed for whoever tended the mill to cook and sleep down there. There were twelve little windows rather high-up on the walls, had no window lights in 'em.

Jack looked it over right good, says, "Bedad, I believe I might take the job."

The man says, "All right, Jack. I see you're no coward. Now I'll give ye half of what ye make and give ye your rations too. I'll go back to the house and get ye some meat and meal for your supper. And you can start in grindin' as soon as anybody comes."

Well, when word got out that the mill was opened up again, lots of customers started comin' in and Jack had to grind right on till it was plumb dark.

Fin'ly got the last turn ground out and shut the mill down. He hadn't no more'n got the water turned out of the mill race when here came an old man on a sorry-lookin' mule, got off and walked in the mill with a little poke of corn on his shoulder. He had a long gray beard and he was one-eyed.

"Howdy do, Jack," he says. "How you gettin' on?"

"All right, I guess," says Jack. "I hope you're well."

"About like common," says the old man.

[1] From *The Jack Tales: Folk Tales from the Southern Appalachians*, collected and re-told by Richard Chase, by permission of the publishers (Boston: Houghton Mifflin Company; 1943), pp. 76–82.

Then Jack looked at him, says, "I don't believe I ever saw you before."

"No," the old man told him, "I'm a stranger."

"Well, how in the world did you know my name?" Jack asked him.

"Oh, I knowed ye time I saw ye," the old man says. "I've come a long way today, Jack, and I wonder could you grind my corn for me. I couldn't get here no sooner."

"Why, sure," says Jack. "You wait here a minute and I'll go turn the water in again."

So Jack started the mill up and ground the stranger's corn for him; shut the mill down, and when he got back the old man says to him, says, "Jack, you're the first one ever done me right here at this mill, and I'm goin' to give ye a present."

He reached in his big coat and took out a silver knife and handed it to Jack. Jack thanked him and the old man left. Then Jack built him up a fire in the fireplace and got out the skillet. Now Jack didn't have no lamp, but the fire gave out right much light, and it happened the moon was shinin' in all twelve of them windows. Made it pretty near as bright as day.

So Jack was cuttin' up his meat with that silver knife when all at once hit got thick dark in there. Jack looked up and there in ever' one of them little windows sat a big black cat. They all were a-lookin' right at Jack, their eyes just a-shinin'.

Well, Jack wasn't scared, much. He went on and put his meat in the skillet, set it on the fire and stooped down to turn it with his knife; paid no attention to them cats. But just about the time his meat 'gun to fry, Jack heard one cat light down on the floor. He went on cookin', and the next thing he knowed, there was a big black cat a-settin' right up in the fireplace with him. Jack went to turn the meat over and that cat stuck out its paw toward the skillet, says, "Sop doll!"

Jack reached out right quick with his knife, says, "You better not sop your doll in my meat or I'll cut it off."

The old cat jerked its foot back and set there a while. Them other cats stirred around a little; stayed up in the windows.

Then Jack saw that big cat reach for his skillet again, says, "Sop doll-ll.'"

Jack come at it with his knife, says, "I done told you not to sop your doll in there. You try it one more time now, and I'll sure whack it off."

The old cat drawed back, set on there switchin' its tail. Them other cats stirred a little, one or two of 'em sort of meowled.

Then that cat fopped its foot right smack in Jack's gravy, says, "Sop! Doll-ll-ll!"

68

Jack came down with his knife right quick and cut the cat's paw plumb off. The old cat jumped for a window and all twelve of 'em went,

"Whar-r-r-r-r!"

and were gone from there 'fore Jack could turn to look.

Well, Jack went to throw that meat in the fire, and instead of a cat's paw, hit was a woman's hand layin' there in the skillet, had a ring on one finger.

Jack took the hand out and wropped it in some paper, put it up on the fireboard. Then he washed and scoured his skillet, cooked him some more meat, and a pone of bread. Got done eatin' and went on to bed.

The next mornin' the man that owned the mill got up real early, says, "Old lady, you better get up and cook me some breakfast. I reckon I'll have to make arrange-ments about buryin' that boy today."

His old lady just sort of scrouged around in the bed, said she was sick and couldn't get up. So the man fixed himself some breakfast and pulled on down to the mill.

There was Jack, just a-grindin' right on.

The man got in to where Jack was, hollered to him, says, "Well, I wasn't expectin' to see you alive, Jack. Thought I'd be buryin' you today."

Jack hollered back at him, says, "Well, hit's a good thing you don't have to do that."

The man hollered back in Jack's ear, says, "When you get that turn ground out, shut down the mill. I got to talk to ye, right now."

So directly Jack went and pulled the water-gate so's the mill racket 'uld stop and him and that man could talk.

Says, "Now, Jack, you tell me what happened last night."

Jack related to him about all them black cats and he told about the old man givin' him that silver knife.

The man says, "I see through the whole thing now. Hit's a witch gang. They wanted to have their lodge meetin's here in the mill. And when that cat sopped in the grease she pizoned it some way or other."

Jack said he had an idea that was how it was. Said that was why he scoured the skillet. The man said hit was a good thing he done that. Then Jack told him about the cat's paw turnin' into a woman's hand, says, "You might not believe that, but I've got it right here to show ye."

Got that woman's hand and unwropped it.

The man took it, looked it over, looked at the ring on it, says, "Now, I declare! Well, I'd 'a never thought it!" Says, "Now, Jack, you lock the mill up and come on back home with me. We got to tend to this right now. Hit's a good thing that knife was made out of silver. You can't hurt a witch with a knife, or a bullet even, unless it's silver."

So they went back to the house and the man's old woman was still in the bed. He asked her if she felt any better. She said, No, said she'd not get up for a little while longer.

So the man says to her, says, "You want me to send for the doctor?"

She said No, said for him to send for some of the neighbor women. He asked her what women folks she wanted to come and she named out eleven women in the settle-ment. So the man sent word to 'em, and 'fore any of 'em got there he says to his wife, says, "Let me see your right hand."

The old woman sort of twisted around, poked out her left hand. "No," says the old man, "hit's your right hand I want to see."

So she twisted and turned, poked out her left hand again. Then he reached over and pulled out her right arm and there wasn't no hand on it.

Well, the women folks came readily as soon as they got word.

The man says to Jack, says, "I been suspectin' my old woman was mixed up with that gang of witches, but I'd 'a never 'lowed she was the head of it."

Jack says, "Oh, surely not."

Man says, "Yes, I knowed hit was her hand time I saw the ring on it."

Well, when the last of them eleven women got in with his old lady, that man shut the door on 'em and fired the house. Them twelve witches started crackin' and poppin', and ever' one of 'em was burnt plumb up.

So Jack made an end of the witch gang in that settle-ment. And that man never did have no more trouble about his mill.

A NOTE ON THE LANGUAGE OF "SOP DOLL!"

Since the language of the story "Sop doll!" is thoroughly colloquial and the idiom and tone suggest genuine rustic speech, it should be noted here that the collector, Richard Chase, does not profess to have made a verbatim phonetic transcription. His informant, Mr. R. M. Ward, of Beech Creek, North Carolina, told Mr. Chase: "I allers try to tell 'em the old way, but I hardly ever use jest ex-actly the same wor-rds." [1] Chase therefore felt justified in correlating various versions of the stories he collected into, in each case, "one complete version." He adds: "The dialect has been changed enough to avoid confusion to the reading eye; the idiom has been kept throughout." [2]

"Doll" is a puzzling word; it seems to mean "paw," and Chase says that his informant so took it.

It is probably superfluous to point out that the underlying plot is common in European folklore.

[1] *The Jack Tales*, Preface, p. xi.
[2] Ibid.

Lithobolia

Some time in the year 1698 one Richard Chamberlayne, who had been (not very happily) secretary to the Governor of the province of New Hampshire, brought to a London printer a singular narrative. He had given it the name of *Lithobolia* (stone-throwing), and he was anxious that it should circulate widely, for it was a point of honor with him to convince as many people as possible that his tale was true. Whatever Whitlock, the printer, may have thought on this point, he was glad to accept, print, publish, and sell *Lithobolia,* and we may guess, though we have no evidence, that it sold well. Today it is one of the rarest (and most readable) of pamphlets.

The stone-throwing which the credulous and horrified Chamberlayne witnessed had taken place in 1682 near Portsmouth, New Hampshire, and was carried on, he was convinced, by "Infernal Spirits, or Devils Incarnate, Witches, or both," and the missiles had been "Stones, Bricks, and Brick-bats of all Sizes, with several other things, as Hammers, Mauls, Iron-Crows, Spits, and other Domestick Utensils, as came into their Hellish Minds." The "Lithobolia" continued, moreover, for "a quarter of a year." Chamberlayne had been a guest in the house of George Walton, where the events took place, and had kept careful notes of everything as it happened; great, therefore, was his distress of mind when the Governor, to whom he presented this evidence, laughed it off and attributed the whole thing to "the waggery of some unlucky Boys." This explanation seems reasonable enough today, but in 1682 witches were still abroad in New England, and one of George Walton's neighbors, an old woman, was known to have a grudge against him. She was also said to be a witch; at least, says Chamberlayne, "suspected and (I think) formerly detected for such kind of Diabolical tricks and practices."

The stone-throwing had begun on a Sunday evening. As the family sat soberly about, stones suddenly hit the roof and sides of the house, and a gate was "wrung off the Hinges, and cast upon the Ground" by invisible hands. It was bright moonlight; nobody could be seen near the house. Yet the stones, "some pretty great," continued to arrive. How large is "pretty great"? The answer is disappointing—but let Chamberlayne tell it.

There came many stones, and some pretty great ones, some as big as my Fist, into the Entry or Porch of the House; we withdrew into the next Room to the Porch, no Person having received any Hurt, (praised be Almighty Providence, for certainly the infernal Agent, constant Enemy to Mankind, had he not been over-ruled, intended no less than Death or Maim) save only that two Youths were lightly hit, one on the Leg, the other on the Thigh, notwithstanding the Stones came so thick, and so forcibly against the sides of so narrow a Room. Whilst we stood amazed at this Accident, one of the Maidens imagined she saw them come from the Hall, next to that we were in, where searching, (and in the Cellar, down out of the Hall) and finding no Body, another and my self observed two little Stones in a short space successively to fall on the Floor, coming as if from the Ceiling close by us, and we concluded it must necessarily be done by means extraordinary and Praeternatural.

Coming again into the Room where we first were, (next the Porch) we had many of these lapidary Salutations, but unfriendly ones; for, shutting the Door, it was no small surprise to me to have a good big Stone come with great force and noise (just by my Head) against the Door on the inside; and then shutting the other Door, next the Hall, to have the like Accident; so going out again, upon a necessary Occasion, to have another very near my Body, clattering against the Board-wall of the House; but it was a much greater, to be so near the danger of having my Head broke with a Mall, or great Hammer brushing along the top or roof of the Room from the other end, as I was walking in it, and lighting down by me; but it fell so, that my Landlord had the greatest damage, his Windows (especially those of the first mention'd Room) being with many Stones miserably and strangely batter'd, most of the Stones giving the blow on the inside, and forcing the Bars, Lead, and Hasps of the Casements outward.

Was this (it seems fair to ask) an "inside job"? What about the "maidens"? It is noteworthy that Chamberlayne himself says that one of them "imagined" she saw the stones fall. Other imaginations were obviously working; was a practical joker or a malicious mischief-maker supplying them with raw material? Some candlesticks were knocked from a table "and likewise a large Pewter Pot"; when Chamberlayne went to bed ("weary of the noise"), there was presently a great battering on the walls of his bedroom.

But the Noise immediately bringing up the Company below, they assured me no Mischief of that Nature was done, and shewed me the biggest Stone that had as yet been made use of in this unaccountable Accident, weighing eight pound and a half, that had burst open my Chamber Door with a rebound from the Floor, as by the Dent and Bruise in it near the Door I found next Morning, done probably, to make the greater Noise, and give the more Astonishment, which would sooner be effected by three Motions, and consequently three several Sounds, viz. one on the Ground, the next to and on the Door, and the last from it again to the Floor, than if it had been one single Blow upon the Door only; which ('tis probable) wou'd have split the Door, which was not permitted,[1] nor so much as a square of the Glass-Window broken or crack'd (at that time) in all the Chamber. Glad thereof, and desiring them to leave me, and the Door shut, as it was before, I endeavored once more to take my Rest, and was once more prevented by the like passage, with another like offensive Weapon, it being a whole Brick that lay in the Anti-Chamber Chimney, and used again to the same malicious purpose as

---

[1] I.e., by Providence.

before, and in the same manner too, as by the mark in the Floor, whereon was some of the Dust of the Brick, broken a little at the end, apparent next Morning, the Brick itself lying just at the Door. However, after I had lain awhile, harkening to their Adventures below, I drop'd asleep again, and receiv'd no further Molestation that Night.

In the Morning (Monday Morning) I was inform'd by several of the Domestics of more of the same kind of Trouble; among which the most signal was, the Vanishing of the Spit which stood in the Chimney Corner, and the sudden coming of it again down the same Chimney, sticking of it in a log that lay in the fire-place.

Another marvel (not quite as good) was that a flatiron "was conveyed invisibly into the Yard." Chamberlayne had prudently taken and kept the wonderful eight-pound stone that struck his bedroom door, and though unseen hands stole it from him, he recovered it and, he tells us, "had it in my custody a long time to show, for the Satisfaction of the Curious." It is a pity that this satisfactory bit of evidence finally disappeared; captured, presumably, by Satan or his agents.

One of the neighbors, who by now were all agog, was so indiscreet as to say that "Boys" had thrown the stones; this temerarious skepticism was promptly punished, for her little boy "was struck with a Stone on the back, which caused him to fall a-crying, and her (being convinced) to carry him away forthwith."

More dreadful things now happened. A pewter spoon was thrown into the living-room, and a black cat was seen in the orchard. The cat "was shot at, but missed." There was also "an odd dismal sort of whistling," and a sound "as it were the trampling of a young Colt."

The powers of darkness were also active out of doors. Mr. Walton had one day loaded his boat with hay and was rowing across the Piscataqua when, alas,

he found his Boat began to be in a sinking Condition, at which being much surprised, upon search, he discover'd the cause to be the pulling out a Plug or Stopple in the bottom of the Boat, being fixed there for the more convenient letting out of the Rain-Water that might fall into it; a Contrivance and Combination of the old Serpent and the old Woman, or some other Witch or Wizard (in Revenge or innate Enmity) to have drown'd both my good Landlord and his Company.

On Wednesday, as they were at work again in the Woods, on a sudden they heard something gingle like Glass or Metal, among the Trees, as it was falling, and being fallen to the Ground, they knew it to be a Stirrup which Mr. Walton had carried to the Boat, and laid under some Wood, and this being laid by him in this very Boat, it was again thrown after him. The third time, he having put it upon his Girdle or Belt he wore about his Waste, buckled together before, but at that instant taken off because of the Heat of the Weather, and laid there again buckled, it was fetched away, and no more seen. Likewise the Graper,[1] or little Anchor of the Boat, cast overboard, which

---

[1] Grapple.

caus'd the Boat to wind up, so staying and obstructing their Passage. Then the Setting-Pole was divers times cast into the River, as they were coming back from the Great Bay, which put them to the trouble of Padling, that is, rowing about for it as often to retrieve it.

Being come to his own House, this Mr. Walton was charged again with a fresh Assault in the out-Houses; but we heard of none within Doors until Friday after, when, in the Kitchin, were 4 or 5 Stones (one of them hot) taken out of the Fire, as I conceive, and so thrown about. I was then present, being newly come in with Mr. Walton from his middle Field (as he called it) where his Servants had been Mowing, and had six or seven of his old troublesome companions.

That stones were invisibly thrown was on this particular occasion witnessed by nine persons, including Governor Jennings of "West Jarsey" (New Jersey) and Governor Clark of "Road Island." The eager Chamberlayne got them to sign an affidavit. After this deposition was taken, the agents of Satan began to center their fire on Chamberlayne again "as if," he says, "I had been the designed object." And in fact most of the stones, he says, "hit me (sometimes pretty hard) to the number of 20, near 30." The dismal whistling was now heard again, also a snorting and a humming, and George Walton was hit in the back as he sat in his boat

at a Cove-side by his House. It was a very odd prank that was practis'd by the Devil a little while after this. One Night the Cocks of Hay, made the Day before in the Orchard, was spread all abroad, and some of the Hay thrown up into the Trees, and some of it brought into the House, and scattered. Two Logs that lay at the Door, laid, one of them by the Chimney in the Kitchin; the other set against the Door of the Room where Mr. Walton then lay, as on purpose to confine him therein: a Form that stood in the Entry (or Porch) was set along by the Fire-side, and a joint-Stool upon that, with a Napking spread thereon, with two Pewter Pots, and two Candlesticks: A Cheese-Press likewise having a Spit thrust into one of the holes of it, at one end; and at the other end of the Spit hung an Iron Kettle; and a Cheese was taken out and broke to pieces. Another time, I full well remember, 'twas on a Sunday at Night, my Window was all broke with a violent shock of Stones and Brick-Bats, which scarce miss'd my self; among these one huge one made its way through the great square or sash of a Casement, and broke a great hole in it, throwing down Books by the way, from the Window to a Picture over-against it, on the other side of the Chamber, and tore a hole quite through it about half a foot long, and the piece of the Cloth hung by a little part of it, on the back-side of the Picture.

After this, we were pretty quiet, saving now and then a few Stones march'd about for Exercise, and to keep (as it were) the Diabolical hand in use, till July 28, being Friday, when about 40 Stones flew about, abroad, and in the House and Orchard, and among the Trees therein, and a Window broke before, was broke again, and one Room where they never used before.

August 1. On Wednesday the Window in my ante-Chamber was broke again, and many stones were plaid about.

It was clearly time for countermeasures, and the afflicted household judiciously "did set on the Fire a Pot with Urin and crooked Pins in it." Bringing this to a boil would of course "give punishment to the Witch or Wizard," but alas! "a Stone came and broke the top or mouth of it and threw it down, and spilt what was in it; which being made good again, another Stone, as the Pot grew hot again, broke the handle off; and being recruited and filled the third time, was then with a third Stone quite broke to pieces and split; and so the operation became frustrate and fruitless."

This was utterly unanswerable. Any man who could disbelieve "these praeternatural Occurrences," says Chamberlayne bitterly, must be "an enemy to his own Soul"; further, he must be trying to "unhinge or undermine the Fundamentals of the best Religion in the World." And had not Chamberlayne seen to it that the whole story was placed "upon Record in his Majesty's Council-Court"? Of course he had, but in spite of all this, when the skeptical Governor of New Hampshire arrived on the scene, he utterly refused to believe that the phenomena were of supernatural origin. Most perplexing of all to poor Richard Chamberlayne (though not to us) was the fact that with the arrival of this scoffing Governor the "Lithobolia" stopped entirely. There was nothing to do—except to write a book.

The stone-throwing devil of Portsmouth was unique in the variety of his mischief. Unlike some other supernatural stone-throwers, he also threw candlesticks and pewter pots, cheeses and spits; he also stole various small objects. The stone-throwing devils that appeared from time to time in other parts of the United States in the early nineteenth century[1] were mostly less imaginative and attended strictly to stone-throwing, though they might accompany it with whistling and jingling. The accounts of their doings that follow were collected by skeptics; C. M. Skinner found his localized in Georgia, Illinois, and Connecticut, and J. W. Barber's somewhat fuller story comes from Sheffield, Massachusetts. The rationalistic interpretations suggested by Skinner and Barber would shock and grieve Richard Chamberlayne.

---

[1] In the twentieth century stone-throwing by witches would appear to be quite rare. It is said, however, by the editors of *Gumbo Ya-Ya* (Boston: Houghton Mifflin Co.; 1945) that "a few years ago" such manifestations occurred at 1813 St. Anthony Street, New Orleans, and continued for several days. "No cause was ever discovered" (*Gumbo Ya-Ya*, p. 291).

More stone-throwing devils[1]

A t Whitmire Hill, Georgia, the spot where two murders were committed before the war, is a headless phantom that comes thundering down on the wayfarer on the back of a giant horse and vanishes at the moment when the heart of its prospective victim is bumping against his palate. At times, however, this spook prefers to remain invisible, and then it is a little worse, for it showers stones and sods on the pedestrian until his legs have carried him well beyond the phantom's jurisdiction.

The legends of buried treasure . . . frequently include assaults by the ghosts of pirates and misers on the daring ones who try to resurrect their wealth.

Forty-seven years ago,[2] in the township of St. Mary's, Illinois, two lads named Groves and a companion named Kirk were pelted with snowballs while on their way home from a barn where they had been to care for the stock for the night. The evening had shut in dark, and the accuracy of the throwers' aim was the more remarkable because it was hardly possible to see more than a rod away. The snowballs were packed so tightly that they did not break on striking, though they were thrown with force, and Kirk was considerably bruised by them. Mr. Groves went out with a lantern, but its rays lit up a field of untrodden snow, and there was no sound except that made by the wind as it whistled past the barn and fences. Toward dawn another inspection was made, and in the dim light the snowballs were seen rising from the middle of a field that had not a footprint on it, and flying toward the spectators like bullets. They ran into the field and laid about them with pitchforks, but nothing came of that, and not until the sun arose was the pelting stopped. Young Kirk, who was badly hurt, died within a year.

The men of Sharon, Connecticut, having wheedled their town-site from the Indians in 1754, were plagued thereafter by whoops and whistlings and the throwing of stones. Men were seen in the starlight and were fired upon, but without effect, and the disturbances were not ended until the Indians had received a sum of money.

[In Sheffield, Mass., according to Barber,[3]] These occurrences commenced Nov. 8th, 1802, at a clothier's shop. A man and two boys

---

[1] From Charles M. Skinner: *Myths and Legends of Our Own Land* (Philadelphia and London: J. B. Lippincott Co.; 1896), Vol. II, pp. 307–9.

[2] This would place the story in 1849.

[3] John Warner Barber: *Historical Collections of Every Town in Massachusetts* (Worcester: Dorr, Howland & Co.; 1839), p. 93.

were in the shop; the boys had retired to rest, it being between 10 and 11 o'clock at night. A block of wood was thrown through the window; after that, pieces of hard mortar, till the man and boys became alarmed, and went to the house to call Mr. Sage, who arose from bed and went to the shop, and could hear the glass break often, but could not discover from whence it came, notwithstanding the night was very light. He exerted himself to discover the cause without success. It continued constantly till day-light, and then ceased till the next evening at 8 o'clock, when it commenced again and continued till midnight; then ceased till the next evening at dusk, and continued till some time in the evening, and then ceased. The next day it commenced about an hour before sun-down, and continued about an hour, and then it left the shop and began at the dwelling-house of Mr. Ezekiel Landon, 100 rods north, in the town of Sheffield. It continued several hours, and ceased till the next morning: when the family were at breakfast it began again, and continued two or three hours, and ceased till evening, when it began again and continued several hours, and ceased till the next morning, when it began again and continued all the forenoon, and then ceased altogether. The articles thrown into the shop were pieces of wood, charcoal, stone, but principally pieces of hard mortar, such as could not be found in the neighborhood. Nothing but stones were thrown into the house of Mr. Landon, the first of which were thrown into the door. There were 38 panes of glass broke out of the shop, and 18 out of the dwelling-houses: in two or three instances persons were hit by the things that were thrown. What was remarkable, nothing could be seen coming till the glass broke, and whatever passed through, fell directly down on the window-sill, as if it had been put through with a person's fingers, and many pieces of mortar and coal were thrown through the same hole in the glass in succession. Many hundreds of people assembled to witness the scene, among whom were clergymen and other gentlemen, but none were able to detect the source of the mischief. The more credulous readily believed it to be witchcraft, but it was generally thought to be some slight of hand, effected by a combination of individuals, as the windows were broken on different sides of the buildings nearly at the same time.

Satan was much too brazen a person to content himself with invisibility and stone-throwing. In the Old World he had liked personal encounters; he seeks them in American legend also. In New Hampshire Jonathan Moulton played a Faust-like role in his collision with the Evil One; in South Carolina the devil that Barney Oxman called up was a fraud. The Adversary that bargained with the Yankee Jabez Stone (another Faust) was sinister enough, and only Daniel Webster could thwart him. In New Jersey, of recent days, Satan has come down in the world, and is only a vaguely dreadful monstrous visitant. Still, he is called "the Jersey Devil," and that is what he will be called here.

Jonathan Moulton and the Devil[1]

The legendary hero of Hampton is General Jonathan Moulton. He is no fictitious personage, but one of veritable flesh and blood, who, having acquired considerable celebrity in the old wars, lives on through the medium of a local legend.

The General, says the legend, encountered a far more notable adversary than Abenaki warriors or conjurers, among whom he had lived, and whom it was the passion of his life to exterminate.

In an evil hour his yearning to amass wealth suddenly led him to declare that he would sell his soul for the possession of unbounded riches. Think of the Devil, and he is at your elbow. The fatal declaration was no sooner made—the General was sitting alone by his fireside—than a shower of sparks came down the chimney, out of which stepped a man dressed from top to toe in black velvet. The astonished Moulton noticed that the stranger's ruffles were not even smutted.

"Your servant, General!" quoth the stranger, suavely. "But let us make haste, if you please, for I am expected at the Governor's in a quarter of an hour," he added, picking up a live coal with his thumb and forefinger, and consulting his watch with it.

The General's wits began to desert him. Portsmouth was five leagues —long ones at that—from Hampton House, and his strange visitor talked, with the utmost unconcern, of getting there in fifteen minutes! His astonishment caused him to stammer out,—

"Then you must be the—"

"Tush! what signifies a name?" interrupted the stranger, with a deprecating wave of the hand. "Come, do we understand each other? Is it a bargain, or not?"

At the talismanic word "bargain" the General pricked up his ears. He had been often heard to say that neither man nor devil could get the better of him in a trade. He took out his jack-knife and began to whittle. The Devil took out his, and began to pare his nails.

"But what proof have I that you can perform what you promise?" demanded Moulton, pursing up his mouth and contracting his bushy eyebrows, like a man who is not to be taken in by mere appearances.

---

[1] From Samuel Adams Drake: *A Book of New England Legends and Folk Lore* (Boston: Roberta Brothers; 1884), pp. 322-8.

The fiend ran his fingers carelessly through his peruke, when a shower of golden guineas fell to the floor and rolled to the four corners of the room. The General quickly stooped to pick up one; but no sooner had his fingers closed upon it, than he dropped it with a yell. It was red-hot!

The Devil chuckled; "Try again," he said. But Moulton shook his head and retreated a step.

"Don't be afraid."

Moulton cautiously touched a coin; it was cool. He weighed it in his hand, and rung it on the table; it was full weight and true ring. Then he went down on his hands and knees, and began to gather up the guineas with feverish haste.

"Are you satisfied?" demanded Satan.

"Completely, your Majesty."

"Then to business. By the way, have you anything to drink in the house?"

"There is some old Jamaica in the cupboard."

"Excellent! I am as thirsty as a Puritan on election-day," said the Devil, seating himself at the table, and negligently flinging his mantle back over his shoulder, so as to show the jewelled clasps of his doublet.

Moulton brought a decanter and a couple of glasses from the cupboard, filled one, and passed it to his infernal guest, who tasted it, and smacked his lips with the air of a connoisseur. Moulton watched every gesture. "Does your Excellency not find it to your taste?" he ventured to ask; having the secret idea that he might get the Devil drunk, and so outwit him.

"H'm, I have drunk worse. But let me show you how to make a salamander," replied Satan, touching the lighted end of the taper to the liquor, which instantly burst into a spectral blue flame. The fiend then raised the tankard to the height of his eye, glanced approvingly at the blaze,—which to Moulton's disordered intellect resembled an adder's forked and agile tongue,—nodded, and said, patronizingly, "To our better acquaintance!" He then quaffed the contents at a single gulp.

Moulton shuddered; this was not the way he had been used to seeing healths drunk. He pretended, however, to drink, for fear of giving offence; but somehow the liquor choked him. The demon set down the tankard, and observed, in a matter-of-fact way that put his listener in a cold sweat: "Now that you are convinced that I am able to make you the richest man in all the province, listen! Have I your ear? It is well! In consideration of your agreement, duly signed and sealed, to deliver your soul"—here he drew a parchment from his breast—"I engage, on my part, on the first day of every month, to fill your boots with golden elephants, like these before you. But mark me well," said Satan, holding up a forefinger glittering with diamonds, "if you try to play me any trick, you will repent it! I know you, Jonathan Moulton, and shall keep my eye upon you; so beware!"

Moulton flinched a little at this plain speech; but a thought seemed to strike him, and he brightened up. Satan opened the scroll, smoothed out the creases, dipped a pen in the inkhorn at his girdle, and said, laconically, "Sign!"

Moulton hesitated.

"If you are afraid," sneered Satan, "why put me to all this trouble?" and he began to put the gold in his pocket.

His victim seized the pen; but his hand shook so that he could not write. He gulped down a mouthful of rum, stole a look at his infernal guest, who nodded his head by way of encouragement, and a second time approached his pen to the paper. The struggle was soon over. The unhappy Moulton wrote his name at the bottom of the fatal list, which he was astonished to see numbered some of the highest personages in the province. "I shall at least be in good company," he muttered.

"Good!" said Satan, rising and putting the scroll carefully away within his breast. "Rely on me, General, and be sure you keep faith. Remember!" So saying, the demon waved his hand, flung his mantle about him, and vanished up the chimney.

Satan performed his part of the contract to the letter. On the first day of every month the boots, which were hung on the crane in the fireplace the night before, were found in the morning stuffed full of guineas. It is true that Moulton had ransacked the village for the largest pair to be found, and had finally secured a brace of trooper's jackboots, which came nearly up to the wearer's thigh; but the contract merely expressed boots, and the Devil does not stand upon trifles.

Moulton rolled in wealth; everything prospered. His neighbors regarded him first with envy, then with aversion, at last with fear. Not a few affirmed that he had entered into a league with the Evil One. Others shook their heads, saying, "What does it signify?—that man would outwit the Devil himself."

But one morning, when the fiend came as usual to fill the boots, what was his astonishment to find that he could not fill them. He poured in the guineas, but it was like pouring water into a rat-hole. The more he put in, the more the quantity seemed to diminish. In vain he persisted; the boots could not be filled.

The Devil scratched his ear. "I must look into this," he reflected. No sooner said, than he attempted to descend; but in doing so he found his progress suddenly stopped. A good reason. The chimney was choked up with guineas! Foaming with rage, the demon tore the boots from the crane. The crafty General had cut off the soles, leaving only the legs for the Devil to fill. The chamber was knee-deep with gold.

The Devil gave a horrible grin, and disappeared. The same night Hampton House was burned to the ground, the General only escaping in his shirt. He had been dreaming he was dead and in hell. His precious guineas were secreted in the wainscot, the ceiling, and other hiding-places known only to himself. He blasphemed, wept, and tore his hair. Suddenly he grew calm. After all, the loss was not irreparable, he reflected. Gold would melt, it is true; but he would find it all,— of course he would,—at daybreak, run into a solid lump in the cellar,— every guinea. That is true of ordinary gold.

The General worked with the energy of despair, clearing away the rubbish. He refused all offers of assistance; he dared not accept them. But the gold had vanished. Whether it was really consumed, or had passed again into the massy entrails of the earth, will never be known. It is only certain that every vestige of it had disappeared.

When the General died and was buried, strange rumors began to circulate. To quiet them, the grave was opened; but when the lid was removed from the coffin, it was found to be empty.

Barney Oxman is a bare-faced jokester, of course, but we should note that his prank was soundly based on the superstition of his victim, and consequently the devil he conjured up was real enough to her. Like most really superstitious people, this simple old lady needed only to be told of Satan to smell the brimstone.

Barney Oxman and the Devil[1]

O h, wrastling with the evil one," says he, "it ain't a bad story that; didn't I ever tell you that frolic of 'Barney Oxman and the devil?'

"Well, there lived an old woman some years ago at Musquash Creek, in South Carolina, that had a large fortin' and an only darter. She was a widder, a miser, and a dunker. She was very good, and very cross, as many righteous folks are, and had a loose tongue and a tight puss of her own. All the men that looked at her darter she thought had an eye to her money, and she warn't far out o' the way nother, for it seems as if beauty and money was too much to go together in a general way. Rich galls and handsome galls are seldom good for nothin' else but their cash or their looks. Pears and peaches ain't often found on the same tree, I tell you. She lived all alone a'most, with nobody but

---

[1] From *The Attaché; or Sam Slick in England,* by the author of *Sam Slick the Clockmaker,* etc. (New York: Stringer & Townsend; 1856), pp. 290-3.

her darter and her in the house, and some old nigger slaves, in a hut near at hand. The only place they went to, in a gineral way, was meetin', and Jerusha never missed that, for it was the only chance she had sometimes to get out alone.

"Barney had a most beautiful voice, and always went there too, to sing along with the galls; and Barney, hearin' of the fortin' of Miss Eels, made up to her as fierce as possible, and sung so sweet, and talked so sweet, and kissed so sweet, that he soon stood number one with the heiress. But then he didn't often get a chance to walk home with her, and when he did, she darsn't let him come in for fear of the old woman; but Barney warn't to be put off that way long. When a gall is in one pastur' and a lover in another, it's a high fence they can't get over, that's a fact.

" 'Tell you what,' sais Barney, 'sit up alone in the keepin' room, Rushy dear, arter old mother has gone to bed, put out the light, and I'll slide down on the rope from the trap-door on the roof. Tell her you are exercised in your mind, and want to meditate alone, as the words you have heard this day have reached your heart.'

"Jerusha was frightened to death a'most, but what won't a woman do when a lover is in the way. So that very night she told the old woman she was exercised in her mind, and would wrastle with the spirit.

" 'Do, dear,' says her mother, 'and you won't think of the vanities of dress and idle company no more. You see how I have given them all up since I made profession,[1] and never so much as speak of them now, no, nor ever thinks of them.'

"Strange, Squire, ain't it! But it's much easier to cheat ourselves than cheat the devil. That old hag was too stingy to buy a dress, but persuaded herself it was bein' too good to wear it.

"Well, the house was a flat-roofed house, and had a trap-door in the ceilin', over the keepin' room, and there was a crane on the roof, with a rope to it, to pull up things to spread out to dry there. As soon as the lights were all out, and Barney thought the old woman was asleep, he crawls up on the house, opens the trap-door, and lets himself down by the rope, and he and Jerusha sat down into the hearth in the chimney corner courtin', or as they call it in them diggins 'sniffin' ashes.' When daylight began to show, he went up the rope hand over hand, hauled it up arter him, closed to the trap-door, and made himself scarce. Well, all this went on as slick as could be for awhile, but the old woman seed that her daughter looked pale, and as if she hadn't had sleep enough, and there was no gettin' of her up in the mornin'; and when she did she was yawkin' and gapin', and so dull she hadn't a word to say.

---

[1] I.e., of religion.

"She got very uneasy about it at last, and used to get up in the night sometimes and call her darter, and make her go off to bed, and oncet or twice came plaguy near catching of them. So what does Barney do, but takes two niggers with him when he goes arter that, and leaves them on the roof, and fastens a large basket to the rope, and tells them if they feel the rope pulled to hoist away for dear life, but not to speak a word for the world. Well, one night the old woman came to the door as usual, and sais, 'Jerusha,' says she, 'what on airth ails you, to make you sit up all night that way; do come to bed, that's a dear.' 'Presently, marm,' says she, 'I am wrastling with the evil one, now; I'll come presently.' 'Dear, dear,' sais she, 'you have wrastled long enough with him to have throwed him by this time. If you can't throw him now, give it up, or he may throw you.' 'Presently, marm,' sais her darter. 'It's always the same tune,' sais her mother, going off grumbling;—'it's always presently, presently;—what has got into the gall to act so? Oh, dear! what a pertracted time she has on it. She has been sorely exercised, poor girl.'

"As soon as she had gone, Barney larfed so he had to put his arm round her waist to steady him on the bench, in a way that didn't look onlike rompin', and when he went to whisper he larfed so he did nothin' but touch her cheek with his lips, in a way that looked plaguily like kissing, and felt like it too, and she pulled to get away, and they had a most reg'lar wrastle as they sat on the bench, when, as luck would have it, over went the bench, and down went both on 'em on the floor with an awful smash, and in bounced the old woman— 'Which is uppermost?' sais she; 'Have you throw'd Satan, or has Satan throw'd you? Speak, Rushy; speak, dear; who's throw'd?' 'I have throw'd him,' sais her darter, 'and I hope I have broke his neck, he acted so.' 'Come to bed, then,' sais she, 'darling, and be thankful; say a prayer backward, and'—jist then the old woman was seized round the waist, hoisted through the trap-door to the roof, and from there to the top of the crane, where the basket stopped, and the first thing she know'd she was away up ever so far in the air, swingin' in a large basket, and no soul near her.

"Barney and his niggers cut stick double quick, crept into the bushes, and went all round to the road in front of the house, just as day was breakin'. The old woman was then singin' out for dear life, kickin' and squealin', and cryin', and prayin', all in one, properly frightened. Down runs Barney as hard as he could clip, lookin' as innocent as if he'd never heerd nothin' of it, and pertendin' to be horrid frightened, offers his services, climbs up, releases the old woman, and gets blessed and thanked, and thanked and blessed till he was tired of it. 'Oh!' says the old woman, 'Mr. Oxman, the moment Jerusha throwed the evil one, the house shook like an airthquake, and as I entered the room he seized me, put me into a basket, and flew off with me. Oh, I shall never forget his fiery eyeballs, and the horrid smell of brimstone he had!'

" 'Had he a cloven foot, and a long tail?' sais Barney. 'I couldn't see in the dark,' sais she, 'but his claws were awful sharp; oh, how they dug into my ribs! it e'en a'most took the flesh off—oh, dear! Lord have mercy on us! I hope he is laid in the Red Sea, now.' 'Tell you what it is, aunty,' sais Barney, 'that's an awful story, keep it secret for your life; folks might say the house was harnted—that you was possessed, and that Jerushy was in league with the evil one. Don't so much as lisp a syllable of it to a livin' sinner breathin'; keep the secret and I will help you.'

"The hint took, the old woman had no wish to be burnt or drown'd for a witch, *and the moment a feller has a woman's secret he is that woman's master.* He was invited there, stayed there, and married there; but the old woman never know'd who the 'evil one' was, and always thought till her dyin' day it was old Scratch himself."

The Devil and Daniel Webster [1]

It's a story they tell in the border country, where Massachusetts joins Vermont and New Hampshire.

Yes, Dan'l Webster's dead—or at least they buried him. But every time there's a thunderstorm around Marshfield, they say you can hear his rolling voice in the hollows of the sky. And they say that if you go to his grave and speak loud and clear, "Dan'l Webster—Dan'l Webster!" the ground'll begin to shiver and the trees begin to shake. And after a while you'll hear a deep voice saying, "Neighbor, how stands the Union?" Then you'd better answer the Union stands as she stood, rock-bottomed and copper-sheathed, one and indivisible, or he's liable to rear right out of the ground. At least, that's what I was told when I was a youngster.

You see, for a while, he was the biggest man in the country. He never got to be President, but he was the biggest man. There were thousands that trusted in him right next to God Almighty, and they told stories about him that were like the stories of patriarchs and such. They said, when he stood up to speak, stars and stripes came right out in the sky, and once he spoke against a river and made it sink into the ground. They said, when he walked the woods with his fishing rod, Killall, the trout would jump out of the streams right into his pockets, for they

[1] From: *Selected Works of Stephen Vincent Benét*, published by Rinehart & Company. Copyright, 1936, by Stephen Vincent Benét.

knew it was no use putting up a fight against him; and, when he argued a case, he could turn on the harps of the blessed and the shaking of the earth underground. That was the kind of man he was, and his big farm up at Marshfield was suitable to him. The chickens he raised were all white meat down through the drumsticks, the cows were tended like children, and the big ram he called Goliath had horns with a curl like a morning-glory vine and could butt through an iron door. But Dan'l wasn't one of your gentlemen farmers, he knew all the ways of the land, and he'd be up by candlelight to see that the chores got done. A man with a mouth like a mastiff, a brow like a mountain and eyes like burning anthracite—that was Dan'l Webster in his prime. And the biggest case he argued never got written down in the books, for he argued it against the devil, nip and tuck and no holds barred. And this is the way I used to hear it told.

There was a man named Jabez Stone, lived at Cross Corners, New Hampshire. He wasn't a bad man to start with, but he was an unlucky man. If he planted corn, he got borers; if he planted potatoes, he got blight. He had good-enough land, but it didn't prosper him; he had a decent wife and children, but the more children he had, the less there was to feed them. If stones cropped up in his neighbor's field, boulders boiled up in his; if he had a horse with the spavins, he'd trade it for one with the staggers and give something extra. There's some folks bound to be like that, apparently. But one day Jabez Stone got sick of the whole business.

He'd been plowing that morning, and he'd just broke the plowshare on a rock that he could have sworn hadn't been there yesterday. And, as he stood looking at the plowshare, the off horse began to cough—that ropy kind of cough that means sickness and horse doctors. There were two children down with the measles, his wife was ailing, and he had a whitlow on his thumb. It was about the last straw for Jabez Stone. "I vow," he said, and he looked around him kind of desperate—"I vow it's enough to make a man want to sell his soul to the devil! And I would, too, for two cents!"

Then he felt a kind of queerness come over him at having said what he'd said; though, naturally, being a New Hampshireman, he wouldn't take it back. But, all the same, when it got to be evening and, as far as he could see, no notice had been taken, he felt relieved in his mind, for he was a religious man. But notice is always taken, sooner or later, just like the Good Book says. And, sure enough, next day, about supper-time, a soft-spoken, dark-dressed stranger drove up in a handsome buggy and asked for Jabez Stone.

Well, Jabez told his family it was a lawyer, come to see him about a legacy. But he knew who it was. He didn't like the looks of the stranger, nor the way he smiled with his teeth. They were white teeth,

85

and plentiful—some say they were filed to a point, but I wouldn't vouch for that. And he didn't like it when the dog took one look at the stranger and ran away howling, with his tail between his legs. But having passed his word, more or less, he stuck to it, and they went out behind the barn and made their bargain. Jabez Stone had to prick his finger to sign, and the stranger lent him a silver pin. The wound healed clean, but it left a little white scar.

After that, all of a sudden, things began to pick up and prosper for Jabez Stone. His cows got fat and his horses sleek, his crops were the envy of the neighborhood, and lightning might strike all over the valley, but it wouldn't strike his barn. Pretty soon, he was one of the prosperous people of the county; they asked him to stand for selectman, and he stood for it; there began to be talk of running him for state senate. All in all, you might say the Stone family was as happy and contented as cats in a dairy. And so they were, except for Jabez Stone.

He'd been contented enough, the first few years. It's a great thing when bad luck turns; it drives most other things out of your head. True, every now and then, especially in rainy weather, the little white scar on his finger would give him a twinge. And once a year, punctual as clockwork, the stranger with the handsome buggy would come driving by. But the sixth year, the stranger lighted, and, after that, his peace was over for Jabez Stone.

The stranger came up through the lower field, switching his boots with a cane—they were handsome black boots, but Jabez Stone never liked the look of them, particularly the toes. And after he'd passed the time of day, he said, "Well, Mr. Stone, you're a hummer! It's a very pretty property you've got here, Mr. Stone."

"Well, some might favor it and others might not," said Jabez Stone, for he was a New Hampshireman.

"Oh, no need to decry your industry!" said the stranger, very easy, showing his teeth in a smile. "After all, we know what's been done, and it's been according to specifications. So when—ahem—the mortgage falls due next year, you shouldn't have any regrets."

"Speaking of that mortgage, mister," said Jabez Stone, and he looked around for help to the earth and the sky, "I'm beginning to have one or two doubts about it."

"Doubts?" said the stranger, not quite so pleasantly.

"Why, yes," said Jabez Stone. "This being the U. S. A. and me having always been a religious man." He cleared his throat and got bolder. "Yes, sir," he said, "I'm beginning to have considerable doubts as to that mortgage holding in court."

"There's courts and courts," said the stranger, clicking his teeth. "Still, we might as well have a look at the original document." And he hauled out a big black pocketbook, full of papers. "Sherwin, Slater, Stevens, Stone," he mutttered. "I, Jabez Stone, for a term of seven years—Oh, it's quite in order, I think."

But Jabez Stone wasn't listening, for he saw something else flutter out of the black pocketbook. It was something that looked like a moth, but it wasn't a moth. And as Jabez Stone stared at it, it seemed to speak to him in a small sort of piping voice, terrible small and thin, but terrible human. "Neighbor Stone!" it squeaked. "Neighbor Stone! Help me! For God's sake, help me!"

But before Jabez Stone could stir hand or foot, the stranger whipped out a big bandanna handkerchief, caught the creature in it, just like a butterfly, and started tying up the ends of the bandanna.

"Sorry for the interruption," he said, "As I was saying—"

But Jabez Stone was shaking all over like a scared horse.

"That's Miser Stevens' voice!" he said, in a croak. "And you've got him in your handkerchief!"

The stranger looked a little embarrassed.

"Yes, I really should have transferred him to the collecting box," he said with a simper, "but there were some rather unusual specimens there and I didn't want them crowded. Well, well, these little contretemps will occur."

"I don't know what you mean by contertan," said Jabez Stone, "but that was Miser Stevens' voice! And he ain't dead! You can't tell me he is! He was just as spry and mean as a woodchuck, Tuesday!"

"In the midst of life—" said the stranger, kind of pious. "Listen!" Then a bell began to toll in the valley and Jabez Stone listened, with the sweat running down his face. For he knew it was tolled for Miser Stevens and that he was dead.

"These long-standing accounts," said the stranger with a sigh; "one really hates to close them. But business is business."

He still had the bandanna in his hand, and Jabez Stone felt sick as he saw the cloth struggle and flutter.

"Are they all as small as that?" he asked hoarsely.

"Small?" said the stranger. "Oh, I see what you mean. Why, they vary." He measured Jabez Stone with his eyes, and his teeth showed. "Don't worry, Mr. Stone," he said. "You'll go with a very good grade. I wouldn't trust you outside the collecting box. Now, a man like Dan'l Webster, of course,—well, we'd have to build a special box for him, and even at that, I imagine the wing spread would astonish you. But, in your case, as I was saying—"

"Put that handkerchief away!" said Jabez Stone, and he began to beg and to pray. But the best he could get at the end was a three years' extension, with conditions.

But till you make a bargain like that, you've got no idea of how fast four years can run. By the last months of those years, Jabez Stone's known all over the state and there's talk of running him for governor —and it's dust and ashes in his mouth. For every day, when he gets up, he thinks, "There's one more night gone," and every night when he lies down, he thinks of the black pocketbook and the soul of Miser Stevens, and it makes him sick at heart. Till, finally, he can't bear it any longer, and, in the last days of the last year, he hitches up his horse and drives off to seek Dan'l Webster. For Dan'l was born in New Hampshire, only a few miles from Cross Corners, and it's well known that he has a particular soft spot for old neighbors.

It was early in the morning when he got to Marshfield, but Dan'l was up already, talking Latin to the farm hands and wrestling with the ram, Goliath, and trying out a new trotter, and working up speeches to make against John C. Calhoun. But when he heard a New Hampshireman had come to see him, he dropped everything else he was doing, for that was Dan'l's way. He gave Jabez Stone a breakfast that five men couldn't eat, went into the living history of every man and woman in Cross Corners, and finally asked him how he could serve him.

Jabez Stone allowed that it was a kind of mortgage case.

"Well, I haven't pleaded a mortgage case in a long time, and I don't generally plead now, except before the Supreme Court," said Dan'l, "but if I can, I'll help you."

"Then I've got hope for the first time in ten years," said Jabez Stone, and told him the details.

Dan'l walked up and down as he listened, hands behind his back, now and then asking a question, now and then plunging his eyes at the floor, as if they'd bore through it like gimlets. When Jabez Stone had finished, Dan'l puffed out his cheeks and blew. Then he turned to Jabez Stone and a smile broke over his face like the sunrise over Monadnock.

"You'll take it?" said Jabez Stone, hardly daring to believe.

"Yes," said Dan'l Webster, "I've got about seventy-five other things to do and the Missouri Compromise to straighten out, but I'll take your case. For if two New Hampshiremen aren't a match for the devil, we might as well give the country back to the Indians."

Then he shook Jabez Stone by the hand and said, "Did you come down here in a hurry?"

"Well, I admit I made time," said Jabez Stone.

"You'll go back faster," said Dan'l Webster, and he told 'em to hitch up Constitution and Constellation to the carriage. They were matched grays with one white forefoot, and they stepped like greased lightning.

Well, I won't describe how excited and pleased the whole Stone family was to have the great Dan'l Webster for a guest, when they

88

finally got there. Jabez Stone had lost his hat on the way, blown off when they overtook a wind, but he didn't take much account of that. But after supper he sent the family off to bed, for he had most particular business with Mr. Webster. Mrs. Stone wanted them to sit in the front parlor, but Dan'l Webster knew front parlors and said he preferred the kitchen. So it was there they sat, waiting for the stranger, with a jug on the table between them and a bright fire on the hearth—the stranger being scheduled to show up on the stroke of midnight, according to specifications.

Well, most men wouldn't have asked for better company than Dan'l Webster and a jug. But with every tick of the clock Jabez Stone got sadder and sadder. His eyes roved round, and though he sampled the jug you could see he didn't taste it. Finally, on the stroke of 11:30 he reached over and grabbed Dan'l Webster by the arm.

"Mr. Webster, Mr. Webster!" he said, and his voice was shaking with fear and a desperate courage. "For God's sake, Mr. Webster, harness your horses and get away from this place while you can!"

"You've brought me a long way, neighbor, to tell me you don't like my company," said Dan'l Webster, quite peaceable, pulling at the jug.

"Miserable wretch that I am!" groaned Jabez Stone. "I've brought you a devilish way, and now I see my folly. Let him take me if he wills. I don't hanker after it, I must say, but I can stand it. But you're the Union's stay and New Hampshire's pride! He mustn't get you, Mr. Webster! He mustn't get you!"

Dan'l Webster looked at the distracted man, all gray and shaking in the firelight, and laid a hand on his shoulder.

"I'm obliged to you, Neighbor Stone," he said gently. "It's kindly thought of. But there's a jug on the table and a case in hand. And I never left a jug or a case half finished in my life."

And just at that moment there was a sharp rap on the door.

"Ah," said Dan'l Webster, very coolly, "I thought your clock was a trifle slow, Neighbor Stone." He stepped to the door and opened it. "Come in!" he said.

The stranger came in—very dark and tall he looked in the firelight. He was carrying a box under his arm—a black japanned box with little air holes in the lid. At the sight of the box, Jabez Stone gave a low cry and shrank into a corner of the room.

"Mr. Webster, I presume," said the stranger, very polite, but with his eyes glowing like a fox's deep in the woods.

"Attorney of record for Jabez Stone," said Dan'l Webster, but his eyes were glowing too. "Might I ask your name?"

"I've gone by a good many," said the stranger carelessly. "Perhaps Scratch will do for the evening. I'm often called that in these regions."

Then he sat down at the table and poured himself a drink from the jug. The liquor was cold in the jug, but it came steaming into the glass.

"And now," said the stranger, smiling and showing his teeth, "I shall call upon you, as a law-abiding citizen, to assist me in taking possession of my property."

Well, with that the argument began—and it went hot and heavy. At first Jabez Stone had a flicker of hope, but when he saw Dan'l Webster being forced back at point after point, he just scrunched in his corner, with his eyes on that japanned box. For there wasn't any doubt as to the deed or the signature—that was the worst of it. Dan'l Webster twisted and turned and thumped his fist on the table, but he couldn't get away from that. He offered to compromise the case; the stranger wouldn't hear of it. He pointed out the property had increased in value, and state senators ought to be worth more; the stranger stuck to the letter of the law. He was a great lawyer, Dan'l Webster, but we know who's the King of the Lawyers, as the Good Book tells us, and it seemed as if, for the first time, Dan'l Webster had met his match.

Finally the stranger yawned a little. "Your spirited efforts on behalf of your client do you credit, Mr. Webster," he said, "but if you have no more arguments to adduce, I'm rather pressed for time"—and Jabez Stone shuddered.

Dan'l Webster's brow looked dark as a thundercloud.

"Pressed or not, you shall not have this man!" he thundered. "Mr. Stone is an American citizen, and no American citizen may be forced into the service of a foreign prince. We fought England for that in '12 and we'll fight all hell for it again!"

"Foreign?" said the stranger. "And who calls me a foreigner?"

"Well, I never yet heard of the dev—of your claiming American citizenship," said Dan'l Webster with surprise.

"And who with better right?" said the stranger, with one of his terrible smiles. "When the first wrong was done to the first Indian, I was there. When the first slaver put out for the Congo, I stood on her deck. Am I not in your books and stories and beliefs, from the first settlements on? Am I not spoken of, still, in every church in New England? 'Tis true the North claims me for a Southerner and the South for a Northerner, but I am neither. I am merely an honest American like yourself—and of the best descent—for, to tell the truth, Mr. Webster, though I don't like to boast of it, my name is older in this country than yours."

"Aha!" said Dan'l Webster, with the veins standing out in his forehead, "then I stand on the Constitution! I demand a trial for my client."

"The case is hardly one for an ordinary court," said the stranger, his eyes flickering. "And, indeed, the lateness of the hour—"

"Let it be any court you choose, so it is an American judge and an American jury!" said Dan'l Webster in his pride. "Let it be the quick or the dead; I'll abide the issue!"

"You have said it," said the stranger, and pointed his finger at the door. And with that, and all of a sudden, there was a rushing of wind outside and a noise of footsteps. They came, clear and distinct, through the night. And yet, they were not like the footsteps of living men.

"In God's name, who comes by so late?" cried Jabez Stone, in an ague of fear.

"The jury Mr. Webster demands," said the stranger, sipping at his boiling glass. "You must pardon the rough appearance of one or two; they will have come a long way."

And with that the fire burned blue and the door blew open and twelve men entered, one by one.

If Jabez Stone had been sick with terror before, he was blind with terror now. For there was Walter Butler, the loyalist, who spread fire and horror through the Mohawk Valley in the times of the Revolution; and there was Simon Girty, the renegade, who saw white men burned at the stake and whooped with the Indians to see them burn. His eyes were green, like a catamount's, and the stains on his hunting shirt did not come from the blood of the deer. King Philip was there, wild and proud as he had been in life, with the great gash in his head that gave him his death wound, and cruel Governor Dale, who broke men on the wheel. There was Morton of Merry Mount, who so vexed the Plymouth Colony, with his flushed, loose, handsome face and his hate of the godly. There was Teach, the bloody pirate, with his black beard curling on his breast. The Reverend John Smeet, with his strangler's hands and his Geneva gown, walked as daintily as he had to the gallows. The red print of the rope was still around his neck, but he carried a perfumed handkerchief, in one hand. One and all, they came into the room with the fires of hell still upon them, and the stranger named their names and their deeds as they came, till the tale of twelve was told. Yet the stranger had told the truth—they had all played a part in America.

"Are you satisfied with the jury?" said the stranger mockingly, when they had taken their places.

The sweat stood upon Dan'l Webster's brow, but his voice was clear.

"Quite satisfied," he said. "Though I miss General Arnold from the company."

"Benedict Arnold is engaged upon other business," said the stranger, with a glower. "Ah, you asked for a justice, I believe."

He pointed his finger once more, and a tall man, soberly clad in Puritan garb, with the burning gaze of the fanatic, stalked into the room and took his judge's place.

"Justice Hathorne is a jurist of experience," said the stranger. "He presided at certain witch trials once held in Salem. There were others who repented of the business later, but not he."

"Repent of such notable wonders and undertakings?" said the stern old justice. "Nay, hang them—hang them all!" And he mutttered to himself in a way that struck ice into the soul of Jabez Stone.

Then the trial began, and, as you might expect, it didn't look anyways good for the defense. And Jabez Stone didn't make much of a witness in his own behalf. He took one look at Simon Girty and screeched, and they had to put him back in his corner in a kind of swoon.

It didn't halt the trial, though; the trial went on, as trials do. Dan'l Webster had faced some hard juries and hanging judges in his time, but this was the hardest he'd ever faced, and he knew it. They sat there with a kind of glitter in their eyes, and the stranger's smooth voice went on and on. Every time he'd raise an objection, it'd be "Objection sustained," but whenever Dan'l objected, it'd be "Objection denied." Well, you couldn't expect fair play from a fellow like this Mr. Scratch.

It got to Dan'l in the end, and he began to heat, like iron in the forge. When he got up to speak he was going to flay that stranger with every trick known to the law, and the judge and jury, too. He didn't care if it was contempt of court or what would happen to him for it. He didn't care any more what happened to Jabez Stone. He just got madder and madder, thinking of what he'd say. And yet, curiously enough, the more he thought about it, the less he was able to arrange his speech in his mind.

Till, finally, it was time for him to get up on his feet, and he did so, all ready to bust out with lightnings and denunciations. But before he started he looked over the judge and jury for a moment, such being his custom. And he noticed the glitter in their eyes was twice as strong as before, and they all leaned forward. Like hounds just before they get the fox, they looked, and the blue mist of evil in the room thickened as he watched them. Then he saw what he'd been about to do, and he wiped his forehead, as a man might who's just escaped falling into a pit in the dark.

For it was him they'd come for, not only Jabez Stone. He read it in the glitter of their eyes and in the way the stranger hid his mouth with one hand. And if he fought them with their own weapons, he'd fall into their power; he knew that, though he couldn't have told you how. It was his own anger and horror that burned in their eyes; and he'd have to wipe that out or the case was lost. He stood there for a moment, his black eyes burning like anthracite. And then he began to speak.

He started off in a low voice, though you could hear every word. They say he could call on the harps of the blessed when he chose. And this was just as simple and easy as a man could talk. But he didn't start out by condemning or reviling. He was talking about the things that make a country a country, and a man a man.

And he began with the simple things that everybody's known and felt—the freshness of a fine morning when you're young, and the taste of food when you're hungry, and the new day that's every day when you're a child. He took them up and he turned them in his hands. They were good things for any man. But without freedom, they sickened. And when he talked of those enslaved, and the sorrows of slavery, his voice got like a big bell. He talked of the early days of America and the men who had made those days. It wasn't a spread-eagle speech, but he made you see it. He admitted all the wrong that had ever been done. But he showed how, out of the wrong and the right, the suffering and the starvations, something new had come. And everybody had played a part in it, even the traitors.

Then he turned to Jabez Stone and showed him as he was—an ordinary man who'd had hard luck and wanted to change it. And, because he'd wanted to change it, now he was going to be punished for all eternity. And yet there was good in Jabez Stone, and he showed that good. He was hard and mean, in some ways, but he was a man. There was sadness in being a man, but it was a proud thing too. And he showed what the pride of it was till you couldn't help feeling it. Yes, even in hell, if a man was a man, you'd know it. And he wasn't pleading for any one person any more, though his voice rang like an organ. He was telling the story and the failures and the endless journeys of mankind. They got tricked and trapped and bamboozled, but it was a great journey. And no demon that was ever foaled could know the inwardness of it—it took a man to do that.

The fire began to die on the hearth and the wind before morning to blow. The light was getting gray in the room when Dan'l Webster finished. And his words came back at the end to New Hampshire ground, and the one spot of land that each man loves and clings to. He painted a picture of that, and to each one of that jury he spoke of things long forgotten. For his voice could search the heart, and that was his gift and his strength. And to one, his voice was like the forest and its secret and to another like the sea and the storms of the sea; and one heard the cry of his lost nation in it, and another saw a little harmless scene he hadn't remembered for years. But each saw something. And when Dan'l Webster finished he didn't know whether or not he'd saved Jabez Stone. But he knew he'd done a miracle. For the glitter was gone from the eyes of judge and jury, and, for the moment, they were men again, and knew they were men.

"The defense rests," said Dan'l Webster, and stood there like a mountain. His ears were still ringing with his speech, and he didn't hear anything else till he heard Judge Hathorne say, "The jury will retire to consider its verdict."

Walter Butler rose in his place and his face had a dark, gay pride on it.

"The jury has considered its verdict," he said, and looked the stranger full in the eye. "We find for the defendant, Jabez Stone."

With that, the smile left the stranger's face, but Walter Butler did not flinch.

"Perhaps 'tis not strictly in accordance with the evidence," he said, "but even the damned may salute the eloquence of Mr. Webster."

With that, the long crow of a rooster split the gray morning sky, and judge and jury were gone from the room like a puff of smoke and as if they had never been there. The stranger turned to Dan'l Webster, smiling wryly.

"Major Butler was always a bold man," he said. "I had not thought him quite so bold. Nevertheless, my congratulations, as between two gentlemen."

"I'll have that paper first, if you please," said Dan'l Webster, and he took it and tore it into four pieces. It was queerly warm to the touch. "And now," he said, "I'll have you!" and his hand come down like a bear trap on the stranger's arm. For he knew that once you bested anybody like Mr. Scratch in fair fight, his power on you was gone. And he could see that Mr. Scratch knew it too.

The stranger twisted and wriggled, but he couldn't get out of that grip. "Come, come, Mr. Webster," he said, smiling palely. "This sort of thing is ridic—ouch!—is ridiculous. If you're worried about the costs of the case, naturally, I'd be glad to pay—"

"And so you shall!" said Dan'l Webster, shaking him till his teeth rattled. "For you'll sit right down at that table and draw up a document, promising never to bother Jabez Stone nor his heirs or assigns nor any other New Hampshireman till doomsday! For any hades we want to raise in this state, we can raise ourselves, without assistance from strangers."

"Ouch!" said the stranger. "Ouch! Well, they never did run very big to the barrel, but—ouch!—I agree!"

So he sat down and drew up the document. But Dan'l Webster kept his hand on his coat collar all the time.

"And, now, may I go?" said the stranger, quite humble, when Dan'l'd seen the document was in proper and legal form.

"Go?" said Dan'l, giving him another shake. "I'm still trying to figure out what I'll do with you. For you've settled the costs of the case, but you haven't settled with me. I think I'll take you back to Marshfield," he said, kind of reflective. "I've got a ram there named

Goliath, that can butt through an iron door. I'd kind of like to turn you loose in his field and see what he'd do."

Well, with that, the stranger began to beg and to plead. And he begged and he pled so humble that finally Dan'l, who was naturally kindhearted, agreed to let him go. The stranger seemed terrible grateful for that and said, just to show they were friends, he'd tell Dan'l's fortune before leaving. So Dan'l agreed to that, though he didn't take much stock in fortune-tellers ordinarily. But, naturally, the stranger was a little different.

Well, he pried and he peered at the lines in Dan'l's hands. And he told him one thing and another that was quite remarkable. But they were all in the past.

"Yes, all that's true, and it happened," said Dan'l Webster. "But what's to come in the future?"

The stranger grinned, kind of happily, and shook his head.

"The future's not as you think it," he said. "It's dark. You have a great ambition, Mr. Webster."

"I have," said Dan'l firmly, for everybody knew he wanted to be President.

"It seems almost within your grasp," said the stranger, "but you will not attain it. Lesser men will be made President and you will be passed over."

"And, if I am, I'll still be Daniel Webster," said Dan'l. "Say on."

"You have two strong sons," said the stranger, shaking his head. "You look to found a line. But each will die in war and neither reach greatness."

"Live or die, they are still my sons," said Dan'l Webster. "Say on."

"You have made great speeches," said the stranger. "You will make more."

"Ah," said Dan'l Webster.

"But the last great speech you make will turn many of your own against you," said the stranger. "They will call you Ichabod; they will call you by other names. Even in New England, some will say you have turned your coat and sold your country, and their voices will be loud against you till you die."

"So it is an honest speech, it does not matter what men say," said Dan'l Webster. Then he looked at the stranger and their glances locked.

"One question," he said. "I have fought for the Union all my life. Will I see that fight won against those who would tear it apart?"

"Not while you live," said the stranger, grimly, "but it will be won. And after you are dead, there are thousands who will fight for your cause, because of words that you spoke."

"Why, then, you long-barreled, slab-sided, lantern-jawed, fortune-telling note-shaver!" said Dan'l Webster, with a great roar of laughter, "be off with you to your own place before I put my mark on you! For, by the thirteen original colonies, I'd go to the Pit itself to save the Union!"

And with that he drew back his foot for a kick that would have stunned a horse. It was only the tip of his shoe that caught the stranger, but he went flying out of the door with his collecting box under his arm.

"And now," said Dan'l Webster, seeing Jabez Stone beginning to rouse from his swoon, "let's see what's left in the jug, for it's dry work talking all night. I hope there's pie for breakfast, Neighbor Stone."

But they say that whenever the devil comes near Marshfield, even now, he gives it a wide berth. And he hasn't been seen in the state of New Hampshire from that day to this. I'm not talking about Massachusetts or Vermont.

The Jersey Devil[1]

M rs. Bowen told the story quite simply as we stood there. There had been a Mrs. Shourds, she said, the mother of a family presumably large. One day she was heard to make a wish, as dreadful a wish as ever was made: She hoped that if she was to be burdened by any more children the next would be a devil. And a devil the next offspring, poor dwarfed misshapen being, proved to be! The creature, Mrs. Bowen said, grew painfully in size until the time came when it could move clumsily about in the house in which it was born and where, from most accounts, it was sheltered mercifully from the curious who came to peep in at the windows.

Just think how you would have acted if the story had come to you that Mrs. Shourds had wished for a devil and had begotten it. Wouldn't you have sidled by of an evening, on one imaginary errand or another, to see what you could see? Well, you probably would not have seen very much, even so. Few saw anything at all, according to all the variations of the story. Presumably those who heard a snatch or two filled in the details of the most incredible part of the tale, as it

---

[1] From Henry Charlton Beck: *Jersey Genesis: The Story of the Mullica River* (New Brunswick, N. J.: Rutgers University Press; 1945; copyright 1945 by the Trustees of Rutgers College), pp. 243–9.

was told again by Mrs. Bowen there in the ruin of plaster and cedar siding which by now must be dust again.

One evening when the wind was howling outside and when a shivery fog came creeping in from the sea, the twisted being cried out wildly and with a flapping of its long arms, turned suddenly to wings, swooped up the Shourds' chimney and disappeared forever as far as the family was concerned. As far as the rest of New Jersey is concerned, this was and is The Jersey Devil, Leeds's Devil, or the Devil of Leeds Point which in cycles of years that vary in the manifold accounts has continued to haunt the countryside with one technique or another. This, at least, was Mrs. Bowen's sketchy recollection of it.

The story and mention of it in a letter or two began the turning of many invisible wheels. Our friend, Mr. Gaskill, in Washington, replied that it was an old associate, Frank Lee, who had made a life's business of uncovering information on the Leeds Point phantom. "He kept his notes on scraps of paper, however," warned our correspondent, "and they may have disappeared long ago. But if you will look up Mrs. Lee, who I believe lives in Vincentown, you may get something that ought to be preserved."

I wrote a letter to Mrs. Lee. For a long time there was no answer. When a reply came, finally, it was from Mrs. Rhoda Lee Compton, Mrs. Lee's daughter. Mrs. Lee had died, too, and while there were many old books about, Mrs. Compton was certain there had been no notes about the ghost. Not until some time after that did I realize that Frank Lee, to whom Mr. Gaskill had referred me, was Francis Baizley Lee whose books on New Jersey are well known.

I began to think my luck was out, especially when an obituary appeared telling of the death of Fire Warden Bozarth, at Batsto near The Forks, in which it was declared that he "was the last man known to have seen The Jersey Devil." I had met and talked with Mr. Bozarth, but never in any of our conversations did he reveal the knowledge of such a distinguished visitor. It was while I had reverted to looking up the family history of the Shourds, descended surely from one Cornelius Shourds, a stockbroker who came all the way from Holland, back in 1684, on the urgent invitation of that pioneer of Pennsylvania, William Penn, that a second letter came from Mrs. Compton saying that her cousin, J. Elfreth Watkins of Philadelphia, had come to visit her. "Oddly enough," she wrote, "he was with my father years ago when they were tracking down those Jersey Devil stories. He says he may be able to find some trace of them in his files."

After some friendly correspondence in which Mr. Watkins said that much of the material in his files had been stolen, he came upon a yellowing clipping of an article he syndicated in 1905, headed boldly "On the Trail of Leeds' Devil" and subtitled "The Dread Monster of

Jersey's Big Forest." "Just back of the white and velvety coastline of New Jersey," Mr. Watkins began, with the full glory of early newspaper writing, "there tapers up from its deep base along Delaware Bay to its apex at Long Branch a green triangle known as 'The Pines.' Its black, innermost heart has suffered a hiatus, a quick transition from twentieth to eighteenth century, plunged into a dark sylvan mediaeval realm of witches, wizards, conjurers and monsters. . . ."

His scene established, Mr. Watkins proceeded, saying that he did not believe that "anywhere in your mythologies you will find any reference to 'Leeds' Devil' but it was a pilgrimage in search of the lair of this monster (which has kept the 'pine hawkers' in the State in terror since Colonial days) that made me turn my back upon the sea and sent me trudging along the white floor of 'The Pines' and wading through its dismal cedar swamps." I had joined that quest, you see. Now, so must you.

"I was set upon the monster's trail by Mr. Francis B. Lee, of Trenton," wrote Mr. Watkins, then the head of a news and feature syndicate, "an astute historian who had made a careful study of the folklore and dialect of the 'pine hawker.' The story goes that back in mid-colonial days there lived in Burlington, on the Delaware, a city far beyond the frontier of The Pines, a woman known as 'Mother Leeds.' Witchcraft was then at its height in the Colonies, and she was accused as an adept in its black arts. In 1735, according to the tale, Mother Leeds gave birth to a male child whose father, at first unidentified, was later said to have been none other than the foul fiend and prince of darkness, otherwise known as Old Horny and Beelzebub.

"The child was normal at birth but before the termination of the tempestuous night of its arrival it horrified several old crones gathered about the bedside of Mother Leeds by assuming a serpent-like body, cloven hoofs, the head of a horse, the wings of a bat, and the forked tail of a dragon. The coloring of the terrible monster turned to a dusky brown and after bepummeling its mother and her chapfallen companions it uttered a series of loud, raucous cries and flew up the chimney. Circling about from village to village, while the tempest still screamed through the trees, the monster stopped on its way to devour several sleeping babes and then made for The Pines."

Pause should be made here, interrupting Mr. Watkins's fascinating narrative to point out, for the benefit of Mrs. Bowen and others, that here is direct quotation from the Sunday supplements of over thirty-five years ago. "Mother Leeds" is no more the creature of my imagination than she was of the man who wrote the article after working with Mr. Lee, the "astute historian." Mrs. Bowen's version, it becomes evident at once, lost much more than names in years of retelling the story.

"During the hundred and forty years that have elapsed belated

98

travelers crossing that dark sylvan tract have seen and heard the monster. Joseph Bonaparte, ex-King of Spain, who loved to hunt deer in this forest, is said to have encountered it once, while Commodore Decatur, who came to The Pines to test cannon balls made from the native bog ore at the since crumbled foundry at Hanover, is said to have fired one of these projectiles—designed for the Algerian pirates— directly through the monster 'without halting its mad pace.' The pine hawkers, who tell experiences even more terrible, attribute to it such supernatural powers as were assigned to the black witches of English folklore. It turns the milk sour in the pails, lames horses in their stalls, dries up the cows in the clearing pastures, seres the corn in the fields.

"Accompanied, as it usually is, by the howling of dogs and the hooting of owls, there can be no surer forerunner of disaster. Where the barrens line the shore it flits from one desolate grass-grown dune to another and is especially watchful upon those wild heights when coasting schooners, driving their prows into the sand, pound to splinters upon the bars and distribute upon the waves their freight of goods and human lives.

"Upon such occasions Leeds' Devil is seen in the companionship of a beautiful golden-haired woman in white, or yet of some fierce-eyed, cutlass-bearing disembodied spirit of a buccaneer whose galleon, centuries ago, was wrecked upon the shore of Cape May County. Again this monster is said to share its haunts with a headless seaman who, the Barnegat people say, was decapitated by none other than Captain Kidd himself and whose stiffened trunk that pirate king left sentinel over buried, ill-gotten gold.

"At other times Leeds' Devil is seen to hover, like a giant bird of prey, above some silent, star-bespangled pond within the umbrous recess of a cedar swamp. On such occasions its foul breath blasts the lives of hundreds of fishes, found floating next day upon the surface, tainted and unfit for food. Half cantering, half flying through the shadowy vistas of the forest, it drives before it to their coverts deer, rabbits and squirrels. Such," Mr. Watkins at last concluded his colorful story, "is the black record of Leeds' Devil, transposed from the nasal dialect of the Pine Hawkers—and these human denizens of the forest we must not pass by unnoticed. . . ."

Clearly the original legend, pieced together by Mr. Watkins and the late Mr. Lee, has everything: A monster that combines the worst of the animal, bird and reptile kingdoms, notable witnesses of its frightfulness, the original touch of trying to shoot down a ghost with a cannon—and even a blonde. Besides the narrative in which Mother Leeds, and not Mrs. Shourds, became the mother of the horrific villain of the piece, the more modern derivation is feeble and forlorn. Even so, I had not heard the whole of it.

From Mrs. Blake in Pleasantville came response to a further inquiry. Mrs. Blake wrote me that the Jersey Devil was "positively born" in three places and that Burlington was *not* one of these. In Leeds Point, she said, he was born in a house on the site of a dwelling occupied then by Dr. Rieck at 507 South Main Street. "I presume," she wrote, "that in Estellville the site of his birthplace can be as positively identified."

The story in each instance was the same, Mrs. Blake pointed out— "the unwanted child, the home already filled with numerous offspring from the poor feeble-minded parents. The mother wishes the child may be a devil when born; the child has a cloven foot and hands like claws. He finally claws his mother's breast and flies up the chimney and away into the night with horrible screeches. The same screeches seem to attend his return-visits," said Mrs. Blake, "which, by the way, come every seven years and always portend disaster."

Expressing an opinion that the germ of the legend was traceable to Old World superstitions, "brought with the people from Europe," Mrs. Blake confessed that she never had heard "when the Devil developed the vampire wings he is supposed to have." While the monster may have developed from superstitions, there must have been some foundation to the story of his birth, Mrs. Blake told me later. "Possibly a deformed and degenerate child was born into such a home in each of the locations along the shore," she suggested. "The child may have run away, either perishing from cold or dying when attacked by wild beasts. Parents and neighbors imagine all sorts of stories," she added, "and it is probable that every tragic event along the shore was placed to the credit of 'The Jersey Devil.'"

Alfred M. Heston, the Atlantic County historian, writing as recently as 1928, recounted the legend, favoring Estellville for the opening scene, declaring the mother of the beast to be a Mrs. Leeds who lived there and not in Leeds Point at all. The baby was normal, he said, and it was soon exchanged, in some baffling manner, for the monstrosity that turned up a few days later. Mr. Heston pictures the creature swooping out the window, not up the chimney, and so loses much of the effect. Details for this departure seem to have come from one George Gregory, whom Mr. Heston calls "a matter-of-fact gentleman" whose home was in Philadelphia but whose summers were spent in Cape May County. There it was, in Goshen, that Mr. Gregory obtained the facts from a Mrs. McCormack who, inspired by an "appearance" of the Devil in 1909, spoke at length on the subject with all the authority of her eighty-four years. Mr. Heston said that Mr. Gregory had it from Mrs. McCormack who had it from the nurse, probably midwife, who attended the Mrs. Leeds of Estellville, that "every day, for a time, the child-devil returned to the home of Mrs. Leeds and perched on the fence."

Mr. Heston appends another and singularly flat claim that the mother of the monster was neither a Shourds nor a Leeds but a woman who, having refused food to a gypsy, was consequently cursed, her first-born subsequently performing most of the tricks ascribed to The Jersey Devil, making its debut, as in other variations, in the house at Leeds Point.

The Devil's name could have been Leeds, and it could have been Shourds, too. Daniel Leeds "located land" in Great Egg Harbor in 1694. Samuel Shourds, Sr., came to Little Egg Harbor in 1735. Daniel and his family lived at Leeds Point. The Shourds, almost legion, were scattered all through the Mullica neighborhood within surprisingly few years. It is impossible, however, to speak with any certainty, to conclude that The Jersey Devil gained its aliases from a person or a place, although there may be something more than coincidence in the fact that Sam Shourds moved shoreward from Bristol, Pa., directly across the Delaware from Burlington, reputed home of "Mother Leeds" in 1735, the year of the supposed diabolical visitation.

Writing in 1929, the late Squire Hargrove of Pemberton, whose tall stories have thrust me into many a tight corner, managed to revive The Jersey Devil for a time, giving him birth at Leeds Point but not at any dwelling of the Shourdses—the Squire drops him at the old Leeds homestead, then occupied by Jesse Mathis. The Squire quotes Jesse as saying that people along the Mullica Valley and beyond believed that children born half-witted had been "touched" by Leeds' Devil and that this was the origin of a modern derivation. By 1934, however, the monster had lost so many of his trappings that a man whom police named as Willis Borton, wanted in five states on charges ranging from burglary to murder, glibly called himself "The Jersey Devil," and as such made the headlines.

6. TREASURE-TROVE

If Cotton Mather had not believed in divine interposition, if he had not felt that the most improbable and romantic events had a spiritual or, rather, theological meaning, a story-teller of much gusto would have been lost to the world. The Puritan intellectual appetite that fed on Mather's *Magnalia Christi* was in part an appetite for tall tales. It would never have accepted secular marvel without parable, preaching, and prayer, but these Mather amply provided. At the same time he obviously enjoyed the effects that he was producing in straight narrative; "Lo!" he will cry, or, frequently: "Behold!" or "Behold the issue!" but sometimes he will defensively add: " 'Tis well known." Often, indeed, it must have been very well known. Who, for instance, in Massachusetts, or in all New England, did not know how Sir William Phips made his fortune? Yet we may doubt if anyone has told the tale either more romantically or more truthfully than Mather. If he could not mention that remarkable "sea-feather" without referring to the mad Roman Emperor Caligula and his sea-spoils, we must forgive him; superfluous literary reference was an ailment of the age as well as of Mather. It has style, too, though not the style of the atom-bomb era.

If all New England knew of Phips, all of eastern North America knew of Captain Kidd, and cherished increasingly the conviction that he had buried six hundred pounds of gold, one hundred of silver, and other valuables "two miles from Albany," or near New Orleans, or on Gardiner's Island, or Martha's Vineyard, or in Passamaquoddy Bay, or at Charleston, South Carolina, or Conanicut, Rhode Island, or Block Island, or Tuckernuck, or the Virgin Islands. And elsewhere; nor is faith in this treasure extinct today.

Even if we leave Captain Kidd's elusive hoard out of the count, a hundred Americans have hopefully dug for one who has found buried treasure, and a thousand golden tales have spurred them on. Mr. Sutliff, that respectable miller, is typical of scores who labored vainly for an attractive delusion. Delusion? Mrs. Maggie Clinger could positively see the Davis Mountain treasure—but could not find Davis Mountain. Major Bell is convinced and convincing about the treasure buried near the Hollywood Bowl. (But—just precisely where?) F. L. Olmstead discovered, to his embarrassment, that a treasure-legend is easier to launch [1] than to scuttle. But no wonder, for some of the tall

---

[1] Mr. Olmstead did not invent the yarn, but he found it amusing until the repercussions became, as he says, "apparently endless."

tales of American buried treasure are true. Ask George Frederick Benner if they are not; he is still alive, or was in 1944.

Sea-feather and sea-treasure[1]

N ow, with a small company of other men he sailed from thence to Hispaniola, where, by the policy of his address, he fished out of a very old Spaniard (or Portuguese) a little advice about the true spot where lay the wreck which he had been hitherto seeking, as un-prosperously as the chymists have their *aurific*[2] *stone*: that it was upon a *reef of shoals,* a few leagues to the northward of Port de la Plata, upon Hispaniola, a port so called, it seems, from the landing of some of the *shipwrecked* company, with a boat full of plate, saved out of their sinking frigot: nevertheless, when he had searched very narrowly the spot, whereof the old Spaniard had advised him, he had not hitherto exactly hit upon it. Such thorns did vex his affairs while he was in the Rose-frigot; but none of these things could retund the edge of his expectations to find the *wreck;* with such expectations he re-turned then into England, that he might there better furnish himself to prosecute a *new discovery;* for though he judged he might, by pro-ceeding a little further, have come at the right *spot;* yet he found his present company too ill a crew to be confided in.

So *proper* was his behaviour, that the best noblemen in the kingdom now admitted him into their conversation; but yet he was opposed by powerful enemies, that clogged his affairs with such demurrages, and such *disappointments,* as would have wholly discouraged his designs, if his patience had not been *invincible.* "He who can wait, hath what he desireth." Thus his indefatigable *patience,* with a proportionable *diligence,* at length overcame the difficulties that had been thrown in his way; and prevailing with the Duke of Albemarle, and some other persons of quality, to fit him out, he set sail for the *fishing-ground,* which had been so well *baited* half a hundred years before; and as he had already discovered his *capacity for business* in many considerable actions, he now added unto those discoveries, by not only *providing* all; but also by *inventing* many of the instruments necessary to the prosecution of his intended *fishery.* Captain Phips arriving with a ship and a tender at Port de la Plata, made a stout canoe of a stately cotton-tree, so large as to carry eight or ten oars, for the making of

---

[1] From Cotton Mather, D.D., F.R.S.: *Magnalia Christi Americana, or the Ec-clesiastical History of New England* (Hartford: Silas Andrus & Son; 1855; copyright 1852), pp. 170–2.

[2] Aurific = gold-making. (The alchemists' stone.)

which *periaga* (as they call it) he did, with the same industry that he did everything else, imploy his own *hand* and *adse,* and endure no little hardship, lying abroad in the woods many nights together. This periaga, with the tender, being anchored at a place convenient, the periaga kept busking to and again, but could only discover a *reef of rising shoals* thereabouts, called "The Boilers,"—which, rising to be within two or three foot of the surface of the sea, were yet so steep, that a ship striking on them, would immediately sink down, who could say how many fathom, into the ocean? Here they could get no other pay for their long *peeping* among the *boilers,* but only such as caused them to think upon returning to their captain with the bad news of their total disappointment. Nevertheless, as they were upon the return, one of the men looking over the side of the periaga, into the calm water, he spied a *sea feather,* growing, as he judged, out of a rock; whereupon they had one of their Indians to dive, and fetch this feather, that they might, however, carry home *something* with them, and make, at least, as fair a triumph as Caligula's.[1] The diver, bringing up the feather, brought therewithal a surprizing story, that he perceived a number of great guns in the *watery world* where he had found his feather; the *report* of which *great guns* exceedingly astonished the whole company; and at once turned their despondencies for their ill success into *assurances* that they had now lit upon the *true spot* of ground which they had been looking for; and they were further confirmed in these assurances, when, upon further diving, the Indian fetched up a *sow,* as they stiled it, or a lump of silver worth perhaps two or three hundred pounds. Upon this they prudently *buoyed* the place, that they might readily find it again; and they went back unto their captain, whom for some while they distressed with nothing but such *bad news* as they formerly thought they must have carried him: nevertheless, they so slipt in the sow of silver on one side under the table, where they were now sitting with the captain, and hearing him express his resolutions to wait still patiently upon the providence of God under these disappointments, that when he should look on one side, he might see that *odd thing* before him. At last he *saw* it; seeing it, he cried out with some agony, "Why! what is this? whence comes this?" And then, with changed countenances, they told him *how* and where they got it. "Then," said he, "thanks be to God! we are made"; and so away they went, all hands to work; wherein they had this one further piece of remarkable prosperity, that whereas if they had first fallen upon that part of the Spanish wreck where the pieces of eight had been stowed in bags among the ballast they had seen a more laborious, and less enriching time of it; now, most happily,

---

[1] Caligula gathered shells, and called them "Spoils of the Ocean." Suetonius: *Caligula,* 46.

104

they first fell upon that room in the wreck where the bullion had been stored up; and so they prospered in this *new fishery*, that in a little while they had, without the loss of any man's life, brought up *thirty-two tuns* of silver; for it was now come to measuring of silver by *tuns*. Besides which, one Adderly, of Providence, who had been formerly very helpful to Captain Phips in the search of this wreck, did, upon former agreement, meet him now with a little vessel here; and *he,* with his few hands, took up about *six tuns* of silver; whereof, nevertheless, he made so little use, that in a year or two he died at Bermudas, and, as I have heard, he ran *distracted* some while before he died. Thus did there once again come into the light of the sun a treasure which had been half an hundred years *groaning under the waters*: and in this time there was grown upon the plate a crust like limestone, to the thickness of several inches; which crust being broken open by iron contrived for that purpose, they knocked out whole bushels of rusty pieces of eight which were grown thereinto. Besides that incredible treasure of plate in various forms, thus fetched up, from seven or eight fathom under water, there were vast riches of *gold,* and *pearls* and *jewels,* which they also lit upon; and, indeed, for a more comprehensive *invoice,* I must but summarily say, "All that a Spanish frigot uses to be enriched withal." Thus did they continue *fishing* till their provisions failing them, 'twas time to be gone; but before they went, Captain Phips caused Adderly and his folk to swear, that they would none of them discover the place of the wreck, or come to the place any more till the next year, when he expected to be there again himself. And it was also remarkable, that though the sows came up still so fast, that on the very last day of their being there they took up twenty, yet it was afterwards found, that they had in a manner wholly cleared that room of the ship where those *massy things* were stowed.

NOTE. The sea-feather can best be defined by quoting Captain John Smith.[1]

---

[1] Captain John Smith: *The Generall Historie of Virginia, New England, and the Summer Isles* (London, 1624; reprinted Glasgow: J. MacLehose & Sons; 1907).
In the West Indies, says Captain Smith, "In the bottom of the sea there is growing upon the rocks a large kind of Plant in the form of a Vine leafe, but far more spread with veines in the colour of a pale red, very strangely interlaced and woven into one another, which we call the Feather."

Sutliff's search[1]

I n the south part of this town,[2] near the Naugatuc river, lived Mr.
John Sutliff, a respectable miller, who died perhaps 10 or 12
years since. Mr. Sutliff, when a young man, became possessed with the
idea, that by digging into the mountain near his house, he should be
able to find silver, gold, and other precious metals. He expected to
find the silver and gold in a state of fusion, so that he could dip it up
with a ladle. He commenced digging by the Waterbury road, near the
Watertown turnpike. In digging into the mountain, in order to avoid
the rocks, stones and other obstructions, his course became very circuitous; and while digging, as he supposed, into the mountain, he in fact
got round under the turnpike road. This was found to be the case in the
following manner. Some person travelling on the road, hearing a
noise under ground beneath his feet, conjectured that it must be
Sutliff digging. Having obtained assistance, he accordingly dug down
and found Mr. Sutliff, who was quite angry in being interrupted in
this manner. Although perfectly sane on all other subjects, he continued digging a little almost every day for the greater part of his
life, for a period of perhaps 30 or 40 years, till the infirmities of old
age compelled him to desist.

Who could fail to believe in two gunny sacks full of money and a
cigar box full of diamonds, if these were described by a dying man,
who, moreover, furnished a map to show where they were buried?
Many believed, and many sought. Walter Noble Burns has pieced
together the story of their quest, but he adds a cynical epilogue—it
was, perhaps, only a pipe dream induced by marihuana. So said Rube
Hadden, of Paradise. The reader must judge.

If I could find Davis Mountain[3]

W e came out of Mexico with two four-horse wagons loaded with
plunder."—This is Zwing Hunt's deathbed story as related by
his uncle.—"Our raid had lasted three months. We numbered twenty-
nine men when we went in. Only eighteen of us got out alive. In

---

[1] From John Warner Barber: *Connecticut Historical Collections* (Improved edition, 1838, published by Durrie & Peck and John Warner Barber), p. 484.

[2] Plymouth, Connecticut.

[3] From *Tombstone,* by Walter Noble Burns, copyright 1927 by Doubleday &
Company, Inc., pp. 288–94.

Monterey, while Billy Grounds and I sat on our horses shooting up and down the street, our partners robbed the bank. They brought out two gunny sacks filled with money and a cigar box full of diamonds. We took possession of Matamoras and sacked the town. From the cathedral there we brought away statues of the Virgin Mary and the Saviour. These figures are life-size and of pure gold. When we got back on this side of the Rio Grande, we got rid of some of our loot. The rest we hauled to Davis Mountain.

"One of our men who had been shot in Mexico died at Davis Mountain and we buried him by Silver Spring. Five hundred dollars in gold had fallen to his share. He had risked his life for that money, and at last he gave his life for it. We decided to let him keep it forever, and we buried the dead man's money in a tin can at the head of the grave."

When he had finished his story, Hunt, it is said, wrote out instructions as to how the treasure could be found. Then he drew a map on a piece of writing paper, and on this map he set down in their relative positions Davis Mountain, Silver Spring, the wreck of the burned wagon, the rock of the two crosses, and the spot at which the treasure was buried. This old map is still in existence, and several copies of it are owned in Arizona.

Hunt, as his uncle declared, added several casual details to his story. He said that the outlaws bathed in the waterfall in the cañon, that they played poker in a cave on Davis Mountain, and that, from the mountain, with a pair of field glasses, they could see into New Mexico. Of Davis Mountain, he said, according to his uncle, "We called it Davis Mountain because a man named Davis was killed and is buried there."

But Zwing Hunt failed to say where Davis Mountain was.

Virgil Boucher, an elder brother of Billy Grounds, whose real name was Billy Boucher, fell under the spell of the romantic tale Zwing Hunt is alleged to have told his uncle. Virgil Boucher came from Texas to Arizona for the first time to hunt the treasure in 1884, bringing with him what purported to be Zwing Hunt's original map and written directions. For more than thirty years, intermittently, he followed the trail of the treasure, making eighteen expeditions into the mountains of southeastern Arizona—the Chiricahuas, Stein's Pass, Peloncillo, Guadalupe, and Silver Creek ranges. Failure after failure did not discourage him, and when he died three years ago in Duncan, New Mexico, he still believed, with the unshaken faith of a religious zealot, that the tale of the Davis Mountain treasure was true.

Mrs. Maggie Clinger of San Antonio is Billy Grounds's sister, and she is troubled with no doubts whatever that the treasure is right where Zwing Hunt's uncle said Zwing Hunt said it was.

"I'm just as sure about that treasure as that my name is Maggie Clinger," said Mrs. Maggie Clinger; "I can see Silver Spring, the rock of the two crosses, and all the rest of it just as plain as if I had been in the cañon myself. I know I could walk straight to the spot where the treasure is buried, if," said Mrs. Maggie Clinger, "I ever got to Davis Mountain."

Bill Sanders, of West Turkey Creek Cañon, has been one of the most inveterate as well as most optimistic searchers for the treasure. He has lived in southeastern Arizona since early times, and knows the mountains as few men know them. He went on several expeditions with Virgil Boucher. He has acted as guide for a dozen parties of treasure-hunters. He has seen the original Zwing Hunt map and studied the written directions. He, too, has implicit faith in the truth of the story.

"There are Davis Mountains in west Texas," said Bill Sanders. "But there is no Davis Peak. I heard a few months ago that the wreck of a burned wagon had been found on top of a mountain in the Davis group. I went there and spent three weeks. The wreck of an old burned wagon was there, and I couldn't figure out how it ever got on top of the mountain, but there was nothing in the Davis range that answered in any way Zwing Hunt's description of the Davis Mountain country.

"But after twenty years of puzzling over Davis Mountain, I believe I have at last identified it. Harris Mountain, in my opinion, is Davis Mountain. I think Zwing Hunt got the two names twisted. Harris Mountain is the eastern gatepost of Turkey Creek Cañon, a few miles from the site of old Galeyville. It is a bald, rounded sugar-loaf. The plains of the San Simon Valley run off from it on the east. The state line of New Mexico is only twenty miles away, and you can see into New Mexico with the naked eye. And there is a tunnel-like cave in Harris Mountain in which the outlaws could have played poker. The grave 'of a man named Davis' is not there, but the grave of a man named Harris is. Also the grave of Harris's wife and two children, all murdered by the Apaches in 1873. The Indians carried off Harris's fifteen-year-old daughter, and she married a buck and had a papoose. She was rescued from the Indians in 1876 by a detachment of the Second Cavalry, and while she was being taken to Fort Bowie she pointed out the spot on the mountain where her family had been massacred. The soldiers found the skeletons and buried them. The peak has been known as Harris Mountain ever since.

"At the foot of Harris Mountain, to the west, is Turkey Creek Cañon, which is not in any feature like the Silver Spring Cañon described by Hunt. But 'a mile or a mile and a half due west' of Harris Mountain is a little cañon running up into Round Valley, and I have

108

an idea this is the cañon of the treasure story. I am going to explore this Round Valley Cañon thoroughly, pretty soon, on a hunt for Silver Spring and Gum Spring and the rock of the two crosses."

Hearken now to the words of Rube Hadden of Paradise.

"I knew all the fellows in the fight in Skeleton Cañon," said Rube. "There were only six. They were Jim Hughes, Milt Hicks, Jack McKenzie, Ike and Billy Clanton, and another fellow whose name I've forgotten. Zwing Hunt and Billy Grounds were not within fifty miles of the fight. I heard all about the fight from Hughes, Hicks, and McKenzie a day or two afterward. They got only $4,000 out of the robbery. Of this, $1400 was in Mexican dollars. The rest was in gold bullion, which they sold. Only three Mexicans were killed. For a few days, Hughes, Hicks, and McKenzie hid the gold bars in a log cabin at the mouth of Cave Creek Cañon below Galeyville and left Al George to watch them, while they hunted up a buyer. When they had disposed of the bullion, the three of them went on a big drunk in Tombstone. Hughes and his bunch buried nothing in Skeleton.

"As for the story of the big treasure buried by Zwing Hunt and Billy Grounds at Davis Mountain, it's pure bunk. I told Virgil Boucher so when he was through here. But he was a nut over this treasure, and God Almighty couldn't have made him believe the yarn was not true. All this about the cigar box full of diamonds and the life-size gold figures of the Virgin and Christ is simply bosh. Zwing Hunt and Billy Grounds never were in Mexico in their lives.

"As outlaws, they didn't amount to much. I knew Zwing Hunt when he was driving a lumber wagon for Morse's saw-mill. He was a better mule-skinner than he was a bandit. Billy Grounds, whom I knew also, was only nineteen when he was killed. If these two boys had had all the experience as bold freebooters in Mexico they are credited with in this fool story, they would never have acted like scared amateurs when they tried to stick up the stamp mill at Charleston.

"Zwing Hunt was killed by Apaches. There's no doubt about that. Billy Breakenridge and Phil Montague and several others who had known Hunt well identified the body. So you can bet everything you've got Zwing Hunt never got back to his old home in San Antonio and never told any deathbed story. The way I figure out this buried treasure romance is that Zwing Hunt's uncle faked it. It sounds like a *marahuana* pipe dream. There is no Davis Mountain. It is not on any map, and nobody in this country ever heard of a peak by that name. In my opinion, it never had any existence except in the crazy imagination of Zwing Hunt's uncle."

Major Horace Bell, who died in 1918 at the age of eighty-seven, had been a soldier, ranger, lawyer, and editor in early California.

From his papers, dictated in 1901, but published in 1930,[1] emerge many fascinating yarns, abounding in circumstantial detail. One of the best is a complicated story of buried treasure. Major Bell had heard of a hoard buried near the spot where the Hollywood Bowl now stands; it was buried near a fresno (wild ash) tree. A Basque sheepherder, said one story, had dug up some portion of this treasure and then disappeared. But a friend of the major, Captain Henry Malcolm, a soldier of fortune from Maine, added some remarkable details. What he told the major, what became of him, and what is otherwise known of the treasure, the major relates as follows:

Who will be next?[2]

D uring the Maximilian War in Mexico, Captain Malcolm was a trusted aide to Gen. Placido Vega, the great patriot fighter of Sinaloa. Vega had held Mazatlán manfully against the Maximilian forces, but in 1865 the siege was reducing the Mexican cause to desperate straits. It became absolutely imperative to raise funds with which to purchase arms, ammunition and supplies from outside sources. The general made a fervid appeal to the whole state to contribute toward a fund to be sent to San Francisco for supplies. A wealthy woman of Mazatlán set the example by contributing her whole family fortune in jewels. Contributing jewelry became a patriotic craze and all the wealthy families turned over their heirlooms.

"Why," said Malcolm, "talk about patriotism, you never saw anything like it. Women with rings on their fingers not worth a dollar would rush in and contribute them, while aristocrats with diamonds and pearls that had been heirlooms for generations threw them into the common heap until it was estimated that $200,000 had been acquired in this way, without counting the cash contributions."

A friend of General Vega, a man of great character and prudence, was selected as the special agent to convey this treasure to San Francisco. Captain Malcolm, an Englishman, and a Mexican captain named Davila went along as escorts.

On the voyage up the special agent, who alone had authority to spend the treasure, died suddenly and mysteriously.

"We had to be extremely careful of our treasure," said Malcolm,

---

[1] *On the Old West Coast, Being Further Reminiscences of a Ranger.*

[2] From *On the Old West Coast, Being Further Reminiscences of a Ranger*, by Major Horace Bell, edited by Lanier Bartlett, copyright 1930 by William Morrow and Company, Inc., by permission of William Morrow & Co.

"for we knew that not only had Mazatlán been infested with Maximilian spies, but that San Francisco was full of them; and we suspected now, of course, that there were enemy agents aboard our ship. We finally landed with it safely in San Francisco and went to the Russ House, where we held a consultation. I suggested that we deposit it with some business house in San Francisco until we could communicate with General Vega, but Captain Davila insisted that it should be buried somewhere so that the secret of its presence in California should rest with us alone. The Englishman seconded him, so we took it out into the hills, first making our own inventory of it, taking out enough to defray additional expenses which would now face us, and wrapping it up in six separate packages covered with buckskin.

"We buried the packages in the hills beyond San Bruno, smoothed over the ground and built a fire over the spot. Of course we took bearings in detail so that we could return to the location without difficulty.

"In response to our urgent message sent by return steamer, Gen. Placido Vega himself came to San Francisco to expend the treasure.

"Captain Davila, the Englishman, and myself rode out to our secret spot in the hills and dug for our six precious packages. They had been removed! They were gone!

"Our consternation was beyond words. The Mexican turned on the Englishman and accused him of stealing the treasure. The Englishman answered him with a blow. The Mexican drew his knife and the Englishman his revolver. Before I could realize what was taking place these two were on the ground weltering in their blood. The Englishman gasped out, 'I die an innocent man.' But the Mexican did not hear him. He was already dead. In three minutes the Englishman also was stone dead.

"Well," continued Captain Malcolm, "I have experienced a great many surprises, mortifications, terrors, but I was never in a situation like this before. In a daze I mounted and rode back to San Francisco. I laid the whole matter before General Vega. Crushed as he was by the terrible news, he exonerated me from blame and held me above suspicion."

Now, to continue further with the accounting of our large cast of characters in this tragedy of treasure trove: When the Tombstone gold strike was made in Arizona in the '80's, Captain Malcolm went there. I presented him with a fine shot gun before he left. He settled on a waterhole and laid claim to it. One day a man came along who claimed prior right to the water, and during the ensuing argument the stranger picked up the shot gun which I had presented to Malcolm and shot him dead.

Young Correa, who had accompanied Martínez on the hunt for the fresno tree in Cahuenga Pass, overcame his superstitious dread after he reached manhood and renewed the search for the tree. But he could find none; the inference was that some woodchopper had felled it.

About 1891 or '92 I happened to meet Correa and related to him the circumstance of the Basque sheepherder having actually found treasure in the pass and also told him Captain Malcolm's story. His interest was at once revived and he solicited my aid in a plan to find the treasure. He proposed that we rent the land for farming purposes, that we clear it and plow with an immensely deep plow and then sub-work it with smaller plows so that we would cover every foot of the ground deep enough to root out the buried wealth.

We entered into an agreement to do this. While I was negotiating with the owners of the land poor Gumisindo Correa was shot down in the streets of Los Angeles by an assassin. The murderer or his motive was never known.

Some time later I was conversing with Etchepare, the tavernkeeper, about the startling chain of events connected with the treasure hunt in Cahuenga Pass and he said: "Oh, I forgot to tell you about my friend the Basque sheepherder. He never reached home with his treasure. He was so fearful of losing it that he made himself a buckskin garment extending the length of his body from his arm pits to his hips, with straps from the shoulders. He quilted it and stowed the treasure under the quilting. Arriving at Barcelona he stood on the rail of the steamer in high glee waving to supposed friends on the distant dock. He lost his balance, fell into the sea and sank like a lead brick."

I abandoned my plan to unearth the Mazatlán treasure, and I do not know that anyone else has ever taken up the hunt. There it lies along the road that leads down through La Nopalera [1] to the brea pits [2] and the City of the Angels, waiting to be mined out. Who will be the next to take a chance against the mysterious unseen forces that seem to haunt this reminder of the Emperor Maximilian and his Empress Carlota?

Olmstead vs. Astor •

A vigorous American legend is the one that brought deluded treasure-seekers to Deer Isle, in Penobscot Bay.[3] Frederick Law Olmstead, the landscape architect, had sued the Astor family (it was said) for some five million dollars, an amount that John Jacob Astor

---

[1] The old name of Hollywood (meaning "the cactus-patch").

[2] A local word; it means asphalt-pools.

[3] Henry Buxton, in *Assignment Down East* (Brattleboro: Stephen Daye Press; 1938), pp. 176–7, tells how he organized a dig for this supposed treasure.

was alleged to have dug up (thus founding the Astor fortune) where William Kidd had buried it, on the Olmstead property on Deer Isle. The Astors refused to pay; but could some of the treasure still be on Deer Isle, where a small cave was called Captain Kidd's Cave? It seemed so to some, until in 1922 treasure, lawsuit, and yarn were exploded by a little circular issued by Mr. Olmstead. This is what it said:

The story of Captain Kidd's Treasure and F. L. Olmstead's Lawsuit against the Astor Estate.

Explanation by F. L. Olmstead prepared in this circular form in self-defense because of an apparently endless chain of inquiries from friends, acquaintances, and total strangers.

This interesting and amazing yarn has been in private circulation and has appeared from time to time in the newspapers in garbled form since 1894; when it was written for the amusement of the author and Miss Olmstead and subsequently read before a small literary club in Chicago of which the author was a member. Intended as a burlesque hoax it was so written as to carry a pervading atmosphere of serious verisimilitude interwoven with enough of the preposterous to let the reader gradually catch onto the joke. It is a delightful example of this type of yarn.

Unfortunately in passing from hand to hand and especially from mouth to mouth it has often lost its delightful humorous quality and become a bald hoax story, arousing various degrees either of credulity or of speculation as to what possible basis in fact it could have had.

Its nearest approach to a basis in fact was a dinner conversation between the author and Miss Olmstead in Chicago, during which they talked about legends of Captain Kidd, about Penobscot Bay and the land which her father had recently purchased there, and about a sort of hollow in the rocks on the shore of that land *almost* big enough to call a cave and *almost* fit to weave some kind of a romantic legend about.

Miss Olmstead may even have said that a chest of buried treasure would be indispensable for the proper sort of legend and may have indicated her willingness to stretch the size of the cave as much as might be necessary to make room for a chest of suitable dimensions.

The seed was planted, and in the fertile soil of the author's imagination soon produced the full grown story, bristling with apparent facts. It is hardly surpassed by his pseudo-scientific monograph in the manner of the higher criticism, "Shakespeare's insomnia."

It has been pleasant and amusing to explain all this to my many friends but it is getting to be something of a bore to explain it individually to unnumbered eager inquirers. Hence this impersonal circular.

F. L. O.

Twelve fathom NE[1]

George Frederick Benner of East Boston had a fascinating experience many years ago concerning a pirate's treasure. The story begins at Middlesex, Vermont, around the year 1880. His aunt, Emeline Benner Lewis, was at home one stormy October evening when an ancient seafaring man, resembling a pirate in general appearance, called at the cottage, asking permission to store a small sea chest until his return. Mrs. Lewis consented, and the trunk was placed in the attic. The years went by, and the sailor never returned.

Young George Benner often called at his aunt's cottage, and every year he asked the lady if he could open the chest to find out what was in it. The good woman always refused, claiming that the mariner might come back. Finally, around the year 1900 she admitted that the sailor was probably dead, and gave George permission to open the trunk.

Besides the usual sailor's trinkets, there were a whale's tooth, an old quadrant, a few shells, a copy of Scott's *The Pirate,* and several letters. One letter dated at Bristol, England, in 1830, was the only clue to the sailor's home. The most important find, however, was a piece of folded vellum. George opened it, revealing a map of the Kennebec River in Maine, with a star on a small bay. Underneath the star were these instructions:

"Stand abrest qurtsbolder bring top in line with hill N ½ m it lise 12 fathom N E near big trees under stone."

The map, according to Benner, was about 150 years old. The following fall young Benner and a friend chartered a small boat and sailed to Boothbay, Maine. The day after their arrival they started up the river early in the morning, exploring the bank, hour after hour, until they came to a large quartz boulder which glistened in the sun. The men ran their boat ashore and searched the vicinity half a mile to the northward, but were only able to locate a single tree. By this time the afternoon sun had set, and they decided to return to Boothbay to await the next day.

Leaving Boothbay with the arrival of dawn, they soon found the great rock and again went ashore. When they walked over to the tall tree and discovered the remains of another large elm nearby, they decided they might be on the right trail. By sinking their crowbar into the earth every few feet, the two men located a large flat stone which

---

[1] From Edward Rowe Snow: *Pirates and Buccaneers of the Atlantic Coast* (Boston: Yankee Publishing Co. [1944]), pp. 329–31.

was a few inches under the surface, and after straining and tugging, lifted the stone high enough to roll it over. Another smaller stone was more easily removed. There, exposed to the sunlight, lay a cask, the top stove in, covered with a fine green mold. Excitedly plunging their hands into the rotting cask, they brought up handfuls of decayed wood and discolored coins which proved to be gold! The keg was entirely filled with coins except for a roll wrapped in badly-rotted canvas. They knelt there with hands full of gold, stunned for a moment at their find. With a quick glance around to see if anyone were watching them, the successful treasure hunters threw the treasure into the new canvas bags they had brought with them, and beat a hasty retreat to the boat. Nervous because of the large treasure in their possession, they agreed that it would be safer to travel right to Boston aboard their craft and thus avoid embarrassing questions.

Starting down the coast at once, Benner and his friend reached Boston two days later, and tied up at the Northern Avenue Public Landing. The two men soon made arrangements for the treasure to be taken to a well-known bank, where experts examined and counted the hoard. When they opened the canvas roll, a pearl necklace and a diamond-studded cross nine inches high were revealed.

The bank finally reported that the sum of $20,000 awaited the two men, an amount which they divided equally. Benner's friend finished college with part of his share, but lost the remainder of his money through stock manipulations. George Frederick Benner still is alive and active on the streets of Boston today, his brisk manner and quick step belying the fact that he has long since passed the biblical allotment of years.

7. SPECIAL PROVIDENCES AND STRANGE DELIVERANCES

The idea of special providences has been tersely described [1] by Professor Kenneth B. Murdock as follows: "In simplest terms it held that every event was manipulated by God." The phrase persisted, in New England at least, much longer, it would seem, than did any solid belief in such interposition. Dr. Murdock quotes the *Connecticut Courant* as referring in 1814 to the drowning of a skater as a "Distressing Providence," but we may suspect that by 1814 this was only a way of talking, for most people. (It is true that Ann Saunders, in 1827, never doubted that her life had been saved by a special providence,[2] but both Ann and her adventures were exceptional.) Even as early as 1680 Dr. Murdock has found a New England historian [3] (who was discussing, to be sure, the events of 1640) implying disbelief. His words, rightly regarded by Dr. Murdock as highly significant, are as follows: "Hitherto [i.e., before 1640] divine providence did, with arms of abundant goodness, as a nursing father, uphold this infant province of New England, as was said of Ephraim, when God learned him to go, taking him by the hand. But for the future they were left more to stand upon their own legs, and shift for themselves."

Needless to say, as belief in divine interposition waned, evidences of such interposition seemed to appear more rarely. When Edward Johnson said in 1653 [4] that God allayed the quarrelsome spirits of the Indians, he meant it literally; when Cotton Mather, in 1700, sent his *Magnalia Christi Americana* to the publisher, he was largely actuated by a desire to show how remarkably the Deity had interposed in the affairs of Massachusetts. But whether they knew it or not, both Mather and Johnson liked to tell a good story, preferably an astonishing one. In 1736, when John Gyles published the story of his captivity among the Indians,[5] he contented himself with calling his escape a "strange deliverance," but he makes it plain that he thought his release providential. (But it has been thought that he was assisted by a clergyman

---

[1] In Kenneth B. Murdock: "William Hubbard and the Providential Interpretation of History," *Proceedings of the American Antiquarian Society*, LII, i, 15ff.

[2] Pp. 55–7, above.

[3] William Hubbard. (See note 1, above.) Pp. 17 and 32 of Murdock's article.

[4] *Wonder-Working Providence of Sion's Savior in New England*, edited by J. F. Jameson (New York: Charles Scribner's Sons; 1910), p. 80.

[5] Pp. 241–3, below.

in preparing his narrative; if so, the views of this assistant may have tempered Gyles's own.)

In the late nineteenth century we find the worthy Quaker Thomas R. Hazard (of jonny-cake fame) half believing in the judgments of God, and the evangelist Dwight L. Moody sure that God has intervened to protect one of his servants—that is, Moody himself. But in the twentieth century that humorous medical man Hans Zinsser, describing a cure that in earlier days would have been esteemed miraculous, ascribes it by implication to the leaving off of all medicine. Skepticism can no farther go.

Cannibals, smallpox, more supplies[1]

Of the Lord's gracious protection of his people, from the barbarous cruelties of the Heathen.

About this time the Indians that were most conversant among them, came quaking and complaining of a barbarous and cruel people called the Tarratines who they said would eat such Men as they caught alive, tying them to a Tree, and gnawing their flesh by peece-meales off their Bones, as also that they were a strong and numerous people, and now comming, which made them flee to the English, who were but very few in number at this time, and could make but little resistance, being much dispersed, yet did they keepe a constant watch, neglecting no meanes Christ had put into their hands for their owne safety, insomuch that they were exceedingly weakned with continued labour, watching and hard diet, but the Lord graciously upheld them in all, for thus it befell meere the Towne of Linn, then called Saugust, in the very dead of the night (being upon their watch, because of the report that went of the Indians approach to those parts) one Lieutenant Walker, a man indued with faith, and of a courageous spirit, comming to relieve the Centinell, being come up with him, all of a sudden they heard the Sticks crack hard by them, and withall he felt something brush hard upon his shoulder, which was an Indian arrow shot through his Coat, and the wing of his buffe-Jacket.

Upon this hee discharged his Culliver directly toward the place, where they heard the noise, which being deeply loden, brake in

---

[1] From *Johnson's Wonder-Working Providence, 1628–1651*, edited by J. Franklin Jameson (New York: Charles Scribner's Sons; 1910), pp. 78–80.

pieces, then they returned to the Court of Guard, and raised such small forces as they had; comming to the light they perceived he had an other Arrow shot through his Coat betwixt his Legs. Seeing this great preservation, they stood upon their Guard till Morning, expecting the Indians to come upon them every moment, but when daylight appeared, they soone sent word to other parts, who gathered together, and tooke counsell how to quit themselves of these Indians, whose approach they deemed would be sudden. They agreed to discharge their great Guns. The redoubling echo rattling in the Rocks caused the Indians to betake themselves to flight (being a terrible unwonted sound unto them) or rather he who put such trembling feare in the Assyriens Army, struck the like in these cruell Caniballs. In the Autumne following, the Indians, who had all this time held good correspondency with the English, began to quarrell with them about their bounds of Land, notwithstanding they purchased all they had of them, but the Lord put an end to this quarrell also, by smiting the Indians with a sore Disease, even the small Pox; of the which great numbers of them died, yet these servants of Christ, minding their Masters businesse, were much moved in affection toward them to see them depart this life without the knowledge of God in Christ. And therefore were very frequent among them for all the noysomenesse of their Disease, entring their Wigwams, and exhorting them in the Name of the Lord. Among others one of the chiefe Saggamores of the Mattachusets, whom the English named Saggamore John, gave some good hopes, being always very courteous to them, whom the godly, and much honour'd among the English, visiting a little before his death, they instructing him in the knowledge of God, Quoth hee, "by and by mee Mattamoy, may be my two Sons live, you take them to teach much to know God."

Accordingly the honoured Mr. John Winthrop, and the Reverend Mr. John Wilson tooke them home, notwithstanding the infectiousnesse of the Disease their Father died of. The mortality among them was very great, and increased among them daily more and more, insomuch that the poore Creatures being very timorous of death, would faine have fled from it, but could not tell how, unlesse they could have gone from themselves; Relations were little regarded among them at this time, so that many, who were smitten with the Disease, died helplesse, unlesse they were neare, and known to the English: their Powwowes, Wizards, and Charmers, Athamochas Factors, were possest with the greatest feare of any. The Winters piercing cold stayed not the strength of this hot Disease, yet the English endeavoring to visit their sick Wigwams, helpe them all they could, but as they entred one of their matted Houses, they beheld a most sad spectacle, death having smitten them all save one poore Infant, which lay on the ground, sucking the Breast of its dead Mother, seeking to draw living nourishment from her dead breast. Their dead they left oft-times unburied, wherefore the English were forced to dig holes, and drag their stinking corps into them. Thus did the Lord allay their quarrelsome spirits, and made roome for the following part of his Army. This yeare came over more supplies to forward the worke of Christ.

God jogs the Puritan elbow[1]

Of the death of divers personages, who were in great esteem with the people of New-England, famous for their godliness, and eminent parts, both for Magistracy and Ministry, and of the correcting hand of the Lord upon his N. E. people.

This year, after the death of this godly Governour, was chosen to succeed in the place Jo. Endicut Esq., and Tho. Dudly Esq. to be Deputy Governor, to the place of Major-General Edw. Gibbons; and seeing that the Lord is pleased to call this people to mourning, the Author will proceed to relate what further occasion this people have had to lament their miscarriages, that have caused the rod to be stretched out towards them, for of a truth they are no Antinomians. The next loss was the death of that famous Preacher of the Lord M. Hooker, Pastor of the Church of Christ at Hartford, and M. Philips, Pastor of the Church of Christ at Watertown, and the holy heavenly, sweet-affecting, and soul-ravishing Minister M. Tho. Shepheard, Pastor of the Church of Christ at Cambridg, whose departure was very heavily taken by all the people of Christ round about him. And now N. E. that had such heaps upon heaps of the riches of Christs tender compassionate mercies, being turn'd off from his dandling knees, began to read their approaching rod in the bend of his brows and frowns of his former favourable countenance toward them; their plenty of all things, which shold have cheared their hearts, and quickened their spirits in elevating both soul and body to a thankful frame, through the work of his blessed Spirit; on the contrary, it brought a fulness on many, even to loath the very honey-comb, insomuch that good wholesome truths would not down, yet had the Lord those that were precious unto him, who were not wanting to help one another out of this distemper, and with more warmer affections exhort one another, Come let us go up unto the house of the Lord, and he will teach us his wayes. Also the Lord was pleased to awaken us with an Army of

---

[1] Ibid., pp. 252–4.

caterpillers, that had he not suddainly rebuked them, they had surely destroyed the husbandmans hope; where they fell upon trees, they left them like winter-wasting cold, bare and naked; and although they fell on fields very rarely, yet in some places they made as clear a riddance, as the harvest mans hand, and uncovered the gay green Medow ground, but indeed the Lord did by some plats shew us what he could have done with the whole, and in many places cast them into the high-wayes, that the Cartwheels in their passage were painted green with running over the great swarms of them; in some fields they devoured the leaves of their pease, and left the straw with the full crop, so tender was the Lord in his correction; this minded all these Jacobites of the end of their coming over, but chiefly the husbandman, whose over eager pursuit of the fruits of the earth made some of them many times run out so far in this Wilderness, even out of the sweet sound of the silver Trumpets blown by the laborious Ministers of Christ, forsaking the assembly of the Lords people to celebrate their Sabbaths in the chimney-corner, horse, kine, sheep, goats, and swine being their most indeared companions, to travel with them to the end of their pilgrimage, or otherwise to gather together some of their neerest neighbors, and make a preachment one unto another, till they had learn'd so much, that they could away with none other teaching. As also the Lord was pleased to command the wind and Seas to give us a jog on the elbow, by sinking the very chief of our shipping in the deep, and splitting them in shivers against the shores; a very goodly Ship called the *Seaforce* was cast away, and many N. E. people put to hard shifts for their lives, and some drowned, as the godly and dearly beloved servant of Christ, Mr. Tho. Coitmire, a very able Seaman, and also a good Scholar, one who had spent both his labour and estate for the helping on of this Wilderness-work: as also another ship set forth by the Merchants of New-Haven, of which the godly Mr. Lamberton went Master, neither ship, persons, nor goods ever heard of; another ship also built and set forth by the inhabitants of Cambridg, split and cast away neer the same place where the *Seaforce* was lost; as also another Barque mostly set forth by Dorchester men, sunk in the Sea, and never heard of the manner how, with divers others which might be here inserted; this seemed the sorer affliction to these N. E. people, because many godly men lost their lives, and abundantly the more remarkable, because the Lord was pleased to forbid any such things to befal his people in their passage hither; herein these people read, as in great capital letters, their suddain forgetfulness of the Lords former received mercy in his wonderful preservation, bringing over so many scores of ships, and thousands of persons, without miscarriage of any, to the wonderment of the whole world that shall hear of it, but more especially were the Merchants and traders themselves sensible of the hand of the Lord out against them, who were in some of the ships, and had their lives given them for a prey; as also Vintners, and other men of trade, whose gain is increased by Merchants men, being so taken up with the income of a large profit, that they would willingly have had the Commonwealth tolerate divers kinds of sinful opinions to intice men to come and sit down with us, that their purses might be filled with coyn, the civil Government with contention, and the Churches of our Lord Christ with errors; the Lord was pleased after this, to let in the King of Terror among his new-planted Churches.

Sea-deliverances and divine warnings[1]

The Wonderful Story of Major Gibbons

Among remarkable sea-deliverances, no less than three several writers have published that wherein Major Edward Gibbons of Boston in New England was concerned. A vessel bound from Boston to some other parts of America was, through the continuance of contrary winds, kept so long at sea, that the people aboard were in extream straits for want of provisions; and seeing that nothing here below could afford them any relief, they look'd upwards unto Heaven in humble and fervent supplications. The winds continuing still as they were, one of the company made a sorrowful motion that they should by a *lot* single out *one* to die, and by death to satisfie the ravenous hunger of the rest. After many a doleful and fearful debate upon this motion, they come to a result, that *it must be done!* The *lot* is cast; one of the company is taken; but where is the executioner that shall do the terrible office upon a poor innocent? It is a death now to think who shall act this bloody part in the tragedy; but before they fall upon this involuntary and unnatural execution, they once more went unto their zealous prayers; and, behold! while they were calling upon God, he answer'd them: for there leaped a mighty *fish* into their boat, which, to their double joy, not only quieted their outrageous hunger, but also gave them some token of a further deliverance. However, the *fish* is quickly eaten; the horrible famine returns, the horrible distress is renewed; a black despair again seizes their spirits; for another morsel they come to a second lot, which fell upon another person; but still they cannot find an executioner: They once again fall to their im-

---

[1] Cotton Mather: *Magnalia Christi Americana* (Hartford: Silas Andrus & Son; 1853), pp. 345–6.

portunate prayers: and behold, a second answer from above! A great *bird* lights and fixes itself upon the mast: one of the men spies it; and there it stands until he took it by the wing with his hand. This was a second *life from the dead*. This fowl, with the omen of a further deliverance in it, was a sweet feast unto them. Still their disappointments follow them; they can see no land, they know not where they are; irresistible hunger once more pinches them; they have no hope to be saved, but by a third miracle: they return to another lot; but before they go to the heart-breaking task of slaying the person under *designation,* they repeat their addresses unto the God of heaven, their former "friend in adversity." And now they look, and look again, but there is nothing: their *devotions* are concluded, and nothing appears: yet they hoped, yet they stayed, yet they lingered. At last one of them spies a ship, which put a new hope and life into 'em all. They bear up with their ship, they man their long-boat, they beg to board their vessel, and are admitted. It proves a French *pirate*. Major Gibbons petitions for a little bread, and offers all for it; but the commander was one who had formerly received considerable kindnesses of Major Gibbons at Boston, and now replied chearfully, "Major Gibbons, not a hair of you or your company shall perish, if it lies in my power to preserve you." Accordingly he supplied their necessities, and they made a comfortable end of their voyage.

Mantissa (over measure)[1]

Over and above the number of *sea-deliverances* intended for this chapter, we will add one more, which is a late and a fresh instance, and attested beyond all contradiction.

On the 16th of October, in this present year, 1697, there arriv'd at New-Haven a sloop of about 50 tuns, whereof Mr. William Trowbridge was master: The vessel belong'd unto New-Haven, the persons on board were seven; and seventeen long weeks had they now spent since they came from their port, which was Fayal. By so unusually tedious a passage, a terrible famine unavoidably came upon them; and for the five last weeks of their voyage they were so destitute of all food, that thro' faintness they would have chosen death rather than life. But they were a praying and a pious company; and when "these poor men cry'd unto the Lord, he heard and sav'd them." God sent his dolphins to attend 'em; and of these they caught still one every day, which was enough to serve 'em: only on Saturdays they still

---

[1] *Ibid.*, p. 54.

catch'd a couple; and on the Lord's Days they could catch none at all. With all possible skill and care they could not supply themselves with the fish in any other number or order; and indeed with a holy *blush* at last they left off trying to do anything on the *Lord's Days,* when they were so well supplied on the *Saturdays.* Thus the Lord kept feeding a company that put their trust in him, as he did his Israel with his manna: and this they continu'd until the dolphins came to that change of water, where they us'd to leave the vessels. Then they so strangely surrendred themselves, that the company took twenty-seven of 'em; which not only suffic'd them until they came ashore, but also some of 'em were brought ashore dry'd, as a monument of the divine benignity.

Three warnings[1]

A lewd young man, being dissatisfied with the service wherein he lived, at the house of an honest man, in a neighboring town, when they told him that his bad courses would bring him to hell at the last, he wickedly said, "He had rather be in hell than in his master's house." Immediately after this, he was in a very strange manner drowned off a little bank in the river.—Take one example more:

There was an old *professor* in one of our churches, who being under the *admonition* of the church for some offences, was by his friends called upon to *repent,* and *reform,* and *humble* himself. But he flew into this outrageous answer: "No! I will burn, before I will turn." And behold the issue! This man some time after fell into the fire, and was burnt to death.—Take one more example yet. 'Tis well known to all the neighbors:

A man in our Narragansett country, having set his dog to *mischief* his neighbours cattel, deny'd the fact with imprecations "that he might never stir from the place, if he had so done." The neighbor to whom he deny'd it, expressing himself troubled at his impudent lying, this Atheist hereupon used the name of the great God in his imprecations, "that God would never let him stir from that place, if he did the thing." The words were scarce out of his mouth, but he sunk down dead in the place, and never stirred any more.

---

[1] Ibid., p. 393.

God sends rain[1]

Concerning the Drought, the true narrative of that Providence is this,

In August last, such was the want of rain, that the Indian corn was not only dried and parched up, but the apple-trees withered, the fruit and leaves fell off as in Autumn, and some trees seemed to be dead with that Drought: the Indians came into town and lamented their want of rain, and that their *Powawes* could get none in their way of worship, desiring me that I would seek to God for rain: I appointed a Fast day for that purpose. The day being come, it proved cleer without any clouds, untill sun-setting, when we came from the Meeting, and then some Clouds arose; the next day remained cloudy, then *Uncas* with many Indians came to my house, Uncas lamented there was such want of Rain; I asked whether if God should send us Rain, he would not attribute it to their *Powawes*: He answered no, for they had done their uttermost and all in vain: I replyed, if you will declare it before all these Indians, you shall see what God will doe for us; For although this year he hath shewn his anger against the English, and not only against the Indians, yet he hath begun to save us, and I have found by experience twice in the like case, when we sought by Fasting and Prayer, he hath given us Rain, and never denyed us. Then *Uncas* made a great speech to the Indians (which were many) confessing that if God should then send rain, it could not be ascribed to their powawing, but must be acknowledged to be an answer of our prayers. This day the clouds spread more and more, and the next day there was such plenty of rain that our River rose more than two foot in height.

God sends rats

In the seventeenth century it was not only Puritans like the Mathers who accepted the idea of special divine intervention. We find Captain John Smith, for example, telling of some ill-judged adminis-

---

[1] From Increase Mather: *A Brief History of the War with the Indians* (London, 1676); quoted from G. L. Kittredge: *The Old Farmer and His Almanack* (Boston: W. Ware & Co.; 1904), p. 364.

tration that the English colonists practiced in the West Indies in 1617. He then describes what he regarded as the direct result, as follows: [1]

> But the great God of heaven being angry at somewhat happened in those proceedings, caused such an increase of silly rats in the space of two years so to abound, before they regarded them, that they filled not onely those places where they were first landed, but swimming from place to place, spread themselves into all parts of the Countrey . . . nay they so devoured the fruits of the earth that they were destitute for a yeere or two.

The judgments of God [2]

A nd here I can't help but say, that I more than half believe in the judgments of God, for of the five boys that were stoning the poor little young robin to death, I know that three of them have since died violent deaths, whilst of the remaining two, one died in jail and the other in a poor-house.

A divine interposition [3]

Y esterday in looking through some papers I found a letter dated March 24, 1909, addressed to my sister, Mrs. A. P. Fitt, of this place, making inquiry in regard to some important experience in connection with our father, the late Mr. D. L. Moody. The letter I remember was referred to me by my sister, and at her request I had consented to reply to it, and how it was mislaid I do not know. Please accept my apologies for the tardiness in its acknowledgment.

I could better answer the inquiry if I knew exactly what the nature of the incident was to which you refer, but it is possible, and even probable, that the incident deals with the occult, and I infer, therefore, that the experience is one of which you have probably heard, which I have heard my father describe several times, although he never made reference to it in public, feeling that it was too sacred an experience and too open to misunderstanding.

On his first evangelistic mission to Great Britain, in the early seven-

---

[1] From Captain John Smith: *The Generall Historie of Virginia, New England, and the Summer Isles* (London, 1624; reprinted Glasgow: J. MacLehose & Sons; 1907), Vol. I, p. 365.

[2] From Thomas Robinson Hazard: *The Jonny-Cake Papers of "Shepherd Tom"* (Boston: Printed for the Subscribers; 1915), p. 262.

[3] From *Noted Witnesses for Psychic Occurrences*, compiled by the Research Officer of the Society (Boston; Boston Society for Psychic Research; 1928), pp. 301-2.

ties, he was invited to the city of Liverpool. You will remember that the prejudice against Americans, especially Yankees, was strong in the city of Liverpool, and even when Beecher made his famous trip to England in the interests of the North during the War he had his greatest difficulty in pleading the cause of the North in the city of Liverpool. How far this feeling influenced the press against my father I do not know, but during the earlier part of the meetings the opposition on the part of the secular press was very strong, and Mr. Moody was made the object of numerous bitter attacks, his motives being impugned, and himself being made the object of all sorts of ridicule. To this he paid no attention. My mother was not with him at the time, being with friends for a few days, when suddenly he had come over him a peculiar sense of fear or nervousness. My father was one of the most fearless men that I have ever known, and the experience was so new to him that he began to feel anxiety about his own condition, questioning whether he might have been overworking, with the result that his mind was affected. He would frequently cross the street if he heard anyone coming up behind him, and at night was careful to look under his bed, examine the closet, and always see that his door was locked. This experience lasted for several days and left him as suddenly as it had come, one day while going to the hall where he was preaching. At the close of his service he was surrounded by the gentlemen who constituted the committee who had invited him to Liverpool, and on one pretext or another they detained him for a few minutes until a police officer came to them and explained that everything was now satisfactory. The chairman of the committee then explained to my father that they had learned that day that for a week there had been at large in the city of Liverpool an escaped lunatic from a neighboring asylum, who was obsessed with the idea that he was commissioned to assassinate my father. For days he had been trying to get an opportunity to stab him and he had only just been caught and placed under arrest.

The experience was one that left a deep impression upon my father, and he felt that it was a distinct interposition of Divine care. For that very reason he felt it was too sacred to speak of frequently, and as I have said, he never referred to it in public, although I have heard him relate the incident on several occasions. If this is the incident regarding which you make inquiry I am very glad to have been able to give it to you for your records, although I share with my father in the conviction that if it has a scientific value it has also to us a spiritual significance, and that it was a case where there was a Divine interposition in behalf of one of God's servants.

Respectfully yours,

W. R. Moody

A life saved[1]

Speaking of Dr. T. reminds me of a case in which I was credited with saving a life under peculiar circumstances. While still House Physician at the hospital, during Dr. T.'s visiting period, we had a poor fellow on the male ward who appeared to suffer from advanced nephritis. Dr. T., as I have remarked, was a virtuoso at compounding drugs. During his short annual reign of three months, the order sheets of every patient were covered with the red ink in which medication orders were entered. They got something or other "t.i.d." (three times a day), other things with meals, something else on waking up, another before the lights went out, and a few odd pills or injections "p.r.n." (pro re nata). Many of them had to be waked out of sound sleep to get one of his "black draughts" or "blue pills" or "brown decoctions"—all of them proudly originated by the Chief himself, and most of them quite complicated, with strong medicaments. The particular old boy of whom I write was getting a formidable sequence of daily doses and was slipping out of our hands—taking it patiently, with good humor and courage. We all liked him, and during his month on the ward he became a favorite. One night, when he was pretty low, I was making my midnight rounds with the ward nurse. We stopped at his bed and held a whispered conversation. He was in bad condition, the nurse said, and she didn't think he'd last long. She hated to force all that medicine down his throat. It bothered him and didn't seem to be doing him any good.

"All right," I said. "He's going to die soon anyway, and we'll stop all medication. Just leave the orders on the chart, and we'll steer the old boy around him as well as we can. Give him anything he wants to eat, within reason, and a shot of my Scotch when you come on at night. I'll bring you a bottle. He might as well die happy."

From that moment, our friend began to improve. Pretty soon, by respectful and adroit suggestion, I arranged to have official sanction for the omission of one pill and "draught" after another. In two weeks our patient began to sit up in bed for extraordinarily hearty meals. In three weeks he was up—his old self, he said. In four, he was out and I forgot about him.

The sequel came one Sunday afternoon during the following winter, when I was sitting in my office. The doorbell rang, and in walked a short, fat, ruddy man of about sixty, behind him a shorter, fatter, and

[1] From Hans Zinsser: *As I Remember Him: The Biography of R. S.* (Boston: Little, Brown & Company; Atlantic Monthly Press; 1940), pp. 178-9.

ruddier boy of twenty or so. Neither of them did I recognize. Yet the older man stuck out his ham of a hand and said: "God bless you, doctor, how are you?" Then I suddenly remembered him. "I hope you're not sick again," I said.

"Oh, no, doctor! I'm fine. I just brought in my son" (who, apparently in the horse business, was embarrassedly rolling a flat-topped derby in one hand while he kept adjusting a white piqué tie with a horseshoe pin) "to show him the man who saved my life. You remember, doctor, that night in the hospital when I was nigh dead? You came around about midnight with the nurse. I was feelin' awful low, an' everybody thought I was goin' to die. I was thinkin' so my own self. You thought I was sleepin', but I wasn't. I was just pretendin'. You had a long talk with the nurse in front of my bed an' then you give her some orders. From that minute, I begun to mend.

"This is the man, my boy, as pulled your Pa out of the claws of the Reaper," he said poetically.

Wound and unwound[1]

Of all the white men I ever knew, the one that understood nature best was old Dr. Mersereau. He was a water doctor who had a sort of sanitarium up in the mountains on the road to Soulsbyville, and made many wonderful cures by natural methods. I never knew him to give any medicine. He considered that his only business was to assist nature, and he would only prescribe natural remedies, the outdoor elements—sunshine, air, water, and earth.

People used to send crippled and ailing and rickety children up from down below and he'd put them in little cotton shirts and turn them loose to play in the dirt and sunshine. He would have them drink a lot of pure mountain water, and eat fresh watercress and other greens, and he cured sores and skin diseases by mud baths or the putting on of earth.

His most remarkable cure, though, was of an Austrian miner.

One day an express wagon drove up to Dr. Mersereau's sanitarium. On the seat was two big Austrians, and lying on a mattress in the bed of the wagon was another; a great hulk of a fellow, lying there totally helpless. Well, Dr. Mersereau come out to the wagon and inquired what was the matter. The two Austrians explained that their friend's

---

[1] Reprinted from *Ghost Town* by G. Ezra Dane, in collaboration with Beatrice J. Dane, by permission of Alfred A. Knopf, Inc. Copyright 1941 by G. Ezra Dane. Pp. 294-7.

legs had been paralyzed for many months; they had taken him every-where, to doctors and to hospitals up here and down below, but no one had been able to do him any good.

The doctor asked them then if they knew what their friend had done that might have caused this paralysis. They said no, he had just been working with them in a little placer mine; his job was to wheel dirt in a wheelbarrow, up an incline.

Well, the doctor climbed into the wagon and looked the fellow over. Then he said to the other two: "You don't need to move him from the wagon," he says, "just take him home, stand him up between you, and have him take one step backward one day, two the next day, three the next, and so on till he is able to walk backwards alone."

They asked what the doctor would charge for his advice.

"Nothing," he says.

Several months later a big powerful man came to the doctor's door and asked: "Don't you remember me, doctor?"

"Why, no," says the doctor.

"Well," says the man, "I'm the miner who was brought to you paralyzed a few months back, and now here I am cured and as healthy as a ram, and ready to pay you for your advice." With that, he handed the doctor five hundred dollars that he had been able to put aside from his earnings since his cure.

What Dr. Mersereau had realized, you see, was that this man, from wheeling his wheelbarrow up the incline for so long, was like a clock that had been wound up too tight; all he needed was to be unwound a bit.

Yes, sir, and they's plenty of people in this world all wound up like the big Austrian, but they don't know it, because, you see, it's not their legs that get paralyzed—it's their heads.

BOOK II

WONDERS OF NATURE—
AND SOME OTHERS

WONDERS OF NATURE—AND SOME
OTHERS: *American fact as the background to American folklore.*
The animal kingdom

It is a short step, and quickly taken, from the tornado that blows a house away or the hurricane that ruins a forest, to the gale that blows a ship's anchor and chain out into a horizontal line; a short step, too, from porpoises to sea-serpents, from rats that comprehend traps (thus reversing our plans) to rats that read letters, from Jersey mosquitoes to Gargantuan ones, and from animals that bark or mew or roar, to animals that talk. The shading off from natural to unnatural history is a rapid process when there is no scientist at hand, and, to say truth, there are many border-line cases.

Since Æsop told of talking animals, and Pliny[1] of dolphins accustomed to bear human riders, we cannot say that unnatural history was born in America. But it has flourished mightily here. The next group of stories glides, via fish stories, from the probable to the impossible, and includes a few which the teller hardly pretends to believe. Such a wink to the audience is not usually favored by the best raconteurs, but those who employ it seem to know what they are about. Thus H. L. Mencken[2] almost persuades us that his Shetland pony was "a cheat, a rogue, and a scoundrel" and that he not only laughed, but chuckled. Thus, too, John Gould[3] almost persuades us that Oscar, the bull, used the telephone. These gentlemen do not, I think, expect more than three-quarter belief from us. With Mark Twain's Jim Baker[4] the case is different. His admiration for the singular talents of bluejays is sincere, outspoken, argumentative, even passionate. He may not convince us that a jay uses good grammar, as he alleges, but as to profanity and sense of humor—well, he proves that the jay has them.

The zoo is a wonderful place, but the zoo of American animal-lore is even more fascinating. This is one region in which fiction is stranger than truth.

[1] *Natural History,* ix, 26.
[2] In "Memoirs of the stable," below.
[3] In "No ordinary bull," below.
[4] In "Jim Baker's bluejay yarn," below.

The perennial old reliable topic. Nobody does anything about it, according to Mark Twain,[1] but there is plenty of talk.

The following account[2] of the Great Snow of February, 1717, by Dr. Mather, is perhaps the most particular description which can now be obtained.

An horrid snow

Boston, 10th Dec. 1717

Sr.

Tho' we are gott so far onward as the beginning of another Winter, yett we have not forgott the last, which at the latter end whereof we were entertained and overwhelmed with a Snow, which was attended with some Things, which were uncommon enough to afford matter for a letter from us. Our Winter was not so bad as that wherein Tacitus tells us, that Corbulo made his expedition against the Parthians, nor that which proved so fatal to the Beasts and Birds in the days of the Emperor Justinian, and that the very Fishes were killed under the freezing sea, when Phocas did as much to the men whom Tyrants treat like the Fishes of the Sea. But the conclusion of our Winter was hard enough, and was too formidable to be easily forgotten, and of a piece with what you had in Europe a year before. The snow was the chief Thing that made it so. For rarely does a Winter pass us, wherein we may not say with Pliny *Ingens Hyeme Nivis apud nos copia,*[3] yet our last Winter brought with it a Snow, that excelled them all. The Snow, 'tis true, not equal to that, which once fell and lay twenty Cubits high, about the Beginning of October, in the parts

---

[1] Or somebody, most probably Charles Dudley Warner. But the saying is usually attributed to Mark. Robert Underwood Johnson, for instance, says it was Mark's (Robert Underwood Johnson: *Remembered Yesterdays;* Boston: Little, Brown & Co., 1923; p. 322).

[2] From *The History and Antiquities of New England, New Jersey, and Pennsylvania,* collected and compiled from authentic sources by John Warner Barber (Portland: William C. Lord; 1848), pp. 476–8.

[3] We have heavy snows in the winter.

about the Euxine Sea, Nor to that which the French Annals tell us kept falling for twenty Nine weeks together, nor to several mentioned by Boethius, wherein vast numbers of people and of Cattel perished, Nor to those that Strabo finds upon Caucasus and Rhodiginus in Armenia. But yett such an one, and attended with such circumstances as may deserve to be remembered.

On the twentieth of the last February there came on a Snow, which being added unto what had covered the ground a few days before, made a thicker mantle for our Mother than what was usual: And the storm with it was, for the following day, so violent as to make all communication between the Neighbors everywhere to cease. People, for some hours, could not pass from one side of a street unto another, and the poor Women, who happened at this critical time to fall into Travail, were put unto Hardships, which anon produced many odd stories for us. But on the Twenty-fourth day of the Month, comes Pelion upon Ossa: Another Snow came on which almost buried the Memory of the former, with a storm so famous that Heaven laid an Interdict on the Religious Assemblies throughout the Country, on this Lord's day, the like whereunto had never been seen before. The Indians near an hundred years old, affirm that their Fathers never told them of any thing that equalled it. Vast numbers of Cattel were destroyed in this Calamity. Whereof some there were, of the Stranger sort, were found standing dead on their legs, as if they had been alive many weeks after, when the Snow melted away. And others had their eyes glazed over with Ice at such a rate, that being not far from the Sea, their mistake of their way drowned them there. One gentleman, on whose farms were now lost above 1100 sheep, which with other Cattel, were interred (shall I say) or Innived, in the Snow, writes me word that there were two sheep very singularly circumstanced. For no less than eight and twenty days after the Storm, the People pulling out the ruins of above 100 sheep out of a Snow Bank which lay 16 foot high, drifted over them, there was two found alive, which had been there all this time, and kept themselves alive by eating the wool of their dead companions. When they were taken out they shed their own Fleeces, but soon gott into good Case again. Sheep were not the only creatures that lived unaccountably, for whole weeks without their usual sustenance, entirely buried in the Snow-drifts.

The Swine had a share with the Sheep in strange survivals. A man had a couple of young Hoggs, which he gave over for dead, But on the twenty-seventh day after their Burial, they made their way out of a Snow-Bank, at the bottom of which they had found a little Tansy to feed upon. The Poultry as unaccountably survived as these. Hens were found alive after seven days; Turkeys were found alive after five and twenty days, buried in the Snow, and at a distance from the ground, and altogether destitute of any thing to feed them. The number of creatures that kept a Rigid Fast, shutt up in Snow for diverse weeks together, and were found alive after all, have yielded surprizing stories unto us.

The Wild Creatures of the Woods, the outgoings of the Evening, made their Descent as well as they could in this time of scarcity for them towards the Sea-side. A vast multitude of Deer, for the same cause, taking the same course, and the Deep Snow Spoiling them of their only defence, which is to run, they became such a prey to these Devourers, that it is thought not one in twenty escaped. These carniverous Sharpers, and especially the Foxes, would make their Nocturnal visits to the Pens, where the people had their sheep defended from them. The poor Ewes big with young, were so terrified with the frequent Approaches of the Foxes, and the Terror had such Impression on them, that most of the Lambs brought forth in the Spring following, were of Monsieur Reinard's complexion, when the Dam, were either White or Black. It is remarkable that immediately after the Fall of the Snow an infinite number of Sparrows made their Appearance, but then, after a short continuance, all disappeared.

It is incredible how much damage is done to the Orchards, For the Snow, freezing to a Crust, as high as the boughs of the trees, anon Split ym to pieces. The Cattel also, walking on the crusted Snow a dozen foot from the ground, so fed upon the Trees as very much to damnify them. The Ocean was in a prodigious Ferment, and after it was over, vast heaps of little shells were driven ashore, where they were never seen before. Mighty shoals of Porpoises also kept a play-day in the disturbed waters of our Harbours. The odd Accidents befalling many poor people, whose Cottages were totally covered with the Snow and not the very tops of their chimneys to be seen, would afford a Story. But there not being any relation to Philosophy in them, I forbear them.

Ain't seen no water [1]

You know, when it lightnings, de angels is peepin' in de lookin' glass; when it thunders, they's rollin' out de rain-barrels; and when it rains, somebody done dropped a barrel or two and bust it.

One time, you know, there was goin' to be big doin's in Glory and all de angels had brand new clothes to wear and so they was all peepin'

---

[1] From Zora Neale Hurston: *Mules and Men*, Copyright, 1934, by Zora Neale Hurston, published by J. B. Lippincott Company, pp. 27–9.

in de lookin' glasses, and therefore it got to lightning all over de sky. God tole some of de angels to roll in all de full rain barrels, and they was in such a hurry that it was thunderin' from the east to the west and the zigzag lightning went to join the mutterin' thunder and, next thing you know, some of them angels got careless and dropped a whole heap of them rain barrels, and didn't it rain!

In one place they call Johnstown they had a great flood. And so many folks got drownded that it looked jus' like Judgment Day.

So some of de folks that got drownded in that flood went one place and some went another. You know, everything that happen, they got to be a nigger in it—and so one of de brothers in black went up to Heben from de flood.

When he got to the gate, Ole Peter let 'im in and made 'im welcome. De colored man was named John, so John ast Peter, says, "Is it dry in dere?"

Ole Peter tole 'im, "Why, yes it's dry in here. How come you ast that?"

"Well, you know Ah jus' come out of one flood, and Ah don't want to run into no mo'. Ooh, man! You ain't *seen* no water. You just oughter seen dat flood we had at Johnstown."

Peter says, "Yeah, we know all about it. Jus' go wid Gabriel and let him give you some new clothes."

So John went on off wid Gabriel and come back all dressed up in brand new clothes and all de time he was changin' his clothes he was tellin' Ole Gabriel all about dat flood, jus' like he didn't know already.

So when he come back from changin' his clothes, they give him a brand new gold harp and handed him to a gold bench and made him welcome. They was so tired of hearing about dat flood they was glad to see him wid his harp 'cause they figgered he'd get to playin' and forget all about it. So Peter tole him, "Now you jus' make yo'self at home and play all de music you please."

John went and took a seat on de bench and commenced to tune up his harp. By dat time, two angels come walkin' by where John was settin' so he throwed down his harp and tackled 'em.

"Say," he hollered, "Y'all want to hear 'bout de big flood Ah was in down on earth? Lawd, Lawd! it sho' rained, and talkin' 'bout water!"

Dem two angels hurried on off from 'im jus' as quick as they could. He started to tellin' another one and he took to flyin'. Gab'ull went over to 'im and tried to get 'im to take it easy, but John kept right on stoppin' every angel dat he could find to tell 'im about dat flood of water.

Way after while he went over to Ole Peter and said: "Thought you said everybody would be nice and polite?"

137

Peter said, "Yeah, Ah said it. Ain't everybody treatin' you right?"

John said, "Naw. Ah jus' walked up to a man as nice and friendly as Ah could be and started to tell 'im 'bout all dat water Ah left back there in Johnstown and instead of him turnin' me a friendly answer he said, 'Shucks! You ain't seen no water!' and walked off and left me standin' by myself."

"Was he a *ole* man wid a crooked walkin' stick?" Peter ast John.

"Yeah."

"Did he have whiskers down to here?" Peter measured down to his waist.

"He sho' did," John tol' 'im.

"Aw shucks," Peter tol' 'im, "Dat was Ole Nora. You can't tell *him* nothin' 'bout no flood."

The lightning-icon[1]

In the summer of that year (1736) a surgeon of a ship, whose name was Davis, came ashore at York to visit a patient. He was no sooner got into the house, but it began to rain with many terrible claps of thunder. When it was almost dark there came a dreadful flash of lightning which struck the surgeon dead as he was walking about the room, but hurt no other person, though several were near him. At the same time it made a large hole in the trunk of a pine tree, which grew about ten feet from the window. But what was most surprising in this disaster was, that on the breast of the unfortunate man that was killed was the figure of a pine tree, as exactly delineated as any limner in the world could draw it, nay, the resemblance went so far as to represent the color of the pine, as well as the figure. The lightning must probably have passed through the tree first before it struck the man, and by that means have printed the icon of it on his breast. But whatever may have been the cause, the effect was certain, and can be attested by a cloud of witnesses who had the curiosity to go and see this wonderful phenomenon.

---

[1] From William Byrd: *A Journey to the Land of Eden and Other Papers* (1841; reprinted, New York: by Macy-Masius, The Vanguard Press; 1928), p. 189.

Remarkables about thunder and lightning[1]

There are who affirm, that although terrible lightnings with thunders have ever been frequent in this land, yet none were hurt thereby (neither man nor beast) for many years after the English did first settle in these American desarts, but that of later years fatal and fearful slaughters have in that way been made amongst us, is most certain; and there are many who have in this respect been as brands plucked out of the burning, when the Lord hath overthrown others as God overthrew Sodom and Gomorrah. Such solemn works of Providence ought not to be forgotten. I shall now, therefore, proceed in giving an account of remarkables respecting thunder and lightning, so far as I have received credible information concerning them; the particulars whereof are these which follow:—

In July, 1654, a man whose name was Partridge, esteemed a very godly person, at Salisbury in New England, was killed with thunder and lightning, his house being set on fire thereby, and himself with others endeavouring the quenching of it, by a second crack of thunder with lightning (he being at the door of his house), was struck dead, and never spake more. There were ten other persons also that were struck and lay for dead at the present, but they all revived, excepting Partridge. Some that viewed him report that there were holes (like such as were made with shot) found in his clothes and skin. One side of his shirt and body was scorched, and not the other. His house, though, (as was said) set on fire by the lightning in divers places, was not burnt down, but preserved by an abundance of rain falling upon it.

July 31, 1658, there hapned a storm of thunder and lightning with rain, in the town of Marshfield, in Plymouth colony, in New England. Mr. Nathaniel Thomas, John Phillips, and another belonging to that town, being in the field, as they perceived the storm a coming, betook themselves to the next house for shelter. John Phillips sat down near the chimney, his face toward the inner door. A black cloud flying very low, out of it there came a great ball of fire, with a terrible crack of thunder; the fire-ball fell down just before the said Phillips; he seemed to give a start on his seat, and so fell backward, being struck dead, not the least motion of life appearing in him afterwards. Captain Thomas, who sat directly opposite to John Phillips, about six feet distance from him, and a young child that was then within three feet of him, through the providence of God, received no hurt; yet many of the bricks in the

---

[1] From Increase Mather: *Remarkable Providences* (1684; reprinted, London: Reeves & Turner; 1890), pp. 51–3.

chimney were beaten down, the principal rafters split, the battens next the chimney in the chamber were broken, one of the main posts of the house into which the summer [1] was framed rent into shivers, and a great part of it was carried several rod from the house; the door before Phillips, where the fire came down was broken.

On the 28th of April, A.D. 1664, a company of the neighbors being met together at the house of Henry Condliff, in North Hampton, in New England, to spend a few hours in Christian conferences and in prayer, there hapned a storm of thunder and rain; and as the good man of the house was at prayer, there came a ball of lightning in at the roof of the house, which set the thatch on fire, grated on the timber, pierced through the chamber-floor, no breach being made on the boards, only one of the jouyces [2] somewhat rased. Matthew Cole, who was son-in-law to the said Condliff, was struck stone dead as he was leaning over a table, and joyning with the rest in prayer. He did not stir nor groan after he was smitten, but continued standing as before, bearing upon the table. There was no visible impression on his body or clothes, only the sole of one of his shoes was rent from the upper leather. There were about twelve persons in the room; none else received any harm, only one woman (who is still living) was struck upon the head, which occasioned some deafness ever since. The fire on the house was quenched by the seasonable help of neighbours.

July 15, 1665, there were terrible cracks of thunder: an house in Boston was struck by it, and the dishes therein melted as they stood on the shelves; but no other hurt done in the town, only Captain Davenport, a worthy man, and one that had in the Pequot war ventured his life, and did great service for the countrey, then residing in the castle, where he commanded, having that day wrought himself weary, was killed with lightning as he lay upon his bed asleep. Several of the soldiers in the castle were struck at the same time, but God spared their lives. It has been an old opinion, mentioned by Plutarch (Sympos. lib. 4, Q. 2) that men asleep are never smitten with lightning; to confirm which it has been alledged, that one lying asleep, the lightning melted the money in his purse, without doing him any further harm; and that a cradle, wherein a child lay sleeping, was broken by lightning, and the child not hurt; and that the arrows of King Mithridates, being near his bed, were burnt with lightning, and yet himself being asleep, received no hurt. But as much of all this may be affirmed of persons awake; and this sad example . . . of Captain Davenport, whom the lightning found and left asleep, does confute the vulgar error mentioned.

---

[1] Main beam of the ceiling.
[2] Joists.

Increase Mather's "Remarkables" were just that: he refrained from taking the easy next step into fiction. How that step is taken may be illustrated by quoting two consecutive paragraphs from Stanley Vestal's account of the American "dust-bowl" [1]

> In most countries the weather is unusual some of the time; on the High Plains it is unusual all of the time. It is generally agreeable. But if you do not like it, never mind; in half an hour's time it will be different.
> One hot day a man was driving a team, when one horse died of sunstroke. Before he could get the harness off the dead horse, they say, a norther struck, and the live horse froze to death.

In the following tale, which he calls "Oklahoma rain," Mr. Vestal has guarded himself as before; this time he inserts one sentence at the point where his account of the terrible dust-storm of March 1935 slides off from fact into fiction, and we are given to understand that the fiction is not Mr. Vestal's. He records it appreciatively, however.

Oklahoma rain [2]

F eeding the family was a hard job, and at first it seemed as if everybody would starve to death. Food was no sooner placed on the table than it was covered with what seemed to be a layer of fine black salt. Every morsel was grit between the teeth at the first bite, and then mud on the tongue. Hungry children, tired men, could not down such food, and quickly gave up trying. Milk and coffee were liquid mud, and added to disgust was the fear of infection.

But as storm after storm followed, smart housewives found ingenious ways of preparing food with a minimum of dust. Liquids they put into Mason jars with screw tops and rubber collars. They learned to mix dough in a bureau drawer—almost closed—thrusting their arms through two holes cut in a cloth covering the opening. They baked nearly everything in the oven of the range, and fried meat on a hot stove, so that the warm air, rising from the pan, carried the dust upward. All food was kept in covered containers, and those women who had ice-boxes and electric refrigerators sealed tight against the outer air counted themselves lucky, and thanked God for American ingenuity. As soon as food was cooked, it was served from the stove pip-

---

[1] Reprinted by permission of the publishers, Duell, Sloan & Pearce, Inc., from Stanley Vestal: *Short Grass Country*, p. 188. Copyright 1941 by Stanley Vestal.
[2] Ibid., pp. 202–6.

141

ing hot, and every plate was immediately covered by a cloth. Milk and coffee were drunk through straws from bottles.

The moment the first sign of a coming dust cloud appeared, everyone hurried to fill every available container with drinking water to last through the ordeal. At that, the only person who got his ration clean was the baby at his mother's breast.

People learned not to leave the house during a storm, and if caught out driving, would stop and park the car to wait until the storm was over, though it lasted half a day. Men on foot clung to some shrub, or tree, or followed a wire fence hand over hand until they reached shelter. It was a perfect blackout.

As for sleeping—how could anyone sleep with his bedding and clothing thick with dust? To leave the window open or the door ajar was intolerable. Yet to keep them closed on a warm night was suffocating. Everyone was coughing and wheezing, and a man who could spit at all, spat mud. The only way one could sleep was with a wet cloth masking the face, and young children were in danger of their lives because they threw off their masks. No one could watch them, for no one could see to watch. Houses in the Southern country are not so tightly built as they are in the North, and the dry winds had a way of warping wood, or finding crevices around windows and doors, even of stone or brick buildings. Nothing it seemed, would keep out the dust. You could not see a person across the room. At school, with the lights on, the teacher could not see the pupils in the second row. The dust seemed able to pass through the very walls and windowpanes.

Sometimes the dust storm was followed by thunder, lightning, hail, and rain. People rushed out when the rain began—only to find, as the drops fell through the dusty air, that these had turned to pellets. Their clothing was ruined. It was raining mud.

Travel was dangerous, for no driver could see the ditch, or make out his radiator cap in such a fog. Headlights helped hardly at all, and cars bumped into each other fore and aft, went into the ditch, or swung crossways of the road. The road itself was so blocked with drifted sand that it was often impassable. Worst of all, dust got into the motors and stalled—or ruined—them in a few minutes' time.

Those who drove horses or mules were "just as bad off." The eyes of the animals soon filled with dust, mud would form from the tears, and the lids stuck together and remained sealed as the mud dried and locked the eyelashes together. For, if the people suffered, the livestock suffered more. Dust clogged the noses of the helpless creatures, soon turning to mud and hardening there, so that all were choked and suffocated. When the farmer swilled his hogs, or poured milk in the trough for his calves, the stuff turned to mud before it could be swallowed. Forage was blown away while the bawling, blinded cattle drifted with

142

the wind and cut themselves up on barbed-wire fences. Horses went frantic with the dust, coughing and snorting. And chickens smothered —even in the snuggest henhouses.

No sooner had the dust stopped blowing than people began to laugh and joke about their troubles.

It was reported that dust had been found in the vault at the bank, that a banana crate used as a waste-paper basket by the local editor was full and running over with dust. One man claimed that gravel had come through his window pane and wakened him during the night. Another, finding his car stalled by the grit in the engine, opened the door and shot ground squirrels overhead which were tunneling upward for air! A local paper reported finding gold nuggets in the street which had been blown from the mines in New Mexico. The county farmer advised his clients that it would be unnecessary to rotate crops in the future, since the wind was rotating soils. One of the natives proposed a test for wind velocity: "Fasten one end of a logchain to the top of a fence-post. If the wind does not blow the chain straight out from the post, the breeze is moderate. You have a calm day."

Allergy in its various forms became so common that, it was said, even the snakes had learned to sneeze; in the night you could tell when a duster was coming by the sneezing of the rattlesnakes on the prairie. Everyone jestingly referred to a dust storm as an "Oklahoma rain." A man caught some huge bullfrogs, so he said, and put them in his water-tank to multiply; but, he said, the poor things all drowned immediately. It hadn't rained for so long that they had never had a chance to learn to swim.

A housewife claimed that she scoured her pans by holding them up to a keyhole. The sand coming through in a stream polished them better than she could by the usual method. One old lady, on hearing a man compare the climate to that of hell, put her chin up and declared that if the good Lord sent *her* to hell, he'd have to give her a constitution to stand it.

They laughed about the Black Snow which covered their fields. One farmer said he was going to leave Texas and move to Kansas to pay taxes—"There's where my farm is now."

Another said he could not keep up with his farm, which had taken a trip north. "But next week she'll be back," he said. "I can plow then."

One leather-faced dry farmer said, "I hope it'll rain before the kids grow up. They ain't never seen none."

Even Texans have said—nay, boasted—that Texas weather is especially irresponsible. How irresponsible, is suggested in the story of a discomfited meteorologist that John C. Duval wrote under the title

"Old Prob's Visit to Texas." [1] Rediscovered by J. F. Dobie, this yarn tells how Old Prob,[2] after forecasting the Texas weather scientifically but inaccurately for weeks, became quite discouraged. His host (the supposed narrator of the tale) prescribed an abundance of medicine —namely, whisky—to relieve this depression. The concluding episode is as follows:

Won't stay in sich a country [3]

W hen he had got all his calcerlations figgered down to his satisfaction he says, "I've got it this pop shore."

"Well, what is it?" says I.

"High thermometer, low barometer, and a warm wave for the Gulf States durin' the next forty-eight hours."

"And for Texas too?" says I.

"Yes, for Texas too," says he. "And I hope it will be hot enough to scorch hell out of it from the Sabine to the Rio Grande." (And from that you may know the medicin was workin' splendid.)

"Now," says he, "I reckon I kin make a satisfactory report to the Bureau at Washington."

And he tuck his cheer to a table and begun scribblin' as hard as he could. I sot patiently waitin' to hear what he had to say to the Bureau for more'n an hour, but still he kept on writin'. At last when I was tired of waitin' for him to git through, I hearn a door go slam! and then the shutters went bang! and the house shivered from top to bottom. I stepped to the door and looked out, though I knowed well enough what was the matter.

"What's the row now?" says Old Prob, layin' down his pen and lookin' oneasy-like towards me. For by this time, you see, he was gettin' mity suspicious of Texas weather.

"Oh, it's nothin'," says I, "but a reg'lar ole blue norther comin' butt-end foremost."

Ole Prob jumped up from his cheer like a stingin' lizard had popped his behind.

"Git my horse right off," says he, screwin' his azermuth past the last notch and wrenchin' the left limb clean off. "Git my horse at once,"

---

[1] *Southwest Review*, Vol. XXIV, pp. 285ff.

[2] I.e., Old Probabilities. A favorite heading for the "weather column" of American newspapers during much of the nineteenth century was "Old Probabilities Says—"

[3] *Southwest Review*, Vol. XXIV, pp. 295-7.

says he, "and I'll quit this confounded Texas of yourn as soon as I kin git on top of him. And if the Bureau at Washington," says he, "don't knock Texas out'n my beat, I'll resign," says he, "as shore as shootin'."

I tried my best to get him to hold on till the norther had blowed out, tellin' him it was impossible to travel agin' it, but he wouldn't listen to me. (You see, the medicin was just gittin' down to its work.)

"I don't care a durn," says he, "if it's rainin' cats an' dogs and hailin' millstones—git my horse quick," says he, "for I won't stay in sich a country another minit."

Findin' I had give Ole Prob ruther an overdost of the medicin, and that he was bent on goin', I went to the stable, saddled up old Whitey and hitched him under the lee of the house out'n the wind. Then I helped Ole Prob tie all his contraptions to his saddle (except the left limb of his azermuth, which was layin' on the floor where he had throwed it in his tantrum).

When he had mounted ole Whitey and was ready to start, I says to him, "Well," says I, "if you will go, there's one little favor I would like to ask of you afore you leave."

"What's that?" says he.

"Well," says I, "off-hand like, what sort of weather are we goin' to have for the next forty-eight hours?"

Ole Prob laughed—he couldn't help it.

"Well," says he, lookin' up at the sky and then around at the mottes [1] of timber scattered over the perara, "off-hand like, my perdiction is high thermometer, low barometer, and warm and pleasant in the Gulf States for the next forty-eight hours."

"And for Texas?" says I.

"No," says he, "for Texas it will be as hot as Hades, er cold as flugens,[2] as wet as a drowned rat, er as dry as a dried apple, jest whichever it damn pleases."

And saying this, he sot his spurs inter ole Whitey's flanks, and the last thing I seed of Ole Prob, he was weatherin' a pint of post oak timber in the direction of Washington with his coat-tails stickin' out straight behind and his long nose splittin' as cold a norther as ever blowed over the pereras of Texas.

---

[1] Clumps.
[2] Probably same as flucans—clay deposits in a mine.

Something considerable and awful[1]

From time immemorial, East Haddam has been the seat of uncommon subterranean noises, called Moodus noises. The Indian name of the town was *Mackimoodus,* which in English is *the place of noises;* a name given with the utmost propriety to the place. The accounts given of the noises and quakings there are very remarkable. Were it not that the people are accustomed to them, they would occasion great alarm. The Rev. Mr. Hosmer, in a letter to Mr. Prince, of Boston, written Aug. 13th, 1729, gives this account of them:—"As to the earthquakes, I have something considerable and awful to tell you. Earthquakes have been here (and no where but in this precinct, as can be discerned; that is, they seem to have their centre, rise and origin among us,) as has been observed for more than thirty years. I have been informed, that in this place, before the English settlements, there were great numbers of Indian inhabitants, and that it was a place of extraordinary *Indian Pawaws,* or in short, that it was a place where the Indians drove a prodigious trade at worshipping the devil. Also I was informed, that, many years past, an old Indian was asked, What was the reason of the noises in this place? To which he replied, that the Indian's God was very angry because Englishman's God was come here.

"Now whether there be anything diabolical in these things, I know not; but this I know, that God Almighty is to be seen and trembled at, in what has been often heard among us. Whether it be fire or air distressed in the subterranean caverns of the earth, cannot be known; for there is no eruption, no explosion perceptible, but by sounds and tremors, which sometimes are very fearful and dreadful. I have myself heard eight or ten sounds successively, and imitating small arms, in the space of five minutes. I have, I suppose, heard several hundreds of them within twenty years; some more, some less terrible. Sometimes we have heard them almost every day, and great numbers of them in the space of a year. Oftentimes I have observed them to be coming down from the north, imitating slow thunder, until the sound came near or right under, and then there seemed to be a breaking, like the noise of a cannon shot, or severe thunder, which shakes the houses and all that is in them. They have in a manner ceased since the great earthquake. As I remember, there have been but two heard since that time, and those but moderate."

A worthy gentleman, about six years since, gave the following ac-

---

[1] From John Warner Barber: *Connecticut Historical Collections* (1838), pp. 526–7.

146

count of them. "The awful noises, of which Mr. Hosmer gave an account, in his historical minutes, and concerning which you desire further information, continue to the present time. The effects they produce are as various as the intermediate degrees between the roar of a cannon and the noise of a pistol. The concussions of the earth, made at the same time, are as much diversified as the sounds in the air. The shock they give to a dwelling house, is the same as the falling of logs on the floor. The smaller shocks produced no emotions of terror or fear in the minds of the inhabitants. They are spoken of as usual occurrences, and are called Moodus noises. But when they are so violent as to be heard in the adjacent towns, they are called earthquakes. During my residence here, which has been almost thirty-six years, I have invariably observed, after some of the most violent of these shocks, that an account has been published in the newspapers, of a small shock of an earthquake, in New London and Hartford. Nor do I believe, in all that period, there has been any account published of an earthquake in Connecticut, which was not far more violent here than in any other place. By recurring to the newspapers, you will find that an earthquake was noticed on the 18th May, 1791, about 10 o'clock P.M. It was perceived as far distant as Boston and New York. A few minutes after there was another shock, which was perceptible at the distance of seventy miles. Here, at that time, the concussion of the earth, and the roaring of the atmosphere, were most tremendous. Consternation and dread filled every house. Many chimneys were untopped and walls thrown down. It was a night much to be remembered; for besides the two shocks which were noticed at a distance, during the night there was here a succession of shocks, to the number of twenty, perhaps thirty; the effects of which, like all others, decreased in every direction, in proportion to the distances. The next day, stones of several tons weight were found removed from their places; and apertures in the earth, and fissures in immovable rocks, ascertained the places where the explosions were made. Since that time, the noises and shocks have been less frequent than before; though not a year passeth over us, but some of them are perceptible."

—Trumbull's Hist. Con.

From the *Connecticut Gazette* (New London) Aug. 20, 1790. No. 1397.[1]

East Haddam, August 5, 1790.

The town of East Haddam was formerly much noted for earthquakes—from which it obtained its ancient Indian name, Moodus; which in their language, it is said, signifies a great noise. They were supposed to take their rise near Salmon river, which runs between

---

[1] Quoted, ibid., pp. 528–9.

this town and Chatham. Several years ago, they were said to be very loud and frequent, and that they shook the ground for several miles around; and it has been reported, that the ground has been opened in several places, and trees torn up by the roots, and carried to some distance, near the above-mentioned river:—and that some persons were under fearful apprehensions that the town would sooner or later be sunk. Various have been the conjectures concerning the cause of these earthquakes or Moodus noises, as they are called. The following account has gained credit with many persons.—It is reported, that between 20 and 30 years ago, a transient person came to this town, who called himself Doct. Steel, from Great Britain, who having had information respecting these noises, made critical observations at different times and in different places, till at length he dug up two pearls of great value, which he called Carbuncles, near Salmon river:—and that he told people the noises would be discontinued for many years, as he had taken away their cause; but as he had discovered others in miniature, they would be again heard in process of time. The best evidence of the authenticity of this story is that it has happened agreeably to his prophecy. The noises did cease for many years, and have again been heard for two or three years past, and they increase—three shocks have been felt in a short space, one of which, according to a late paper, was felt at New London, though it was by the account much more considerable in this and the adjacent towns.

NOTE: The Moodus noises are presumably caused by a species of miniature underground landslides. See *Connecticut* (American Guide Series, Boston: Houghton Mifflin Co.; 1938), pp. 404–5 for a good brief discussion.

2. SNAKES AND SERPENTS

Of snakes, most people believe the worst, whatever zoologists may say. Perhaps this is because parents teach children to "look out" for reptiles, perhaps it has something to do with original sin, perhaps (a little more probably) we have lumped the evil with the good. Generally speaking, we either run from them or chase them, and if we can, we kill them. We not only think them worse than they are, we think them stranger. Belief in the hoopsnake dies hard. Few men could be driven even by desperation to Deacon Nauhaught's bold act, and few can read Thomas Benton's rattlesnake story without squirming. (Mr. Benton says it is not his, but he has told it, and there is no other sponsor visible.)

As for the sea-serpent, that is another book, or set of books. He turns up along our Atlantic coast (why not the Pacific?—but no) when news is dull and rum plentiful, and, like most marvels, he contrives to get the most respectable people to vouch for him. He appears briefly (as is his wont) in this group of stories. It would be a good joke on the editor, and on three centuries of Americans, should it turn out that there really is a sea-serpent. Some say so.

Hoopsnakes, pro [1]

The "Hoop Snake" and "Stinging Snake" are considered by many very intelligent people to be mere fable. But are they? Here is an account set down by W. C. Bryant, of Bryant, Mississippi, and sent in by Wm. B. Mershon.

"I just read a newspaper statement that authorities in Washington have declared there are no such animals as Stinging Snakes, Hoop Snakes, and Jointed Snakes. They explain that the Jointed Snake is a lizard, the sharp point on the tail of another snake gave the uninitiated the wrong impression that it was a stinger hung onto his shoe heel, and the Hoop Snake is a fable of rather fabulous dimensions, emanating from a low grade of 'hooch.' I have seen each of these snakes perform nearly if not exactly as reported by old negroes and small boys and their conduct was scandalous. They were not 'bottle' snakes, either.

[1] From *Field & Stream*, April 1926, p. 130.

149

"The Stinging Snake and the Hoop Snake are true snakes and have no lizard in them, as has that mongrel the Jointed Snake of which I shall not speak further as he is admittedly not entitled to registration papers in any snake club of merit or standing. I shall take up first, figuratively speaking of course, the Stinging Snake, for 'thereby hangs a tail' and it is a stinging tail.

"The Stinging Snake is a little thicker through the equator than the usual snake of his length, and the south pole end of him tapers to a blunted point out of which, when he is very dead, you can squeeze a bony tough piece shaped like a .22 cartridge with a sharp point of the darning needle variety.

"He is a deep blue color on the back, no other lines or stripes, and lying out in the dead leaves (I have never seen a stinger coiled, though I doubt not he coils as do other snakes) has the appearance of a section of new rubber hose. Turn him over and his belly is a reddish cream color or a yellow color with red cast. I have never killed but three or four of these snakes when full grown though a good many small ones. They are very active and use their vigor and speed to get out of sight and out of danger. My field hands have shown me several over five feet in length that they had killed, and frequently press out the long sting to examine it.

"The largest of these Stinging Snakes that I have killed was gotten on a dry June day while I was watching three of my farm hands doing some cleaning up around a rustic summer house on my place in the Scuna Valley, Mississippi.

"I was roused on hearing one of my men in his grumbling negro voice say, 'Look at dat snake!' Bill followed with a yell 'Lookout; he's coming!' I looked out all right. For about thirty yards distant out of the leaves a blue snake of large size emerged and came directly for me with great speed.

"I picked up my gun and as I did so the snake, now at a distance of 15 or 16 yards, threw its tail up from the ground and extended it forward over its head. Its speed diminished but it kept its course—a direct line toward me. The closer it came the lower and more extended forward it held its tail, until it was in the form of an eclipse [*sic*] which was rolling and sagging as it rolled. When some 3 or 3½ yards away I fired and killed it. It measured over 5½ feet, and its sting was like a polished pencil point. It was a female and I was over a den of her young and her attack was to move me from its entrance.

"The Stinging Snake is a reality, and the Hoop Snake is the Stinging Snake in the act of attacking its foe."

Have you ever seen one of these snakes? If so—let's hear about it.

Hoopsnakes, con, with some other doubts[1]

During the strawberry season, when my back began to ache with stooping, I used to relieve the monotony by begging Gram to tell—for the hundredth time—how she saw the hoopsnake.

Her memory of that event improved with the years and each retelling of the story brought forth some fresh, corroborative detail. I would exclaim in delight:

"You never told me *that* before!"

And Gram would answer in all sincerity:

"I just remembered it. It comes back now as clear as day."

The story always started out the same and I desired no other beginning.

"It was in the early days," Gram would say, "long before you were born. Deer lived here then and a few remaining Indians. Father had planted his first strawberry patch on the slope near the spring."

"The same spring we have now?" I would ask, seeking to stretch out the story.

"Yes, the very same spring. A hayfield ran along the eastern edge of the berry patch. Well, one June day we were picking berries there. I remember I had a tin pail full and was just straightening up when I saw the snake."

"Was it really rolling along like a wheel?"

"No, it was crawling along like any other snake when I first saw it. It was blackish and about six feet long. It was coming straight for us. As I stood up, it saw me and turned toward the hayfield. It ran along the edge, just inside the grass, and as it went its head kept rising higher and higher, and just below where the pasture fence is now, it grabbed its tail in its mouth and rolled away like a hoop out of sight. I was so excited, I remember, I tipped over the whole pail of berries and had to pick them up again."

"Did you see it too, Gramp?" I always wanted to know.

"Well, kind uv," he would reply judiciously. "But Mother saw 't best."

I used to query Gramp in private about that "kind uv." But all he would volunteer was: "Yer gran-maw wouldn't tell a lie. Ef she says she saw 't roll, she prob'ly did—at least, I'm sartin she thinks she did."

---

[1] From *Dune Boy: The Early Years of a Naturalist*, by Edwin Way Teale, pp. 79–86. Copyright, 1943, by Edwin Way Teale. Reprinted by permission of Dodd, Mead & Company.

Gram was not the only one in the dune country ready to swear to a first-hand glimpse of a hoopsnake. These legendary rolling reptiles were commonplace in the folk-lore of the time and the region. Wherever an erroneous belief, such as the idea of hoopsnakes or of reptiles that swallow their young, gains wide acceptance, there must be some explanation in accord with facts. My belief is that the hoopsnake story had its origin in the ability of blue racers and blacksnakes to run along the ground with their heads lifted for a surprising distance into the air.

When fleeing through tall grass, such snakes sometimes lift their heads higher and higher, the better to see or sense their foes. Possibly glimpses of these reptiles speeding through the waving grass, with heads held so high they seemed bending backwards, have given rise to the widespread belief in rolling hoopsnakes.

Similarly that other perennial among serpent misconceptions—the belief that mother snakes swallow their young when danger approaches —may have a simple and logical explanation. When close to the mouth of the burrow, the mother serpent may take her stand, with her head weaving and held close to the ground and her mouth opening in repeated menacing movements, while the little reptiles wriggle down to the comparative safety of their underground retreat. To the excited observer the little snakes—disappearing suddenly from sight—would appear to be rushing into the open mouth of their mother. In fact, instead of their mother, it is the ground which swallows them up.

An interesting instance, illustrating how superstitions start and false premises have their beginning, occurred a mile or so from Lone Oak several years before I appeared on the scene.

On a back-road farm a woman was looking for eggs laid in out-of-the-way places about the barnyard. Coming to a great hollow stump, she leaned over to look inside. A huge "puff adder" was coiled within. With a great hiss, it blew its cloud of "poisonous vapor" directly into her face. The frightened woman ran to the house. On the back of the stove she noticed some neglected toast which had burned to a crisp. She started eating the charred bread, in her distraction, and in a few minutes felt better. The burned toast had proved a miraculous antidote —it had neutralized the venom of the adder!

The story of her escape from death was repeated many times in my boyhood. Burned toast was accepted by numerous people as a sure-cure for the vapor-poison of the puff adder. The weak link in this circumstantial story, as I learned in later years, is the fact there isn't any puff-adder poison. In fact, there isn't any puff adder!

The great hiss which the woman heard was formed by harmless air; the deadly adder she saw was simply that poor, pitiful pretender, the hog-nosed snake. No more venomous than a kitchen mouse, this reptile tries to frighten its enemies with sound and fury signifying nothing. If they are not intimidated, it flops over on its back and feigns death. This, then, was the sinister, deadly monster which burned toast had miraculously conquered!

How other erroneous beliefs in the realm of natural history, which were current in the dune country at that time, came into being, I do not know. But they were spread, by word of mouth, until acceptance seemed universal. Undoubtedly many were brought to America from the Old Country as representatives of many races lived on the farms of the region. Most of the time, Gramp and Gram quoted folklore beliefs with their tongues in their cheeks. But there were neighbors who clung firmly to the old opinion that bats come down chimneys at night to dine on ham; that snakes suck milk from cows; that a butterfly alighting on a person's head means good luck is coming and that a bird flying into a house indicates important news is on the way.

I remember one Sunday morning when Gram was energetically swatting houseflies with a folded-up piece of newspaper.

"That," said Gramp, looking up from his *Chesterton Tribune*, "makes four hun'red more flies yer bringin' t' th' house. Y've jest killed forty flies an' every time y' kill a fly, ten more come t' its funeral!"

Odd beliefs about insects were many. In numerous ways they were supposed to affect the fortunes of humans. Dream of ants, one superstition stated, and prosperity would come your way. See a ladybug in the house in winter, another declared, and you would receive as many dollars as there were spots on the insect's back. A honey-bee buzzing around your head was supposed to indicate a letter was on its way. A measuring worm crawling on a man's shoulder was "measuring him for a shroud." If the same moth larva found its way along a woman's hand, it was "measuring her for new gloves." Thousand-legged worms were thought to crawl into babies' ears and to make them crazy. And dragonflies—usually known as darning needles—were likely, many people affirmed, to sew up the ears of children.

These swift and beautiful insects were associated with numerous other superstitions. They were thought to feed and to doctor snakes and, according to some people, to sting horses. When a country boy went fishing in a place where dragonflies were numerous, he found himself between the horns of a dilemma. If a dragonfly alighted on his pole, it meant the fish wouldn't bite; if he injured a dragonfly, it meant he would have bad luck.

In the lower pasture, near the spring, large numbers of great, tender mushrooms pushed their way above the ground each summer. Gram and I sometimes picked a milkpail full in a quarter of an hour while the morning dew was still on the grass. After removing and discarding the upper skins, Gram would fry them in butter on the kitchen range.

When Gramp came in from his chores, we would all enjoy a special treat for breakfast. While we picked the mushrooms in the cool fresh air of the dawn, Gram often told me stories or recalled the queer beliefs she had encountered when she first came west.

A sliver off a hog-trough, many inhabitants of the region thought, was a sure-cure for a sty. Anyone who saw a boy with his shirttail hanging out would be sure to find a letter waiting for him the next time he went to the post office. If a person's ears grew close to his head, it meant he was stingy; if a person had a large nose, it indicated he possessed a generous nature. In setting the table, if anyone made a mistake and put two knives and no fork at a plate, it presaged a funeral in the family. If, on the other hand, there were two forks and no knife, it indicated the approach of a wedding. Anyone who started off on an errand or a journey and forgot something and had to return, should always sit on a chair before starting out again—otherwise bad luck would follow.

These beliefs, and many more I cannot now recall, were ones that Gram heard in early days. Of all such folklore oddities the ones that interested me most were those which related to the living creatures of the fields and woods.

"Straddle-Bugs," as Gramp called the harvestmen or daddy-longlegs, were thought to have some mystic connection with cattle. Kill a daddy-longlegs, a popular superstition had it, and your cows would go dry. Many a farm-boy, in the dune country, tried the time-honored procedure of holding one of these grandfather-graybeards by two of its legs and noting the direction the others pointed in order to obtain a clew as to the direction taken by strayed cattle.

One summer night, as Gram was reading *When Wilderness Was King* and Gramp and I sat on the front porch outside the screen door, Gramp suddenly exclaimed:

"Listen! There's the first katydid o' th' year. They say it's just six weeks t' frost from th' time y' hear the first katydid."

Other humble creatures were also imagined to be related in some way to the weather. In autumn the sight of a woolly-bear caterpillar hurrying across an open space indicated that an early winter was on its way. Some country-people maintained, in addition, that you could tell whether the early winter would be mild or severe by examining the central band around its body. A wide band meant a severe winter; a narrow band, a mild one.

"Step on a spider," Gramp used to quote a superstition of the time, "an' it'll rain next day."

"What if you step on a spider on a rainy day?" I once asked.

"Then y'll hev two days o' rain in succession."

Stepping on a cricket was also thought to bring on a rainstorm. I remember that I used to be puzzled by the fact that even the people who quoted this belief never put the prescription to the test by stepping on crickets during a drought.

"All signs fail in dry weather," Gramp explained in answer to my question.

Deacon Nauhaught's dilemma[1]

Deacon Nauhaught was once attacked by a number of large *black snakes*. Being at a distance from any inhabitants, he was, to be sure, in a very precarious situation; for, unfortunately, he had not even a knife about him for his defence. To outrun them, he found utterly impossible; to keep them off, without any weapon, was equally so. He therefore came to the determination to stand firm on his feet. They began winding themselves about him; in a little time, one of them had made his way up to the Indian's neck, and was trying to put his black head into his mouth. Nauhaught opened it immediately. The black serpent thrust in his head, and Nauhaught, putting his jaws together, bit it off in a moment! As soon as the blood, streaming from the beheaded, was discovered by the rest of the snakes, they left their intended prey with great precipitation, and Nauhaught was liberated from the jaws of impending death.

Thomas Benton's rattlesnake story[2]

There's a crazy, farfetched tale of an old cattleman who bought a new pair of boots. On his way home from town he got off his horse for some reason or other and was bitten by a rattlesnake. He died. Some time later his son, seeing the old man's boots in a corner, put them on and went to work. That night he got sick, swelled up, and died. There was a scratch on one of his legs. Nobody knew why he died. A little later another member of the family put on the boots, which were still new. He died also with a scratch on his leg. I've forgotten how many people died from wearing the boots, but the tale has it that the mystery was finally solved by discovering a couple of rattlesnake fangs in the boots. They had broken off there when the

---

[1] From John Warner Barber: *Historical Collections: Massachusetts*, p. 59.

[2] From Thomas Hart Benton: *An Artist in America* (New York: Robert M. McBride & Co.; 1937), pp. 210–11.

old man had been bitten and had continued to bite all those who wore the boots later!

Miracles are wrought by faith, but faith is no antidote for rattlesnake venom. Mr. Kerman's account of what he calls "rattlesnake religion" is a tall story. As he tells it, it is strictly true, and his wonder at the apparent immunity of the fanatics who submit themselves to rattlesnake bites is a wonder that we must all share. When he wrote, in 1942, however, the returns were not all in. In September 1945 two "believers" died after being bitten. These were Mrs. Harve Kirk, a preacher's wife of Wise County, Virginia, and Lewis Ford, a preacher at the Dolly Pond Church of God at Grasshopper, Texas. At his funeral snake-handling was practiced. There was also music—guitars, cymbals, and tambourines (*Time*, Vol. XLVI, p. 23; September 17, 1945).

Rattlesnake religion[1]

Handling venomous snakes as a religious rite has been going on in a few obscure churches in America, I've been told, for close to thirty years, but I think the general public of America first heard of it in the summer of 1938, when the Associated Press sent out a story from Harlan, Kentucky, about the trial of three members of the Pine Mountain Church of God. A farmer named John Day, who didn't like snakes and who didn't want his wife, a member of the church, fooling with them, had the three men arrested. He charged that the reptile handling was a breach of the peace. At the trial—which resulted in acquittals—it came out that rattlesnakes were passed around frequently among the members in the Pine Mountain Church as part of the service. The idea was not to prove their faith by inviting snakes to bite them and then refusing medical attention; cases of that kind have got into the papers from time to time. This was a ritualistic matter, an act of worship, for which scriptural sanction was claimed.

Realizing the novelty of the thing for most readers, the editor of *Pictures*, Sunday rotogravure section of the St. Louis *Post-Dispatch*, sent Arthur Witman, a staff photographer, and me, a reporter, to get a story, in words and pictures, of the doings. Through a Harlan newspaperman, I arranged without much difficulty for permission from the church people for us to carry out the assignment. The congregation co-operated with us to a degree that amazed me.

---

[1] By Keith Kerman, from *Eve's Stepchildren*, selected and edited by Lealon N. Jones (Caldwell, Idaho: The Caxton Printers; 1942), pp. 93–102.

Snakes and Serpents

The Church of God of Pine Mountain perches on a steep wooded slope of that mountain, about seventeen miles from Harlan. It is a frame structure, unpainted, and was built by the volunteer labor of members on land donated by a member. Inside, there are benches of split logs, and the pulpit, at the edge of a platform extending across one end of the building, is merely a plain board table on long legs.

The church has a congregation of forty adults, mostly farmers and poor. (In all this general description I am speaking of conditions that existed when I was there in early September of 1938; I don't know what changes have taken place since.) It is an independent church, but may be classified as to beliefs and practices with that group of sects often spoken of loosely as "Holy Rollers." It is fundamentalist in doctrine and believes in sanctification and a baptism of the Holy Spirit which confers supernatural gifts, such as ability to speak in unknown tongues and to heal by prayer, the laying on of hands, or anointing with oil. Because of the importance it attaches to divine gifts, religious experts would probably use the word "charismatic" in describing the church. It forbids theatregoing, dancing, smoking, drinking, immodest dress, and the cutting of women's hair. Emotionalism characterizes the services; people shout and sing ecstatically, go through queer bodily movements, including the well-known jerks, sometimes yell unintelligible things in what is taken to be an "unknown tongue." The members call one another "saints," and the men kiss in greeting.

J. D. Browning, a ruddy-faced, pleasant-mannered man of early middle age, had been pastor of the church for four years when I visited it. He was unordained and received no salary, but made his living farming fifty acres of hillside near by. He had no monopoly on the preaching; anyone in the congregation could get up behind the pulpit and preach whenever the spirit so moved him.

Pastor Browning had introduced snake handling into the service of the Pine Mountain Church soon after becoming its pastor. The principal scriptural authority for the rite, he told me, was found in the words of Christ to the Apostles as given in the sixteenth chapter of St. Mark.

"And he said unto them, Go ye forth into all the world, and preach the gospel to every creature. He that believeth and is baptized shall be saved; but he that believeth not shall be damned. And these signs shall follow them that believe: In my name shall they cast out devils; they shall speak with new tongues; they shall take up serpents; and if they drink any deadly thing, it shall not hurt them; they shall lay hands on the sick, and they shall recover."

He also cited these words in the tenth chapter of St. Luke: "Behold I give you power to tread on serpents and scorpions. . . ." It is apparent that in the passage in St. Mark the Pine Mountain saints find

157

support for their belief in other divine gifts as well as the ability to "take up serpents."

While snake handling was practiced in a number of other churches, the pastor thought his was the only one in which all the members took part. None of the snakes on hand, he said, had been captured more than a week before; they were never kept more than a month because they became ill in captivity. They were supplied to the congregation by "unbelievers," who had caught them. Sometimes a box of snakes would be sent from one church to another.

We drove up a steep, narrow, winding road to the Pine Mountain Church on a hot, still Sunday. Pastor Browning and several of the other male saints greeted us gravely and pleasantly in a little clearing in front of the building, and we stood there talking as other people arrived in trucks, small automobiles, and on foot—plain people whose plain clothing looked neat and clean. It was odd to see rawboned mountain men kiss a newcomer when he joined our group.

The men talked with us and with one another about the scriptures and matters of doctrine. They talked of these matters with an interest such as lawyers might show in discussing some nice legal point. In answer to questions, they said they were afraid of snakes—wouldn't touch them except when the spirit was on them in church. Practically all said they had been bitten but hadn't suffered more than temporary discomfort. A lean, black-haired timberman, picturesque in a broad-brimmed black slouch hat, showed several scars on hand and arm, pointing them out—"thar, and thar and thar."

Church time came and all filed inside, members taking seats on the platform and the front benches, spectators in the rear. There were probably seventy-five in the church—men, women and children. Art Witman, with camera and a satchel full of flash bulbs, took a position near the platform.

The sound of singing began to come from within the church, but I lingered a while outside. Out across a wide valley were the sedate, orderly ranks of the Great Smoky Mountains, fading decently into the horizon. The woods and fields of the valley were peaceful in the sun. On the slope where I stood the air was warm and still with the typical tranquillity of a summer Sunday. It was a drowsy, normal, familiar world.

I stepped into the Pine Mountain Church of God, and it was like passing abruptly from a comfortable fireside doze into delirium. Within those four rough walls there was a scene which to me had the strange, unreal—and disturbing—quality of a fevered dream.

The congregation was singing "Jesus Is Getting Us Ready for the Great Day" to the clash of cymbals and the jingle of a tambourine. Feet were stamping and hands were clapping in time with the music, and bodies were jerking violently. And the snakes were out. Two rattlers and a copperhead had been taken from a wooden box, and the saints, men and women, were passing them from hand to hand, worshiping with them.

The men took the snakes without hesitation or a sign of fear. They handled them familiarly, as if they were friends. Women seemed to be less at ease with the reptiles.

A thin young farmer of Pine Mountain whose voice rose piercingly above all the rest took one of the snakes and pranced along the front row of benches, singing and shouting. In front of a young mother who sat holding a baby in her lap, he paused and gleefully held the reptile extended before the baby's eyes. As he laughed and the mother smiled, the baby gravely reached out and touched the snake. The man pranced away, collected the other two serpents, and draped all three about his head. A tail bearing a half-dozen rattles lay across one shoulder, and three reptilian heads swayed within a hand's span of his eyes. He smiled, his eyes glowed, and he shouted, "Hallelujah!"

The picturesque, black-haired timberman was another who handled the snakes as if happy to be doing it. He left the cymbals he had been beating together, arranged the three snakes on one big, hairy hand, and held them aloft as if making an offering. Presently he held the mouth of one rattler open to show its fangs.

An elderly, bespectacled man coiled a snake around the top of his head and sat with hands clasped on his chest, face serene, wearing the serpent like a crown. A woman in a white dress, who had been singing fervently, shouting and finally jerking, reached a mood of exaltation and took a snake on her two palms. She held it stiffly before her. Her eyes were shut, a babble of scriptural phrases came from her mouth, and sweat ran down her face.

The church was full of din, movement, emotion—a mass excitement that was almost tangible. The singing never stopped. Over and over the worshipers chanted the refrain of the "Great Day" hymn. It was provocative, urgent music. The cadence was strongly marked. Cymbals, tambourine, stamping feet, and clapping hands all accented the beat, so that as foundation or background for the wild scene—a kaleidoscope of agitated bodies, sweating, open-mouthed, ecstatic faces and dangling serpents—there was an insistent, rhythmic pulsation that pounded the nerves.

The snakes alone did not appear to share in the excitement. Their movements seemed sluggish. If they tried to escape it was not apparent. They behaved as if they were voluntarily joining in that fantastic ceremony.

At the height of the tumult, a gray-shirted, bare-armed young mountaineer, singing lustily, seized the pulpit Bible, opened it, and placed

· 159

it on his head. He took the three snakes in his hands and held them on the opened Book, the head of one resting on his right hand. Another scaly head was supported on the hand of a saint who stood close by, and its forked tongue could be seen, outlined against his skin. The congregation shouted in wild enthusiasm.

Almost immediately after that the serpent ritual ended. The singing stopped, the snakes were returned to their box. Men and women who had been taking part in the ceremony returned to their seats, or strolled over to a water bucket to drink out of a tin dipper. No one had been bitten.

Witman, whose photographic bulbs had been flashing almost constantly, his camera often so close he could have handled the snakes himself, sat down by me. A bead of sweat dropped off the end of his nose. He whispered, "I can't believe it." Maybe he was thinking of the opportunity he had had to take such pictures; he had been in a cameraman's paradise.

The snake handling lasted about half an hour. The service went on for an hour longer, but the rest was anticlimax—even a demonstration of fire handling, a speech in an "unknown tongue," and various striking displays of religious emotionalism.

The pastor and several others preached from the pulpit. Several persons told of miraculous cures effected through the power of religion. One woman concluded such a recital with a chant of praise to heaven and a sort of jig of jubilation. Another woman asked to be prayed over. She knelt at the edge of the platform, and eight or ten other members formed a circle around her. All prayed earnestly, not only aloud but loud, and each one prayed in his own words. A babble of voices rose above the woman's bowed head.

During a great part of the service women kept going through peculiar evolutions in the space between the front benches and the platform. Eyes shut, hands waving, they moved their feet in a rhythmic step and wheeled slowly in backward circles. Frequently their bodies would jerk as if the spine were being snapped like a whip. Some of the men also performed this jerk. I wasn't sure whether it was an involuntary action or an accomplishment, a bit of religious technique.

It was a chubby man, coatless, tieless, and suspendered, who delivered a message in what was taken to be an "unknown tongue." Being made the mouthpiece for such a message is supposed, among Church of God people, a special mark of divine favor. He went behind the pulpit and spoke in an unintelligible jargon for ten minutes, then translated. He strode and skipped about the platform as he spoke; he shivered and sweated and his eyes rolled. When he finally slumped down on a bench he seemed to be in a state of nervous exhaustion, almost of collapse.

The fire handling was, in a way, as impressive as the snake rite, but was not carried out in an atmosphere so tense with excitement. Only a few of the male saints took part in this display; most of the members don't try it. They produced a kerosene torch and a miner's acetylene lamp and held their hands in the flames. The demonstration was given at close range, practically under our noses. Hands were kept steadily in the fire at various distances and in various positions while the camera was sighted and snapped. No one appeared to be hurt. I examined the hands, and, aside from their being smoke-blackened, saw no marks to show they had been in fire.

Despite all the shouting, prancing, and sensationalism, I observed that day a simple kindliness among these people, one to another. Once during the service I saw a woman vainly trying to quiet her baby. Presently, as it continued to fret and cry, a rawboned mountain man, whose hands had been full of rattlesnakes a few minutes before, went over to the woman—who was not his wife—took the baby with a smile and returned to his seat. In thirty seconds he had soothed the youngster into stillness; then he returned it to its mother.

Anticlimactic also was a snake-handling service I attended at a Church of God in Harlan the next night—although a man was bitten at that service. Some two hours later, when his wound was photographed, he said it didn't bother him much. But I met that night a man who said he had originated snake-handling as a religious rite. He was G. W. Hensley, pastor of the East Pineville Church of God, near Harlan. He said he had introduced the practice twenty-eight years before, in Sale Creek, Tennessee; that he had been bitten 250 times, and had been ill from a snakebite only once.

I don't know if there was trickery in the handling of snakes and fire in the Pine Mountain Church. I did not detect any. It would not have been difficult, however, to deceive me, as I was not there to attempt an exposé. There was no doubt that I saw men's hands actually in fire and that the fire was hot. There was no doubt the snakes were alive, and I had the word of one of their custodians that their poison sacs had not been removed and they had not been induced to discharge their venom before the service. My newspaper friend in Harlan told me: "These people might shoot you if you were an enemy, but they wouldn't lie to you." Beyond suggesting that the strong monotonous beat of the saints' music might have a numbing or hypnotic effect on snakes, and that hysteria does curious things, I offer no explanation of the strange religious rites in the Pine Mountain Church of God.

Big as a barrel

Little explored (and for good reasons), the Florida Everglades are haunted by many a terrible tale—of man-killing mosquitoes, of web-footed panthers, of ghostly fires, and of crocodiles. Most of all, and naturally so, there are stories of snakes. The greatest of these is—or was —the Cape Sable snake. Karl A. Bickel tells of it thus: [1]

The story of the great snake of the Cape Sable country is embedded deep in folklore not only of the Seminoles but also of the white settlers in that district. For years the Cow Seminoles, who live on the Brighton reservation, refused to venture into the Cape Sable region because of a huge serpent which, they asserted, made that area its habitat and chased and devoured human beings. The Florida State Department of Agriculture, in its pamphlet "The Seminole Indians of Florida," prepared by the Florida Writers' Project, tells the story in full and as follows:

"According to Uncle Steve Roberts of Homestead, the serpent 'wasn't no legend but a fact. Buster Farrel, an Indian, killed the critter in 1892,' he explained. 'Buster was hunting when he come across a trail where the grass was all beat down in a wide path, and thinking it was a whopping big 'gator, he followed it. Pretty soon he spotted the snake. It was more'n a good rifle shot from him but he fired anyhow, and the critter went threshing off in the grass makin' more noise than a hurricane. Buster didn't go to see whether he'd hit it or not remembering the stories about the serpent swallowing Indians whole. Wasn't 'til some days later he seen a flock of buzzards flyin' around the place, and when he went down there he found the snake. The buzzards had tore and scattered the carcass so bad Buster couldn't measure it, but he swore the snake was all of sixty feet long and as big as a barrel. He cut off and kept the jaw bones, which were so big he could open them up and drop them over his body.' "

The Seminoles believed the snake lived in a lake back of Cape Sable and that this lake had an underground connection with the gulf which permitted it to make its way, in and out, between the Gulf and the Everglades.

"Acorn," one of the many pseudonymous writers who contributed to *The Spirit of the Times*, told in its columns in 1846 a story that has reappeared in many parts of America. "Acorn" makes it the climax of a lying contest, which appears to take place in New England. This is his version:

---

[1] Reprinted from *The Mangrove Coast*, by Karl A. Bickel; copyright, 1942, by Coward-McCann, Inc.; p. 233.

Hoe-handle

A snake story was proposed. Our old stand-by spun out a most marvelous and serpentine narrative indeed, and when he had finished his story it was apparent that it had told well on his listeners. He was sure of winning the bet. All eyes were now directed on his antagonist. A smile of incredulity played upon his countenance as he remarked—

"Stranger, that's a pretty keen sort of lie you've been telling, but I can relate an affair that actually took place, and I can bring witnesses to prove it, that eclipses your yarn all holler. You see, I was engineering on the Rail Road up here, and one day the cars being a little late, we put on the steam until she made everything crack. We had very little freight, but there was a lot of niggers along who was sitting on the sides of the freight car, amusing themselves by cutting the weeds with their hoes, when all at once up started a large copper-colored snake, one of the real poison sort, just in range of one of the hoes. We were going at the rate of sixty miles an hour,[1] and quick as thought off came the snake's head. Well, gentlemen, what do you think was the consequence? Why, gentlemen, believe me, as true as I'm a living sinner, no sooner had the hoe come in contact with the snake's head, than a particle of the poison flew into the eye of the hoe, *and,* gentlemen, as true as I'm a sinner, the hoe-handle instantly swelled up with such force, that it burst the eye of the hoe into a thousand fragments, killing two of the best niggers in the gang—"

"Stop! stop!" shouted all hands, "you've won the bet."

Up the Hudson, above Corinth, Carl Carmer met Jack Loveland, a more or less veracious story-teller. Inspired by Mr. Carmer's statement that he liked true stories better than tall tales, Mr. Loveland delivered himself of the following:

Not weird, but puzzlin'[2]

I was drivin' logs downstream with Grover Lynch, the fellow that married Polly Bissell and made Jack Casey kill himself. We seen a rock out in the river that was about twelve feet wide and on the edge of it sat a big bullfrog. We had one o' them small fish scales with us and we grabbed that frog and weighed him and he weighed twelve pounds. We set him back down and walked away and just then I seen a big black snake crawl up on that rock and I says "I'll bet you twelve

---

[1] This, in 1846, was no small part of the lie.

[2] From *The Hudson*, copyright, 1939, by Carl Carmer, and reprinted by permission of Rinehart & Company, Inc., Publishers.

dollars that snake swallows that frog," and he says, "You're on." That snake inched up on that frog and he was twelve feet long because he was just as long as the rock and we measured it afterwards.

"Well, sir, just as that snake got a good holt on that frog's behind the frog sees the end of the snake's tail, makes one jump for it, and ketches it in his mouth. So there we set with the snake takin' in more of the frog every minute and the frog gettin' about a foot of snake down his gullet in the same time. It got to be mighty excitin' to see which one was goin' to get the other swallowed first. Just as the twelfth minute was up they both give one last big gulp—and they'd each swallowed the other at the same moment. We saw 'em both disappear right before our eyes. We could never settle our bet. I claimed it, but Grover says it was ridiculous to suppose that the frog had swallowed the snake if the snake had swallowed the frog. So we sort of broke up after that."

Mr. Carmer observed that that was a weird experience, but Loveland demurred.

"Not weird," said Jack, striking the bowl of his pipe contemplatively, "not weird exactly—but puzzlin'."

The sea-serpent is an international monster, though often seen off the Atlantic coast of North America. He is very old; Pliny and the medieval naturalists knew about him, and if we are to go by weight of evidence, he must surely exist. Unfortunately, or otherwise, the quality of the evidence is inferior to its quantity. It is also a suspicious circumstance that New England newspapers are apt to receive tidings of this rare visitant at periods when news is otherwise rather dull.

In view of the suspicion which most men entertain on this subject, it seemed best to take our account from a particularly careful and respectable witness. Even so, some will think he has not proved anything, and it is certainly unfortunate that, as he admits frankly, he had not been "much accustomed to look through a glass."

Supposed to be a serpent[1]

The following is taken from a pamphlet, entitled "Report of a Committee of the Linnaean Society of New England, relative to a large Marine Animal, supposed to be a Serpent, seen near Cape Ann, Massachusetts, August, 1817." The letter is from the Hon. Lonson Nash, of Gloucester.

---

[1] From John Warner Barber: *Historical Collections: Massachusetts*, p. 180.

Gloucester, Sept. 9, 1817.

Sir: Your favor of the second inst. has been received. The vote of thanks of the Linnaean Society for my services was highly gratifying to me, not simply on account of the high consideration I entertain for the members of that laudable institution, but likewise for the agreeable manner and respectable channel through which their vote of thanks was communicated to me.

I have seen and conversed with the woman who was said to have seen the serpent dormant on the rocks, near the water, to whom you refer in yours; but she can give no material evidence. She says that she saw something resembling a large log of wood on the rocks, on the extreme eastern point of Ten Pound Island, (a small island in our harbor) resting partly on the rocks and partly in the water. The distance was about half a mile. She took a glass, looked at the object, and saw it move. Her attention was for a short time arrested by some domestic avocation, and when she looked for the object again it had disappeared.

You request a detailed account of my observations relative to the serpent. I saw him on the fourteenth ultimo, and when nearest I judged him to be about two hundred and fifty yards from me. At that distance I judged him in the larger part about the size of a half barrel, tapering towards the two extremes. Twice I saw him with a glass, only for a short time, and at other times with the naked eye for nearly half an hour. His color appeared nearly black—his motion nearly vertical. When he moved on the surface of the water, the track in his rear was visible for at least half a mile.

His velocity, when moving on the surface of the water, I judged was at the rate of a mile in about four minutes. When immersed in the water, his speed was greater, moving, I should say, at the rate of a mile in two, or at most in three minutes. When moving under water, you could often trace him by the motion of the water on the surface, and from this circumstance I conclude he did not swim deep. He apparently went as straight through the water as you could draw a line. When he changed his course, it diminished his velocity but little—the two extremes that were visible appeared rapidly moving in opposite directions, and when they came parallel they appeared not more than a yard apart. With a glass I could not take in at one view the two extremes of the animal that were visible. I have looked at a vessel at about the same distance, and could distinctly see forty-five feet. If he should be taken, I have no doubt that his length would be found seventy feet, at least, and I should not be surprised if he should be found one hundred feet long. When I saw him I was standing on an eminence on the sea-shore, elevated about thirty feet above the surface of the water, and the sea was smooth. If I saw his head I could not distinguish it from his body, though there were sea-faring men near me who said they could distinctly see his head. I believe they spoke truth, but, not having been much accustomed to look through a glass, I was not so fortunate.

I never saw more than seven or eight distinct portions of him above the water at any one time, and he appeared rough, though I suppose this appearance was produced by his motion. When he disappeared he apparently sunk directly down like a rock. Capt. Beach has been in Boston for a week past, and I am informed that he is still there. An engraving from his drawing of the serpent has been or is now making in Boston, but I have not been able to ascertain how far his drawing is thought a correct representation.

Respectfully, Sir, your most ob't,
Lonson Nash.

Hon. John Davis.

Fish stories are not peculiar to America, but they are bigger here. If Herodotus tells of a ring found in a fish's belly, *Anonymous Americanus* can and does tell of anything from a ticking alarm-clock to a live woman playing a grand piano. The fish whose scales were hay-scales, the trout that learned to follow his owner on land, but later fell in a stream and drowned—these creatures are migrants and have no single discoverable author. And they are told *pour le sport*. Nobody believes them. But when it comes to fish of wondrous size or catches of tremendous quantity, the case is a little different. It is as well to pause before pronouncing judgment. Especially is this true of stories that go back for a half-century, a century, or more. Certain fish come and go in certain regions, and the interval between the coming and going may be the greater part of a man's lifetime. Among the following fish stories, therefore, are included some true ones. (As the English littérateur H. H. Garrod remarked in another connection, "Those who know what is what, will know which is which.")

Tarpon[1]

W ood suffered many a jeer from the local fishing colony. Late in March his day arrived, fifty-six years ago.

He was working from a skiff close in shore toward a beach lined with mangroves. He was using mullet for bait. He noted tarpon playing close in, and as his guide moved toward the rolling fish he caught sight of another tarpon fifty feet out. He cast his bait six feet ahead of the tarpon and the big fish whirled and took it. Then his booty trailed off slowly with the bait apparently held lightly in his mouth.

"I gave him fifteen or twenty feet of extra line," said Mr. Wood, thereby establishing himself once and for all as a sound tarpon fisherman, "and I waited until he had taken up all of the slack. When it seemed he had it firmly in his mouth, I drew in sharply and hooked him.

"Instantly the big fish was up and out of the water, gleaming in the sun, and shaking his head to dislodge the hook. We paddled toward

---

[1] Reprinted from *The Mangrove Coast*, by Karl A. Bickel; copyright, 1942, by Coward-McCann, Inc.; pp. 278–88.

him to pick up line and he made off through the water. He must have carried us half a mile and during the run made six other leaps in the air, fighting hard to rid his mouth of the hook. Then he slowed down, and in his next leap hardly cleared water. As he tired I slowly worked him close to the rowboat. I wanted to gaff him but my guide was afraid if we brought him into the boat he would knock it to pieces. So I waited. When a sailboat came along I stepped into it and began reeling him in. It was Mr. Smith who gaffed him finally, and then we brought him into our boat. A tarpon had been caught with a twenty-one thread line, on a five-foot bamboo rod with never more than two hundred and fifty feet of line out. It could be done! We had taken only twenty-six and a half minutes to land him."

That was the first. Wood took his fish in good time. Even with modern tackle and with all the experience in tarpon fishing that has been piled up in the last half century, landing a ninety-three-pound tarpon from a rowboat, with no friendly and powerful engine to help, in twenty-six and a half minutes is a remarkable performance.

Without realizing it at the time, Wood invented a new and fascinating sport and initiated a great tourist attraction. Ten thousand tarpon-fishing tourists, at least, visit the resorts of the Mangrove Coast every year between May 15th and August 1st. Around three thousand tarpon are landed yearly, at times more. Tarpon fishing has become a cult. One man I know has caught one thousand three hundred and seventy-five tarpon in the last twenty-five years and hopes to make it fourteen hundred before his fishing days are over. There seem to be as many of the great fish as ever but old guides will tell you that the tarpon are becoming smarter. They take the lure less easily. On the other hand the tarpon fishermen are no longer so hungry for the kill. Dozens of tarpons are caught each year; their weight estimated, snapshots taken and then returned to the sea. The fish have no value as food, and several of the best tarpon tournaments no longer require the "body" in order to participate in the awarding of the prizes. The report of the fisherman and his guide are all that is required.

"A man who will fight a tarpon for thirty minutes to an hour and a half and then release him isn't the sort of fellow who would lie about ten or twenty pounds," says one club official, "and a good guide is a reliable estimator of weight. We want the tarpon to live."

Tarpon caught in recent years along the Mangrove Coast have weighed up to two hundred and three pounds. Twenty-five years ago several caught in Sarasota Bay weighed up to two hundred and sixteen pounds but today the tarpon, though often playing in the bay, rarely take the lure except outside in the main body of the gulf. Tarpon seldom show up until May 15th, but a few have been caught in upper Sarasota Bay as early as mid-January. Generally speaking, baby tarpon

—meaning small tarpon weighing from three to six pounds and every pound a ton of fight—start showing in the Shark River section early in February. From then on the march of the tarpon up the coast depends on the increasing warmth of the water and the behavior of the crabs on which they feed. The tarpon follow the crabs and the crabs go north according to the heat.

Tarpon fishing is a cross between hunting elephants, searching for whale and picking up a live wire. You do not cast your lure into a likely "spot." There simply isn't such a thing. There are places, like Boca Grande channel, Mansota beach near Venice or off "the Pines" on Longboat Key where they do seem to gather more certainly than elsewhere, but by and large, tarpon are where you find them. The boats go out in the early morning just before dawn, and, as the sun moves up through the pink and blue mists, the guides and fishermen eye the horizon line for signs of fish. Sometimes you will spot them—fifty or a hundred of them—madly thrashing about in circles, their tails flashing in the sun like propeller blades, the water churned foamy. Again you will sight them, slowly and solemnly marching, two by two, in almost equidistant lines, down some invisible sea lane. You can bring your boat down between them and often they will not even sound at your approach. Another time they will roll and dive about your boat so close you can touch them with a pole, or a pair of them will start ahead of your boat and play tag with you for miles without ever stopping to show the slightest interest in bait. At times when there will be hundreds of tarpons exploding about you, boiling up in clusters on all sides, not a fish will be taken.

Then suddenly the fish will bite!

When the biting streak occurs, about once or twice in twenty-four hours, they all seem to bite at once furiously, recklessly, at almost anything. Then the mood will seem to pass as suddenly as it started. Between times there is little to do but wait, and hope. Occasionally there will be short biting periods at midday. Once in a while a single tarpon will be caught when the rest of the school seem to be utterly devoid of any interest in food. That does not happen often. Generally speaking tarpon bite when they bite and they don't when they won't.

The fishing varies slightly in different localities. After a school has been located, the fishing boat, generally a gas driven vessel from twenty to thirty feet in length, fishing two rods, will approach slowly. No great care has to be taken as the fish pay no attention to the boats when they are at play. In the Boca Grande Channel sportsmen usually fish off the bottom, baiting their hooks with crab and keeping around fifteen feet off the floor of the gulf. The boats push along at about two miles an hour dragging the bait and tackle behind them. The strike is invariably light. The fish takes the bait gently into its mouth, as if it were afraid of crushing it, and will run for fifteen or twenty feet with it. The fish will then come down on the bait and then is the time to strike. Hundreds of tarpon are lost every year through a too quick jerk back on the pole. Men who are used to casting for bass, for instance, find it hard to overcome the tendency to pull back wildly when they feel the strike. If they do, almost invariably the tarpon drops the bait and gets away. This explains why freshmen tarpon fisherwomen are often more successful than men. When a man feels a strike he almost always instinctively responds with a quick jerk. Women, on the other hand, will often drop the pole and scream, "I've got a fish, what'll I do?" The tarpon begins to move away and about the time she seizes her rod and swings it back, the tarpon has bitten down upon the crab—and she has her fish hooked on her line.

North of Boca Grande it is customary to use a big white and red bobber with about fifteen or eighteen feet of line floating free with the bait. When the tarpon are sighted and a safe approach has been made, the fisherman casts his line in front of the game fish he hopes to attract as they swim past. If the fish are in a biting mood, the move brings success.

The instant the tarpon feels the hook the battle is on. There are few feeble fighters. The big silver-sides will be in the air with a smashing rush, the water will fall away in waves as he comes up, his head shaking madly to throw off the hook. Three—four—five times he will make the leap and then will probably sound deeply and see-saw all the way up. An average weight for tarpon is around sixty-five pounds and a sixty-five pounder can keep a fisherman in a state of nervous hysteria for twenty-five minutes without exerting himself at all. I have seen tarpon fishermen so exhausted after a twenty-five-minute continuous leaping, sawing and jumping match with a tarpon as not to be able to stand or to speak from sheer mental and physical exhaustion for ten minutes. These men only want one tarpon a season.

Some men come to the Mangrove Coast year after year and fail to get their tarpon. Others will average a tarpon a tide for a week at a time. Jesse Tucker, a well-known Sarasota tarpon fisherman, holds a Mangrove Coast record for catching five tarpon, ranging from fifty-five pounds to one hundred and two pounds, in four hours. But Jesse once hooked a tarpon off a bay bridge, while casting for mackerel, and held it for two jumps before the startled fish was able to run the line out and get away. Lassoing a tarpon is not frequent, but both Kirk Lincoln and V. T. Hamlin, the well-known newspaper cartoonist, have so cast their lines as to have them whip about the flourishing tail of a tarpon and both were able to bring their fish to gaff. A few years ago on a bet Bert Cohen floated out into the gulf in a barrel, made a cast and caught and killed his tarpon—a 125 pounder.

The guides tell you that only ten per cent of any school of tarpon are ever seen on the surface at one time. If the proportion is correct, a school of five hundred tarpon cannot be at all unusual, for I have often seen fifty tarpon rolling and tossing at one time.

Even a school of five hundred tarpon the guides will say is no great shucks. From Clearwater to Boca Grande every guide will swear to having seen that many at one time rolling in a long creaming line in the moonlight. That would mean schools of at least five thousand fish.

Once I was out fishing the late afternoon tide. Tarpon fishermen as a rule are a conservative lot and resist innovation, but Oscar Babcock had cut a trap door in the cabin of his new thirty footer, thus enabling Wesley, his guide, to stand on the high steersman's chair, operate the steering wheel with the big toe of his right foot and yet keep an eager eye out for signs of fish.

The sun was slipping into an explosion of turquoise and red clouds and the boat was rising and falling easily with gentle roll. In the tiny galley Archie was working over the stove heating up the soup and the coffee. As he worked he talked.

"Once in a while you will see a school of tarpon a thousand fish or more," said Archie. "I saw a school like that last week almost a quarter of a mile long. And there wasn't a bite in the whole parade."

Wesley came down from his standing perch and resumed his seat at the wheel.

"Best time to see tarpon," he said, "is at night. And the best night is a dark one. A dark night when the phosphorus is burning good. After a shower, in the dark of the moon. The water fires up fine then and you can see the tarpon cutting through the water a hundred yards off. You can see them from head to tail then, looking like they had their insides trimmed with neon signs.

"I was off the 'Pines' north of Sarasota last summer," he went on, "when one night I saw a glow off toward the shore. I brought the boat up within thirty yards of it. You could see plain it was nothing but tarpon. Must have been thousands of them. A glowing line for almost a quarter of a mile down the beach. The streak was a full hundred yards wide. Sometimes the mass would run three and four feet deep. They weren't hitting it up and they didn't seem to be going any place. It took 'em about half an hour to pass me. Once in a while one or two would come to the top and roll, and the drops of water would look like pinwheels sparkling. That was the greatest tarpon show I ever saw."

Offshore there was some sort of disturbance in the water. In the late sunlight a light brown patch could be seen just under the surface of the water. A broad, sharply pointed head came up and swung into the air, almost erect.

"Look at that loggerhead," said Arch. "Now if we had a jig I'd go over and let him have it."

"Can one get in that close to them?"

"Lots of times they are asleep but you can slide up pretty close almost any time. Those big loggerheads aren't afraid of anything. You will find them often sloshing about on the surface dead asleep. On a light line they'll give you quite a fight but they aren't worth much. The hawkbill turtle shell sells pretty well sometimes and then again it doesn't. We don't hunt them often. A green turtle will give you a pretty good steak but the brown ones aren't good eating. If you want a real fight in these gulf waters take on a manta ray."

"Isn't that a skate?" asked one of the passengers. "I saw one once that was six feet across."

"Six foot," replied Wesley with polite scorn, "is nothing. We don't bother with six footers. We take them on when they run to fifteen to twenty feet across. The biggest one I ever saw was twenty-five foot across. It weighed three thousand pounds and it dragged the boat, a fishing cruiser as big as this, ten miles before it slowed down. The big manta ray are kings of the gulf. Nothing can touch them. They almost let you run into them before they move. But the instant they feel the harpoon sink into them they drop fifty or sixty feet into the water. Then those big flappers of theirs get to working and they head out to sea. As quick as we land a harpoon into one we always throw the boat into reverse until he gets to going good. When he tires after an hour or so we go into reverse again and start pulling just to keep him from getting any rest. A big ray will fight from six to eight hours. I heard of one once that pulled a boat for seventeen miles before he slowed down. Manta ray is the biggest, wildest game in the whole gulf!"

"I saw a manta ray eating once," said Arch. "Something to look at. All there is to their heads is a couple of big eyes that look like tail lights to an automobile and a mouth as big as a bushel basket. We were laying off Venice looking for tarpon and then suddenly this old chap comes up in the middle of a school of sardines. He opens his mouth and brings his big flippers around and scoops up sardines by the bucketful. I mean it—a regular bucketful at every scoop. We took a shot at him with a .30–.30. It didn't even feaze him. It did scare the sardines and they flipped up their tails and shot off."

Sharks[1]

B ut I was going to tell you about sharks. The next year I was out in
the *Cape Ann* again and we took along a clever boy from
Woburn that had been to college and the Institute of Technology and
all that, and was finishing off to be an engineer, when the spondulix
ran short, or something. He heard about what happened to Joe
Folsom and happened to others and he thought he'd see what he
could do about it. He said it would be fun. If he'd got caught in the
fog, he'd seen the other side of the fun. But he was the clever boy, all
right. He went up town and got him an electric battery and things,
and when we got to the Banks he told us about his great scheme.

He fixed up a charge of gunpowder or dynamite or something, and
hid it in a bottle in a roll of salt pork. Then he hitched on his wires,
insulated wires, you know, and set out his battery and trailed the pork
overboard.

Mr. Shark came along, snapped the pork, and just then the college
boy turned on his switch and blew the gizzard out of that shark, all
right. He never bit anybody else.

"Your man stole that from Charles Reade," said I.

"Maybe he did, but I didn't," said The Fisherman, testily. "It happened just as I was telling you. The men on the schooner all said it
was a bully scheme and they'd carry a battery and things like that
on every trip. But they didn't. They forgot all about it. Everybody
forgets everything when he gets into the fishing business."

The following brief extract from "Shepherd Tom" Hazard's reminiscences is included not for intrinsic improbability—I accept it fully
—but because it has been doubted by more recent and less fortunate
observers. It had better be assumed, by the way, that Mr. Hazard is
speaking of bluefish when he uses the term "horse mackerel." The word
was often used vaguely, and was sometimes applied to what we now
call tuna; certainly that meaning does not fit in the following passage.

---

[1] From Charles Edward Russell: *From Sandy Hook to 62°* (New York: The Century Co.; 1929), pp. 317–18. By permission of D. Appleton-Century Co.

Narragansett fishing[1]

So I think I will just copy from a letter I received more'n six months ago from my brother Joseph, who has visited nearly every country and coast in the world, and besides that, owns "Sea Side," called by the summer visitors "Hazard's Castle," situated just south of Narragansett Pier, directly opposite the best fishing-ground in Rhode Island, the world inclusive. Says he: "As late as 1845, I reco'lect that Stephen A. Chase and myself caught 101 black-fish (tautog) on my shore, at Sea Side, on one afternoon. I used to see striped bass by the hundred in the breakers in the autumn, some of them very large. I have seen people at the north pier wading in the dock and pitching out flounders by the hundreds with a pitchfork, as they would hay in the field at mowing time. Menhaden (bony fish) were sold at twelve cents and less, a barrel, for manuring land, and thousands of barrels were sometimes landed at a haul on the beach, north of the Pier. Farmers used to come to the Pier from towns bordering on the Connecticut line, in the autumn, to catch codfish for their winter's supply, and go back with as many as they would need for many months to come, all caught in one day with hook and line. I have known two farmers to take a boat at the south Pier and go about the quarter of a mile from shore, and come back before night with over a ton of codfish to salt for their winter's use. Some seasons in October, I have seen the shore lined with fishing boats and smacks, some coming long distances. I remember seeing Capt. Williams, that most original, honest, interesting old fisherman, (a regular Norseman, one might readily imagine), come ashore one Sunday morning at about 11 o'clock, at the Pier, with three halibut in his boat, aggregating from six to seven hundred pounds weight. I remember seeing our nephew Rowland, when he was a boy, land at the Pier with one hundred and twenty-two horse mackerel he had just caught along the shore between the Pier and Point Judith."

---

[1] From Thomas Robinson Hazard: *The Jonny-Cake Papers of "Shepherd Tom"* (Boston: Printed for the Subscribers; 1915), pp. 304-5.

Arkansaw fishing[1]

W hen it comes to catching large fish Arkansaw has all the states
beat. The largest fish I ever saw, read, or heard tell of, was caught
out of the Arkansaw River below Little Rock. It kept getting their
bait and breaking their lines. Finally they had a blacksmith to make
a fish-hook out of a crowbar; they tied it to a steamboat cable and
baited it with a muly cow that had died with the holler horn, tied the
cable to a tree, and the next morning they had him; they was afraid
he would pull a team in the river, so they got all the negroes for miles
around and pulled him out on the bank, and hauled him to town in
sections. When they cut him open they found inside of him another
fish that weighed two hundred pounds (by guess), three fat hogs, one
yoke of oxen, and an acre of burnt woods.[2]

The saucer-back halibut[3]

W hiskery as a "porkypine," tanned to the color of an old leather
boot, Jereboam Thacher of Provincetown, longshore fisherman,
looked old enough to have fished in the flood. One leg, missing from
the knee-joint, was pieced out with the loom of an oar.

"How did I lose my leg?" asked he. "It's a tale that would turn your
hair gray. I don't often tell about it, for folks won't believe me. Haint
nobody left these days that kin remember what the fishin was like when
I was a young feller. But I'm tellin you life was different when a man
could walk alongshore with a pitchfork and load up a cart with
squiteague, and when the cod shoaled right in to the rocks and laid
there for days. In them times the lobsters used to crawl in on the
marshes and bed down for the winter as soon as the weather cooled
up, and men dug 'em out by the bushel along in Januwary–Febuwary.

"'Twas a halibut took my leg off, although the critter didn't mean no

---

[1] From Marion Hughes: *Three Years in Arkansas* (Chicago, 1904), p. 31 but
taken from James R. Masterson: *Tall Tales of Arkansaw* (Boston: Chapman &
Grimes; 1942), p. 70.

[2] Compare the contents of the alligator's stomach in the yarn on page 31 of the
present volume.

[3] By Joseph Chase Allen, from Elizabeth Reynard: *The Narrow Land* (Boston:
Houghton Mifflin Co.; 1934), pp. 255-7. By permission of the publishers, Houghton
Mifflin Company.

harm. Used to be a lot of em around inshore in them days, big fellers, shaped like a sole or a flounder, broad, with both eyes on one side of their heads; spotted light and dark brown on the back and dead white underneath. Only place they get em now is well offshore, but in them days they used to run right in to the beach. And they run from twenty-five pound weight up to, waal, no man ever knew how big the biggest one was. They get em now that run to three-four hundred pound.

"There was bigger ones than that when I was young.

"A halibut is a bottom fish, but there's times when they come up. They'll skitter acrost-water, jump out clean, and then there's times when they'll lay almost awash, with their sides and fins curled up like a saucer. Jest lay there. What for? The Lord only knows.

"Waal, this day I had run off-shore into the bay, haulin lobster-pots, doin a little hand-linin and managin to git a hundred or two pounds of lobsters and bout as many fish. I was runnin right along under sail in my smack-boat, makin good time before a light southerly that was blowin, and glad of it too, because the fog was makin. I must have been three mile from land when all to oncst I fetched up solid. Pretty nigh capsized. Figgered 'twas a piece of driftin wreck, and I went forrad to shove clear and look for damage, but it waant a wreck at all. It looked like bottom, but no bottom that I ever seen before. Besides, there was forty foot of water there.

"I got clear, put her on the other tack and stood off, wonderin about it. I run on for mebbe twenty minutes, then tacked in shore and bingo! I was aground agen! Bout six times I hit before I finally tuk in that there was somethin between me and home. What it was I couldn't tell, but it was there. And then, jest as I was pushin off the last time, I noticed a flurry some fathoms ahead of me, and I see somethin big break water, a oval brown thing that opened and shet. It was a head, but, Godfreys, what a head! I could see two eyes, twice the length of a whaleboat oar apart. Lookin around they was.

"Bimeby I reelized what the eyes belonged to. A halibut! Layin awash. And I had been sailin acrost his saucer-back for nigh on an hour!

"Things didn't look too good to me, but I waant real worried. How to git clear, that was the question. Fin'lly I figgered that I'd run on to his fin agen, climb out, stand on it, and hang onto my boat, which might be lightened enough to ride over. I trimmed aft my sheet and headed for where I knew his side laid. I miscalkerlated some, and hit it before expected, hit it hardish, too. Then I passed the slack of my halliards round me, and jumped over the bow. Something hit my knee, and I never felt sech pain before. I crawled over the gunnel, more dead than alive, saw that my leg was bleedin bad, and wound a line tight round it. Then I took an oar, and dizzy with pain, I tried to shove the boat over. As she moved ahead, and went clear, I saw what had done the damage:

"I had struck that fish solid and started up a couple of scales. There they laid, four foot acrost, standin half on edge, sharp as a meat axe, hard as flint. I had stumbled onto the edge of one, and later, when some of the bunch picked me up, they found that my leg was so nigh cut off that they had to finish the job."

Special bait

All fishermen know that fish are choosy about bait, and that even the same fish will bite one thing one day and another (refusing the first) a little later. This fact has begotten some strange tales. A correspondent of Lowell Thomas sent him the following examples, which seem definitely unusual: [1]

Jack Cummings, of Philadelphia, Pennsylvania, tells me of the ferocious trout they have in a lake where he goes fishing. Those trout are so game that not only do they demand live and wiggling bait, but any ordinary kind of bait isn't live and wiggling and fierce enough for them. So the fishermen of those parts bait their hooks with live tomcats.

Mr. Cummings knows of another lake where the fish chew tobacco. The fishermen have a novel way of catching those tobacco-chewing fish. It's done this way: You go out in a boat and throw quids of tobacco into the water. The fish get the quids and start to chew. And then the fisherman just waits until those fish come to the surface to spit, and hits them on the head with a club and kills them.

Sea-horses at drill [2]

But that which brought us the first Dawning of Hope, with respect to the Discovery of Land, was the Discovery which one of the Seamen made, of three or four great Fishes, which he called Sea-Horses; and not without reason, for their fore-parts were the perfect figure of a Horse, but their hinder parts perfect Fish; when the rest of the Seamen saw these Creatures, they all rejoyc'd, and said we were not far from

---

[1] Lowell Thomas: *Tall Stories* (New York: Funk & Wagnalls Co.; 1931), pp. 51–2.
[2] From John Dunton: *Letters Written from New-England*, A.D. *1686* (Boston: Published for the Prince Society; 1867), pp. 47–8.

Land; the reason of which was, That these Sea-Horses were Creatures that took a great delight in sleeping on the Shore, and therefore were never seen but near the Shore: This was but a collateral Comfort, for tho' these Sea-Horses delight in Sleeping on the Shore, yet they might swim two or three hundred Leagues into the Sea for all that: But we that looked upon our selves in a perishing Condition, were willing to lay hold on any little Twigg of Hope, to keep our Spirits up. One of the Seamen that had formerly made a Greenland Voyage for Whale-Fishing, told us that in that Country he had seen very great Troops of those Sea-Horses ranging upon Land, sometimes three or four hundred in a Troop: Their great desire, he says, is to roost themselves on Land in the Warm Sun; and Whilst they sleep, they appoint one to stand Centinel, and watch a certain time; and when that time's expired, another takes his place of Watching, and the first Centinel goes to sleep, &c. observing the strict Discipline, as a Body of Well-regulated Troops. And if it happen that at any time an Enemy approach, the Centinel will neigh, and beat, and kick, and strike upon their Bodies, and never leave till he has wak'd 'em; and then they run together into the Seas for shelter. But for all this Caution, the Sailors are, it seems too cunning for them; and get between them and the Sea, and beat out the Brains of the first that comes to hand; and so have done, till that they have kill'd so long, that they have wanted strength to kill another; and that which moves the Seamen to this cruelty is, because their Teeth are of great worth and value, and are a very vendible Commodity in the Southern parts of the World. And since it is the Shore on which these Creatures meet with this Destruction; and that if they had kept at Sea, they had been safe: I cou'd not but reflect, That those who leave their settled stations, whether out of Principles of Profit or of Pleasure, and will be trying New Experiments, and putting of New Projects on the Tenters, do oftentimes make very poor Returns; and are convinc'd it had been better for 'em to have kept that station which Providence at first had put 'em in.

The perch motor[1]

It is in violation of the law of the commonwealth to use live decoys in hunting wildfowl, but F. M. (Bucky) Rhodes of Vineyard Haven believed that he had developed a most successful substitute of late, and his disillusionment was painful.

Said decoy was of cork, painted in a lifelike manner, and equipped

---

[1] By J. C. Allen in *Vineyard Gazette*, November 9, 1945.

with a "quacker" to which a long rubber tube and bulb were attached. Anchored in the water, the "quacker" could be operated, and the decoy appeared very life-like indeed. But Cap'n Harry Norton added the final touch when he attached a short piece of fish-line and a baited hook to the decoy's beak. Once anchored, a perch took the bait, and diving, caused the decoy to "tip up" in a most natural manner. The fish swam this way and that, towing the decoy as if it was a swimming duck.

Thrilled and delighted, Bucky prepared a demonstration for the benefit of admiring friends, and made all preparations in an elaborate manner. But the friends brought along their retrievers, who sprang over board and brought the decoy ashore as fast as it could be anchored, and the perch had no opportunity at all to do their stuff!

A Yankee among the mermaids, a yarn, by a Cape Codder[1]

We pulled quietly back to the ship. The barrel of brandy had not been found, and I wish I may be sniggered if the capting did not fly into the biggest kind o' quarter-deck passion I ever did see. He stormed great guns and fired hull broadsides at the boat's crews, swearin' that they should keep on dredgin' till the tub was found, if it was the day arter eternity. So, you see, the hands was piped to dinner, but I was ordered tew keep in the boats and take care they didn't stave each other.

Waell, I laid down in the capting's gig, and what with the parson's licker, and the talk abeout marmaids, and syringes, and water-galls, and one thing and t'other, a very pretty muss began mixin' in my brain pan. So, as I was layin' comfortably moored in the starn sheets, with my head a leetle over the boat's quarter, I thought it highly unwrong that the brandy tub hadn't been fotched up, and that the men usin' the grapnels must have shirked as we did, cos, if they'd sarched as they oughter, they must have seed the barrel, for the water was so petickler clear that you could dissarn the crabs crawlin' over the korril rocks at the bottom of twenty fathom.

Waell, while I was lookin' into the ocean to see if I could light upon the barrel, a leetle o' the largest fish I ever did see come and swum

---

[1] From *Traits of American Humour,* by Native Authors, edited and adapted by the author of *Sam Slick, The Old Judge, The English in America,* etc., etc., in three volumes (London: Colburn & Co.; 1852), Vol. I, pp. 252–6.

right close to the bottom of the sea, jest under the boats. Then it kept risin' and risin' till I seed its long fins were shaped like mens' arms; and when it come near the sarfis, it turned on its back, and then I seed a human face! I know'd at once that it was a marmaid, or a marman, or one o' them amfibberous critters called fabbelus syringes, as the chaplain had been spinnin' his yarns abeout. So, the critter popt its head up jest above the water, which was smooth as glass, and a little smoother tew, by a darned sight, and jest as clear and jest as shiny, and says he to me:

"Look here, strannger, you and your shipmates ain't doin' the genteel thing to me no how you can fix it, for they're playin' old hub with my garding grounds and oyster beds by scratchin' and rakin' 'em all over with them ar' darned anchors and grapnel fixins, in a manner that's harrowin' to my feelins. If the capting wants his thundernation licker tub, let him just send eeny decent Christian down with me, and I'll gin it him."

Waell, I'm not goin' to say that I didn't feel kinder skeered, but the chaplain's yarns had rubbed the rough edge off, and the notion o' findin' the capting's cask pleased me mightily, cos I knowed it would tickle the old man like all creation, and sartingly get me three or four liberty days for shore goin' when we returned to Port Mahon. So, as I hadn't on nothin' petikler as would spile, only a blue cotting shirt and sail-cloth pantys, and the weather bein' most uncommon warm, I jest told the marman I was ready, and tortled quietly over the boat's side into the blue transparent sea.

The marman grappled me by the fist, and we soon touched bottom, now I tell ye. I found as I could walk easy enough, only the water swayed me abeout jest as if I war a leetle tight, but I didn't seem to suffer nothin' from want o' breath, nyther.

We soon reached whar' the brandy cask was lyin' right under the ship' keel, which accounts for its not bein' seen nor nothin' by the boats' crews. I felt so everlastically comical abeout findin' the tub, that I told the half-bred dolphing fellow that pinted it out, that if I knowed how to tap it, I wish I might die if I wouldn't give him a gallon of the stuff as a salvage fee.

"What's in it?" says the marman.

"Why, licker," says I.

"Waell," says the marman, "so I heerd them scrapin' fellers in the boat say; but I guess I've licker enough to last my time, tho' I recking your licker is something stronger than salt water, seein' that its hooped in that almighty way."

"Why, you lubber," says I, "it's brandy—the raal ginnewine coney-hack."

"And what's that?" says the marman.

180

"Why, dew tell—want to know?" says I; "have you lived to your time o' life without tastin' spirretus licker? Waell, I swow, you oughter be the commedore of all them cold water clubs, and perpetual president of all temp'rance teetotallers. Go ahead, matey; pilot the way to your shanty, and I'll roll the barrel arter you. I'll sune give you a drink o' licker that will jest take the shirt-tail off eeny thing you ever did taste, now I tell you."

Waell, the critter flopped ahead, for you see its the natur' o' the marmen, seein' as they've no legs, only a fish's tail what's bent under them, jest like the lower part o' the letter J, to make way by floppin' their starns up and down, and paddlin' with their hands—somethin' between a swim and a swagger—but the way they get through the water is a caution. I rolled the tub along over the smooth white shiny sand, and the crabs and lobsters skeeted off right and left sides out o' my way regular skeered, and big fishes of all shapes and makes, with bristlin' fins, swum close alongside me, and looked at me quite awful with their small gooseberry eyes, as much as to say, "What the nation *are* you at?"

Bymeby, the marman brought up in front of a rayther largeish cave or grotto of rock and shell work, kivered with korril and sea-weed. So, you see, the tub was put right on eend in one corner. I made an enquirry o' the marman if he had a gimblet, and he said he b'lieved there was such a thing in the hold or cellar; he'd found a carpenter's toolchest in a wreck a few miles to the easterd, and he fotched away six or seving of the leetle fixins, thinkin' they might be useful to hum [1]—so, he opened the back door and hailed a young marman to bring him the gimblet.

Seein' as there was no benches nor nothin' to sit down on, which marmen and marmaids don't desire, cos they've no sittin' parts to their bodies, which is all fish from their waistbands, I jest sot on the top o' the brandy-tub, and took an observation of the critter before me. His face was reglar human, only it looked rayther tawney and flabby like a biled nigger, with fishy eyes, and a mouth like a huge tom cod. His hair hung stret down his shoulders, and was coarse and thick, like untwisted rattlin'; his hands were somethin' like a goose's paw, only the fingers were longer and thicker; and his body was not exactly like an Injin's nor a nigger's, nor a white man's—nor was it yaller, nor blue, nor green—but a sorter altogether mixed up colour, lookin' as if it were warranted to stand the weather. Jest abeout midships, his body was tucked into a fish's belly, with huge green scales right down to the tail.

Whilst I was surveyin' the marman fore and aft, the back door opened and a she critter flopped in, with a young marman at the

---

[1] To hum = at home.

breast. The leetle sucker was not bigger than a pickerel, with a tail of a delicate sammon colour, and a head and body jest like one o' them small tan monkeys, with a face as large as a dollar. The marman introduced the she critter as his wife, and we soon got into a coil of talk right slick, all abeout the weather, and the keare and trouble o' a young family—and I wished I may be swamped if the marmaid warn't a dreadful nice critter to chatter. Like all wimming folks, she was plaguey kewrous as to whar' I was raised and rigged—and when I said I guess I hailed from Cape Cod, and all along shore thar', she looked at the marman, and said to me:

"Waell, I never—Cape Cod! why, strannger, I guess there must be some finnity in our breeds."

Waell, you see, I grew rayther kewrous tew, and wanted to log the peticklers o' the nateral history o' the race o' marmen—so I made a few enquerries respectin' their ways o' life.

"I guess," says I, "you've a tarnal good fish market in these here parts, and keep your table well supplied with hallibut and sea-bass, and black-fish, eh?"

"Why, strannger," says the marman, rayther wrathy, "seein' its you I won't be offended, or, by hevving, if that speech ain't enough to make a marman feel scaly, why then it ain't no matter. We claim to be half fish in our natur', and I reckon you don't kalkilate we gobbles our relations? there's sea varmint enough in all conscience, sitch as oysters, and clams, and quahogs, and muscles, and crabs, and lobsters. We go the hull shoat with them; and then we cultivates kail and other sea truck in our gardings, and sometimes we swims under the wild fowl as they're floatin' and jerks down a fine duck or a gull, or gathers their eggs off the rocks, or the barnacles off drift wood."

Jest then, the marman's eldest son-fish fotched in the gimblet, and brought up the marman's jawin' tacks with a round turn. The young un was about the size of an Injin boy, just afore he runs alone—half papoose, half porpus. He got a leetle skeered when he clapt eyes on me, but I gave him a stale quid o' backer to amuse himself, and the sugar plum made the marmaster roll his eyes above a bit, now I tell you.

Waell, I bored a hole in the brandy tub, and pickin' up an empty clam-shell, handed a drink to the lady, and told her to tote it down. She swaller'd it down pretty slick, and the way she gulped afterwards, and stared, and twisted her fishy mouth, was a sin to Davy Crockett. The marman looked rayther wolfy at me, as if I'd gin her pison; so I drawed a shell-full and swallered it myself. This kinder cooled him down, and when the marmaid got her tongue tackle in runnin' order agin, she said she guessed the licker was the juice of hevving, and she'd be darned if she wouldn't have another drink right off the reel.

Seein' this, the marman swallered his dose, and no sooner got it down than he squealed right out, and clapped his webby hands together, and wagged his tail like all creation. He swore it was elegant stuff, and he felt it tickle powerful from the top of his head to the eend of his starn-fin. Arter takin' two or three horns together, the sonny cried for a drink, and I gin him one that sent him wrigglin' like an eel in an un-easiness. So the marman said, as the licker was raal first-rate, and first-rater than that tew, he guessed he'd ask in his next door neighbor and his lady, jest to taste the godsend. Waell, in a minnit, in comes a huge marman of the most almighty size, looking jest like Black Hawk when he was bilious; he fotched up his lady with him, and his eldest son, a scraggy hobbadehoy marman, and his darters, two young mar-maids or marmisses, jest goin' out o' their teens, who flapped their yaller-skinned paws over their punking-colored chops, pretendin' to be almighty skeered at comin' before a strannge man in a state o' natur'—but they forgot all abeout that thar' when the licker was handed to them.

Arter takin' a few swallers, the fresh marman said he guessed the clam-shell was altogether tew leetle to get a proper amount o' licker whereby a feller could judge correctly of the raal taste o' the stuff—so he went to his berth in the next cave, and fotched a large blue and silver shell that held abeout a pint.

The news o' the brandy tub spred pretty slick, for in half an hour, I'd the hull grist o' the marmen belongin' to that settlement cooped up in the cavern. Sich a noisy swillin' set o' wet souls I never did see; the drunk come on 'em almighty strong, for they kept me sarvin' out the licker jest as quick as it would run. I thought if the capting could have seen me astridin' his brandy-cask, in an underground grocery at the bottom o' the sea, surrounded by sich a skeul of odd fish, how many dozen at the gangway would he have ordered the bosen's mate to have sarved me out?

The way the drunk affected the different critters was right kewrous, now I tell you. One great scaly feller stiffened his tail all up, and stood poppindickler erect on the peaked pints of the eend fin, like a jury-mast, and jawed away raal dignified at all the rest, wantin' them to appoint him a sort o' admiral over the hull crew. Another yeller feller, with a green tail, was so dreadful blue, that he doubled himself into a figgery 5, and sung scraps and bits o' all sorts o' sea songs, till he got tew drunk to speak at all. Some o' the marmen wanted to kiss all the marmaids, and tew o' the ladies begun scratchin' and fightin' like two pussies, cos one trod on t'other's tail. Some went floppin' and dancin' on the sand like mad, rasin' sich a dust that I could not see to draw the licker—but the party round the tub soon druv' them to the right abeout, as interferin' with the interest o' the settlement. Every minnit some fresh marman dropped on the ground with the biggest kind of load on; I never seed a set o' critters so almighty tight, yellin', swearin', huggin', and fightin', till they growed so darned savagerous that I kinder feared for my own safety amongst them drunken moffradite sea aborgoines. So, you see, I up and told them that I'd clapt my veto on the licker, and that they should not have any more.

Waell, if ever you did hear a most etarnal row, or see a hull raft o' drunken fellers cut didoes, then *was* the time. It was voted that I were a public enemy, and every half drunken marman suddenly become very 'fishus to have me Linched, and it were settled at last that I were to be rode on a rail, and tarred and feathered. But, while some o' the varmint went arter the rail and the tar, the rest o' the critters begun quarrelin' who was to sarve out the licker; and as each marman, drunk or sober, wanted to have the keare o' the precious stuff, they soon raised a pretty muss, and kept on tearin' at each other like a pack o' wolves. Seein' this, I jest kinder sneaked quietly away from the cave grocery till I come in sight o' the ship, when I struck upperd for the sarfis, and swum for dear life. I soon seed that the boats' crew were musterin' for another bout o' draggin' for the brandy-cask; so, fearin' least the capting should miss me, I jest laid hold o' the edge o' the gig, and crawled in pretty quickly, and laid myself down in the starn-sheets, as if I'd never been out o' the boat.

I hadn't laid thar' half a second, when I heerd a noise jest for all the world as if somebody was squeezin' a small thunder cloud right over my head. I ruz up, and thar' were the capting and the hull crew lookin' over the ship's side at me—the officers in a tarnel rage, and the men grinnin' like so many hyenas.

"Rouse up, you long-sided lazy swab, and bring the boats in from the boom. Are you goin' to sleep all day?"

"Ay, ay, Sir," said I, jumpin' up in the boat, when all the water run off me like forty thousand mill-streams—I'd been so outrageous soaked when down with the marmen. I felt kinder skeered lest the capting should see it, but when I stood up he laughed right out, and so did the hull crew tew.

"Why, he's not awake yet," said the capting. "Bosen, give him another bucket."

You see they wanted to persuade me that I'd fell asleep in the gig, as fast as a meetin' house, and slept thar' the hull while the crew were at dinner, and that no shoutin' nor nothin' couldn't wake me up—so, the bosen run along the boom and jest give me a couple o' buckets o' sea-water right over me. When I told 'em my yarn abeout the marman poppin' up his head, and invitin' me down, and all abeout findin' the brandy-tub and the rest, they swore that I'd got drunk on the parson's licker, and dreampt it all in the boat. But I guess I know what I did see, jest abeout as slick as anybody; and the chaplain b'lieved the hull story; and said that as I'd learnt the marmen the valley o' licker, they'd get huntin' up all the tubs and barrels out of the different wrecks in all the various seas; and that intemperance would spile the race, and thin 'em off till they became one o' the things that was—jest like the Injins what's wastin' away by the power o' rum and whiskey given 'em by the white men.

I recking the parson warn't far out in his kalkilashing. The love o' licker has had its effect upon the marmen and marmaids; they must have thinned off surprisin'ly, for I ain't seed none since, nor I don't know nobody that has nyther.

Among pests whose misdemeanors are exaggerated by man, the name of the mosquito, in America, leads all the rest. Yet I have dodged him, so far as might be. To compile a thesaurus of mosquito stories would indeed be possible; but that way madness lies. In the other direction lies boredom, unless one ventures but a very short way, for tales of the mosquito merely ring changes upon a small number of standard themes, some of them unfunny. The mosquito who strips a schooner of its rigging must come from the coast, and the one who bites through an iron kettle [1] would seem to have originated in a place and time in which cooking was done out of doors. But they have "been around" and may appear anywhere in these United States.

Stewart Holbrook's story of Ethan Allen and Remember Baker (p. 268 below) is perhaps more of a snake story than a mosquito one.

'Hoppers and history [2]

Among the greatest of the calamities which a hostile nature visited upon the pioneers of the western prairies were the devastating grasshopper plagues. In 1818 a swarm of grasshoppers descended upon the Red River Valley in North Dakota and devoured all trace of vegetation. They made destructive raids in '57, '66 and '67. The great calamity of 1874, however, surpassed anything before or since. On the plains it is still called "The Grasshopper Year."

The 'hoppers came suddenly out of the north on an afternoon late in July. They traveled with a strong wind; rising high in the air with their wings spread, they were carried along with little effort, and their ravages reached from the Dakotas to Texas.

To observers of their approach it seemed at first that a squall might be in the offing. Gradually the sun was darkened by a cloud in the northwest. Presently the insects began to alight, and the cry went up: "Grasshoppers!"

They came like a driving snow, filling the air, covering the earth,

---

[1] This one got into this book, p. 48.

[2] As condensed in *The Reader's Digest*, November 1937, pp. 59–60, from Everett Dick: *The Sod-House Frontier* (New York: D. Appleton-Century Co.; 1937).

the buildings, the shocks of grain, everything. According to one observer, their alighting on the roofs sounded like continuous hail. They alighted on trees in such numbers that their weight broke off large limbs. Chickens and turkeys were frightened at first and ran from them, but they soon identified the 'hoppers and ate themselves sick. One pioneer reported that a herd of 40 hogs and 50 turkeys fattened themselves on nothing but grasshoppers and a little hay. The pork and fowl had a peculiar taste of grasshoppers.

At times the insects were four to six inches deep on the ground, and continued to alight for hours. Men were obliged to tie strings around their trousers to keep the pests from crawling up their legs. The 'hoppers gathered so thick on the tracks that Union Pacific trains were stopped. The rails were so oily and greasy that the wheels spun and would not pull a train.

People brought out sheets and blankets to protect the most valuable crops. Yet the insects ate holes in the bedclothes or crawled underneath and destroyed everything. In Dakota old straw was piled around a field and set on fire; some put a salt solution on the grain, all to no avail. Men with clubs walked down the corn rows knocking the 'hoppers off, but on looking back they saw the insects as numerous as ever. They alighted in such numbers that the cornstalks were bent toward the ground and the potato vines mashed flat. The sound of their feeding was like a herd of cattle eating in a corn field.

Every green thing except castor beans, cane, native grass, and the leaves of certain trees was eaten. Onions and turnips were eaten right down to the end of the roots, leaving holes in the ground. Trees, denuded of their leaves and stripped of their bark, died. The water in the creeks, stained with the excrement of the insects, assumed the color of strong coffee. The cattle refused to drink until compelled by extreme thirst. Even the fish tasted like grasshoppers.

A piece of harness or a garment left on the ground was quickly ruined. Pitchfork and scythe handles were gnawed so rough as to become uncomfortable to the hands, and the weather-beaten boards on houses and fences were so eaten that within a few hours they looked like new lumber.

If any of the creatures were tramped underfoot, their companions quickly devoured them. They ate the mosquito bar off the windows and even invaded houses and ate the window curtains. The jaunty waving fields of corn were reduced to bent-over denuded stalks in 12 hours, and even the large weeds were destroyed.

When the insects left, the country was a scene of ruin and desolation. Those who had the money to get out of the country did so. Those who remained were largely dependent upon relief appropriations, which were quickly voted by federal and state governments, and supplies provided by churches, benevolent societies, and relatives in the East. To the clergy, the calamity proved a blessing in disguise. It made the individualistic frontiersman see how helpless he was in the face of God's providence, and there were wonderful revivals.

There have been other grasshopper plagues since the disaster of '74, but none which caused such desolation. The terrible news deterred prospective homeseekers, and it was years before western migration was restored to its former proportions.

Conjuring rats[1]

In New England, as well as in other parts of the United States, it is still believed, by certain persons, that if a house is infested with rats, these can be exiled by the simple process of writing them a letter, in which they are recommended to depart, and make their abode in another locality. The letter should indicate precisely the habitation to which they are assigned, and the road to be taken, and should contain such representations of the advantages of the change as may be supposed to affect the intelligence of the animal in question. This method of freeing a house from its domestic pests is well known, but is commonly regarded as a jest. As in most such cases, however, what is supposed to be mere humor is, in fact, the survival of a perfectly serious and very ancient usage. This custom, still existing in retired places, is illustrated by the following document, the genuineness of which may be relied on.

The country house of a gentleman, whose permanent home in Boston, being infested by rats, the owner proposed to use poison; but the caretaker, who was in charge of the empty house, represented that there was a better way, namely, to address an epistle to the creatures; he prepared a letter, of which the following is a reproduction.

... Maine, October 31, 1888

Messrs. Rats and Co.,—Having taken quite a deep interest in your welfare in regard to your winter quarters, I thought I would drop you a few lines which might be of some considerable benefit to you in the future seeing that you have pitched your winter quarters at the summer residence of ... No. 1, Seaview Street, I wish to inform you that you will be very much disturbed during cold winter months as I am expecting to be at work through all parts of the house, shall take down ceilings, take up floors, and clean out every substance that would serve to make you comfortable, likewise there will be nothing left for you to feed on, as I shall remove every eatable substance; so

[1] From William Wells Newell: "Conjuring Rats," *Journal of American Folk-Lore*, Vol. V, pp. 23–5.

you had better take up your abode elsewhere. I will here refer you to the farm of . . . No. 6, Incubator Street, where you will find a splendid cellar well filled with vegetations of (all) kinds besides a shed leading to a barn, with a good supply of grain, where you can live snug and happy. Shall do you no harm if you heed to my advice; but if not, shall employ "Rough on Rats."

Yours,

. . .

This letter was greased, rolled up, and thrust into the entrance of the rat-holes, in order that it might be duly read, marked, and inwardly digested; the result being, as the owner of the house was assured, that the number of the pests had been considerably diminished.

The reader cannot but admire the persuasive style of the Yankee farmer, and the judicious mixture of argument, blandishment, and terror, exhibited in the document; while in the choice of the barn of a neighbor, recommended as a desirable place of abode, is shown a shrewdness worthy of its reward.

That the practice of writing letters to rats is not confined to New England will appear from the following extract, taken from the "Baltimore Sun," February 21, 1888, (as cited in the "New York Times," February 23):—

The testimony in the contest over the will of George Jessup, of "Kenilworth," near Cockneyville, in Baltimore County, was completed yesterday. The will bequeaths "Kenilworth," the ancestral home of the Jessup family, to George Jessup, Esq., son of the testator, after the death of his stepmother, and the widow, and other children of the testator seek to have the will set aside, on the ground that the elder Mr. Jessup, who died April 3, 1887, in the 84th year of his age, was of unsound mind. Among the witnesses for the defence examined yesterday was Mr. James Howard, residing in Baltimore County, about two miles from "Kenilworth." He testified that Mr. Jessup was entirely competent. On cross-examination, Colonel Charles Marshall asked him if he ever proposed to Mr. Jessup to try to drive the rats away from the house.

"I did, sir," replied the witness.

"How did you tell him you were going to drive them away?"

"By letters."

"How were you going to do it by letters?"

"By reading them."

"To whom?"

"To the rats."

"How much was he going to give you for doing that?"

"There was no contract between us."

"You were to write the letter and he was to read it?"

"I was to write the letter and Mr. Jessup was to read it."

"You thought that would drive them away?"

"I didn't think anything about it; I tried it, and I know it."

"You have done that?"

"I have done it."

"Did you write a letter to Mr. Jessup's rats, or ask him to write one to them?"

"Mr. Jessup wanted to write it, but I would not let him; I wrote it when I went home that night; at least I got my daughter to write it, and I took and gave it to Mr. Jessup."

"What had he to do with it?"

"I told him to take the letter to the meat-house, and read it, and lay the letter down on the meat-house floor."

"Did he do that?"

"He told me he did."

"In that letter didn't you tell them they had lived on Mr. Jessup long enough?"

"Yes, sir."

"Didn't you tell them they must leave?"

"Yes, sir, I did."

"Didn't you tell them to go straight to the lane?"

"Yes, sir."

"Past the stone house, and keep on up the hill, right past the church, and not to go down the turnpike or up the turnpike, but to keep on until they came to the large white house on the right, and turn in there; that it was Captain Low's house and they would get plenty to eat there?"

"I did."

"Did Mr. Jessup report to you that the paper had disappeared?"

"Yes, sir, he did."

"Didn't you tell him that broke the charm?"

"Yes, sir."

"What did he say had become of the paper?"

"He didn't know, and I didn't know."

"He came to tell you that it had disappeared—the rats did not go?"

"The last time I called on him, he said that he really believed a great many of them did go, but they hadn't all gone."

"All who understood the letter had gone?"

"I don't know about that. May be some understood it, and didn't go, too."

During this examination the attorneys and their clients, the jury, court officials, and the large audience were convulsed with laughter, and during the day the slightest allusion to the "rat story" was the signal for a fresh outburst.

Mrs. Katie Barker, one of the contestants of the estate, confirmed the evidence of Mr. Howard, and said the episode occurred in 1882. Her father, she said, shut the door, and refused to allow her to accompany him any farther when he went out to read the letter to the rats.

Aunt Weed's rat letter [1]

It was found tucked away in a crevice in the cellar wall, after the old house in East Sandwich was "gone in ruins." It was a piece of paper, good old paper made from linen rags, or it would not have remained intact and the writing on it legible after long years in that interstice between granite block and granite block of the potato pit. It was damp, of course, even in that inner cellar far from the bulkhead door; it had been damp even before the roof leaked and the floors began to sag. The piece of paper, apparently a second sheet of a folded over note, had weathered successfully under those unfavorable conditions some forty years' immuration, the last ten of which the house was unoccupied.

Since it has come into the possession of Mrs. Leon Currier, the great-great-niece of the Mrs. Abigail Weed who wrote it, it has had a certain local currency as "Emmy's Rat Letter." It now hangs, framed, in Mrs. Currier's parlor. It has for fellows there other relics of old times, an inlaid candle stand, fanback windsors, a Currier and Ives of Lincoln, the most generous flip glass I ever saw, a Washington and Lafayette pitcher in blue and white, a pewter wafer box and a sugar shaker in soft paste Staffordshire known in the family as "Mrs. Phillpotts." It has been widely copied, and it has been photographed, but I cannot discover that any one in recent years has tried the efficacy of its formula by inserting a copy in cellar or chamber or corn loft. Perhaps they feel that what banished, three generations ago, the gentle creatures of dark mole gray known as black rats, would fail in this day and generation with the predatory brown rats that have supplanted them.

Inasmuch as the exorcism is written with a dearth of punctuation and capitalization, and as it has a word or two of unfamiliar or uncertain meaning, I cannot reproduce it exactly as it was written. I must print it so that its meaning can be followed as it is read, and I must add a little exegesis. It is dated "Sandwich May the 9th 1845." It reads as follows:

---

[1] From *New Hampshire Neighbors* by Cornelius Weygandt (New York: Henry Holt and Co.; 1937), pp. 191–4. Copyright, 1937, by Henry Holt and Co., Inc.

191

"I have bourne with you till my patience is all gone. I cannot find words bad enough to express what I feel, you black devils you are, gnawing our trace corn while we are asleep! And even when we are awake you have the audacity to set your infernal jaws to going. Now, spirits of the bottomless pit, depart from this place with all speed! Look not back! Begone, or you are ruined! If you could know as much as I do, you would never take another thing from here. I will keep nothing to myself. You shall hear the whole. We are preparing water (to) drown you; fire to roast you; cats to catch you; and clubs to maul you. Unless you want your detested garments dyed in fire and brimstone, you satans, quit here and go to Ike Nute's! This is for cellar rats. Please give notice to those in the chamber. There are many of us in the garret plotting against you, when our eyes are open all but one poor female who is affraid of life. But the rest is not affraid I can tell you. There is our bill, and I leve if they get hold of you (you) would think you're in wire cage. A hint to the wise is sufficient.

To the bigest and most inventive rat.

Mrs. Weed."

It is necessary, perhaps, to explain that "trace corn" is seed corn bound together in a long string by the plaiting together of the husks turned back from the ears. Twenty such strung ears make a "trace." "Leve" is the old word of the countryside for "believe." The chamber is the low attic over the ell of the one-story house, as the garret is the high attic over the main part of that house. One-story house proper and ell, together with garret and chamber, make the story-and-a-half house typical of New England.

A re-reading of the exorcism tells us the writer is playful as well as earnest. She is making game at the same time that she is half hoping the letter will rid her home of rats. She is laughing at herself for writing the charm and trusting there is enough power in it to induce her to feel the thrill of making magic. Light from her family on her personality and character make clearer, perhaps, certain of the letter's phrases. She was a prim and exact little person who was, as she says in the letter, "affraid of life." Her great-grandniece says she was timorous about everything from mice to tramps. Mistress Abigail lost her husband and returned with her daughter to her childhood's home where she lived with her brothers William and Steven Cogan.

As I read it first I could not but wonder if the hocuspocus of it was veiled language threatening reprisals against some one who was vilifying the old lady or some of her family. "To the bigest and most inventive rat" would so well suit a fabricator of lies. I have dismissed any such interpretation. I think it is a charm, an exorcism to rid the house of black rats. Written apparently on the back of a sheet from an old letter, which was saved, no doubt, because it had little writing on it, for scrap paper, it has not the importance of a document written on unused paper. It is not to be taken too seriously. I say this, not because charms and incantations are taboo to Puritanism. They are not, as the world knows. There was witchcraft in Sandwich, New Hampshire, as well as in Salem, Massachusetts, plenty of it when witchcraft was in season. I say the exorcism is not to be taken too seriously because of the mockery with which it is written. The writer had a sense of humor. She was play-acting in writing it, but many a play-actor has convinced herself that her role was real life. I believe that she had by her in some old almanac, that repository of strange odds and ends, some sort of incantation against rats; or that she remembered the phrases of some evangelist tearing into the Devil. I believe she was half satiric, half serious in what she wrote, that it is a mock exorcism as well as an exorcism. It has affiliations with well-known charms, even to those in Anglo-Saxon days. Whatever your interpretation of Aunt Weed's Rat Letter, it drives you to own that there were complexities as well as simplicities in back-country life three generations ago.

It should perhaps be added that it is the tradition of the countryside that the rats did leave the cellar of the old lady's house after she put in it the letter to them, and that they did go, as she exorcised them, to Ike Nute's.[1]

---

[1] Mr. Weygandt may or may not be right in his guesses about the mood in which Aunt Weed wrote. Mary Heaton Vorse tells (*Time and the Town;* New York: Dial Press; 1942, p. 259) of getting rid of a skunk by writing (as advised by an old lady): "Dear Skunk: I would not willingly hurt the feelings of one of God's creatures, but circumstances beyond my control make it necessary for me to ask you to go. Regretfully, Mary Vorse."

Jim Baker's bluejay yarn[1]

Animals talk to each other, of course. There can be no question about that; but I suppose there are very few people who can understand them. I never knew but one man who could. I knew he could, however, because he told me so himself. He was a middle-aged, simple-hearted miner who had lived in a lonely corner of California, among the woods and mountains, a good many years, and had studied the ways of his only neighbors, the beasts and the birds, until he believed he could accurately translate any remark which they made. This was Jim Baker. According to Jim Baker, some animals have only a limited education, and use only very simple words, and scarcely ever a comparison or a flowery figure; whereas, certain other animals have a large vocabulary, a fine command of language and a ready and fluent delivery; consequently these latter talk a great deal; they like it; they are conscious of their talent, and they enjoy "showing off." Baker said, that after long and careful observation, he had come to the conclusion that the bluejays were the best talkers he had found among birds and beasts. Said he:

"There's more *to* a bluejay than any other creature. He has got more moods, and more different kinds of feelings than other creatures; and, mind you, whatever a bluejay feels, he can put into language. And no mere commonplace language, either, but rattling, out-and-out book-talk—and bristling with metaphor, too—just bristling! And as for command of language—why *you* never see a bluejay get stuck for a word. No man ever did. They just boil out of him! And another thing: I've noticed a good deal, and there's no bird, or cow, or anything that uses as good grammar as a bluejay. You may say a cat uses good grammar. Well, a cat does—but you let a cat get excited once; you let a cat get to pulling fur with another cat on a shed, nights, and you'll hear grammar that will give you the lockjaw. Ignorant people think it's the *noise* which fighting cats make that is so aggravating, but it ain't so; it's the sickening grammar they use. Now I've never heard a jay use bad grammar but very seldom; and when

[1] From Mark Twain: *A Tramp Abroad* (Author's National Edition; New York: Harper & Brothers; 1907) , Vol. I, pp. 24–32.

they do, they are as ashamed as a human; they shut right down and leave.

"You may call a jay a bird. Well, so he is, in a measure—because he's got feathers on him, and don't belong to no church, perhaps; but otherwise he is just as much a human as you be. And I'll tell you for why. A jay's gifts, and instincts, and feelings, and interests, cover the whole ground. A jay hasn't got any more principle than a Congress-man. A jay will lie, a jay will steal, a jay will deceive, a jay will betray; and four times out of five, a jay will go back on his solemnest promise. The sacredness of an obligation is a thing which you can't cram into no bluejay's head. Now, on top of all this, there's another thing; a jay can outswear any gentleman in the mines. You think a cat can swear. Well, a cat can; but you give a bluejay a subject that calls for his reserve-powers, and where is your cat? Don't talk to *me*—I know too much about this thing. And there's yet another thing; in the one little particular of scolding—just good, clean, out-and-out scolding—a blue-jay can lay over anything, human or divine. Yes, sir, a jay is every-thing that a man is. A jay can cry, a jay can laugh, a jay can feel shame, a jay can reason and plan and discuss, a jay likes gossip and scandal, a jay has got a sense of humor, a jay knows when he is an ass just as well as you do—maybe better. If a jay ain't human, he better take in his sign, that's all. Now I'm going to tell you a perfectly true fact about some bluejays.

"When I first begun to understand jay language correctly, there was a little incident happened here. Seven years ago, the last man in this region but me moved away. There stands his house,—been empty ever since; a log house, with a plank roof—just one big room, and no more; no ceiling—nothing between the rafters and the floor. Well, one Sunday morning I was sitting out here in front of my cabin, with my cat, taking the sun, and looking at the blue hills, and listening to the leaves rustling so lonely in the trees, and thinking of the home away yonder in the states, that I hadn't heard from in thirteen years, when a bluejay lit on that house, with an acorn in his mouth, and says, 'Hello, I reckon I've struck something.' When he spoke, the acorn dropped out of his mouth and rolled down the roof, of course, but he didn't care; his mind was all on the thing he had struck. It was a knot-hole in the roof. He cocked his head to one side, shut one eye and put the other one to the hole, like a 'possum looking down a jug; then he glanced up with his bright eyes, gave a wink or two with his wings —which signifies gratification, you understand,—and says, 'It looks like a hole, it's located like a hole,—blamed if I don't believe it *is* a hole!'

"Then he cocked his head down and took another look; he glances up perfectly joyful, this time; winks his wings and his tail both, and

195

says, 'Oh, no, this ain't no fat thing, I reckon! If I ain't in luck!—why
it's a perfectly elegant hole!' So he flew down and got that acorn, and
fetched it up and dropped it in, and was just tilting his head back,
with the heavenliest smile on his face, when all of a sudden he was
paralyzed into a listening attitude and that smile faded gradually out
of his countenance like breath off'n a razor, and the queerest look of
surprise took its place. Then he says, 'Why, I didn't hear it fall!' He
cocked his eye at the hole again, and took a long look; raised up and
shook his head; stepped around to the other side of the hole and took
another look from that side; shook his head again. He studied a while,
then he just went into the *de*tails—walked round and round the hole
and spied into it from every point of the compass. No use. Now he
took a thinking attitude on the comb of the roof and scratched the
back of his head with his right foot a minute, and finally says, 'Well,
it's too many for *me*, that's certain; must be a mighty long hole; however, I ain't got no time to fool around here, I got to 'tend to business;
I reckon it's all right—chance it, anyway.'

"So he flew off and fetched another acorn and dropped it in, and
tried to flirt his eye to the hole quick enough to see what become of it,
but he was too late. He held his eye there as much as a minute; then he
raised up and sighed, and says, 'Confound it, I don't seem to understand this thing, no way; however, I'll tackle her again.' He fetched
another acorn, and done his best to see what become of it, but he
couldn't. He says, 'Well, *I* never struck no such a hole as this before;
I'm of the opinion it's a totally new kind of a hole.' Then he begun to
get mad. He held in for a spell, walking up and down the comb of the
roof and shaking his head and muttering to himself; but his feelings
got the upper hand of him, presently, and he broke loose and cussed
himself black in the face. I never see a bird take on so about a little
thing. When he got through he walks to the hole and looks in again
for half a minute; then he says, 'Well, you're a long hole, and a deep
hole, and a mighty singular hole altogether—but I've started in to
fill you, and I'm d—d if I *don't* fill you, if it takes a hundred years!'

"And with that, away he went. You never see a bird work so since
you was born. He laid into his work like a nigger, and the way he
hove acorns into that hole for about two hours and a half was one of
the most exciting and astonishing spectacles I ever struck. He never
stopped to take a look any more—he just hove 'em in and went for
more. Well, at last he could hardly flop his wings, he was so tuckered
out. He comes a-drooping down, once more, sweating like an ice-
pitcher, drops his acorn in and says, '*Now* I guess I've got the bulge
on you by this time!' So he bent down for a look. If you'll believe me,
when his head come up again he was just pale with rage. He says, 'I've
shoveled acorns enough in there to keep the family thirty years, and if

I can see a sign of one of 'em I wish I may land in a museum with a belly full of sawdust in two minutes!'

"He just had strength enough to crawl up on to the comb and lean his back agin the chimbly, and then he collected his impressions and begun to free his mind. I see in a second that what I had mistook for profanity in the mines was only just the rudiments, as you may say.

"Another jay was going by, and heard him doing his devotions, and stops to inquire what was up. The sufferer told him the whole circumstance, and says, 'Now yonder's the hole, and if you don't believe me, go and look for yourself.' So this fellow went and looked, and comes back and says, 'How many did you say you put in there?' 'Not any less than two tons,' says the sufferer. The other jay went and looked again. He couldn't seem to make it out, so he raised a yell, and three more jays come. They all examined the hole, they all made the sufferer tell it over again, then they all discussed it, and got off as many leather-headed opinions about it as an average crowd of humans could have done.

"They called in more jays; then more and more till pretty soon this whole region 'peared to have a blue flush about it. There must have been five thousand of them; and such another jawing and disputing and ripping and cussing, you never heard. Every jay in the whole lot put his eye to the hole and delivered a more chuckle-headed opinion about the mystery than the jay that went there before him. They examined the house all over, too. The door was standing half open, and at last one old jay happened to go and light on it and look in. Of course, that knocked the mystery galley-west in a second. There lay the acorns, scattered all over the floor. He flopped his wings and raised a whoop. 'Come here!' he says, 'Come here, everybody; hang'd if this fool hasn't been trying to fill up a house with acorns!' They all came a-swooping down like a blue cloud, and as each fellow lit on the door and took a glance, the whole absurdity of the contract that that first jay had tackled hit him home and he fell over backwards suffocating with laughter, and the next jay took his place and done the same.

"Well, sir, they roosted around here on the housetop and the trees for an hour, and guffawed over that thing like human beings. It ain't any use to tell me a bluejay hasn't got a sense of humor, because I know better. And memory, too. They brought jays here from all over the United States to look down that hole, every summer for three years. Other birds, too. And they could all see the point, except an owl that come from Nova Scotia to visit the Yo Semite, and he took this thing in on his way back. He said he couldn't see anything funny in it. But then he was a good deal disappointed about Yo Semite, too."

Ab Yancey's bee-hunt[1]

A b Yancey's great bee-hunting yarn is still remembered in several different versions and variants. A man who knew Yancey very well indeed offered to tell me the tale "jest like I've heerd Ab tell it hisse'f a thousand times," and I noted it down as follows: "Wal, sir, my Gran'pap Paisley allus was a great feller t' bee-hunt, an' one Fall he was alinin' 'em way over yander t'other side o' Pappaw Cove. Seemed like thar was bees ever' place, morn he ever seen afore, an' th' fu'ther he follered 'em th' thicker they got. Finally he come to a place whar they was so dang many bees a-flyin' he couldn't see the sun scarcely, an' a-buzzin' so loud hit like t'deefened him. Most fellers would of tuck out, I reckon, but Gran'pap Paisley was a bee-hunter from who laid th' chunk, an' he was jest obleeged to find out whar all them bees was a-goin' to. He knowed in reason they warn't no tree in th' world big enough t' hive sich a swarm as that 'ar.

"Wal, sir, atter a while he come t' a great big bluff, an' he seen right off that's whar all them bees was a-usin' round. Th' hull dang cliff was jest plum black with bees, an' they was a-hangin' down in clusters forty foot long. They was beemartins thar from all over creation, a-ketchin' th' stragglers, an' dead bees four foot deep in th' creek bottom! Gran'pap he looked ever'thing over keerful, an' he figgered they must be anyhow two hundred million pound o' honey in that 'ar clift, an' maybe more. Th' hull dang bluff was jest *made* out o' comb honey, with a few rocks in it! But thar wasn't no way on Gawd's earth t' git th' dang stuff, fur as Gran'pap could figger. Nobody cain't smoke no beegum four hundred foot long an' a hunderd an' fifty foot high, an' it'd be as much as a feller's life was worth t' go a-projectin' round thar if them bees *warn't* smoked.

"Finally th' ol' man he went home an' told th' folks 'bout it, an' th' next day him an' th' boys come back an' snooped round thar some more, all of 'em a-studyin' how t' git that 'ar honey out o' th' bee-bluff. They pondered 'bout it all Winter, an' come Spring th' ol' man he figgered it out. First thing they done was t' build a new cabin right on top o' th' bluff, an' th' hull kit an' b'ilin' of 'em moved over thar—lock, stock, bar'l an' hound-dawgs. Th' boys they rid into town an' filed on th' place, so's t' git Guv'mint papers an' ever'thing. Th' fellers round th' court-house was all laughin' 'bout it—wanted t' know if they'd found a gold-mine over thar, or somethin'. Th' boys didn't

---

[1] Reprinted from *Ozark Mountain Folks* by Vance Randolph (New York: Vanguard Press; 1932), pp. 146–50. Copyright, 1932, by Vanguard Press, Inc.

git mad, though, jest grinned at 'em an' 'lowed maybe they had at that.

"Soon as they got th' fences up an' th' corn-patch broke an' planted they all went to work a-diggin' a well right on top o' th' honey-bluff. Ever'body 'lowed they had all went plumb ravin' crazy, 'cause thar was a good spring right back o' th' house, but th' folks never said nothin', jest kept right on a-diggin'. They dug an' they dug, a-buildin' windlasses an' a-pilin' up rock higher'n fodder-stacks. Hit was th' Gawd-awfullest job o' work ever saw in these parts. Them boys growed calluses on their hands big as walnuts, an' they all got kinder hump-backed from diggin'—some of 'em never did git over it. One mornin' when they'd got down 'bout sixty foot, a leetle trickle o' yeller come a-oozin' out under a rock! One o' th' boys seen it an' begun t' holler for Gran'pap. Th' ol' feller come down th' bucket-rope spry as a bitch-mink, an' soon as he seen th' stuff an' tasted it he sings out: 'We've struck honey, boys, an' th' job's done! Bail her out good, an' let her cl'ar up! Put a good lid on top, t'keep th' bugs out'n the well! An' when you'uns git that done, just go up an' set on th' gallery like a gentleman—ye won't have t' do ary 'nother lick o' work long as ye live!' An' they never did, neither.

"Naw, sir, th' Yanceys never done a lick o' work for two hull genera-tions—they *shore* didn't. Strained honey was sellin' for four cents a pound in them days, an' th' Yancey honey was th' best ever—strained through fifty feet o' rocks an' gravels, ever' drap of it. They jest put it up in bar'ls an' hauled it t' Springfield an' Fayetteville. . . . Th' Yanceys was th' richest family in th' hull state o' Arkansas them days, an' they jest 'bout run th' country, I tell you! They'd be a-runnin' it yit, I reckon, if it warn't for them ornery no-count Hammonses— Gawd damn 'em one an' all forever! You see, th' Yanceys got t' fightin' with th' Hammonses 'bout somethin' or other, an' atter two-three of 'em got kilt th' Hammons boys snuck over one night an' drapped more'n two hundred pound o' gunpowder down th' honey-well! Th' hull Hammons tribe mortgaged their farms t' git th' money t' buy that 'ar powder.

"Wal, sir, when they tetched fire t' that fuse hit jest blowed th' hull clift plumb off, an' scattered comb honey an' bee-bread all over Snake County! I reckon more'n a million ton o' honey fell slap-dab into the creek! . . . Hit ruint th' Yanceys forever, 'cause th' honey was gone an' th' market was plumb sp'ilt anyhow. For ten year atter that folks jest used the creek water for long sweetenin', an' a mill-pond six mile down th' valley tasted kinder sweet-like up till three-four year ago. Th' big clift is still known fur an' wide as Bee Bluff, though, an' th' ol' mill-pond whar th' honey was at is called Honey Lake t' this day!"

Animals are intelligent, that is the trouble. If all of them were notoriously and admittedly stupid, a whole great section of American folklore would have died a-borning, for the lack of a sympathetic audience is fatal. This group of stories contains nothing that is impossible, though some of it is a little strange. Really improbable animals have been herded into the next corral.

The bears' jubilee [1]

We have alluded to the unsociability of the bear; but it should be stated that there are occasionally times when they have their friendly gatherings, and assemble from all the surrounding country to exchange ideas, cultivate short-lived friendships, and have one grand jubilee. The Indians describe these meetings with becoming gravity, and ascribe to them all the intellectual character and importance which they give to their own "talks." The antics of the bear on these occasions are represented as exceedingly amusing; the young cubs are displayed before the visitors with due ceremony, their anxious mothers evidently very proud of their shining coats of black hair and promising strength. They are taken up and dandled with all care, and rocked to and fro, and also, for waywardness, have their ears severely boxed, and are otherwise disciplined into juvenile obedience. On the occasions of the grand dances, an obscure thicket is selected, the grass is beaten down, and protruding roots torn away. The old bears then form a circle, generally sitting upon their haunches, assuming most solemn and critical expressions. The performer meanwhile goes through his pantomime of bowing and prancing, evidently anxious to secure applause; presently a partner volunteers, and an old-fashioned minuet follows. The spectators the while keep time with their paws, and give no mean imitations of "patting Juba"; and warming with the excitement, they will all suddenly spring up and join in a general double-shuffle, the award of superiority being given to the last who, from inclination or positive exhaustion, quits the field. It is from these "backwoods assemblies" that the Indians profess to have learned their most

[1] From "Bears and Bear-Hunting," *Harper's New Monthly Magazine*, Vol. XI, p. 597 (June–November 1855).

difficult steps and most complicated dances; and to be able to perform like a bear is with them a compliment always desired, but one they seldom have the vanity to believe they truly deserve.

The bear's revenge[1]

D own at the Rhodes ranch at New Meadows the boys had caught a very young bear. The cub soon got on to all sorts of tricks until finally some one had the bright idea of teaching him how to box. He got so that every time anyone came around he'd get up on his hind legs and start biffing around. Once in awhile, when he got on one of his drunks, Sheepherder Bill would wake up to find himself out in the bed that had been built for the bear. Neither the bear nor Bill seemed to mind the other's presence much.

One day a big Tennessean came to the ranch. He was walking around the fields and happened to be standing by an irrigation ditch when he looked around and saw a bear coming at him. No one had warned him about the pet, and when the bear started scuffling with him the fellow really thought he meant business and started to fight for his life. He managed to get the cub down in the irrigation ditch and for more than an hour he worked in a vain endeavor to get the bear's head under water long enough to drown him. The bear finally squirmed away, got up, and trundled off toward home, but apparently he was not soon to forget the incident.

The next time Sheepherder Bill came to the ranch on his usual spree, and went to sleep in the bear's box, he awakened to find himself in the irrigation ditch with the cub doing his best to drown him. He was so stupefied from the effects of the liquor that only the efforts of the men who had come over to see what the cub was up to saved him from a watery grave.

The squirrel fleet[2]

A good story is told by an old lumberman, who, in the early days of steamboating on the Ohio river, contracted to deliver on board of steamboat one hundred thousand shingles at a "wood-land-

---

[1] From *Idaho Lore* (Federal Writers Project, Vardis Fisher, State Director; Caldwell, Idaho: Caxton Printers; 1939), p. 38.

[2] From N. E. Jones, M.D.: *The Squirrel Hunters of Ohio, or Glimpses of Pioneer Life* (Cincinnati: Robert Clarke Co.; 1898), pp. 168–70.

ing" of one of the river counties in Ohio. The shingles were stacked on the bank of the river ready for shipment. A few days after, the lumberman heard most of his "stuff" had been stolen, and it was probable it had gone to Pittsburg. On receiving this unwelcome news, he drove down to the river to look after the condition of things. Before he reached the place he found the woods alive with squirrels marching toward the river.

On his return the workmen asked what discoveries were made. The reply was, "The shingles never went to Pittsburg"; "they all went down the river, and it is useless to look in Pittsburg or any other place for them.". . . "I got to the river just in time to know all about it. You see, the squirrels are marching and crossing the river at that point; and the commanding general is not much on a swim, and he carried one of my shingles down to the water and rode over on it, and every colonel, captain, lieutenant and commissioned and non-commissioned officer did what they saw their general do, and finally the rank and file made a raid, and I got there just as an old squirrel came down to the water dragging a shingle, which he shoved into the water, jumped upon it, raised his brush for a sail and went over high and dry; and when near enough to the other shore leaped off and let his boat float down the stream. As soon as these observations were taken in, I went up on the high bank where the shingles had been stored, and found there was not a shingle left—they are down the river, gentlemen—down the river, sure."

This story receives a shadow of support from the learned and cautious Buffon, who observes: "Although the navigations of the grey squirrels seem almost incredible, they are attested by so many witnesses that we cannot deny the fact." And in a note on the subject says: "The grey squirrels frequently remove their place of residence, and it not unoften happens that not one can be seen one winter where they were in multitudes the year before; they go in large bodies, and when they want to cross a lake or river they seize a *piece of the bark of a birch or lime, and drawing it to the edge of the water, get upon it, and trust themselves to the hazard of the wind and waves, erecting their tails* to serve the purpose of *sails;* they sometimes form a fleet of three or four thousand, and if the wind proves too strong, a general shipwreck ensues . . . but if the winds are favorable they are certain to make their desired port."

Memoirs of the stable[1]

H orses, taking one with another, are supposed to be the stupidest
creatures (forgetting, of course, horse-lovers) within the confines
of our Christian civilization, but there are naturally some exceptions,
and they probably include the whole race of Shetland ponies. During
the interminable epoch stretching from my eleventh year to my fourteenth I was on confidential terms with such a pony, and came to have
a very high opinion of his sagacity. As the phrase ran in those days, he
was as sharp as a trap, and also excessively immoral. The last word, I
should say at once, I do not use in the Puritan or Freudian sense, for
Frank was a gelding; what I seek to convey is simply the idea that he
was also a cheat, a rogue and a scoundrel. Nearly all his waking hours
were given over to deceiving and afflicting my brother Charlie and me.
He bit us, he kicked us, he stepped on our toes, he crowded us against
the walls of his stall, and he sneezed in our faces, and in the intervals
he tried to alarm us by running away, or by playing sick or dead.
Nevertheless, we loved him, and mixed with our affection there was a
great deal of sincere admiration.

Where he was bred we never heard, and, boy-like, did not inquire.
One day in the Autumn of 1891 a couple of carpenters appeared in
Hollins street and began to throw up a miniature stable at the end of
the long backyard, and by the time they got the roof on Frank was in
it, along with a yellow go-cart, a tabloid buggy with fringe around its
top, a couple of sets of harness, and a saddle. It soon turned out that
there was not room enough in the stable for both the go-cart and the
buggy, so the buggy was moved to Reveille's livery-stable two blocks
away, where my father's horse John was in residence. Simultaneously,
a colored intern was brought in from the same place to instruct Charlie
and me in the principles of his art, for we were told that we were to
have the honor of caring for Frank. Inasmuch as we had been hanging
about stables since infancy, watching the blackamoors at their work,
this hint that we needed tutelage rather affronted us, but we were
so delighted by the privilege of becoming hostlers—the dream of every
American boy in that horsy age—that we let it pass, and only too soon
learned that there was a great deal more to servicing a Shetland pony
than could be picked up by watching blackamoors service full-grown
horses.

Charlie, I believe, got the first kick, but I got the first bite. It was

[1] Reprinted from *Heathen Days,* by H. L. Mencken (New York: Alfred A. Knopf;
1943), pp. 15–26, by permission of Alfred A. Knopf, Inc. Copyright 1941, 1942, 1943
by Alfred A. Knopf, Inc.

delivered with sly suddenness on the second morning after the intern from Reveille's had graduated me *cum laude* and gone back to his regular job. He had cautioned me that, in currying any sort of horse it was necessary to pay particular heed to the belly, for it tended to pick up contamination from the stall litter, and he had added the warning that the belly was a sensitive area, and must be tackled gently. I was gentle enough, goodness knows, but Frank, as I was soon to learn, objected to any sort of currying whatsoever, top or bottom, and so, as I stooped down to reach under his hull—he was only nine hands high at the withers—he fetched me a good nip in the seat of my pants. My reaction was that of a coiled spring of high tension, and it was thus hardly more than a split second before I was out in the yard, rubbing my backside with both hands. When I tell you that Frank laughed you will, of course, set me down as a nature-faker; all the same, I tell you that Frank laughed. I could see him through the window above his feed-trough, and there were all the indubitable signs —the head thrown back, the mouth open, the lips retracted, the teeth shining, the tears running down both cheeks. I could even hear a sound like a chuckle. Thereafter I never consciously exposed my caboose to him, but time and again he caught me unawares, and once he gave me a nip so severe that the scar remains to this day. Whenever I get to hospital—which is only too often in these later years—the sportive young doctors enter it upon their chart as a war wound.

Frank quickly developed a really marvelous technic of escape. He had a box-stall that, considering his size, was roomy, and Charlie and I kept it so clean that hostlers from all the other stables in the alley would drop in to admire it. There was a frame of soft red clay to ease his forefeet, and a large piece of rock-salt to entertain him on lazy afternoons. He got hearty meals of substantial horse-victuals three times a day, and in cold weather the water used to mix his mill-feed was always warm. Through the window above his trough he could look out into the yard, and a section of it about twenty feet square was fenced off to give him a paddock. In this paddock he was free to disport a couple of hours every day, save only when there was snow on the ground. But when he was in it he devoted most of his time to hanging his head over the paling-fence, lusting for the regions beyond. Just out of his reach was a peach tree, and beyond it a pear tree, both still young and tender. One fine spring day, with both trees burgeoning, he somehow cracked the puzzle of the catch on the paddock gate, and by the time he was discovered he had eaten all the bark off the peach tree, from the ground to a height of four feet. Charlie and I found it hard to blame him, for we liked the peach gum ourselves and often chewed it, flies and all, but my mother wept when the tree died, and the paddock gate was outfitted with an iron bar and two chains.

Frank never got through it again—that is, by his own effort. But one day, when a feeble-minded hired girl left it open, he was in the yard instantly and made a killing that still lives in the family tradition. Rather curiously, he did not molest the pear tree, but by the time he was chased back to his own ground he had devoured a bed of petunias, all my mother's best dahlias, the better part of a grape vine, and the whole of my father's mint patch. I have been told by eminent horse-lovers that horses never touch mint, but I am here dealing, not with a horse, but with a Shetland pony. Frank gradually acquired many other strange appetites—for example, for ice cream. Every time it was on tap in the house he would smell it, and begin to stamp and whinny, and in the end it became the custom to give him whatever happened to be left. Once, when the hired girl got salt into it and the whole batch was spoiled, he devoured all of it—probably a gallon and a half —and then drank two buckets of water. He also ate oranges (skin and all), bananas (spitting out the skin), grapes, asparagus and sauerkraut. One day Charlie tried him with a slab of rat trap cheese, but he refused it. Another day Charlie gave him a piece of plug tobacco wrapped in a cabbage leaf, but again without success. This last trick, in fact, offended him and he sought revenge at once. When he bit through the cabbage into the tobacco he gave a sudden and violent cough, and the plug hit Charlie in the eye.

When we were in the country in Summer Frank had my father's horse John for a stable-mate, and they got on together well enough, though it was plain to see that Frank regarded John as an idiot. This was a reasonable judgment, for John, who was a trotter, was actually very backward mentally, and could be easily scared. Whenever the two were in pasture together Frank would alarm John by bearing down upon him at a gallop, as if about to leap over him. This would set John to running away, and Frank would pursue him all over the pasture, whinnying and laughing. John himself could no more laugh than he could read and write. He was a tall slim sorrel with a long narrow head, and was so stupid that he even showed no pride in his speed, which was considerable. Life to him was a gloomy business, and he was often in the hands of horse-doctors. If there was a stone on the road he always picked it up, and when we were in the country and Charlie and I had charge of him we never bedded him down for the night without investigating his frogs. In the course of an average Summer we recovered at least twenty nails from them, not to mention burrs and splinters. Like most valetudinarians he lived to a great age. After my father's death we sold him to an animal show that had Winter quarters in Baltimore, and he spent his last years as a sort of companion to a herd of trained zebras. The zebras, I heard, had a lot of fun with him.

One night, an hour or so after midnight, there was a dreadful kicking and grunting in our stable in the country, and my father and Charlie and I turned out to inquire into it. We found John standing in the middle of his box-stall in a pitiable state of mind, his coat ruffled and his eyes staring. Frank, next door, was apparently sleeping soundly. We examined John from head to foot, but could find nothing wrong, so we contented ourselves with giving him a couple of random doses from his enormous armamentarium of medicine bottles, and talking to him in soothing tones. He seemed quite all right in the morning, and my father drove him to and from town, but that night there was another hullabaloo in the stable, and we had to turn out again. On the day following John was put to grass and Charlie and I went for a colored horse-doctor in Cross Keys, a nearby village. He advised us to throw away all of John's medicines, and prescribed instead a mild course of condition powders, with a handful of flaxseed once a day. This was begun instantly, but that night the same dreadful noises came from the stable, and again the night following, and again the night after that, and so on for a week. Two or three other horse-doctors were called in during that time, but they were all baffled, and John took to looking seedy and even mangy. Meanwhile, my father began to suffer seriously from the interruptions to his sleep, and talked wildly of having the poor horse shot and his carcass sent to a glue-factory. Also he began to discover unpleasant weaknesses in his old friend Herman Ellis, from whom John had been bought. Ellis, hitherto, had been held up to Charlie and me as a model, but now it appeared that he drank too much, kept two sets of books, was a Methodist, and ought to be expelled from the Freemasons.

Charlie and I, talking over the business at length, came to the conclusion eventually that there must be more to it than met the eye, and so decided to keep watch at the stable. There was already floating through our minds, I think, some suspicion of Frank, for we were at pains to prevent him learning what we were up to. At our bedtime we sneaked into the carriage house on tiptoe, and there made ourselves bunks in the family dayton-wagon. We were soon sound asleep, but at the usual time we were aroused by a great clomping and banging in the stalls adjoining, and turned out to take a stealthy look. It was a moonlight night, and enough of the gentle glare was filtering into the stable to give us an excellent view. What we saw scarcely surprised us. All the uproar, we discovered, was being made by Frank, not by John. Frank was having a whale of a time flinging his heels against the sides of his stall. The noise plainly delighted him, and he was laughing gaily. Presently poor John, waking in alarm, leaped to his feet and began to tremble. At this Frank gave a couple of final clouts, and then lay down calmly and went to sleep—or, at all events, appeared to. But

206

John, trying with his limp mind to make out what was afoot, kept on trembling, and was, in fact, still half scared to death when we announced our presence and tried to comfort him.

My father had arrived by this time, his slippers flapping, his suspenders hanging loose and blood in his eye, and we soon made him understand what had happened. His only comment was "Well, I'll be durned!" repeated twenty or thirty times. We soon had a bridle on Frank, with a strap rigged from it to his left hind leg, and if he tried any more kicking that night he knocked himself down, which was certainly no more than he deserved. But we heard no more noise, nor was there any the next night, or the next, or the next. After a week we removed the strap, and then sat up again to see what would happen. But nothing happened, for Frank had learned his lesson. At some time or other while the strap was on, I suppose, he had tried a kick—and gone head over heels in his stall. He was, as I have said, a smart fellow, and there was never any need to teach him the same thing twice. Thereafter, until the end of the Summer, he let poor John sleep in peace. My father fired all the horse-doctors, white and black, and threw out all their remedies. John recovered quickly, and a little while later did a mile on the Pimlico road in 2.17½—not a bad record, for he was pulling a steel-tired buggy with my father and me in it, and the road was far from level.

In that same stable, the next Summer, Frank indulged himself in a jape which came near costing him his life. To recount it I must describe briefly the lay-out of the place. He inhabited a box-stall with a low wall, and in that wall was a door fastened by a movable wooden cleat. He was in the habit of hanging his head over the door, and drooling lubriciously, while Charlie and I were preparing his feed. This feed came down from the hayloft through a chute that emptied into a large wooden trough, and he often saw us start the feed by pulling out a paddle in the chute. One night either Charlie or I neglected to fasten the door of his stall, and he was presently at large. To his bright mind, of course, the paddle was easy. Out it came, and down poured an avalanche of oats—a bushel, two bushels, and so on to eight or ten. It filled the trough and spilled over to the floor, but Frank was still young and full of ambition, and he buckled down to eat it all.

When Charlie and I found him in the morning he was swelled to the diameter of a wash-tub, his eyes were leaden, his tongue was hanging out dismally, peppered with oats that he had failed to get down. "The staggers!" exclaimed Charlie, who had become, by that time, an eager but bad amateur horse-doctor. "He is about to bust! There is only one cure. We must run him until it works off." So we squeezed poor Frank between the shafts of the go-cart, leaped in, gave him the whip, and were off. Twice, getting down our hilly road to the pike, he sank to his fore-knees, but both times we got him up, and thereafter, for three hours, we flogged him on. It was a laborious and painful business, and for once in his life Frank failed to laugh at his own joke. Instead, he heaved and panted as if every next breath were to be his last. We could hear his liver and lights rumbling as we forced him on. We were so full of sympathy for him that we quite forgot his burglary, but Charlie insisted that we had to be relentless, and so we were. It was nearing noon when we got back to the stable, and decided to call it a day. Frank drank a bucket of water, stumbled into his stall, and fell headlong in the straw. We let him lie there all afternoon, and all of the night following, and for three days thereafter we kept him on a strict diet of condition powders and Glauber's salt.

The bloating that disfigured him, when it began to go down at last, did not stop at normalcy, but continued until he was as thin as a dying mule, and that thinness persisted for weeks. There came with it, perhaps not unnaturally, a marked distaste for oats. His old voluptuous delight in them was simply gone. He would eat them if nothing else offered, but he never really enjoyed them again. For a year, at least, we might have made him free of a feed-trough full of them without tempting him. What John thought of the episode we could never find out. My guess is that he was too dumb to make anything of it.

From Maine to Idaho, from the Adirondacks to Arkansas, unlikely creatures crawl, prowl, whine, and roar through the jungle of America's imagination. They are native, no matter what analogies may be found. The Swan Valley monster, for example, is not only older than the Loch Ness monster, he is bigger and more terrifying and, let's say it, better.

If it be questioned whether Uncle Heber's flytrap belongs to the animal kingdom, that, of course, is just the point, and an uncanny one too. And if it be said that the tar-baby story was meant for children, that is indubitable, but it was the grown-ups who took it so warmly and immediately to their hearts that it has been a miniature American classic for more than half a century.

The sidehill-gouger, whose legs are shorter on one side than on the other, is not peculiar to the Adirondacks, but may be found wherever the American countryside is sufficiently hilly. As for the Guyascutus, he was probably born in Boston, but certainly acclimated in Oregon, Arkansas, and elsewhere.[1]

No ordinary bull[2]

O scar was no ordinary bull, but had several unusual escapades to his credit. Some might have been apocryphal, but mostly they were like the time he charged the Ladies' Farm Bureau picnic and ate one hundred twenty-seven cream cheese and olive sandwiches. Another time he was being used as a demonstrator in a safety bull pen invented by a neighbor, and before a crowd of seven hundred he proved the pen was far from safe. He also proved that seven hundred men and women can't all get up in the same pear tree.

The time he telephoned Aunt Hulda in Cleveland stands out as his

---

[1] The curious may read the history of his wanderings and transformations in an article by B. J. Whiting in the *Southern Folklore Quarterly* for December 1944, pp. 251–75.

[2] From John Gould: *Farmer Takes a Wife* (New York: William Morrow & Co.; [1945]), pp. 5–7. Copyright 1945 by John Gould; by permission of William Morrow & Co., Inc.

finest achievement. Aunt Hulda Banter, then living in Cleveland, was about to observe her eighty-eighth birthday anniversary, and her only child, Mrs. Matthew Nute (our neighbor), was minded to telephone congratulations. Mrs. Nute had finished churning and was wiping her hands prior to putting in the call. Everyone for miles around was on the Farmers' Line in those days, so she cranked for Central and yelled, "Now git off'n the line, everybody; I'm calling long distance."

Central took the number, and Mrs. Nute heard it relayed. She mused on what she would say to her mother. With half-closed eyes she stared vacantly at the wallpaper and weighed this phrase against that.

While she was waiting the connection, Oscar moved toward the house. He had already torn down his stanchion, put the hired man up on the scafflings, and pulled up half the cabbages in the kitchen garden. He bounded into the kitchen and shoved one foot through the cane bottom of the Boston rocker. This commotion brought Mrs. Nute from her reverie and sent her headlong through the sitting room to round up a posse.

Oscar limped, rocker and all, to the telephone. He smelled at the dangling receiver and ran his tongue into the mouthpiece. He did not know, of course, that the operators had performed their duties, that Aunt Hulda was excitedly holding her receiver to her ear, and that the Cleveland operator was intoning sweetly, "Here is your party; go ahead—please!"

Oscar didn't know that. But he might just as well. He laid back his ears, humped up his back, sucked in a torrent of wind, rolled his eyes, and blatted so the house shook. He then kicked the rocking chair into the pantry, knocked over a crock of buttermilk, swished a pan of cookies off the table with his tail, and went back to the kitchen garden, where he was presently retrieved.

To this day Aunt Hulda believes she was struck by lightning.

The Swan Valley monster[1]

On August 22, 1868, I wuz crossin' the river at Olds Ferry when I seen somethin' stickin' outa the water. It pears tuh be alive, fur it don't jist drift with the current but keeps a-movin' this way an that, an they's big ripples all around it. Purty soon it comes nearer an I see somethin' like a elephant's trunk shootin' up, and the dang thing starts tuh spoutin' water—then somethin' comes tuh the surface that looks like the head uv a snake, but it's ez big ez a washtub, only flat-

---

[1] From *Idaho Lore* (Federal Writers Project, Vardis Fisher, State Director; Caldwell, Idaho: Caxton Printers; 1939), pp. 104–6.

like an hez that gol-darned horn a-stickin' up out uv it an hez long
black whiskers at the sides uv its face.

By that time I wuz on the other side so I whips up my horse an
rides up the side uv the hill where I cud git a good sight uv it. I gits
off my horse an ties him tuh a quakin' asp behind some brush an then
I watches the thing. It's swimmin' towards the bank. Purty soon it gits
there an heaves itself outa the water an starts slitherin' up the hill in
my direction—an say, yuh never smelt such a stink in all your life! My
horse starts a-snortin' an a-rarin', an breaks loose an lights out through
the timber. An all the time that stinkin' reptile is gittin' closter tuh
me. I make out it's about twenty feet long, an outside uv that horn
that keeps shootin' up an down out uv its head, and the whiskers, an
a pair uv big fins, er wings, er whatever they is, all shiny-like in the
sun, that comes outa the sides uv its neck, it looks down tuh the middle
like a big snake, ez big around ez a calf—uv a kinda greenish-yaller
color with red an black spots on it. An then all uv a suddint right then
it pears tuh turn intuh a fish, with scales ez big ez yer hand, all colors
uv the rainbow, shinin' like big pieces uv colored glass in the sun—an
then all the shinin' peters out an all the rest uv it is jist a grayish
colored horny tail, like a big lizard's er mebbe a crocodile's—an all
the way from where that doggone horn kep shootin' up an down on its
head clear down tuh the tail they's a line of shiny black spines with a
hook on the end uv 'em like a porcupine's.

It keeps a-comin' closter an closter to where I'm a-standin' with my
rifle cocked and the closter it come, the worst it stunk. I'm feelin' purty
sick but I sez tuh myself no sech critter ez that oughta be let tuh live.
An I gits a draw on it and lets it have a slug in the eye. It gives a beller
an raises up on its tail twenty feet high an starts fer me a-hissin' an
a-snarlin'. Its mouth is open a foot wide showin' fangs ten inches long
an a red forked tongue that keeps a-dartin' in an out a-spurtin' green
pizen. I lets it heve another slug in its yaller belly—an it drops an
thrashes around on the ground a-hissin' an a-snarlin' an a-bellerin'
somethin' awful, tearin' up the earth, an knockin' down brush an trees,
an smashin' everythin' around it.

Bye an bye it's still, an I goes tuh take a look. It's a-layin' on its
back an I see it's got twelve short legs a-growin' out uv its belly; the
first pair, next tuh the tail, hez hoofs on 'em, the next pair hez long
claws, ez sharp ez razors, an the next hoofs agin, then two pairs uv
claws, an the last below the fins, er wings, er whatever they is, is hoofs
agin. An everywhere I see, they's black patches where it's spit pizen, an
everythin' it's teched is a-witherin' an a-dyin'—trees an bushes an grass
an everythin'.

Well, I goes tuh git me some kind uv a rig tuh take the critter tuh
town in. I calculate tuh have it stuffed an show it at the fair fer so

much a head, an mebbe make a little money off'n it. I gits a team an a dead-ax wagon and six fellers tuh help me haul it down tuh the wagon an load it, fer we can't drive right up tuh where it is on accounta the timber. I tell 'em tuh wear gloves an I takes an old tarp along tuh wrap around the speciment so's when we handle it we won't none uv us git pizened.

When we're a hundred yards or so from the place, we begins tuh smell that stink agin an the horses ack skeered. I'm a-drivin' an I try tuh quiet 'em down but they keep on a-snortin' an a-rarin' an two uv the other fellers has tuh git out an hold 'em down but we can't do nothin' with 'em so I got tuh back a ways till I find a place tuh turn an then I turns round an heads 'em the other way. We leave one feller there with the team an the rest uv us goes on.

It tain't no pleasant trip fer the nearer we git the worse the atmosphere gits. I don't know how I looked but the other fellers hez aholda their noses an wuz lookin' purty pale around the gills. One feller got sick an didn't come no further.

When we gits there we see where the ground is all tore up, an the brush all trampled down fer fifty foot, an quakin' asps an cottonwoods knocked down an a-layin' on the ground—an everythin' the pizen hit wuz dead. But nary sight uv the critter. But we finds its trail along the flattened grass an busted brush, an it leads down an smack intuh the river.

We waited round fer the rest uv the day an half the town wuz there with us watchin' the river, fer they'd heard about the strange critter; but nobody sees hide nor hair uv it, ner spout ner tail.

They say a snake don't die till sundown. I dunno what the derned thing wuz, but mebbe it went down in the water tuh die—or mebbe it *didn't* die.

Boy an man, I've hunted an trapped an fished all over the state fer nigh ontuh seventy-five year, I've ketched some purty queer fish by hook an trap, but I ain't never seen nothin' to compare with that speciment.

Powerful changed[1]

W ell, you know when de Flood was and dey had two of everything in de ark—well, Ole Nora didn't take on no trees, so de woodpecker set 'round and set 'round for a week or so then he felt like he just had to peck himself some wood. So he begin to peck on de Ark.

---

[1] From Zora Neale Hurston: *Mules and Men*, Copyright, 1934, by Zora Neale Hurston, published by J. B. Lippincott Company, pp. 137–41.

Ole Nora come to him and tole him, "Don't peck on de Ark. If you peck a hole in it, we'll all drown."

Woodpecker says, "But Ah'm hungry for some wood to peck."

Ole Nora says, "Ah don't keer how hongry you gits don't you peck on dis ark no mo. You want to drown everybody and everything?"

So de woodpecker would sneak 'round behind Ole Nora's back and peck every chance he got. He'd hide hisself way down in de hold where he thought nobody could find him and peck and peck. So one day Ole Nora come caught him at it. He never opened his mouth to dat woodpecker. He just hauled off and give dat peckerwood a cold head-whipping wid a sledge hammer, and dat's why a peckerwood got a red head today—'cause Ole Nora bloodied it wid dat hammer. Dat's how come Ah feel like shootin' every one of 'em Ah see. Tryin' to drown *me* before Ah was born.

"A whole lot went on on dat ole Ark," Larkins White commented. "Dat's where de possum lost de hair off his tail."

"Now don't you tell me no possum ever had no hair on dat slick tail of his'n," said Black Baby, " 'cause Ah know better."

Yes, he did have hair on his tail one time. Yes, indeed. De possum had a bushy tail wid long silk hair on it. Why, it useter be one of de prettiest sights you ever seen. De possum struttin' 'round wid his great big ole plumey tail. Dat was 'way back in de olden times before de big flood.

But de possum was lazy—jus' like he is today. He sleep too much. You see Ole Nora had a son name Ham and he loved to be playin' music all de time. He had a banjo and a fiddle and maybe a guitar too. But de rain come up so sudden he didn't have time to put 'em on de ark. So when rain kept comin' down he fretted a lot 'cause he didn't have nothin' to play. So he found a ole cigar box and made hisself a banjo, but he didn't have no strings for it. So he seen de possum stretched out sleeping wid his tail all spread 'round. So Ham slipped up and shaved de possum's tail and made de strings for his banjo out de hairs. When dat possum woke up from his nap, Ham was playin' his tail hairs down to de bricks and dat's why de possum ain't got no hair on his tail today. Losin' his pretty tail sorta broke de possum's spirit too. He ain't never been de same since. Dat's how come he always actin' shame-faced. He know his tail ain't whut it useter be; and de possum feel mighty bad about it.

"A lot of things ain't whut they useter be," observed Jim Presley. "Now take de 'gator for instance. He been changed 'round powerful since he been made."

"Yeah," cut in Eugene Oliver, "He useter have a nice tongue so he could talk like a nat'chal man, but Brer Dog caused de 'gator to lose his tongue, and dat's how come he hate de dog today."

213

"Brer 'Gator didn't fall out wid Brer Dog 'bout no tongue," retorted Presley.

Brer Dog done de 'gator a dirty trick 'bout his mouth. You know God made de dog and de 'gator without no mouth. So they seen everybody else had a mouth so they made it up to git theirselves a mouth like de other varmints. So they agreed to cut one 'nothers' mouth, and each one said dat when de other one tole 'em to stop cuttin' they would. So Brer Dog got his mouth first. Brer 'Gator took de razor and cut. Brer Dog tole him, "Stop," which he did. Den Brer Dog took de razor and begin to cut Brer 'Gator a mouth. When his mouth was as big as he wanted it, Brer 'Gator says, "Stop, Brer Dog. Dat'll do, I thank you, please." But Brer Dog kept right on cuttin' till he ruint Brer 'Gator's face. Brer 'Gator was a very handsome gent'man befo' Brer Dog done him that a way, and everytime he look in de lookin' glass he cry like a baby over de disfiggerment of his face. And dat's how come de 'gator hate de dog.

"My people, my people," lamented Oliver. "They just will talk whut they don't know."

"Go on Oliver."

De 'gator didn't fall out wid de dog 'bout no mouth cuttin' scrape. You know all de animals was havin' a ball down in de pine woods, and so they all chipped in for refreshments and then they didn't have no music for de dance. So all de animals what could 'greed to furnish music. So de dog said he'd be de trumpet in de band, and de horse and de frog and de mockin' bird and all said they'd be there an help out all they could. But they didn't have no bass drum, till somebody said, "Whut's de matter wid Brer 'Gator, why don't he play bass drum for us?" Dey called Brer 'Gator but he wasn't at de meetin' so de varmints deppitized Brer Dog to go call on Brer 'Gator and see if he wouldn't furnish de drum music for de dance. Which he did.

"Good evenin', Brer 'Gator."

"My compliments, Brer Dog, how you makin' out? Ah'm always glad when folks visit me. Whut you want?"

"Well Brer 'Gator, de varmints is holdin' a big convention tonight in de piney woods and we want you to furnish us a little bit of yo' drum music."

"It's like this, Brer Dog, tell de other animals dat Ah'm mighty proud they wants me and de compliments run all over me, but my wife is po'ly and my chillun is down sick. But Ah'll lend you my drum if you know anybody kin play it, and know how to take keer of it too!"

"Oh, Ah'll do *dat*, Brer 'Gator. You just put in in my keer. You don't have to worry 'bout dat atall."

So de dog took Brer 'Gator's tongue to de ball dat night and they beat it for a drum. De varmints lakted de bass drum so well till they didn't play nothin' else hardly. So by daybreak it was wore clean out. Brer Dog didn't want to go tell Brer 'Gator they had done wore his tongue out so he hid from Brer 'Gator. Course de 'gator don't like it 'bout his tongue so he's de sworn enemy of de dog.

Uncle Heber's flytrap [1]

There ain't no question 'bout my ole Uncle Heber being the goldurnest laziest man in these parts, I reckon. Spent his full life trying to hatch up new ways of gitting outen work. Lots of folks 'cused him of shirking his dooties, and when he didn't make no comeback they said he didn't have no shame even, but I reckon the truth is he jes didn't have no energy to make argyment.

He never took no wife 'cause he was too lazy to go courting, and doing his own housekeeping like he done, he jes nacherly let his place go to rack and ruin. The shingles of his house all blowed off, and part of the roof caved in. Cracks come in the walls, and it rained so hard that ever'thing in the house was wet. Uncle Heber stuck it out until the cracks got so big that the wind'd come in and blow the civers offen his bed. He caught cold and almost died 'cause he was too lazy to sneeze, even. At last the house sorta give up and caved in, and then even Uncle Heber knowed he'd got to move sommers else.

Feller told him 'bout a little island, eight mile up Brice's Crick, what nobody claimed, and Uncle Heber jes moved on up there. Was too lazy to explore it first, jes put his stuff together in a duffel bag, called his dog, and off he set.

The ground on that island was the richest, I reckon, anywhere could be found. No crops had ever been growed on it, and it was made up of silt washed up from the crick. Uncle Heber was in the best piece of luck anybody ever heerd of, I reckon. All he had to do was push a stick in the ground, and goldurn if it didn't take root and grow. On the island was enormous trees of all kinds, some of 'em as thick in the trunk as a house. They was apple trees with apples as big as punkins, and persimmon trees with persimmons as big as your head and sour as an old maid schoolteacher's mouth. The catfish in the crick was as big as alligators. Only trouble was that ever'thing else was in perportion. The good things was the bestest, but the bad things was the worstest anybody ever heerd tell of.

Uncle Heber sure was in clover. He found a big holler tree what he makes into a house, and there's plenty of fruit and fish and ever'thing he needs. He had brung along his old clay pipe and some fine-cut backer, and of course when he filled his pipe he spilt some backer and jes let it lay. Well, the backer took roots and growed up into the biggest and strongest backer leaves anybody ever heerd of.

He figgered out a good way to catch catfish and not tire hisself out. He'd balance his pole on a forked stick, and put a rock on the limb of a tree jes over the shore end of the pole. On the rock he tied a string. Then in the limb of the tree he rigged up a sharp knife atween two tater graters. He'd stretch hisself out on the crick bank, puffing on his pipe and cogerate hisself how to cut down on his work. When he sees a nibble on the fishline, he pulls the string. The rock falls off on the end of the pole. This jerks the fish outen the water, 'cross the knife which guts it, and through the tater graters what takes off the scales. He didn't bother 'bout the heads and tails, jes cooked the fish thataway and left the rest for his dog.

Uncle Heber'd lost all his teeth when he was a young feller, 'cause he was too lazy to chew his food, I reckon, but he got 'round that all right. He traded a man outen a set of store teeth and then rigged up some clockwork to make the teeth champ up and down. Uncle Heber'd wind up the clockwork and put them in his mouth and let his jaw hang loose. Then he'd feed in his rations and the teeth'd chew it up for him. He used to keep the teeth in his hip pocket, but oncet they got started running in his pocket and bit a hunk outen Uncle Heber, and after that he kept 'em out on the table where he could see 'em.

Oncet he was laying on his back 'longside his fishpole on the crick bank, smoking his pipe and figgering how he was getting tired of catfish and wanted some fresh meat and how he could get some meat without trubble, when a big idee hit him. He 'membered 'bout a little plant he'd seen down near Wilmin'ton what folks call the Venus flytrap and this plant catches flies and little frogs. He figgered that in his fertile land mebbe one of them flytraps'd grow big enough to trap him some game.

After worrying 'bout it two or three months, he got up enough energy to push his raft acrost the crick, walk to the road, and pick up a ride to Wilmin'ton. He got a Venus plant and took it back to his island and planted it in a clear space.

In no time atall that plant begin to grow, and Uncle Heber see he had figgered proper and correct and the plant is going to be as big as a live-oak tree. When the Venus plant was six foot high, it caught a rabbit one night. In the morning Uncle Heber see the jaws of the trap shet tight and a rabbit tail sticking out. He figgered and figgered how to git the rabbit out and fin'ly he hit on it. I be goldurn if he didn't light up his pipe with that strong backer and blow at the Venus trap. The plant got real white and began to shiver and opened up its trap and let the rabbit drop out.

Uncle Heber figgered this was the best luck of all. The Venus plant kept on catching him game, most every night, and in a few months it was big enough to catch a deer or a bear. Uncle Heber had so much game he didn't bother to fish no more, jes eat his fill on game. This went on for quite a spell, and Uncle Heber was sitting purty and the only thing he was worrying 'bout was how to find a easy way to dress his game.

Then late one night he was woke up by a awful yammering going on outside. He got up and crawled outen his holler tree, and it was bright moonlight, and he sees his dog chasing a big skunk 'round the Venus tree. The dog was right behind the skunk, but couldn't quite catch it. All a-sudden the tree reaches out one of its traps and grobs up the skunk and the dog in one gulp.

Now Uncle Heber thunk a lot of his dog. It was his onliest friend, and the only thing he could talk to, and he ruther have 'most anything happen to him 'cept lose his dog. So he runs back to his tree house to fetch his pipe so he can blow smoke on the trap and make it open up.

But I reckon that skunk was too goldurn potent for the Venus trap. When Uncle Heber come up, the Venus tree is shaking all over. It shake back and forth and dip up and down. Big gobs of sticky sap, like 'lasses, come oozing out and run down on the ground. First thing Uncle Heber knowed one of the traps dip down and grob him up entire.

The Venus tree keeps on shaking like it's sick to its stummick. Then it gives a powerful lunge and tore itself up by the roots and landed smack in the middle of the crick.

Iffen it hadn't been that Uncle Heber was smoking his pipe when the trap grobbed him he'd a-been a goner, I reckon. The Venus tree started down stream with him in one trap and the dog and the skunk in 'nother, and he jes puffed up a couple good puffs of that pipe and the Venus tree wilted right down in the water and opened up its traps, wide open. Uncle Heber landed in the water, and the skunk and the dog landed in the water, and the three struck off for shore. Uncle Heber smelt the skunk, and the skunk smelt Uncle Heber, and the skunk jes turned 'round and jumped back in the Venus trap.

Uncle Heber was a changed man after that. He moved to town and got a job in a livery stable, and he give up smoking. Said he couldn't stand that sissy stuff they sold in town and called it backer.

The wonderful tar-baby story[1]

"Didn't the fox *never* catch the rabbit, Uncle Remus?" asked the little boy the next evening.

"He come mighty nigh it, honey, sho's you bawn—Brer Fox did. One day atter Brer Rabbit fool 'im wid dat calamus root, Brer Fox went ter wuk en got 'im some tar, en mix it wid some turkentime, en fix up a contrapshun wat he call a Tar-Baby, en he tuk dish yer Tar-Baby en he sot 'er in de big road, en den he lay off in de bushes fer ter see wat de news wuz gwineter be. En he didn't hatter wait long, nudder, kaze bimeby here come Brer Rabbit pacin' down de road—lippity-clippity, clippity-lippity—dez ez sassy ez a jay-bird. Brer Fox, he lay low. Brer Rabbit come prancin' 'long twel he spy de Tar-Baby, en den he fotch up on his behime legs like he wuz 'stonished. De Tar-Baby, she sot dar, she did, en Brer Fox, he lay low.

" 'Mornin'!' sez Brer Rabbit, sezee—'nice wedder dis mawnin',' sezee.

"Tar-Baby ain't sayin' nuthin', en Brer Fox, he lay low.

" 'How duz yo' sym'tums seem ter segashuate?" sez Brer Rabbit, sezee.

"Brer Fox, he wink his eye slow, en lay low, en de Tar-Baby, she ain't sayin' nuthin'.

" 'How you come on, den? Is you deaf?' sez Brer Rabbit, sezee. 'Kaze if you is, I kin holler louder,' sezee.

"Tar-Baby stay still, en Brer Fox, he lay low.

" 'Youer stuck up, dat's wat you is,' says Brer Rabbit, sezee, 'en I'm gwineter kyore you, dat's w'at I'm a gwineter do,' sezee.

"Brer Fox, he sorter chuckle in his stummuck, he did, but Tar-Baby ain't sayin' nuthin'.

" 'I'm gwineter larn you howter talk ter 'specttubble fokes ef hit's de las' ack,' sez Brer Rabbit, sezee. 'Ef you don't take off dat hat en tell me howdy, I'm gwineter bus' you wide open,' sezee.

"Tar-Baby stay still, en Brer Fox, he lay low.

"Brer Rabbit keep on axin' 'im, en de Tar-Baby, she keep on sayin' nuthin', twel presently Brer Rabbit draw back wid his fis', he did, en blip he tuck 'er side er de head. Right dar's whar he broke his merlasses jug. His fis' stuck, en he can't pull loose. De tar hilt 'im. But Tar-Baby, she stay still, en Brer Fox, he lay low.

" 'Ef you don't lemme loose, I'll knock you agin,' sez Brer Rabbit,

[1] From Joel Chandler Harris: *Uncle Remus: His Songs and His Sayings; The Folk-Lore of the Old Plantation* (New York: D. Appleton & Co.; 1888), pp. 23-5.

sezee, en wid dat he fotch 'er a wipe wid de udder hand, en dat stuck. Tar-Baby, she ain't sayin' nuthin', en Brer Fox, he lay low.

" 'Tu'n me loose, fo' I kick de natal stuffin' outen you,' sez Brer Rabbit, sezee, but de Tar-Baby, she ain't sayin' nuthin'. She des hilt on, en de Brer Rabbit lose de use er his feet in de same way. Brer Fox, he lay low. Den Brer Rabbit squall out dat ef de Tar-Baby don't tu'n 'im loose he butt 'er cranksided. And den he butted, en his head got stuck. Den Brer Fox, he sa'ntered fort', lookin' des ez innercent ez wunner yo' mammy's mockin'-birds.

" 'Howdy, Brer Rabbit,' sez Brer Fox, sezee. 'You look sorter stuck up dis mawnin', sezee, en den he rolled on de groun', en laft twel he couldn't laff no mo'. 'I speck you'll take dinner wid me dis time, Brer Rabbit, I done laid in some calamus root, en I ain't gwineter take no skuse,' sez Brer Fox, sezee."

Here Uncle Remus paused, and drew a two-pound yam out of the ashes.

"Did the fox eat the rabbit?" asked the little boy to whom the story had been told.

"Dat's all de fur de tale goes," replied the old man. "He mout, en den agin he moutent. Some say Jedge B'ar come 'long en loosed 'im— some say he didn't. I hear Miss Sally callin'. You better run 'long."

Arkansaw hogs

A mong improbable animals the Arkansaw hog ranks high. The clas- sical description of him seems to have appeared in a pamphlet, now rare, that was published at Chicago in 1904. J. R. Masterson [1] de- scribes it in his *Tall Tales of Arkansaw*. His description, and a quota- tion that he gives, are as follows: [2]

Three Years in Arkansas is a paper-bound pamphlet, the yellow cover of which is decorated with an engraving of a saw-backed hog. About its author, Marion Hughes, we know little more than we can learn from his books. He was a native of Pike County, Indiana, where he was born about 1855 on a little backwoods farm. He "never went to school," he tells us, "only a little in the fall after the farm work was dun." In 1879 he began five years of farming in Nebraska, where later

[1] James R. Masterson: *Tall Tales of Arkansaw* (Boston: Chapman & Grimes; 1942).
[2] P. 96.

he raised cattle and ran a hotel. In 1889 he went to Rock Springs, Wyoming, and next to Guthrie, Oklahoma, supporting himself as hotel-keeper, carpenter, lawyer, and proprietor of a second-hand store. During the 1890's he passed three years in the hills of southwestern Arkansas, in Sevier and Polk Counties. By 1904 (when he was living at Muskogee) he had removed forty-eight times; and later he did so at least twice again—to Stillwater and to Oklahoma City.

[1] From Hughes's book we may satisfy our curiosity about the hogs of Arkansas. Wolves and bears, we are informed, would eat any Poland China, Berkshire, Chester White, or Jersey Red, "but a wolf or bear can't catch a native hog, and if it did the hog would whip it in a fair fight." The native hogs include ten varieties. (1) The razorback must be shot at sideways; to shoot at it endways would be like aiming at the end of a shingle. (2) The hazel splinter, which runs wild in the mountains west of Hot Springs, has a nose so sharp that when it strikes a bush it will split a twig. It is like the razorback except that it grows to be very large. "I saw one," says Hughes, "that dressed fourteen pounds with its head on, and six and a half with its head cut off." (3) The fish hog sits on the bank of a river or on a log in a swamp, like a cat watching for a mouse; it dives into the water and almost always comes out with a fish. "They dress them," we are told, "like a bullfrog —save the hind legs and throw the rest away." (4) The center breed is as long from the ears to the end of the tail as from the ears to the end of the nose. (5) The steelyard hog, when caught, is held up by the ears. If the head goes down and the tail flies up, the hog is released to grow for another year. (6) The tryo hog, as small and active as a cat, lives mostly on bugs and flies. They are called Tryo hogs (says our informant) because they always go three in a group when out far away or in search of food, when they come to a small flat rock one will lie down for the chunk; number two will put his nose under the rock and over the one that is lying down and then suddenly jerk up his legs and pry up the rock, and number three is ready to jump under and catch the bug or worm that may be under the rock. One tryo hog may be large enough to season a pot of beans. (7) Handspiked hogs in droves lift up rail fences with their sharp snouts and go into and out of cornfields at will. (8) A stone hog is distinguished by a stone tied to the tail, since its head overbalances its rear. (9) Saw hogs are "the original Arkansaw saw mills." They catch an old and poor sow, buckle a strap on her nose to keep her from biting their legs, then they turn her over on her back across a log, one man at each end ahold of her legs for handles, one boy ahold of her ears and one ahold of her tail, to help pull her through. When they get started you can hear the bark and

---

[1] Ibid., pp. 100–1.

splinters flying and the old sow squeeling for three miles. (10) The chicken-footed hog roosts in trees but does not lay eggs.

Adirondack fauna[1]

Stranger creatures than rattlers have been seen in our mountains. Again and again the sea-serpent has been reported in Lake Champlain; once at least there *was* a sea-serpent there, manufactured by a nationally famous artist with a sense of humor, loudly applauded by journalists and keepers of hotels. In 1895 another sea-serpent was reported in the very unlikely location of Long Lake. Personally I am much more interested in those numerous creatures of fantasy described by guides, such as the Side-Hill Gouger, or Walloper, which has legs short on one side so that he can manage the steepest hill. Willard Howland of Cranberry Lake had an assortment of these creatures which one of his clients put into an amusing long poem; it tells about the Vociferous Antissmus, the Swamp Auger, the barking Moon Crumbler, and the Woolly Nig—which has five legs and two tails.

Some of the guides could have schooled Lewis Carroll. Of these lords of fancy the Prince seems to be Herbert Clark. He is the master-guide who has accompanied Bob and George Marshall, sons of the famous New York lawyer, up every one of the forty-six major peaks of the Adirondacks; Herbert Peak is named for him, and Mount Marshall for the brothers whom he guided. Through the year 1919, when he was fifty years old, Clark was the champion oarsman of the Saranacs; Mr. Bob Marshall says that in one day the guide rowed sixty-five miles, twenty-four of them in a heavy freight-boat. According to this mighty man, a rock on lower Saranac showing a queer dent is the place where Captain Kidd, the pirate, bumped his head; a reach in the Ausable River below the Olympic ski-jump is where the *Merrimac* and the *Monitor* fit their famous battle. Newcomers have been warned by Clark against the ferocious *rugarues*—perhaps related to the *loup-garou* (werewolf) of the French "Canucks." Among the guide's gallery of imaginary characters is the Shiny Slatt, the opposite of Paul Bunyan in that he did everything badly; Jacob Whistletricker, compounder of marvelous drugs; Joe McGinnis, who was subject to the Fantod, a disease in which the patient shrinks to the size of a baseball; and Susie Soothingsyrup, a gay lass of colorful accomplishments. Beside his ambition to scale all the major peaks, Herbert Clark has aspired to catch

---

[1] From Harold W. Thompson: *Body, Boots and Britches*, Copyright, 1939, by Harold W. Thompson, published by J. B. Lippincott Company, pp. 299–300.

221

the Grandfather Pickerel of the Adirondacks, to be easily identified by his gold teeth and spectacles.

The guyascutus

It is almost a century now [1] since the guyascutus appeared in print. In Oregon he was described as appearing in Maine, and in Philadelphia he was declared to have originated in Boston. These are suspicious circumstances; the story, which became a country-wide fable, is about as follows:

Two soldiers of fortune, living by their wits, advertised that they would exhibit, for a price, a living guyascutus, captured at great risk. The tickets were sold, the crowd assembled, and one of the sharpers gave a lecture on the fearful animal, while the other, behind a curtain, emitted dreadful howls and roars. But the audience becoming restless, the lecturer, with presence of mind, turned pale and shouted: "Run for your lives! The guyascutus is loose!" The audience promptly escaped, and so did the swindlers.

Since the guyascutus has never been seen, it is not practicable to describe it.

---

[1] One version in F. A. Durivage and G. P. Burnham: *Stray Subjects Arrested and Bound Over* (Philadelphia: Carey & Hart; 1848), and a slightly different one in the Oregon *Spectator* for October 16, 1846. (Reference to *Spectator* from Whiting, *Southern Folklore Quarterly*, Vol. VIII, p. 267.)

BOOK III

GOOD YARNS GROW
BIGGER

GOOD YARNS GROW BIGGER:

American deeds and

American imaginings

In America, as elsewhere, interesting stories drive dull ones out, of course; but the same process goes on within individual stories; picturesque details supplant dull ones, and the odd tends to displace the commonplace. Miss Ratchford has given us (in the article quoted below) some excellent examples of this, and what she tells us about her own memories of stories heard in childhood may serve to remind us that the memory is incurably romantic. Montaigne complained that his memory retained only what interested it, but this is true of us all, and especially true of us collectively. Thus, any middle-aged American from the Atlantic seaboard, if he ever heard of the *Mary Celeste* at all, can tell you that she was found abandoned, shipshape, with all sails set, and even with food cooking on the galley stove. These false details have crystallized into legend. Why these and not certain others, attached to the tale by Conan Doyle and others? Who can say? A typical writer's version is here given, followed by the cautious solution of the late George S. Bryan. A comparison of the two is instructive, but the public prefers the good old myth to either.

The passage of time is, of course, favorable to mythology. Mere carelessness or ignorance may twist a story; for example, the tale of the rescue of the ship *Sharon* from mutineers was famous a century ago, and told with reasonable accuracy; recently I have seen three different printed accounts, all written within ten years, and all placing the events in the Atlantic Ocean; they took place in the Pacific. If a sea story cannot even remain in the right ocean, what may we expect of detail more subtle than geography, when the event is a century old?

Perhaps it was a desire to see their experiences truly set down in black and white, their form fixed for posterity, that led so many men in the seventeenth, eighteenth, and early nineteenth centuries to publish True Narratives, True Relations, True Accounts, and the like. This class of literature (if that be the word) would repay close study, which it has hardly received. In America it is, rightly regarded, a part of our history, but it is also the prototype of the "true" pulp fiction that is fobbed off on a section of the reading public today. The old narratives, at their worst, were better written than the pulp fiction, to be sure, but they must have fed the same appetite. Sometimes they had an ulterior motive; Ethan Allen's narrative of his captivity became a very effective recruiting document for the American cause in the War of 1812, though Ethan says he wrote it for the information of the curious in all nations. A pompous motive, it may be, but not a bad one.

But the first-personal narrative, even in the hands of an egotist, is in some ways cramped. John Hersey can tell the saga of Jack Kennedy with more ease, no doubt, than Kennedy could tell it himself, and the outsider sees more. Nathaniel Bowditch did not—perhaps could not—tell of one of his great feats of navigation, but his crew could and did. It is true that they exaggerated a little.

Exaggeration is a great American game. Conventionally regarded as "Western," it is hardly unknown in Yankee-land. Maine liars, it will be seen, can hold their own with any in America. The fireside, the cracker-barrel, and the tent are the backgrounds against which our robust imagination likes to spread its wings inordinately, but it is the gentlemen of the press who go furthest when they can indulge in a vacation from fact. Who invented the hen that laid square eggs? It was a newspaperman. The folklorist properly seeks out the hunter, the trapper, the lumberman, the railroader, and the oldest villager, but he sometimes makes a fetish of oral transmission. Let him step into a country newspaper office, let him talk with the leg-men of a metropolitan daily, let him find one of the underpaid lucky fellows who are allowed some freedom in "special stories"—and he will learn something to his advantage.

Among the most thrilling of our country's favorite stories are, it must be admitted, some of its murders. The most famous one of all, which need not be named, has been overwritten until at last we know too much (as well as not quite enough) about it; it will not be found here. Belle Gunness is a dreadful figure, and her story is less known than that other. The subway murder has several merits. It is plausible, mysterious, and disturbingly loaded with a suggestion of what might (very unpleasantly) further have happened. No doubt that is why it has been a recurrent legend, usually told as true, for over forty years.

On the Concho[1]

Near Paint Rock, Texas, there is a long bluff of rocks running parallel with the Concho River, about a quarter of a mile from its banks. The region was once used as a camping place by the Comanche Indians, as is shown by Indian pictographs covering the face of the bluff, giving it the name Painted Bluff. At one point a spring gushes out from two ledges of rock and goes cascading to the foot, pouring itself into a rocky basin. Near the basin, watered by the spring, there formerly stood several large pecan trees.

A great many years ago a letter addressed to "An Old Settler, Paint Rock, Texas," was delivered to my father. The writer inquired if there were, in that locality, a group of pecan trees at the foot of a spring coming out of a bluff. The letter gave definite measurements indicating the relative positions of the trees to the bluff and to each other, which my father listed one day, while surveying near the spring. If allowance were made for the change of terrain over a number of years, the bluff, spring, and trees might be said to fit the description contained in the letter; so my father wrote the inquirer.

A second letter came promptly. The writer had a map showing the location of a treasure buried near the spring. He proposed that Father undertake the search on shares. This letter was not answered, and no more was heard of the matter.

Later, a young man named Dave Ransbarger, who lived on the Colorado River about fifteen miles from town, brought in a bar of dark metal taken from the gravel of an abandoned crossing on the Colorado. The bar was melted down and found to be lead. The local assayer could detect no trace of silver. Of course, there was much speculation as to how the bar came to be embedded in the gravel, and as the crossing where it was found lay on the old Spanish road to the San Saba Mission, someone suggested that it must have been dropped by a mule train carrying metal from the San Saba mines.

As a child I heard these two incidents mentioned by older members of the family, who certainly had no thought of connecting them. Yet in recent years they have been combined into a typical buried treasure

---

[1] By Fannie E. Ratchford, from *Coyote Wisdom*, Texas Folk-Lore Society Publications, No. XIV (Austin: Texas Folk-Lore Society; 1938), pp. 175-9.

story of wide circulation: mule train of silver bullion from the San Saba mines, pursuit by Indians, hasty burial of treasure, battle with the Indians, escape of a sole survivor, etc. No circumstantial detail is wanting, except an explanation of how the Spanish mule-train carrying the treasure came to be at the Painted Bluff, which is fifteen miles or more off the San Saba road.

It often happens that a story offered originally as a mere hypothesis, or even as a frank joke, through much repetition, gains currency as a reputable legend. One of the favorite local stories among the children of my generation was that of Uncle Rich Coffee's escape from the Indians by hiding in the cave at the Painted Bluff. Now this cave is hardly more than an angle in the bluff enclosed by a fallen rock. We could never understand why the Indians, who must have known the cave quite as well as we did, did not find him. The question was put one day to an older friend who had taken us to the Painted Bluff for a picnic. I well remember his teasing smile as he said, "Oh, I guess Uncle Rich must have crawled through the crack in the back of the cave into another cave that runs so far back the Indians couldn't find him."

Now, we knew that the crack in the back of the cave was too small for any one of us to wriggle through, and Uncle Rich Coffee, according to tradition, was a tremendously big man. We knew also from our own investigation that the crack did not lead into a second cave. But the suggestion was too fascinating to reject on the mere ground of facts, and it has become an interesting and orthodox part of the Uncle Rich Coffee story.

Several years ago, in the course of a terrible drouth in West Texas, I was teaching in the high school of a small town in the stricken section. By the time the third winter without grass or feedstuffs of any kind had rolled round, many of the stockmen were without resources or credit for buying feedstuff, and the miserable cattle in the pastures were left to die of starvation.

Day by day the unclouded sky became more and more thickly dotted with buzzards, which hung over the country like the spirit of drouth itself. The children on the school ground amused themselves, first, by trying to see who could count the greatest number of buzzards during one recess. From this simple sport, the high school children passed on to the more complicated game of working out a set of superstitions that would cover every possible grouping of the birds in the sky. One buzzard seen alone was bad luck; groups of even numbers were bad luck; odd numbers were good luck. If one caught sight of a buzzard over his left shoulder he must find one on his right to balance it before he took his eyes from the sky. When four buzzards were seen symmetrically placed at the four cardinal points of the compass with one directly overhead the drouth would be broken.

228

These signals, made up purely out of the imaginations of the older girls, were accepted without question by the younger ones, and came to be half-believed even by their authors. I have no doubt that a visitor to that community twenty years hence will find distinct survivals of this game in the luck beliefs of the people.

The most fertile source of legends on the Concho was the Old Ostrander House. Sometime in the early or middle 80's a man named Ostrander, from Syracuse, New York, came out as head of a ranching company, enclosing with wire fence a large stretch of land lying between Paint Rock and San Angelo. Part of the enclosed land was bought outright, but much of it was state school land. The pastures were stocked with fine horses and cattle; barns and stock sheds were built over the ranch; and on a hill overlooking Kickapoo Creek was erected a large stone ranch house, called Thornfield, the wonder of the country round. The whole was a mere speculative bubble. This was the period of investment of foreign capital in western ranches, and it has been supposed that Ostrander hoped to unload on some innocent English or Scotch younger son with more money than judgment. Before a victim was found, however, the passage of the Texas Alien Land Law ruined his plans. Suddenly Ostrander, with his wife and daughter, took French leave—so suddenly, indeed, that, according to tradition, they left the evening meal they were eating unfinished, and took with them only the clothes they were wearing.

For fifteen years or more Thornfield stood unoccupied and uncared for, the resort of picnickers and sightseers, when suddenly one day Ostrander reappeared and sold off such furniture as he could find buyers for in the neighborhood and again vanished.

Out of the many surmises concerning the sudden departure of the Ostrander family has arisen a cycle of legends, most of them having some basis in fact, but the story that has gained the widest circulation is fiction pure and simple. It arose after this fashion. When I was a child, about twelve years old, I went one day with friends who were taking a visiting relative to see the Ostrander House. The visitor was an old lady of a fluffy, romantic turn of mind, who firmly believed that she had the gift of prophetic dreams. As we walked around the house to the flag-stone porch at the back, she caught sight of a half fallen-in cistern curbing.

"Just exactly as I saw it in a dream!" she exclaimed, and then she related with dramatic gusto a dream which had for its climax the drowning of a beautiful young girl in this very cistern. Whether the tragedy of the original dream was suicide or accident I have forgotten. I have since heard both versions told as legends. But I well remember being tremendously impressed with the story she made of it, and I have no doubt I did my part in spreading it.

229

I had forgotten the incident until a few years ago, when I read a feature story concerning the Ostrander House. In this account, published in one of the Texas daily newspapers, the ghost of the drowned girl played a spectacular part. Through the name of the writer I was able to trace the story to the source I have indicated. Only a few months ago, while at home on a visit, I sought information concerning the actual operations of the Ostrander Ranch in its heyday. An old-timer whom I approached said, "For heaven's sake, don't go telling that yarn about the ghost of a drowned girl again."

"How do you suppose such a story got started?" I asked.

"I'm sure I don't know," he answered, "but it is told everywhere now, and half the people in this country believe it."

On December 5, 1872 the "half-brig" *Mary Celeste* was found, abandoned but seaworthy, east of the Azores. From that day to this no man has been able to say with certainty what happened to her company of ten (in maritime legend thirteen, and other numbers) persons. Fraud, madness, pestilence, sea-monsters—these are some of the commoner explanations that have been put forward, orally and in print, during nearly three quarters of a century. The most circumstantial and least fragmentary account is said by its author [1] to be based on the testimony of survivors, especially of one John Pemberton. According to this narrative, Captain Briggs went mad and disappeared (overboard?), and the captain of the salvaging vessel, the *Dei Gratia,* got rid of the *Mary Celeste's* crew, falsely represented her as found derelict, and enriched himself with salvage money. This solution explains everything, but some of the most knowledgeable amateurs of our legend will have none of it. William McFee scoffed, George S. Bryan [2] referred to it as "flinging printer's ink in the public face"; and Charles E. Fay, [3] an expert student of the mystery, declared (in 1942): "This unpleasant book has been thoroughly dissected and refuted." Unpleasantness, of course, need not count against the book, nor need melodrama, for seafaring life has enough of that, but it is true that Pemberton's tale conflicts repeatedly with recorded fact.

To me, much the likeliest solution, though it is disappointingly simple, seems to be that offered by Dr. Oliver W. Cobb, a cousin of both Captain Briggs and Mrs. Briggs. That solution, as adopted (and

---

[1] Laurence J. Keating: *The Great Mary Celeste Hoax* (London: Heath Cranton; 1929).

[2] George S. Bryan: *Mystery Ship.* See below.

[3] Charles Edey Fay: *Mary Celeste, the Odyssey of an Abandoned Ship* (Salem: Peabody Museum; 1942; 1,000 copies). There is also an abridged edition, but the full one is largely "documented." It also contains a fifteen-page bibliographical review of the case.

slightly adapted) by George S. Bryan, is here given, but is prefaced by a typical *Mary Celeste* romance.

It seems unlikely that more evidence—after seventy-four years—will or can appear. I vote with Dr. Cobb and William McFee, with G. S. Bryan and Charles E. Fay, for an unwarranted alarm, a premature abandonment, and a sudden gale that swamped the boat (or boats) and left the *Mary Celeste* a true derelict. And yet could Pemberton, with all his gross errors of fact, and they are very gross, be right on the essential point? We must leave it there.

The *Mary Celeste*, in fiction—and in fact, an unsolved mystery[1]

The circumstances under which the brig *Marie* [sic] *Celeste* was found deserted in mid-ocean are matters of official record, but that only. No trace of any member of the ship's company of thirteen souls has ever been found. Thirteen, that unlucky number! "Had that anything to do with it?" asks the superstitiously inclined sailor.

Today (1913) many years after the disaster, we know practically no more about it than did the skipper who found the deserted ship. There is ample room for imagination, for from the recorded facts no one has been able to construct even a tenable theory. However, here are the facts in the case, all that has been learned after thirty-eight years. . . .

Early in September, 1872, Capt. Ben Griggs, a New Englander, stood on an East River wharf, in New York, watching the loading of the last article for his ship's cabin. It was a sewing-machine belonging to his wife, for Mrs. Griggs was to go with her husband for the voyage, on the *Marie Celeste* of 500 tons, bound for Genoa. As the machine was slung aboard, the captain's wife, with their seven-year-old daughter and their twelve-year-old son and accompanied by the vessel's owner, appeared on the wharf. The boy ran up to Capt. Griggs crying: "Oh, father, do please take me for a trip as well as sister." "Stop there, my lad, not so fast," replied his father, "you've been two voyages with me, and now it's proper that you stay at home so as to attend school." "But I'll be lonesome without Mother and Sister," replied the boy. "Aye, I dare say you will," said the old man thoughtfully. Then, turning to his owner, "What do you say, sir, as to the boy coming with his mother

---

[1] From George S. Bryan: *Mystery Ship* (Philadelphia: J. B. Lippincott Co.; 1942), pp. 130–40; abstracted by G. S. Bryan from the *Strand Magazine* for 1913. Copyright 1942 by George S. Bryan. Reprinted by permission of George S. Bryan.

and sister?" The owner of the ship shook his head. "I believe, captain, the lad should stick to his books." That settled it. When the brig hauled off, the captain's son was left standing on the jetty beside his father's employer, and he wept as though he was brokenhearted, till the owner took him to a shop and bought him some sweets and toys. In not taking his son on that voyage of the *Celeste* the skipper spared the lad—what? No one can answer that question. The weeks passed, two months or more. Then suddenly through the State Department there came to the owner, from the United States Consul at Gibraltar, this notice.

> Gibraltar, 2nd January, 1873
> The American brig *Marie Celeste* of New York was brought into this port by the British barque *Dei Gratia; Marie Celeste* picked up on high seas on the 5th December, abandoned. Brig in perfect condition, but was taken possession of by Admiralty Court as a derelict. Fate of crew unknown.

The owner of the ill-fated brig at once took passage for Gibraltar. Before his departure, however, he sent a copy of the letter to Capt. Griggs's little son. "If father only had taken me along with him," the little boy said, "we would have been together and happy now. For when they left me and took mother and sister, that made the ship's company up to thirteen."

At noon on 5th December, 1872, the Atlantic, at a point 300 miles due west from Gibraltar, was as smooth as a mill pond and there were three vessels within sight of each other. One was a German tramp steamer holding a course for the West Indies, and crossing the bows of the brig about three miles off. The steamer ran up a signal that called for an answer from the brig. But the brig sent no answer. She was silent. Then, as if saying to the brig, "Well, if you don't want me to speak to you or report you, it's all the same to me," the tramp held on her course due south, dropping at last over the horizon. The third vessel was the British barque *Dei Gratia,* Captain Boyce, bound for Gibraltar. Captain Boyce, through his telescope, had seen the signal displayed by the tramp steamer when trying to speak to the brig. Also, he had waited in vain for an answering flag from the *Marie Celeste,* the reply demanded by the common code of courtesy on the high seas. "Queer, jolly impolite, when I come to think of it," was the British skipper's comment, and he determined to investigate. "A confounded, surly churl of a sea-dog who refused to be spoken at sea," for the Briton was not as lacking in curiosity as his brother skipper of the steamer seemed to be. Taking every advantage of the catspaw of wind from the southward, Captain Boyce ran within hailing distance of the silent brig. "There seems to be something amiss with that vessel," he said to his mate, Adams.

"Aye, sir," replied the mate, "she should by rights have every inch of sail spread. And how she yaws, sir. She acts to me, sir, as though the crew were all drunk."

They were now within half a mile of the *Marie Celeste,* and both captain and mate were scrutinizing closely the queer actions of the brig, the captain through his telescope and the mate through binoculars. Suddenly, at the same moment, both cried, "Not a soul in sight on her decks!"

"It must be our eyes; we can't see them, but they're there somewhere, of course," said the skipper.

There was still no response from the brig.

"Damme! Give 'em an urgent hoist, Adams, that'll get 'em sure."

Forthwith, the urgent hoist was run up. Still no reply. Meanwhile, the behaviour of the brig became stranger than ever. The wind had veered slightly, and the brig's sails were flapping in an irresponsible way.

"The fools," cried the skipper of the British ship. "Strange we can't see them. What are they hiding for? But they're there, sure, 'cause they're bringing her about. Hang me, if they ain't trying to run away from us."

Captain Boyce now formed a trumpet with his hands and shouted, "Brig ahoy!" the mate joining in the yell, for they were within easy hailing distance. But the mysterious brig still failed to answer, and, though all hands on the British ship could now examine the decks of the brig with the naked eye, not a sign of life could they discover.

"Lower a boat," thundered Captain Boyce. "Mr. Adams, we must board that craft. Her crew is either drunk, or murdered, or dead of fever, or starved to death, or—" he turned to look into the mate's eyes.

"Or they've abandoned the ship, sir," said the mate understandingly. "And yet never that, sir. Why should they abandon her? She's not showing signs of distress, not one."

On the calm sea a boat, manned by two sailors and carrying both captain and mate from the *Dei Gratia,* pulled toward the strange brig. As they drew near, they read, on the vessel's stern, "*MARIE CELESTE, NEW YORK.*"

"Celeste, ahoy! on deck, there," cried Boyce, as he came alongside, well forward. The only answer was the flapping of the somnolent sails aloft. "Bless me, if she ain't pretty near all right aloft," said the skipper. "It's below the wrong is." Whereupon he ordered his sailors to stand by, while he and the mate boarded the brig, climbing up by the chain-plates. Then, after one swift glance over the bulwarks, the captain said, "All hands must be below, for there's not a man in sight, not even a man at the wheel."

The two Britons then made their way aft, noting the ship's condition as they went. Not a thing was missing. Nothing was wanting that

233

would be needed by such a vessel at sea. She was obviously a first-class craft, freshly painted, newly outfitted, spick and span in every way. But that uncanny silence on such a fine ship was something awesome. The two men felt their flesh creep. Was the ship deserted? To them the brig seemed a floating graveyard, a ghost ship, the kind of phantom craft they had read about. From stem to stern, in cabin and forecastle, the two men searched, but not a human being dead or alive could they find.

"Mutiny!" exclaimed the skipper. "Master and mate have been thrown overboard. But where are the mutineers? Why this game of hide-and-seek?"

After a second examination of every part of the mysterious brig, the mariners returned to the cabin.

"Well, it hasn't been mutiny, sir," said the mate, " 'cause there's no sign of a struggle."

"Nor was it piracy," said the captain, " 'cause the money-box has not been disturbed, and the cargo's valuable, but not touched, and there's no indication of any violence."

"Nor starvation, sir, with fever, and all hands going luny and jumping over the side, 'cause there's tons of grub, and the medicine-chest ain't been used to any account."

"And there was no storm, Adams, nor waterspout, nor tidal wave to wash 'em overboard. The log shows nothing since leaving Sandy Hook."

"Well, then, sir, if it weren't mutineers, nor pirates, nor storm, nor wreck, nor leak, nor famine, nor sickness, what could it have been, sir, except a sea-serpent sticking his snout aboard and swallowing 'em one by one?"

"They've abandoned ship, Adams, that's plain," said the skipper, ignoring the sea-serpent theory.

"Yes, sir, they've left the ship, but why?"

"Why? It's most extraordinary, you know. They were not forced off, that's easy to see. They went willingly, and they had not made any preparations to go, that's certain. They didn't know they were going till the very moment they went. They went all in a most unaccountable hurry, 'cause they left the ship in the middle of their breakfast. And they didn't take a stitch of clothing with them except what they had on their backs. Hang it! they took nothing but the ship's chronometer. Why the chronometer? We can't find the chronometer, can we? And I firmly believe they took the ship's papers too, at least we haven't found the papers, though they may be locked in some drawer we've failed to open."

"That's straight, sir, they abandoned ship with nothing but the chronometer and possibly the ship's papers. But why did they quit a

234

ship that's as sound as the day she was launched? We've tried the pumps, and there's not an unnecessary drop of water in the old hooker. The ship's just perfect in every particular. Hullo! Here's blood!" The mate had drawn a cutlass from a scabbard that hung on the cabin wall. He pointed to spots on the blade. "Blood, sir, yet why did the man that used the cutlass take the trouble to put it back in its sheath? And" —looking at the woodwork of the cabin round about the scabbard,— "see these marks, more blood. Piracy, sir, that's it. There's a Captain Kidd in this job, and he's made 'em all walk the plank."

"Pirates, Adams, yes! But then, there's the valuables—the two watches in the mate's room, and the lady's rings and other jewels, and the full money-chest."

"Well, Captain, anyway, she is our prize."

"Aye, Adams; but what I can't make out is how did they leave the ship? Not in their own boats, eh?"

"No, sir, not in their own boats, 'cause the boat that would be carried by a craft like this is here present and accounted for."

"Well, then, Adams, they got away in a boat belonging to another vessel."

"How else could they get away, sir?"

"So all we've got to do, Mr. Adams, is to tow her into Gibraltar, and try and find out why this A-1 craft was abandoned by her people."

The reader may wish to try and unravel this hard nautical knot for himself. Therefore, here are further details of the examination made by the two British sailors on the abandond ship *Marie Celeste.*

First, it was clear that the abandonment of the vessel was not due in any way to a storm or even bad weather.

"Look at the sewing-machine," said the skipper, as he and the mate discussed the situation in the brig's cabin. "There's been a woman here—probably the captain's wife—and she was using that machine not long before she went wherever she went. Note this thimble lying on its side on a corner of the machine. There could have been no storm at the time the woman separated from the ship, for any kind of sea-roll would have caused the cotton to tumble off the machine."

"There's been a child here, too, sir," put in the mate. "It was a girl, for the thing the woman was sewing on the machine 'pears to me like a pinafore. The child was possibly the skipper's kiddie. And the woman stopped sewing in the middle of stitching a sleeve to leave the ship, however she left it."

"No, she didn't," said the captain. "She stopped sewing to get her breakfast," and the captain pointed to the table, the appearance of which showed that four persons had risen from a half-eaten meal to leave the cabin forever. The four at the table were accounted for as the captain, his wife, and the little girl, and the mate. That the meal was breakfast was indicated by the nature of the food—oatmeal, coffee, bacon and eggs. The child had almost finished her porridge. At the captain's place at the table, lay the two halves of a hard-boiled egg in the shell. It was evident that the moment he broke the shell he left the cabin never to return. At another place at the table—probably his wife's—stood a bottle filled with a then popular brand of cough medicine. It looked as if the woman's last act aboard the brig had been to remove the cork from the bottle, for the cork lay on the cloth; and, as an evidence that there had been nothing but a calm sea since the ship was deserted, the narrow tall bottle stood upright close to the edge of the table, not a drop of the medicine having escaped from the bottle. In the forecastle, too, pans on the stove contained a breakfast cooked, showing that the sailors were about to gather for the morning meal when they went over the side instead.

Second, there was a dearth of evidence of mutiny or piracy. No sign of any kind indicated violence or a struggle. Moreover, as already stated, the money-chest was found to have its contents presumably intact.

Third, how long had the vessel been deserted? The log answered this question, but whether truthfully or not there was no way of knowing. The last entry in the log was made forty-odd hours before the *Marie Celeste* was sighted by the *Dei Gratia.* There was no mention of storm. The log was found in the mate's room. The entry made at seven o'clock on the morning of 2nd September (December), 1872, merely gave the latitude and longitude and slight winds from the southward.

Fourth, there was no sign of any intention to leave the ship, not a trace of any kind of preparation. That the sailors had no expectation of abandoning ship, but that, on the contrary, all hands left in a great hurry on the spur of the moment, was shown by the fact that they had washed their underclothing before breakfast on the morning of the desertion, for, on looking around, Captain Boyce and his mate beheld the sailors' clothes hanging on a line over the forecastle. In the mate's room lay a paper containing a sum in addition. When the mate was summoned to leave the ship, was he eating breakfast or was he doing this sum? For of the three columns only the first two were added.

Fifth, while the binnacle and compasses of the vessel were found, the chronometer was missing. Absolutely not another thing—so far as the two men could see—was missing from the brig, except, possibly, the ship's papers. The sailors—some of them at least—had not even stopped to take their pipes or tobacco. In the forecastle were found eight pipes and several tins of cut plug. Was the thing so terrible that it had induced sailors not to stop even for their smoke?

Sixth, and strongest of all, the boat belonging to the *Celeste* was in its place. How, then, could the crew of thirteen have left the ship except by boats from another vessel? What message of mortal terror could that other boat have brought to necessitate the immediate desertion of a staunch ship?

Seventh, "What I want to know," said the skipper, as he towed his prize to Gibraltar, "is how that blood got on the cutlass and on the woodwork of the brig. And say, Adams, how is it a mother and child would leave a good ship in mid-ocean without taking even the child's nightie?"

For the rest, the official data bearing on the mystery is (sic) very meager. In the archives of the Department of State are the following:

CREW AND PASSENGERS VANISH

Document 136 from U. S. Consul Johnson, dated Gibraltar, 7th January, 1873, "Result of analysis adverse to blood existing on sword and woodwork belonging to the brig *Marie Celeste.*"

Document 137, from the same, dated 20th January, 1873. "Principal owner of brig *Marie Celeste* arrived from New York to claim brig from Admiralty Court. Nothing heard of missing crew. Chronometer and ship's papers not to be found on board the brig."

Document 138, "Brig *Marie Celeste* restored to her original owner 12th February, 1873."

Document 139, "Brig *Marie Celeste* cleared for Naples under command of Captain John Hutchins, sent out by owner from New York for the purpose. Forwarded to Mrs. Bilson, of New York, effects of Henry Bilson, missing mate of brig *Marie Celeste,* the brig's last voyage."

And, meantime, though the representatives of the United States in all the ports of the world had been instructed by the Department of State to watch for the missing crew, not a single incoming vessel anywhere reported picking up the *Celeste's* thirteen.

[1] Let us now endeavor to reconstruct the abandonment as he [Dr. Oliver Cobb, a cousin of Captain Briggs] finally was convinced it must have taken place. The cargo of alcohol had been loaded at New York in cool weather; the *Mary Celeste* had crossed the Gulf Stream and on November 25th was in a comparatively warm belt. There may have been a seepage of alcohol, and vapor may have collected in the hold to such a point that Captain Briggs grew alarmed (unjustifiably so, as events were to prove) and, having Mrs. Briggs and Sophia to think of, quickly decided to remove everybody from possible danger.

It would appear that, having ordered the light sails furled and the mainsail lowered (it would practically furl itself in the lazy jacks, the lines that reached from above to confine it), he gave the helmsman the order "Put your helm down!" and had the vessel hove to on the starboard tack. That she was on the starboard tack (that is, had the

---

[1] Ibid., pp. 244–9.

wind on her starboard side) is evident from the fact that when she was encountered by the *Dei Gratia,* the sheets of the jib and fore-topmast staysail were "fast on the port side" (Deveau). When she was hove to, the yards on the foremast were braced around to starboard to bring the square sails aback. These sails were the foresail, the lower fore-topsail, and the upper fore-topsail. The wind would then blow *against* them and stop the headway. A sailor would be at the wheel. The yards would remain aback until a shift of wind caught them on the other side.

A section of rail was taken out, and the ship's only boat was lowered on the port side without tackle—a method Deveau found possible. The main peak-halyard was unrove for use as a tow-line, one end being left attached to the gaff. The halyard would have a circumference of two and three-quarters inches and a diameter of an inch; and where attached to the gaff on board it would be about eight feet up from the deck. Its length would be about four hundred feet. Inasmuch as the mainsail had been furled, the halyard was available; and when bent on to the boat's painter it would make the longest and best tow-line ready for immediate use.

Captain Briggs got chronometer, sextant, and ship's papers—then there was sudden haste. Leaving the main staysail unfurled and the wheel unlashed, everybody took to the boat. Perhaps the binnacle was displaced and the compass broken by a sailor's unskilful effort to get the compass in a hurry. There would be a boat loaded with ten persons, its painter bent to four hundred feet of slack halyard. A strong and unexpected breeze from the north filled the square sails; the halyard came taut and, as the ship gathered headway, the straining line was drawn at an angle over the side. It parted—and the yawl was adrift.

(At the inquiry, Deveau said that "the main peak-halyards were broken," and Lund filled out the statement by testifying that they "were broke and gone." If the halyards were "broke and gone," where else did they go? The men from the *Dei Gratia* were undoubtedly looking to see whether a rope might have been made fast to the bitts or along the rail. That is why Wright said, "I observed no remains of any tow-line," and Deveau said, "I saw no remains or pieces of a painter or boat's rope fastened to the rail." These men were sure that the halyard was "broke and gone," for they could not set the mainsail until they got a coil of rope from the lazarette and rove off a new halyard—the one that Surveyor Austin mentioned in his report.)

Eight men, Mrs. Briggs, and infant Sophia were on the open ocean in a small boat. They had no compass; we do not know of a surety that they had provisions or water. (The provisions that Austin found tumbled about may have been left thus by the men from the *Dei*

Gratia: "We used the provisions found on board the *Mary Celeste*," said Deveau.) Perhaps the men rowed for a while, hoping to overtake the ship—it was a vain hope. No vessel picked them up, they never reached the Azores.

The ship drifted on; ran into a squall; lost her foresail and upper fore-topsail. She turned about, heading toward the west, and shipped a sea—this would account for water in the forward house and the cabin, the doors of both having been left open. The fore hatch had been left off too—or possibly blown off—and this might explain some of the water between decks. The ship would come to from time to time and hang in the wind, raising the hopes of those in the boat,—if they still followed. Then her staysail and jib would fill again, and she would run before the wind once more. First on one tack, then on the other, she would for the most part keep a reasonably straight course— just as she was doing when she approached the *Dei Gratia*.

Capt. W. M. Collins of Nova Scotia has stated (1941) to the present writer: "Doctor Cobb has his own theory as to the actual abandonment, which is as near as any. To the experienced seaman it is just another *premature abandonment*. They have cost thousands of lives. I watched that phase of sea life (and death) through the years, and had some experience of my own."

In 1926, Mrs. D. R. Morehouse stated in an interview (*Boston Sunday Post*, August 15th) that Captain Morehouse had said undoubtedly Captain Briggs and the entire crew had abandoned the ship because the rumbling of alcohol gases in the hold caused them to fear an explosion. "I've heard him tell the story a hundred times and shake his head and say, 'Poor Briggs! He and his wife and crew all perished in that small, open yawl. There can be no other way out of it.'"

This coincides in a general way with the opinion of Capt. J. H. Winchester, the *Mary Celeste's* principal owner. Winchester had been a sea-captain, with first-hand experience of such matters. He knew Captain Briggs well, and (according to Mrs. Priscilla Shelton, Richardson's sister) a niece of his own was married to Mate Albert G. Richardson. He went to Gibraltar to attend the salvage inquiry before the Vice-Admiralty Court, and at that time he had opportunity to inspect the *Celeste* as she lay in the harbor under arrest by the Court, as well as to discuss various particulars of the evidence with Cornwell, who acted as Proctor for him, and with Consul Sprague. Living until January 30th, 1912, he was enabled to weigh the case thoroughly and to mature his own views.

Winchester Noyes, a grandson, who became president of the firm of J. H. Winchester & Co., ship brokers, said (in the Nautical Gazette of December 24th, 1913) that Captain Winchester "always held" that "after a spell of rough weather" there was a "spontaneous combustion" of gas, which blew off the fore hatch. Alarmed by the report and the smoke-like vapor that followed it, all hands got safely into the boat. But no further explosions occurred, nor did the ship take fire. Fresh air cooled the hold, and with a fair breeze the *Celeste* ran away from the boat, whose occupants were lost in "another sea tragedy." To the present writer Mr. Noyes gave a practically identical version.

No more eloquent tales, no stranger ones have been told in America than those told by men and women captured by pirates, by Indians, by foreign foes. Their published narratives are today a treasured (if seldom read) segment of our early literature, but when first published, they were news to Americans who well knew that the same thing might have happened, might still happen, to them. The stories are usually related in plain and unsophisticated language, sometimes with a rather affected elegance; sometimes they show all too plainly the mark of the ghost-writer, but even so they are unmistakably genuine; even when wooden or when (at the other pole) rhetorical, they carry the reader on as few works of fiction can do. Amazing records of human endurance, they are also true; the victims had no desire to exaggerate, no desire and no need. Unconscious overstatement of their sufferings may occur; just what, for instance, did happen to the first joint of John Gyles's great toes? Could Philip Ashton really have thrown a hat into the snake's mouth? Did Captain Carver subsist three days without any food? And so on; but these questions can by no means shake the essential credibility and power of a plain story told by people who have suffered much and narrowly escaped alive.

The captive is froze![1]

O ne winter as we were moving from place to place, our hunters killed some moose; and one lying some miles from our wigwams, a young Indian and myself were ordered to fetch part of it. We set out in the morning when the weather was promising, but it proved a very cold, cloudy day. It was late in the evening (when) we arrived at the place where the moose lay; so that we had no time to provide ma-

---

[1] From John Gyles: *Memoirs of Odd Adventures and Strange Deliverances* (Boston: S. Kneeland & T. Green; 1736), pp. 16–17. (This passage was reprinted by Henry Beston in *American Memory;* New York: Farrar & Rinehart; 1937.) In the Boston Public Library copy, which belonged to Jeremy Belknap, the historian, is a manuscript note in Belknap's hand, saying that the little book was "said to have been written and embellished by Joseph Seccombe, Chaplain of the Garrison at St. George's." This seems likely enough, as Gyles had been commander of that Maine garrison, and as the clergy sometimes assisted in the preparation of such narratives. Another example of such assistance will be found in the next selection.

terials for fire or shelter. At the same time a storm came on very thick of snow and continued until the next morning. We made a small fire with what little rubbish we could find around us, which with the heat of our bodies melted the snow upon us as fast as it fell, and filled our clothes with water. Nevertheless, early in the morning, we took our loads of moose-flesh and set out, in order to return to our wigwams; we had not travelled far before my moose-skin coat (which was the only garment that I had on my back, and the hair was in most places worn off) was froze stiff around my knees like a hoop, as likewise my snow-shoes and shoe-clouts to my feet! Thus I marched the whole day without fire or food! At first I was in great pain, then my flesh numbed, and I felt at times extreme sick, and thought I could not travel one foot further; but wonderfully revived again. After long traveling I felt very drowsy, and had thoughts of setting down; which had I done, without doubt I had fallen on my final sleep; as my dear companion, Evans, had done before; for my Indian companion, being better clothed, had left me long before: but again my spirits revived as much as if I had received the richest cordial! Some hours after sunset I recovered the wigwam and crawled in with my snow-shoes on. The Indians cried out, *The captive is froze to death!*

They took off my pack, and where that lay against my back was the only place that was not frozen. The Indians cut off my shoes, and stripped the clouts from my feet, which were as void of feeling as any frozen flesh could be: but I had not sat long by the fire, before the blood began to circulate, and my feet to my ankles turned black, and swelled with bloody blisters, and were inexpressibly painful. The Indians said one to another, *His feet will rot, and he'll die.* Nevertheless, I slept well at night. Soon after the skin came off my feet, from my ankles, whole like a shoe, and left my toes naked without a nail, and the ends of my great toe-bones bare, which in a little time turned black, so that I was obliged to cut the first joint off with my knife. The Indians gave me rags to bind up my feet, and advised me to apply fir-balsam, but withal said, that they believed it was not worthwhile to use means, for I should certainly die. But by the use of my elbows and a stick in each hand, I shoved myself on my bottom, over the snow, from one tree to another, till I got some fir-balsam, then burned it in a clam-shell till it was of a consistence like salve, and applied it to my feet and ankles, and by the divine blessing within a week I could go about upon my heels with my staff. And through God's goodness, we had provision enough, so that we did not remove under ten or fifteen days, and then the Indians made two little hoops something in form as a snow-shoe, and seized them to my feet: and I followed them in their track on my heels from place to place; sometimes half leg deep in snow and water, which gave me the most acute pain imaginable, but I was forced to walk or die. But within a year my feet were entirely well, and the nails came on my great toes: so that a very critical eye could scarce perceive any part missing, or that they had been froze at all!

Philip Ashton, an American merchant seaman, was captured in June 1722 off Nova Scotia, with some other sailors, by the notorious pirate Ned Low of Boston. Later Ashton escaped, on an island in the Bay of Honduras. His adventures, worthy of Robinson Crusoe, were ghost-written by his pastor, the Reverend John Barnard of Marblehead,[1] and published. Barnard explains in a preface: "I have taken the minutes of all from his own Mouth . . . improved the first vacant Hour, I could, to Read it over distinctly to him, that he might correct the Errors. . . . Thus corrected, he set his Hand to it as his own History." This was an admirable method, though it may be suspected that the Reverend John Barnard colored the narrative a little with his own ideas of divine interposition.

Our extract, taken from the London edition of 1726[2] is preceded by the words: "But the Time for Deliverance was now come. God had ordered it that Low and Spriggs were ashour upon an Island distinct from Roatan. . . . He had moved the Cooper to take me into the Boat."

Philip Ashton's misery[3]

W hen we came first to Land, I was very Active in helping to get the Casks out of the Boat, & Rowing them up to the Watering place: then I lay down at the Fountain & took a hearty Draught of the Cool Water; & anon, I gradually strol'd along the Beech, picking up Stones and Shells & looking about me; when I had got about Musket Shot off from them (tho' they had taken no Arms along with them in the Boat) I began to make up to the Edge of the Woods: when the Cooper spying me, call'd after me, & asked me where I was going; I told him I was going to get some Coco-nuts, for there were some Coco-nut trees just before me. So soon as I had recovered the Woods and lost sight of them, I betook myself to my Heels, & ran as fast as the thickness of the Bushes, and my naked Feet would let me. I bent my course, not

---

[1] 1681–1770.

[2] John Barnard, V.D.M.: *Ashton's Memorial, or an Authentic Account of the Strange Adventures and Signal Deliverances of Mr. Philip Ashton* . . . (London: Richard Ford and Samuel Chandler, both in the Poultry; 1726).

[3] Ibid., pp. 41–73.

243

directly from them, but rather up behind them, which I continued till I had got a considerable way into the Woods, & yet not so far but that I could hear their talk, when they spake anything loud; and here I lay close in a very great Thicket, being well assured, if they should take the pains to hunt after me, never so carefully, they would not be able to find me.

After they had filled their Casks and were about to go off, the Cooper called after me to come away; but I lay snug in my Thicket, and would give him no Answer, tho' I plainly eno' heard him. At length they set a hallooing for me, but I was still silent; I could hear them say to one another, The D—g is lost in the Woods, and can't find the way out again; then they hallooed again; and cried, he is run-away and won't come again; the Cooper said, if he had thought I would have served him so, he would not have brought me ashoar. They plainly saw it would be in vain to seek me in such hideous Woods, and thick Brushes. When they were weary with hallooing, the Cooper at last, to shew his good Will to me, (I can't but Love and Thank him for his Kindness) call'd out, If you don't come away presently, I'll go off and leave you alone. But all they could say was no Temptation to me to discover myself, and least of all that of their going away and leaving me; for this was the very thing I desired, that I might be rid of them, and all that belonged to them. So finding it in vain to wait any longer, they put off with their Water, without me; and thus was I left upon a desolate Island, destitute of all help, and much out of the way of all Travellers; however, this Wilderness I looked upon as Hospitable, and this Loneliness as good Company, compared with the State and Society I was now happily Delivered from.

When I supposed they were gone off, I came out of my Thicket, and drew down to the Water side, about a Mile below the Watering place, where there was a small run of Water; and here I sat down to observe their Motions and know when the Coast was clear; for I could not but have some remaining fears lest they should send a Company of Armed Men after me; yet I thought if they should, the Woods and Bushes were so thick that it would be impossible they should find me. As yet I had nothing to Eat, nor indeed were my Thoughts much concerned about living in this Desolate Place, but they were chiefly taken up about my geting clear. And to my Joy, after the Vessels had stayed five Days in this Harbour, they came to sail, and put out to Sea, and I plainly saw the Schooner part from the two Sloops, and shape a different Course from them.

When they were gone and the Coast clear, I began to reflect upon my self, and my present Condition; I was upon an Island from whence I could not get off; I knew of no Humane Creature within many scores of Miles of me; I had but a Scanty Cloathing, and no possibility of

244

getting more; I was destitute of all Provision for my Support, and knew not how I should come at any; every thing looked with a dismal Face; the sad prospect drew Tears from me in abundance; yet since GOD had graciously granted my Desires, in freeing me out of the hands of the Sons of Violence, whose Business 'tis to devise Mischief against their neighbour, and from whom every thing that had the least face of Religion and Virtue was intirely Banished, (unless that Low would never suffer his Men to work upon the Sabbath, (it was more devoted to Play) and I have seen some of them sit down to Read in a good Book) therefore I purposed to account all the hardship I might now meet with, as Light, & Easy, compared with being Associated with them.

In order to find in what manner I was to Live for the time to come, I began to Range the Island over, which I suppose is some 10 or 11 Leagues Long, in the Latitude of 16 deg. 30 min. or thereabouts. I soon found that I must look for no Company, but the Wild Beast of the Field, and the Fowl of the Air; with all of which I made a Firm Peace, and GOD said Amen to it. I could discover no Footsteps of any Habitation upon the Island; yet there was one walk of Lime Trees near a Mile long, and ever now & then I found some broken Shreds of Earthen Pots, scattered here and there upon the Place, which some say are some remains of the Indians that formerly Lived upon the Island.

The Island is well Watered, and is full of Hills, high Mountains, and lowly Vallies. The Mountains are Covered over with a sort of scrubby black Pine, & are almost inaccessible. The Vallies abound with Fruit Trees, and are so prodigiously thick with an underbrush, that 'tis difficult passing.

The Fruit were Coco-Nuts, but these I could have no advantage from, because I had no way of coming at the inside; there are Wild Figs, and Vines in abundance, these I chiefly lived upon, especially at first; there is also a sort of Fruit growing upon Trees somewhat larger than an Orange, of an Oval shape, of a brownish Colour without, and red within, having two or three Stones about as large as a Walnut in the midst: tho' I saw many of these fallen under the Trees, yet I dared not to meddle with them for some time, till I saw some Wild Hogs eat them with safety, and then I thought I might venture upon them too, after such Tasters, and I found them to be a very delicious sort of Fruit; they are called Mammees Supporters, as I learned afterwards. There are also a sort of small Beech-Plumb, growing upon low shrubs; and a large form of Plumb growing upon Trees, which are called Hog-Plumbs; and many other sorts of Fruit which I am wholly a Stranger to. Only I would take notice of the Goodness of GOD to me, in preserving me from destroying myself by feeding upon any Noxious

Fruit, as the Mangeneil Apple, which I often took up in my hands, and look'd upon, but had not the power to eat of; which if I had, it would have been present Death to me, as I was informed afterwards, tho' I knew not what it was.

There are also upon this Island, and the Adjacent Islands and Keys, Deer, and Wild Hogs; they abound too with Fowl of diverse sorts, as Ducks, Teil, Curlews, Galdings, (a Fowl long Legged, and shaped somewhat like a Heron, but not so big) Pellicans, Boobys, Pigeons, Parrotts, &c. and the Shoars abound with Tortoise.

But of all this Store of Beast, and Fowl, I could make no use to Supply my Necessities; tho' my Mouth often watered for a Bit of them; yet I was forced to go without it; for I had no Knife, or other Instrument of Iron with me, by which to cut up a Tortoise, when I had turned it; or to make Snares or Pitts, with which to entrap, or Bows and Arrows with which to kill any Bird or Beast withal; nor could I by any possible means that I knew of, come at Fire to dress any if I had taken them, tho' I doubt not but some would have gone down Raw, if I could have come at it.

I sometimes had thoughts of Digging Pits and covering them over with small Branches of Trees, & laying Brush and Leaves upon them to take some Hogs or Deer in; but all was vain imagination, I had no Shovel, neither could I find or make any thing that would answer my end, and I was presently convinced, that my Hands alone, were not sufficient to make one deep and large eno' to detain any thing that should fall into it; so that I was forced to rest satisfied with the Fruit of the Vine, and Trees, and looked upon it as good Provision, and very handy for one in my Condition.

In length of time, as I was poking about the Beech, with a Stick, to see if I could find any Tortoise Nests, (which I had heard lay their Eggs in the Sand) I brought up part of an Egg clinging to the Stick, and upon removing the Sand which lay over them, I found near an Hundred & Fifty Eggs which had not been laid long eno' to spoil; so I took some of them and eat them: And in this way I sometimes got some Eggs to Eat, which are not very good at the best; yet what is not good to him that has nothing to Live upon, but what falls from the Trees.

The Tortoise lay their Eggs above High Water Mark, in a hole which they make in the Sand, about a Foot, or a Foot and half deep, and cover them over with the Sand, which they make as smooth & even as any part of the Beech, so that there is no discerning where they are, by any, the least sign of a Hillock, or Rising; and according to my best observation, they Hatch in about 18 or 20 days, and as soon as the Young Ones are Hatched they betake themselves immediately to the Water.

There are many Serpents upon this, and the Adjacent Islands. There

246

is one sort that is very Large, as big round as a Man's Wast, tho' not above 12 or 14 Feet long. These are called Owlers. They look like old fallen Stocks of Trees covered over with a short Moss, when they lye at their length; but they more usually lye coiled up in a round. The first I saw of these greatly surprised me; for I was very near to it before I discovered it to be a Living Creature, and then it opened its Mouth wide eno' to have thrown a Hat into it, and blew out its Breath at me. This Serpent is very slow in its motion, and nothing Venemous, as I was afterwards told by a Man, who said he had been once bitten by one of them. There are several other smaller Serpents, some of them very Venemous, particularly one that is called a Barber's Pole, being streaked White and Yellow. But I met with no Rattlesnakes there, unless the Pirates, nor did I ever hear of any other being there.

The Islands are also greatly infested with vexatious Insects, especially the Musketto, and a sort of small Black Fly (something like a Gnat) more troublesome than the Mosketto; so that if one had never so many of the comforts of Life about him, these Insects would render his Living here very burthensome to him; unless he retired to a small Key, destitute of Woods and Brush, where the Wind disperses the Vermin.

The Sea, hereabouts, hath a variety of Fish; such as are good to Eat, I could not come at, and the Sharks, and Alligators, or Crocodiles, I did not care to have any thing to do with; tho' I was once greatly endangered by a Shark, as I shall tell afterwards.

This was the Place I was confined to; this my Society and Fellowship; and this my State and Condition of Life. Here I spent near Nine Months; without Converse with any Living Creature; for the Parrots here had not been taught to Speak. Here I lingred out one Day after another, I knew not how, without Business or Diversion; unless gathering up my Food, rambling from Hill to Hill, from Island to Island, gazing upon the Water, and staring upon the Face of the Sky, may be called so.

In this Lonely and Distressed Condition, I had time to call over my past Life; and Young as I was, I saw I had grown Old in Sin; my Transgressions were more than my Days; and tho' GOD had graciously Restrained me from the Grosser Enormities of Life, yet I saw Guilt staring me in the Face; eno' to humble me and forever to vindicate the Justice of GOD in all that I underwent. I called to mind many things I had heard from the Pulpit, and what I had formerly Read in the Bible, which I was now wholly destitute of, tho' I thought if I could but have one now, it would have sweetened my Condition, by the very Diversion of Reading, and much more from the Direction and Comfort it would have afforded me. I had some Comforts in the midst of my Calamity. It was no small Support to me, that I was about my Lawful Employment, when I was first taken; and that I had no hand in bringing my Misery upon myself, but was forced away sorely against my Will. It wonderfully alleviated my Sorrows, to think, that I had my Parents approbation, and consent in my going to Sea; and I often fancied to myself, that if I had gone to Sea against their will and pleasure, and had met with this Disaster, I should have looked upon it as a designed Punishment of such Disobedience, and the very Reflection on it would have so aggravated my Misery, as soon to have put an end to my Days. I looked upon my self also, as more in the way of the Divine Blessing now, than when I was linked to a Crew of Pirates, where I could scarce hope for Protection and a Blessing. I plainly saw very signal Instances of the Power & Goodness of God to me, in the many Deliverances which I had already experienced (the least of which I was utterly unworthy of) and this Encouraged me to put my Trust in Him: and tho' I had none but GOD to go to for help, yet I knew that He was able to do more for me than I could ask or think: to Him therefore I committed myself, purposing to wait hopefully upon the Lord till He should send Deliverance to me: Trusting that in His own time and way he would find out means for my safe Return to my Fathers House; and earnestly entreating that he would provide a better place for me.

It was my Daily Practice to Ramble from one part of the Island to another, tho' I had a more special Home near to the Water side. Here I had built me a House to defend me from the heat of the Sun by Day, and the great Dews of the Night. I took some of the best Branches I could find fallen from the Trees, and stuck them in the Ground, and I contrived as often as I could (for I built many such Huts) to fix them leaning against the Limb of a Tree that hung low; I split the Palmeto Leaves and knotted the Limb & Sticks together; then I covered them over with the largest and best Palmeto Leaves I could find. I generally Situated my Hut near the Water side, with the open part of it facing the Sea, that I might be the more ready upon the look out, and have the advantage of the Sea Breeze, which both the Heat and the Vermin required. But the Vermin, the Muskettos and Flys, grew so troublesome to me, that I was put upon contrivance to get rid of their Company. This led me to think of getting over to some of the Adjacent Keys, that I might have some Rest from the disturbance of these busy Companions. My greatest difficulty lay in getting over to any other Island; for I was but a very poor Swimmer; and I had no Canoo, nor any means of making one. At length I got a piece of Bamboe, which is hollow like a Reed, and light as a Cork, and having made tryal of it under my Breast and Arms in Swimming by the Shoar; with this help I e'en ventured to put off for a small Key about Gunshot off, and I reached it pretty comfortably. This Key was but about 3 or 400 Feet in compass, clear of Woods & Brush, & lay very low: & I found it so free

248

from the Vermin, by the free Passage of the Wind over it, that I seemed to be got into a New World, where I lived more at ease. This I kept as a place of Retreat, whither I retired when the Heat of the Day rendred the Fly-kind most troublesome to me: for I was obliged to be much upon Roatan for the sake of my Food, Water, and House. When I swam backward and forward from my Night to my Day Island, I used to bind my Frock and Trousers about my Head, but I could not so easily carry over Wood and Leaves to make a Hut of; else I should have spent more of my time upon my little Day Island.

My Swimming thus backward & forward exposed me to some Danger. Once I remember as I was passing from my Day to my Night Island, the Bamboe got from under me e'er I was aware, & the Tide or Current set so strong, that I was very difficultly put to it to recover the Shoar; so that a few Rods more distance had in all probability landed me in another World. At another time as I was Swimming over to my Day Island, a Shovel nos'd Shark, (of which the Seas thereabouts are full, as well as Alligators) struck me in the Thigh just as I set my Foot to Ground, & so grounded himself (I suppose) by the shoalness of the Water, that he could not turn himself to come at me with his Mouth, & so, thro' the Goodness of GOD, I escaped falling a Prey to his devouring Teeth. I felt the Blow he gave me some hours after I had got ashoar. By accustoming myself to Swim, I at length grew pretty dexterous at it, and often gave myself the Diversion of thus passing from one Island to an other among the Keys.

One of my greatest difficulties lay in my being Barefoot, my Travels backward and forward in the Woods to hunt for my Daily Food, among the thick under-brush, where the Ground was covered with sharp Sticks & Stones, & upon the hot Beech among the sharp broken Shells, had made so many Wounds and Gashes in my Feet, & some of them very large, that I was hardly able to go at all. Very often as I was treading with all the tenderness I could, a sharp Stone or Shell on the Beech or pointed Stick in the Woods, would run into the old Wounds, & the Anguish of it would strike me down as suddenly as if I had been shot thro', & oblige me to set down and Weep by the hour together at the extremity of my Pain; so that in process of time I could Travel no more than needs must, for the necessary procuring of Food. Sometimes I have sat leaning my Back against a Tree, with my Face to the Sea, to look for the passing of a Vessel for a whole Day together.

At length I grew very Weak and Faint, as well as Sore and Bruised; and once while I was in this Condition, a Wild Boar seemed to make at me with some Fierceness; I knew not what to do with my self, for I was not able to defend myself against him if he should attack me. So as he drew nearer to me, I caught hold of the Limb of a Tree which

249

was close by me, & drew my Body up by it from the Ground as well as I could; While I was in this Hanging posture, the Boar came and struck at me, but his Tushes only took hold of my shattered Trousers & tore a piece out; and then he went his way. This I think was the only time that I was assaulted by any Wild Beast, with whom I said I had made Peace; and I look upon it as a Great Deliverance.

As my Weakness encreased upon me, I should often fall down as tho' struck with a dead sleep, and many a time as I was thus falling, and sometimes when I lay'd myself down to Sleep, I never expected to wake or rise more; and yet in the midst of all GOD has Wonderfully preserved me.

In the midst of this my great Soreness and Feebleness I lost the days of the Week, & how long I had layn in some of my numb sleepy Fits I knew not, so that I was not able now to distinguish the Sabbath from any other Day of the Week; tho' all Days were in some sort a Sabbath to me. As my Illness prevailed I wholly lost the Month, and knew not whereabouts I was in the Account of Time.

Under all this Dreadful Distress, I had no healing Balsames to apply to my Feet, no Cordials to revive my Fainting Spirits, hardly able now & then to get me some Figs or Grapes to Eat, nor any possible way of coming at a Fire, which the Cool Winds, & great Rains, beginning to come on now called for. The Rains begin about the middle of October, & continue for Five Months together, and then the Air is Raw Cold, like our North East Storms of Rain; only at times the Sun breaks out with such an exceeding Fierceness, that there is hardly any enduring the Heat of it.

I had often heard of the fetching Fire by Rubbing of two Sticks together; but I could never get any this way; tho' I had often tried when I was in Health and Strength, untill I was quite tired. Afterwards I learned the way of getting Fire from two Sticks, which I will Publish, that it may be of Service to any that may be hereafter in my Condition.

Take Two Sticks, the one of harder, the other of softer Wood, the dryer the better, in the soft Wood make a sort of Mortice or Socket, point the harder Wood to fit that Socket; hold the softer Wood firm between the Knees, take the harder Wood between your Hands with the point fixed in the Socket, and rub the Stick in your Hands backward & forward briskly like a Drill, and it will take Fire in less than a Minute; as I have sometimes since seen, upon experiment made of it.

But then I knew of no such Method (and it may be should have been difficultly put to it to have formed the Mortice and Drill for want of a Knife) and I suffered greatly without a Fire, thro' the Chillness of the Air, the Wetness of the Season, and Living only upon Raw Fruit.

Thus I pass'd about Nine Months in this lonely, melancholy,

wounded, and languishing Condition. I often layd my self down as upon my last Bed, & concluded I should certainly Dye alone, & no Body knew what was become of me. I thought it would be some relief to me if my Parents could but tell where I was; and then I thought their Distress would be exceeding great, if they knew what I underwent. But all such thoughts were vain. The more my Difficulties encreased, and the nearer prospect I had of Dying, the more it drove me upon my Knees, and made me the more earnest in my Crys to my Maker for His favourable regards to me, and to the Great Redeemer to pardon me, and provide for my after well being.

And see the Surprising Goodness of GOD to me, in sending me help in my time of trouble, & that in the most unexpected way & manner, as tho' an Angel had been commissioned from Heaven to relieve me.

Sometime in November, 1723, I espied a small Canoo, coming towards me with one Man in it. It did not much surprise me. A Friend I could not hope for; and I could not resist, or hardly get out of the way of an Enemy, nor need I fear one. I kept my Seat upon the Edge of the Beech. As he came nearer he discovered me & seemed greatly surprised. He called to me. I told him whence I was, & that he might safely venture ashoar, for I was alone, & almost Dead. As he came up to me, he star'd & look'd wild with surprise; my Garb and Countenance astonished him; he knew not what to make of me; he started back a little, & viewed me more thorowly; but upon recovering of himself, he came forward, & took me by the Hand & told me he was glad to see me. And he was ready as long as he stayed with me, to do any kind offices for me.

He proved to be a North-Britain, a Man well in Years, of a Grave and Venerable Aspect, and of a reserved Temper. His Name I never knew, for I had not asked him in the little time he was with me, expecting a longer converse with him; and he never told me it. But he acquainted me that he had lived with the Spaniards 22 Years, and now they threatened to Burn him, I knew not for what Crime: therefore he had fled for Sanctuary to this Place, & had brought his Gun, Ammunition, and Dog, with a small quantity of Pork, designing to spend the residue of his Days here, & support himself by Hunting. He seemed very kind and obliging to me, gave me some of his Pork, and assisted me all he could; tho' he conversed little.

Upon the Third Day after he came to me, he told me, he would go out in his Canoo among the Islands, to kill some Wild Hogs & Deer, and would have me to go along with him. His Company, the Fire, and a little dressed Provision something recruited my Spirits, but yet I was so Weak, and Sore in my Feet, that I could not accompany him in Hunting: So he set out alone, and said he would be with me again in a Day or two. The Sky was Serene and Fair, and there was no

251

prospect of any Danger in his little Voyage among the Islands, when he had come safe in that small Float near 12 Leagues; but by that time he had been gone an Hour, there arose a most Violent Gust of Wind and Rain, which in all probability overset him; so that I never saw nor heard of him any more. And tho' by this means I was deprived of my Companion, yet it was the Goodness of GOD to me, that I was not well eno' to go with him; for thus I was preserved from that Destruction which undoubtedly overtook him.

Thus after the pleasure of having a Companion almost Three Days, I was as unexpectedly reduced to my former lonely Condition, as I had been for a little while recovered out of it. It was grievous to me to think that I no longer saw the Dawnings of Light, after so long Obscurity, but the Clouds returned after the Rain upon me. I began to experience the Advantage of a Companion, and find that Two is better than One, and flattered my self, that by the help of some fresh Hogs Grease, I should get my Feet well, and by a better Living recover more Strength. But it pleased GOD to take from me the only Man I had seen for so many Months after so short a Converse with him. Yet I was left in better Circumstances by him than he found me in. For at his going away he left with me about Five Pound of Pork, a Knife, a Bottle of Powder, Tobacco Tongs and Flint, by which means I was in a way to Live better than I had done. For now I could have a Fire, which was very needful for me, the Rainy Months of the Winter; I could cut up some Tortoise when I had turned them, and have a delicate broiled Meal of it; So that by the help of the Fire, and Dressed Food, and the Blessing of GOD accompanying it, I began to recover more Strength, only my Feet remained sore.

Besides, I had this Advantage now, which I had not before, that I could go out now and then and catch a Dish of Crab-Fish, a Fish much like a Lobster, only wanting the great Claws. My manner of catching them was odd; I took some of the best pieces of the old broken small Wood, that came the nearest to our Pitch Pine, or Candle-Wood, and made them up into a small Bundle like a Torch, and holding one of these lighted at one End in one hand, I waded into the Water upon the Beech up to my Wast: the Crab-Fish, spying the Light at a considerable distance, would crawl away till they came directly under it, and then they would lye still at my Feet. In my other hand I had a Forked Stick with which I struck the Fish and tossed it ashoar. In this manner I supplyed my self with a Mess of Shell-Fish, which when roasted is very good Eating.

Between two and three Months after I had lost my Companion, as I was ranging a long shoar, I found a small Canoo. The sight of this at first renewed my Sorrows for his Loss; for I thought it had been his Canoo, and it's coming ashore thus, was a proof to me that he was lost in the Tempest: but upon further Examination of it I found it was one I had never seen before.

When I had got this little Vessel in possession, I began to think my self Admiral of the Neighbouring Seas, as well as Sole Possessor and Chief Commander upon the Islands; and with the advantage hereof I could transport my self to my small Islands of Retreat, much more conveniently than in my former Method of Swimming. In process of time I tho't of making a Tour to some of the more distant and larger Islands, to see after what manner they were inhabited, and how they were provided, and partly to give my self the Liberty of Diversions. So I lay'd in a small parcel of Grapes and Figs, and some Tortoise, & took my Fire-Works with me, and put off for the Island of Bonacco, an Island of about 4 or 5 Leagues long, and some 5 or 6 Leagues to the Eastward of Roatan.

As I was upon my Voyage, I discovered a Sloop at the Eastern End of the Island; so I made the best of my way, and put in at the Western End; designing to travel down to them by Land, partly because there ran out a large point of Rocks far into the Sea, and I did not care to venture my self so far out in my little Canoo as I must do to head them: & partly because I was willing to make a better discovery of them, before I was seen by them; for in the midst of my most deplorable Circumstances, I could never entertain the thoughts of returning on board any Pirate, if I should have the opportunity, but had rather Live and Dye as I was. So I haled up my Canoo, and fastened her as well as I could, and set out upon my Travel.

I spent two Days, and the biggest part of two Nights in Travelling of it; my Feet were yet so sore that I could go but very slowly, and sometimes the Woods and Bushes were so thick that I was forced to Crawl upon my Hands and Knees for half a Mile together. In this Travel I met with an odd Adventure that had liked to have proved fatal to me, and my preservation was an eminent Instance of the Divine Conduct and Protection.

As I drew within a Mile or two of where I supposed the Sloop might be, I made down to the Water side, and slowly opened the Sea, that I might not discover my self too soon; when I came down to the Water side I could see no sign of the Sloop, upon which I concluded that it was gone clear, while I spent so much time in Travelling. I was very much tired with my long tedious March, and sat my self down leaning against the Stock of a Tree facing to the Sea, and fell a Sleep. But I had not slept long before I was awakened in a very surprising manner, by the noise of Guns. I started up in a fright, and saw nine Periaguas, or large Canooes, full of men firing upon me. I soon turned about and ran as fast as my sore Feet would let me into the Bushes; and the Men which were Spaniards, cryed after me, O

Englishman, we'll give you good Quarter. But such was the Surprise I had taken, by being awakened out of Sleep in such a manner, that I had no command of my self to hearken to their offers of Quarter, which it may be at another time under cooler thoughts I might have done. So I made into the Woods, and they continued Firing after me, to the number of 150 small Shot at least, many of which cut off several small Twigs of the Bushes along side of me as I went off. When I had got out of the reach of their Shot, into a very great Thicket, I lay close for several Hours; and perceiving they were gone by the noise of their Oars in Rowing off, I came out of my Thicket, and Travelled a Mile or two along the Water side, below the place where they Fired upon me, and then I saw the Sloop under English Colours, Sailing out of the Harbour, with the Periaguas in tow; and then I concluded that it was an English Sloop that had been at the Bay, whom the Spaniards had met with and taken.

The next Day I went up to the Tree, where I so narrowly Escaped being taken Napping, and there to my surprise I found 6 or 7 shot had gone into the Body of the Tree, within a Foot or less of my Head as I sat down; & yet thro' the wonderful goodness of GOD to me, in the midst of all their Fire, and tho' I was as a Mark set up for them to shoot at, none of their Shot touched me. So did GOD as yet signally preserve me.

After this I Travelled away for my Canoo at the Western End of the Island, and spent near three Days e'er I reached it. In this long March backward and forward, I suffered very much from the Soreness of my Feet, & the want of Provisions; for this Island is not so plentifully stored with Fruit as Roatan is, so that I was very difficultly, put to it for my Subsistence, for the 5 or 6 Days that I spent here; and besides the Musketoes and Black Flys were abundantly more numerous, and vexatious to me than at my old Habitation. The Difficulties I met with here made me lay aside all thoughts of tarrying any time to search the Island. At length much tired and spent I reached my Canoo, and found all safe there, to my great Joy; and then I put off for Roatan, which was a Royal Palace to me in comparison of Bonacco, where I arrived to my great Satisfaction about Ten a Clock at Night, & found all things as I left them.

Here I lived (if it may be called Living) alone for about Seven Months more, from the time of my loosing my North British Companion; and spent my time after my usual manner in Hunting for my Food, and Ranging the Islands; till at length it pleased GOD, to send some Company to me, with whom I could Converse, and enjoy somewhat more of the Comforts of Life.

Sometime in June, 1724, as I was upon my small Island, where I often retired for Shelter from the pestering Insects, I saw two large

Canooes making for the Harbour; as they drew near they saw the
Smoak of the Fire which I had kindled, and wondring what it should
mean came to a stand. I had fresh in my Memory what I met with at
Banacco, and was very loth to run the risque of such another firing,
and therefore stept to my Canoo upon the back side of my small
Island, not above 100 feet off from me, and immediately went over to
my great Mansion, where I had places of Safety to Shelter me from
the Designs of an Enemy, and Rooms large and spacious eno' to give
a kindly welcome to any ordinary number of Friends. They saw me
cross the Ferry of about Gun shot over, from my little to my great
Island, and being as much afraid of Spaniards, as I was of Pirates, they
drew very cautiously towards the shoar. I came down upon the Beech,
shewing my self openly to them, for their caution made me think they
were no Pirates, and I did not much care who else they were; however
I thought I could call to them, and know what they were, before I
should be in much danger from their shot; and if they proved such as
I did not like, I could easily retire from them. But before I called, they,
who were as full of fears as I could be, lay upon their Oars, and
hallooed to me, enquiring who I was, and whence I came; I told them
I was an English Man, and had run away from the Pirates. Upon this
they drew something nearer and enquired who was there besides my
self; I assured them I was alone. Then I took my turn, and asked them
who they were, and whence they came. They told me they were Bay-
men, come from the Bay. This was comfortable News to me; so I bid
them pull ashoar, there was no danger, I would stop for them. Accordingly they put ashoar, but at some distance from me, and first
sent one Man ashoar to me; whom I went to meet. When the Man
came up to me he started back, frighted to see such a Poor, Ragged,
Lean, Wan, Forlorn, Wild, Miserable Object so near him; but upon
recovering himself, he came and took me by the hand, and we fell to
embracing one another, he with surprise and wonder, I with a sort of
Extasy of Joy. After this was over he took me in his Arms and carried
me down to their Canooes, where they were all struck with astonishment at the sight of me, were glad to receive me, and expressed a very
great tenderness to me.

I gave them a short History how I had escaped from Low, and had
lived here alone for Sixteen Months, (saving three days) what hardship I had met with, and what danger I had run thro'. They stood
Amazed! They wondred I was alive! and expressed a great satisfaction
in it, that they were come to relieve me. And observing I was weak,
and my Spirits low, they gave me about a Spoonful of Rhum to re-
cruit my fainting Spirits. This small quantity, thro' my long disuse of
any Liquor higher Spirited than Water, and my present weakness,
threw my Animal Spirits into such a violent Agitation, as to obstruct

their Motion, and produced a kind of Stupor, which left me for some time bereft of all Sense; some of them perceiving me falling into such a strange Insensibility, would have given me more of the same Spirit to have recovered me; but those of them that had more wit, would not allow of it. So I lay for some time in a sort of Fit, and they were ready to think that they should lose me as soon as they had found me. But I revived.

Twice kidnapped, or Fanny Noble
among the Indians[1]

James Whidden, the maternal grandfather of Mrs. Shute, was a captain in the army at the taking of Cape Breton in 1745. He owned a tract of land on Swan Island, in the river Kennebec, where he lived with his family. One of his daughters married Lazarus Noble, of Portsmouth, who lived on the island with her father. The Indians had been accustomed to visit Capt. Whidden for the purposes of trade. There was a garrison on the island to secure the inhabitants from the attacks of the enemy in time of war.

One morning, a little after daybreak, two boys went out of the garrison and left the gate open. The Indians were on the watch, and availing themselves of the opportunity, about ninety entered the garrison. The inhabitants immediately discovered that the enemy was upon them; but there was no escape. Captain Whidden and his wife retreated to the cellar, and concealed themselves. Noble and his hired man met the Indians at the head of the stairs, and fired upon them, wounding one of them in the arm. The Indians did not return the fire, but took Noble, his wife, and seven children, with Timothy Whidden and Mary Holmes, prisoners. The hired man and the two boys escaped. The captives were carried to the water's side and bound; excepting such as could not run away. The Indians then returned to the garrison, burnt the barn and plundered the house, cut open the feather beds, strewed the feathers in the field, and carried off all the silver and gold they could find, and as much of the provisions as they chose. It was supposed they omitted to burn the house from the suspicion that the

---

[1] *Of the Captivity of Frances Noble, who was, among others, taken by the Indians from Swan Island, in Maine, about the year 1755;* compiled by John Kelly, Esq., of Concord, New Hampshire, from the Minutes and Memoranda of Phinehas Merrill, Esq., of Stratham, in the same State; and by the former Gentleman communicated for publication to the Editors of the Historical Collections of New Hampshire. Reprinted by S. G. Drake: *Tragedies of the Wilderness* (Boston, 1846), pp. 165–72.

captain and his wife, from whom they had, in times of peace, received many favors, were concealed in it. Capt. Whidden, after the destruction of his property on the island, returned to Greenland, in this state, which is supposed to have been his native place, and there died.

The Indians also took in a wood on the island an old man by the name of Pomeroy, who was employed in making shingles. Having collected their captives and plunder, they immediately left the island, and commenced their return to Canada to dispose of their prey. Pomeroy was old and feeble, and unable to endure the fatigue of the march, without more assistance than the savages thought fit to render him, and they killed him on the journey. They were more attentive to the children, as for them they undoubtedly expected a higher price or a greater ransom. Abigail, one of the children, died among the Indians. The other captives arrived safe in Canada, and were variously disposed of. Mr. Noble was sold to a baker in Quebec, and his wife to a lady of the same place as a chambermaid. They were allowed to visit each other and to sleep together. Four of the children were also sold in Quebec, as were Timothy Whidden and Mary Holmes. The captives in that city were exchanged within a year, and returned to their homes. Mr. Whidden and Miss Holmes were afterwards united in marriage.

Fanny Noble, the principal subject of this memoir, at the time of her captivity, was about thirteen months old. She was carried by a party of Indians to Montreal. In their attempts to dispose of her, they took her one day to the house of Monsieur Louis St. Auge Charlee, an eminent merchant of that place, who was at that time on a journey to Quebec. His lady was called into the kitchen by one of her maids to see a poor infant crawling on the tile floor in dirt and rags, picking apple peelings out of the cracks. She came in, and on kindly noticing the child, Fanny immediately caught hold of the lady's gown, wrapped it over her head, and burst into tears. The lady could not easily resist this appeal to her compassion. She took up the child, who clung about her neck and repeatedly embraced her. The Indians offered to sell her their little captive, but she declined buying, not choosing probably in the absence of her husband to venture on such a purchase. The Indians left the house, and slept that night on the pavements before the door. Fanny, who had heard again the voice of kindness, to which she had not been accustomed from her savage masters, could not be quiet, but disturbed the slumbers and touched the heart of the French lady by her incessant cries. This lady had then lately lost a child by death, and was perhaps more quick to feel for the sufferings of children, and more disposed to love them, than she would otherwise have been. Early the next morning the Indians were called into the house; Fanny was purchased, put into a tub of water, and having been thoroughly washed, was dressed in the clothes of the deceased child, and put to bed. She awoke smiling, and seemed desirous of repaying her mistress' kindness by her infantile prattle and fond caresses. Fanny could never learn for what price she was bought of the Indians, as her French mother declined answering her questions upon that subject, telling her to be a good girl, and be thankful that she was not still in their power.

Mons. and Mad. St. Auge took a lively interest in their little captive, and treated her with much tenderness and affection. She felt for them a filial attachment. When her parents were exchanged, her mother, on her return home, called upon Fanny, and took the child in her arms, but no instinct taught her to rejoice in the maternal embrace, and she fled for protection to her French mamma. Mrs. Noble received many presents from the French lady, and had the satisfaction to see that her little daughter was left in affectionate hands.

Fanny was taught to call and consider Mons. and Mad. St. Auge as her parents. They had her baptized by the name of Eleanor, and educated her in the Roman Catholic religion. She learned her Pater Nosters and Ave Marias, went to mass, crossed herself with holy water, and told her beads with great devotion.

When four or five years old, she was enticed away from her French parents by Wheelwright, who had been employed by the government of Massachusetts to seek for captives in Canada. He carried her to the Three Rivers, where he had several other captives, and left her, as he pretended, with a relation of her French father's for a few days, when she expected to return to Montreal. But she had not been to the Three Rivers more than twenty-four hours, when the old squaw who had sold her to Mad. St. Auge came along in a sleigh, accompanied by a young sanop, seized upon Fanny, and carried her to St. Francois, where they kept her about a fortnight. She had now attained an age when she would be sensible of her misfortunes, and bitterly lamented her separation from her French parents. The Indians endeavored to pacify and please her by drawing on her coat or frock the figures of deers, wolves, bears, fishes, etc.; and once, probably to make her look as handsomely as themselves, they painted her cheeks in the Indian fashion, which very much distressed her, and the old squaw made them wipe off the paint. At one time she got away from the savages, and sought refuge in the best-looking house in the village, which belonged to a French priest, who kissed her, asked her many questions and treated her kindly, but gave her up to the claim of her Indian masters. While at St. Francois, her brother, Joseph Noble, who had not been sold to the French, but still lived with the Indians, came to see her, but she had a great aversion to him. He was in his Indian dress, and she would not believe him to be a relation, or speak to him if she could avoid it. She was at last turned back by the Indians to Montreal, and to her great satisfaction was delivered to her French father, who rewarded the Indians for returning her. It was doubtless the expectation of much reward which induced the old squaw to seize her at the Three Rivers, as the Indians not infrequently stole back captives, in order to extort presents for their return from the French gentlemen to whom the same captives had before been sold. Before this time she had been hastily carried from Montreal, hurried over mountains and across waters, and concealed among flags, while those who accompanied her were evidently pursued, and in great apprehension of being overtaken; but the occasion of this flight or its incidents she was too young to understand or distinctly to remember, and she was unable afterwards to satisfy herself whether her French father conveyed her away to keep her out of the reach of her natural friends, or whether she was taken by those friends, and afterwards retaken as at the Three Rivers and returned to Montreal. The French parents cautiously avoided informing her upon this subject, or upon any other which should remind her of her captivity, her country, her parents or her friends, lest she should become discontented with her situation, and desirous of leaving those who had adopted her. They kept her secreted from her natural friends, who were in search of her, and evaded every question which might lead to her discovery. One day, when Mons. St. Auge and most of his family were at mass, she was sent with another captive to the third story of the house, and the domestics were required strictly to watch them, as it was known that some of her relations were then in the place endeavoring to find her. Of this circumstance she was ignorant, but she was displeased with her confinement, and with her little companion found means to escape from their room and went below. While raising a cup of water to her mouth, she saw a man looking at her through the window, and stretching out his arm toward her, at the same time speaking a language which she could not understand. She was very much alarmed, threw down her water, and ran with all possible speed to her room. Little did she suppose that it was her own father from whom she was flying in such fear and horror. He had returned to Canada to seek those of his children who remained there. He could hear nothing of his Fanny; but watching the house, he perceived her, as was just stated, and joyfully stretching his arms towards her, exclaimed, "There's my daughter! O! that's my daughter!" But she retreated, and he could not gain admittance, for the house was guarded and no stranger permitted to enter. How long he continued hovering about her is now unknown, but he left Canada without embracing her or seeing her again.

Her French parents put her into a boarding school attached to a nunnery in Montreal, where she remained several years, and was taught all branches of needle-work, with geography, music, painting, etc. In the same school were two Misses Johnsons, who were captured at

Charlestown, N.H., in 1754, and two Misses Phipps, the daughters of Mrs. Howe, who were taken at Hinsdale in 1755. Fanny was in school when Mrs. Howe came for her daughters, and long remembered the grief and lamentations of the young captives when obliged to leave their school and mates to return to a strange, though their native country, and to relatives whom they had long forgotten.

While at school at Montreal, her brother Joseph again visited her. He still belonged to the St. Francois tribe of Indians, and was dressed remarkably fine, having forty or fifty broaches in his shirt, clasps on his arm, and a great variety of knots and bells about his clothing. He brought his little sister Ellen, as she was then called, and who was then not far from seven years old, a young fawn, a basket of cranberries, and a lump of sap sugar. The little girl was much pleased with the fawn, and had no great aversion to cranberries and sugar, but she was much frightened by the appearance of Joseph, and would receive nothing at his hands till, at the suggestion of her friends, he had washed the paint from his face and made some alteration in his dress, when she ventured to accept his offerings, and immediately ran from his presence. The next day Joseph returned with the Indians to St. Francois, but some time afterwards Mons. St. Auge purchased him of the savages, and dressed him in the French style; but he never appeared so bold and majestic, so spirited and vivacious, as when arrayed in his Indian habit and associating with his Indian friends. He however became much attached to St. Auge, who put him to school; and when his sister parted from him upon leaving Canada, he gave her a strict charge not to let it be known where he was, lest he too should be obliged to leave his friends and return to the place of his birth.

When between eleven and twelve years of age, Fanny was sent to the school of Ursuline nuns in Quebec, to complete her education. Here the discipline was much more strict and solemn than in the school at Montreal. In both places the teachers were called half nuns, who, not being professed, were allowed to go in and out at pleasure; but at Quebec the pupils were in a great measure secluded from the world, being permitted to walk only in a small garden by day, and confined by bolts and bars in their cells at night. This restraint was irksome to Fanny. She grew discontented; and at the close of the year was permitted to return to her French parents at Montreal, and again enter the school in that city.

While Fanny was in the nunnery, being then in her fourteenth year, she was one day equally surprised and alarmed by the entrance of a stranger, who demanded her of the nuns as a redeemed captive. Her father had employed this man, Arnold, to seek out his daughter and obtain her from the French, who had hitherto succeeded in detaining her. Arnold was well calculated for this employment. He was secret,

subtle, resolute and persevering. He had been some time in the city
without exciting a suspicion of his business. He had ascertained where
the captive was to be found—he had procured the necessary powers to
secure her, and in his approach to the nunnery was accompanied by a
sergeant and a file of men. The nuns were unwilling to deliver up their
pupil, and required to know by what right he demanded her. Arnold
convinced them that his authority was derived from the governor, and
they durst not disobey. They, however, prolonged the time as much
as possible, and sent word to Mons. St. Auge, hoping that he would be
able in some way or other to detain his adopted daughter. Arnold
however was not to be delayed or trifled with. He sternly demanded
the captive by the name of Noble in the governor's name, and the
nuns were awed into submission. Fanny, weeping and trembling, was
delivered up by those who wept and trembled too. She accompanied
Arnold to the gate of the nunnery, but the idea of leaving forever
those whom she loved and going with a company of armed men she
knew not whither, was too overwhelming, and she sunk upon the
ground. Her cries and lamentations drew the people around her, and
she exclaimed bitterly against the cruelty of forcing her away, declaring that she could not and would not go any further as a prisoner
with those frightful soldiers. At this time an English officer appeared
in the crowd; he reasoned with her, soothed her, and persuaded her to
walk with him, assuring her the guard should be dismissed and no
injury befall her. As they passed by the door of Mons. St. Auge, on
their way to the inn, her grief and exclamations were renewed, and it
was with great difficulty that she could be persuaded to proceed. But
the guard had merely fallen back, and were too near to prevent a
rescue, had an attempt been made. Capt. M'Clure, the English officer,
promised her that she should be permitted to visit her French parents
the next day. She found them in tears, but they could not detain her.
Mons. St. Auge gave her a handful of money, embraced her, blessed
her, and rushed out of the room. His lady supplied her with clothes,
and their parting was most affectionate and affecting. She lived to a
considerably advanced age, but she could never speak of this scene
without visible and deep emotion.

She was carried down the river to Quebec, where she tarried a few
days, and then sailed with Captain Wilson for Boston. She arrived
at that port in July, one month before she was fourteen years of age.
She was joyfully received by her friends, but her father did not long
survive her return. After his death she resided in the family of Capt.
Wilson, at Boston, until she had acquired the English language, of
which before she was almost entirely ignorant. She then went to New-
bury, and lived in the family of a relative of her father, where she
found a home, and that peace to which she had long been a stranger.

Her education had qualified her for the instruction of youth, and she partially devoted herself to that employment. She was engaged in a school at Hampton, where she formed an acquaintance with Mr. Jonathan Tilton, a gentleman of good property in Kensington, whom she married about the year 1776. He died in 1798. In 1801, she married Mr. John Shute, of New-Market, and lived in the village of Newfields in that town till her death, in September, 1819. She was much respected and esteemed in life, and her death was, as her life had been, that of a Christian.

Captain Carver's narrative[1]

G en. Webb, who commanded the English army in North America, which was then encamped at Fort Edward, having intelligence that the French troops under Monsieur Montcalm were making some movements towards Fort William Henry, he detached a corps of about fifteen hundred men, consisting of English and provincials, to strengthen the garrison. In this party I went as a volunteer among the latter.

The apprehensions of the English general were not without foundation; for the day after our arrival we saw Lake George (formerly Lake Sacrament) to which it lies contiguous, covered with an immense number of boats; and in a few hours we found our lines attacked by the French general, who had just landed with eleven thousand regulars and Canadians, and two thousand Indians. Colonel Monro, a brave officer, commanded in the fort, and had no more than two thousand three hundred men with him, our detachment included.

With these he made a gallant defence, and probably would have been able at last to preserve the fort, had he been properly supported, and permitted to continue his efforts. On every summons to surrender sent by the French general, who offered the most honorable terms, his answer repeatedly was, that he yet found himself in a condition to repel the most vigorous attacks his besiegers were able to make; and if he thought his present force insufficient, he could soon be supplied with a greater number from the adjacent army.

But the colonel having acquainted General Webb with his situation, and desired he would send him some fresh troops, the general dis-

---

[1] *Captain Jonathan Carver's Narrative of his Capture, and subsequent Escape from the Indians, at the bloody Massacre committed by them, when Fort William Henry fell into the Hands of the French, under Gen. Montcalm, in the year 1757.* Written by himself. Reprinted by S. G. Drake: *Tragedies of the Wilderness* (Boston, 1846), pp. 172–78.

patched a messenger to him with a letter, wherein he informed him that it was not in his power to assist him, and therefore gave him orders to surrender up the fort on the best terms he could procure. This packet fell into the hands of the French general, who immediately sent a flag of truce, desiring a conference with the governor.

They accordingly met, attended only by a small guard, in the centre between the lines; when Monsieur Montcalm told the colonel, that he was come in person to demand possession of the fort, as it belonged to the king his master. The colonel replied that he knew not how that could be, nor should he surrender it up whilst it was in his power to defend it.

The French general rejoined at the same time delivering the packet into the colonel's hand, "By this authority do I make the requisition." The brave governor had no sooner read the contents of it, and was convinced that such were the orders of the commander-in-chief, and not to be disobeyed, than he hung his head in silence, and reluctantly entered into a negotiation.

In consideration of the gallant defence the garrison had made, they were to be permitted to march out with all the honors of war, to be allowed covered wagons to transport their baggage to Fort Edward, and a guard to protect them from the fury of the savages.

The morning after the capitulation was signed, as soon as day broke, the whole garrison, now consisting of about two thousand men, besides women and children, were drawn up within the lines, and on the point of marching off, when great numbers of the Indians gathered about, and began to plunder. We were at first in hopes that this was their only view, and suffered them to proceed without opposition. Indeed it was not in our power to make any, had we been so inclined; for though we were permitted to carry off our arms, yet we were not allowed a single round of ammunition. In these hopes however we were disappointed; for presently some of them began to attack the sick and wounded, when such as were not able to crawl into the ranks, notwithstanding they endeavored to avert the fury of their enemies by their shrieks or groans, were soon dispatched.

Here we were fully in expectation that the disturbance would have concluded; and our little army began to move; but in a short time we saw the front division driven back, and discovered that we were entirely encircled by the savages. We expected every moment that the guard, which the French, by the articles of capitulation, had agreed to allow us, would have arrived, and put an end to our apprehensions; but none appeared. The Indians now began to strip every one without exception of their arms and clothes, and those who made the least resistance felt the weight of their tomahawks.

I happened to be in the rear division, but it was not long before I shared the fate of my companions. Three or four of the savages laid hold of me, and whilst some held their weapons over my head, the others soon disrobed me of my coat, waistcoat, hat and buckles, omitting not to take from me what money I had in my pockets. As this was transacted close by the passage which led from the lines on to the plain, near which a French sentinel was posted, I ran to him and claimed his protection; but he only called me an English dog, and thrust me with violence back again into the midst of the Indians.

I now endeavored to join a body of our troops that were crowded together at some distance; but innumerable were the blows that were made at me with different weapons as I passed on; luckily however the savages were so close together that they could not strike at me without endangering each other. Notwithstanding which one of them found means to make a thrust at me with a spear, which grazed my side, and from another I received a wound, with the same kind of weapon, in my ankle. At length I gained the spot where my countrymen stood, and forced myself into the midst of them. But before I got thus far out of the hands of the Indians, the collar and wristbands of my shirt were all that remained of it, and my flesh was scratched and torn in many places by their savage gripes.

By this time the war-whoop was given, and the Indians began to murder those nearest to them without distinction. It is not in the power of words to give any tolerable idea of the horrid scene that now ensued; men, women, and children were dispatched in the most wanton and cruel manner, and immediately scalped. Many of these savages drank the blood of their victims, as it flowed warm from the fatal wound.

We now perceived, though too late to avail us, that we were to expect no relief from the French; and that, contrary to the agreement they had so lately signed to allow us a sufficient force to protect us from these insults, they tacitly permitted them; for I could plainly perceive the French officers walking about at some distance, discoursing together with apparent unconcern. For the honor of human nature I would hope that this flagrant breach of every sacred law proceeded rather from the savage disposition of the Indians, which I acknowledge it is sometimes almost impossible to control, and which might now unexpectedly have arrived to a pitch not easily to be restrained, than to any premeditated design in the French commander. An unprejudiced observer would, however, be apt to conclude, that a body of ten thousand christian troops, most christian troops, had it in their power to prevent the massacre from becoming so general. But whatever was the cause from which it arose, the consequences of it were dreadful, and not to be paralleled in modern history.

As the circle in which I stood inclosed by this time was much thinned, and death seemed to be approaching with hasty strides, it was proposed by some of the most resolute to make one vigorous effort, and endeavor to force our way through the savages, the only probable method of preserving our lives that now remained. This, however desperate, was resolved on, and about twenty of us sprung at once into the midst of them.

In a moment we were all separated, and what was the fate of my companions I could not learn till some months after, when I found that only six or seven of them effected their design. Intent only on my own hazardous situation, I endeavored to make my way through my savage enemies in the best manner possible. And I have often been astonished since, when I have recollected with what composure I took, as I did, every necessary step for my preservation. Some I overturned, being at that time young and athletic, and others I passed by, dexterously avoiding their weapons; till at last two very stout chiefs, of the most savage tribes, as I could distinguish by their dress, whose strength I could not resist, laid hold of me by each arm, and began to force me through the crowd.

I now resigned myself to my fate, not doubting but that they intended to dispatch me, and then to satiate their vengeance with my blood, as I found they were hurrying me toward a retired swamp that lay at some distance. But before we had got many yards, an English gentleman of some distinction, as I could discover by his breeches, the only covering he had on, which were of fine scarlet velvet, rushed close by us. One of the Indians instantly relinquished his hold, and springing on this new object, endeavored to seize him as his prey; but the gentleman being strong, threw him on the ground, and would probably have got away, had not he who held my other arm quitted me to assist his brother. I seized the opportunity, and hastened away to join another party of English troops that were yet unbroken, and stood in a body at some distance. But before I had taken many steps, I hastily cast my eye towards the gentleman, and saw the Indian's tomahawk gash into his back, and heard him utter his last groan. This added both to my speed and desperation.

I had left this shocking scene but a few yards, when a fine boy about twelve years of age, that had hitherto escaped, came up to me, and begged that I would let him lay hold of me, so that he might stand some chance of getting out of the hands of the savages. I told him that I would give him every assistance in my power, and to this purpose bid him lay hold; but in a few minutes he was torn from my side, and by his shrieks I judge was soon demolished. I could not help forgetting my own cares for a minute, to lament the fate of so young a sufferer; but it was utterly impossible for me to take any methods to prevent it.

I now got once more into the midst of friends, but we were unable to afford each other any succor. As this was the division that had advanced the furthest from the fort, I thought there might be a possibility (though but a bare one) of my forcing my way through the outer ranks of the Indians, and getting to a neighboring wood, which I perceived at some distance. I was still encouraged to hope by the almost miraculous preservation I had already experienced.

Nor were my hopes in vain, or the efforts I made ineffectual. Suffice to say, that I reached the wood; but by the time I had penetrated a little way into it, my breath was so exhausted that I threw myself into a break, and lay for some minutes apparently at the last gasp. At length I recovered the power of respiration; but my apprehensions returned with all their former force, when I saw several savages pass by, probably in pursuit of me, at no very great distance. In this situation I knew not whether it was better to proceed, or endeavor to conceal myself where I lay till night came on; fearing, however, that they would return the same way, I thought it most prudent to get further from the dreadful scene of my distresses. Accordingly, striking into another part of the wood, I hastened on as fast as the briers and the loss of one of my shoes would permit me; and after a slow progress of some hours, gained a hill that overlooked the plain which I had just left, from whence I could discern that the bloody storm still raged with unabated fury.

But not to tire my readers, I shall only add, that after passing three days without subsistence, and enduring the severity of the cold dews for three nights, I at length reached Fort Edward; where with proper care my body soon recovered its wonted strength, and my mind, as far as the recollection of the late melancholy events would permit, its usual composure.

It was computed that fifteen hundred persons were killed or made prisoners by these savages during this fatal day. Many of the latter were carried off by them and never returned. A few, through favorable accidents, found their way back to their native country, after having experienced a long and severe captivity.

The brave Col. Monro had hastened away, soon after the confusion began, to the French camp, to endeavor to procure the guard agreed by the stipulation; but his application proving ineffectual, he remained there till General Webb sent a party of troops to demand and protect him back to Fort Edward. But these unhappy concurrences, which would probably have been prevented had he been left to pursue his own plans, together with the loss of so many brave fellows, murdered in cold blood, to whose valor he had been so lately a witness, made such an impression on his mind that he did not long survive. He died in about three months of a broken heart, and with truth might it be said that he was an honor to his country.

I mean not to point out the following circumstance as the immediate judgment of heaven, and intended as an atonement for this slaughter; but I cannot omit that very few of those different tribes of Indians that shared in it ever lived to return home. The small-pox, by means of their communication with the Europeans, found its way among them, and made an equal havoc to what they themselves had done. The methods they pursued on the first attack of that malignant disorder, to abate the fever attending it, rendered it fatal. Whilst their blood was in a state of fermentation, and nature was striving to throw out the peccant matter, they checked her operations by plunging into the water; the consequence was that they died by hundreds. The few that survived were transformed by it into hideous objects, and bore with them to the grave deep indented marks of this much dreaded disease.

Monsieur Montcalm fell soon after on the plains of Quebec.

That the unprovoked cruelty of this commander was not approved of by the generality of his countrymen, I have since been convinced of by many proofs. One only, however, which I received from a person who was witness to it, shall I at present give. A Canadian merchant, of some consideration, having heard of the surrender of the English fort, celebrated the fortunate event with great rejoicings and hospitality, according to the custom of that country; but no sooner did the news of the massacre which ensued reach his ears, than he put an immediate stop to the festivity, and exclaimed in the severest terms against the inhuman permission; declaring at the same time that those that had connived at it had thereby drawn down on that part of their king's dominions the vengeance of Heaven. To this he added, that he much feared the total loss of them would deservedly be the consequence. How truly this prediction has been verified we well know.

Ethan Allen's captivity

Ethan Allen was a man about whom legends naturally gathered. Brave, shrewd, profane, he was a popular hero; his religious skepticism, though it led President Stiles of Yale to call him "the profane and impious deist," did little or nothing to decrease his stature as an object of awe. Some of the yarns that were told of him have been collected by Stewart Holbrook in his book on Allen.[1] They make a consistent picture, but since some of them are told of other men as well, I have preferred to give the most famous Allen story in the hero's own words. As has been suggested earlier, he probably told the truth, but not the whole truth.

[1] Stewart H. Holbrook: *Ethan Allen* (New York: The Macmillan Co.; 1940). Copyright by The Macmillan Co. 1940.

Since one of the anecdotes retailed by Mr. Holbrook is also both a mosquito and a rattlesnake story, it must be told here.[1] The colonel, it seems, fell asleep out in the woods, and was bitten repeatedly by a rattler, to the horror of his companion, Remember Baker. But the snake went into convulsions, then into torpor. "Drunk, by Jesus!" exclaimed Remember Baker; for the colonel had been drinking. When he awoke, he complained bitterly of "those eternal damnable bloodsucking mosquitoes" which he thought had been biting him. The language sounds like Allen, but this does not guarantee the complete truth of the anecdote.

Ticonderoga[2]

A nd, while I was wishing for an opportunity to signalize myself in its behalf, directions were privately sent to me from the then colony (now state) of Connecticut, to raise the Green Mountain Boys, and, if possible, with them to surprise and take the fortress, Ticon-

---

[1] Ibid., pp. 268–9.
[2] From pp. 15–20 of

A NARRATIVE OF COL. ETHAN ALLEN'S CAPTIVITY.

From the time of his being taken by the British, near Montreal, on the 25th day of September, in the year 1775, to the time of his exchange, on the 6th day of May, 1778, containing

HIS VOYAGES AND TRAVELS,

With the most remarkable occurrences respecting himself, and many other continental Prisoners, of different ranks and characters, which fell under his observation in the course of the same; particularly the destruction of the prisoners at New-York, by General Sir William Howe, in the years 1776 and 1777; interspersed with some POLITICAL OBSERVATIONS.

Written by himself, and now published for the information of the curious in all Nations.

> *When God from chaos gave this world TO BE,*
> *Man then he form'd, and form'd him TO BE FREE.*
> *American Independence, a poem, by Freneau.*

To which are now added a considerable number of explanatory and occasional notes, together with an index of reference to the most remarkable occurrences in the narrative.
****

WALPOLE. N. H.

Published by THOMAS & THOMAS,
From the press of CHARTER & HALE,
1807.

deroga. This enterprise I cheerfully undertook; and, after first guard-
ing all the several passes that led thither, to cut off all intelligence
between the garrison and the country, made a forced march from Ben-
nington, and arrived at the lake opposite to Ticonderoga, on the
evening of the ninth day of May, 1775, with two hundred and thirty
valiant Green Mountain Boys; and it was with the utmost difficulty
that I procured boats to cross the lake. However, I landed eighty-three
men near the garrison, commanded by Col. Seth Warner; but the day
began to dawn, 'and I found myself under a necessity to attack the
fort, before the rear could cross the lake; and, as it was viewed hazardous, I harrangued the officers and soldiers in the manner following:
"Friends and fellow soldiers, You have, for a number of years past,
been a scourge and terror to arbitrary power. Your valor has been
famed abroad, and acknowledged, as appears by the advice and orders
to me, from the General Assembly of Connecticut, to surprise and
take the garrison now before us. I now propose to advance before you,
and, in person, conduct you through the wicket-gate; for we must this
morning either quit our pretentions to valor, or possess ourselves of
this fortress in a few minutes; and, as it is a desperate attempt, which
none but the bravest of men dare undertake, I do not urge it on any
contrary to his will. You that will undertake it voluntarily, poise your
firelocks."

The men being, at this time, drawn up in three ranks, each poised
his firelock. I ordered them to face to the right; and, at the head
of the centre-file, marched them immediately to the wicket-gate aforesaid, where I found a sentry posted, who instantly snapped his fusee
at me: I ran immediately towards him, and he retreated through the
covered way into the parade within the garrison, gave a haloo, and
ran under a bomb-proof. My party, who followed me into the fort, I
formed on the parade in such a manner as to face the two barracks
which faced each other. The garrison being asleep, except the sentries,
we gave three huzzas which greatly surprised them. One of the sentries
made a pass at one of my officers with a charged bayonet, and slightly
wounded him: My first thought was to kill him with my sword; but, in
an instant, I altered the design and fury of the blow to a slight cut on
the side of the head; upon which he dropped his gun, and asked
quarter, which I readily granted him, and demanded of him the place
where the commanding officer kept; he shewed me a pair of stairs in
the front of a barrack, on the west part of the garrison, which led up to
a second story in said barrack, to which I immediately repaired, and
ordered the commander, Capt. Delaplace, to come forth instantly, or I
would sacrifice the whole garrison; at which the Capt. came immediately to the door, with his breeches in his hand; when I ordered him
to deliver to me the fort instantly; he asked me by what authority I

demanded it; I answered him, "In the name of the great Jehovah, and the Continental Congress." The authority of the Congress being very little known at that time, He began to speak again; but I interrupted him, and, with my drawn sword over his head, again demanded an immediate surrender of the garrison; with which he then complied, and ordered his men to be forthwith paraded without arms, as he had given up the garrison: In the meantime some of my officers had given orders, and, in consequence thereof, sundry of the barrack doors were beat down, and about one third of the garrison imprisoned, which consisted of the said commander, a Lieut. Feltham, a conductor of artillery, a gunner, two serjeants, and forty-four rank and file; about one hundred pieces of cannon, one thirteen inch mortar, and a number of swivels. This surprise was carried into execution in the gray of the morning of the tenth day of May, 1775. The sun seemed to rise that morning with a superior lustre; and Ticonderoga and its dependencies smiled on its conquerors, who tossed about the flowing bowl, and wished success to Congress, and the liberty and freedom of America.

Montreal[1]

T he town of Montreal was in a great tumult. Gen. Carlton and the royal party, made every preparation to go on board their vessels of force, as I was afterwards informed, but the spy, escaping from my guard to the town, occasioned an alteration in their policy, and emboldened Gen. Carlton to send the force, which he had there collected, out against me. I had previously chosen my ground, but when I saw the number of the enemy, as they sallied out of the town, I perceived it would be a day of trouble, if not of rebuke; but I had no chance to flee, as Montreal was situated on an island, and the river St. Lawrence cut off my communication to Gen. Montgomery's camp. I encouraged my soldiery to bravely defend themselves, that we should soon have help, and that we should be able to keep the ground, if no more. This, and much more, I affirmed with the greatest seeming assurance, and which in reality I thought to be in some degree probable.

The enemy consisted of not more than forty regular troops, together with a mixed multitude, chiefly Canadians, with a number of English who lived in the town, and some Indians; in all, to the number of near five hundred.

The reader will notice that most of my party were Canadians; indeed it was a motley parcel of soldiery which composed both parties.

---

[1] Ibid., pp. 31–8.

However, the enemy began the attack from wood-piles, ditches, buildings, and such like places, at a considerable distance, and I returned the fire from a situation more than equally advantageous. The attack began between two and three of the clock in the afternoon, just before which I ordered a volunteer, by the name of Richard Young, with a detachment of nine men as a flank guard, which, under the cover of the bank of the river, could not only annoy the enemy, but at the same time, serve as a flank guard to the left of the main body.

The fire continued for some time on both sides; and I was confident that such a remote method of attack could not carry the ground, provided it should be continued 'till night: But near half the body of the enemy began to flank round to my right; upon which I ordered a volunteer, by the name of John Dugan, who had lived many years in Canada, and understood the French language, to detach about fifty of the Canadians, and post himself at an advantageous ditch, which was on my right, to prevent my being surrounded: He advanced with the detachment, but, instead of occupying the post, made his escape, as did likewise Mr. Young upon my left, with their detachments. I soon perceived that the enemy was in possession of the ground, which Dugan should have occupied. At this time I had but about forty-five men with me; some of whom were wounded; the enemy kept closing round me, nor was it in my power to prevent it; by which means, my situation, which was advantageous in the first part of the attack, ceased to be so in the last; and, being almost entirely surrounded with such vast unequal numbers, I ordered a retreat, but found that those of the enemy, who were of the country, and their Indians, could run as fast as my men, though the regulars could not. Thus I retreated near a mile, and some of the enemy, with the savages, kept flanking me, and others crowded hard in the rear. In fine, I expected, in a very short time, to try the world of spirits: for I was apprehensive that no quarter would be given to me, and therefore had determined to sell my life as dear as I could. One of the enemy's officers, boldly pressing in the rear, discharged his fusee at me; the ball whistled near me, as did many others that day. I returned the salute, and missed him, as running had put us both out of breath; for I conclude we were not frightened: I then saluted him with my tongue in a harsh manner, and told him that, inasmuch as his numbers were so far superior to mine, I would surrender, provided I could be treated with honor, and be assured of good quarter for myself and the men who were with me; and he answered I should; another officer, coming up directly after, confirmed the treaty; upon which I agreed to surrender with my party, which then consisted of thirty-one effective men, and seven wounded. I ordered them to ground their arms, which they did.

The officer I capitulated with, then directed me and my party to advance toward him, which was done; I handed him my sword, and in half a minute after, a savage, part of whose head was shaved, being almost naked and painted, with feathers intermixed with the hair of the other side of his head, came running to me with an incredible swiftness; he seemed to advance with more than mortal speed; as he approached me, his hellish visage was beyond all description; snakes' eyes appear innocent in comparison of his; his features extorted [*sic*]; malice, death, murder, and the wrath of devils and damned spirits are the emblems of his countenance; and, in less than twelve feet of me, presented his firelock; at the instant of his present, I twitched the officer, to whom I gave my sword, between me and the savage; but he flew round with great fury, trying to single me out to shoot me without killing the officer; but by this time I was near as nimble as he, keeping the officer in such a position that his danger was my defence; but, in less than half a minute, I was attacked by just such another imp of hell: Then I made the officer fly around with incredible velocity, for a few seconds of time, when I perceived a Canadian, who had lost one eye, as appeared afterwards, taking my part against the savages; and in an instant an Irishman came to my assistance with a fixed bayonet, and drove away the fiends, swearing by Jasus he would kill them. This tragic scene composed my mind. The escaping from so awful a death, made even imprisonment happy; the more so as my conquerors on the field treated me with great civility and politeness.

The regular officers said that they were very happy to see Col. Allen: I answered that I should rather chose to have seen them at Gen. Montgomery's camp. The gentlemen replied, that they gave full credit to what I said, and, as I walked to the town, which was, as I should guess, more than two miles, a British officer walking at my right hand, and one of the French noblesse at my left; the latter of which, in the action, had his eyebrow carried away by a glancing shot, but was nevertheless very merry and facetious, and no abuse was offered me 'till I came to the barrack-yard, at Montreal, where I met general Prescott, who asked me my name, which I told him: He then asked me, whether I was that Col. Allen, who took Ticonderoga. I told him I was the very man: Then he shook his cane over my head, calling many hard names, among which he frequently used the word rebel, and put himself in a great rage. I told him he would do well not to cane me, for I was not accustomed to it, and shook my fist at him, telling him that was the beetle of mortality for him, if he offered to strike; upon which Capt. M'Cloud of the British, pulled him by the skirt, and whispered to him, as he afterwards told me, to this import; that it was inconsistent with his honor to strike a prisoner.

Young Lochinvar might have taken part in the "ride for a bride" described in our next group of stories; Brady's leap might have been performed by Perseus; and men of other nationalities may have had—doubtless did have—trials as great as Kennedy's in the South Pacific in World War II. It may be doubted, however, whether any other than a young American would, like Kennedy's companion, have emerged into safety with such a song of triumph as

> Jesus loves me, this I know,
> For the Bible tells me so.

And though the attempt was abortive, it may be doubted whether any but Americans would have thought, during World War I, of kidnapping the Kaiser, and would almost have succeeded.

Kidnapping the Kaiser[1]

To understand this incredible yarn of the attempted kidnapping of the German Kaiser in Holland, one has to let his mind go back to the war, when editors and recruiting posters were screaming "Get the Kaiser!" when President Wilson was making a distinction between the German people and their government, and rhetorically making war, not against the people but against the Kaiser; when Lloyd George was thundering to bring the Kaiser to trial and hang him for war guilt.

So eight Tennesseans, all but one of them members of the 114th Field Artillery stationed at Tuntange in Luxembourg, plotted elaborately to kidnap the Kaiser from his sanctuary in Holland. They did not write an important chapter in the story of the World War, because they failed; but they did write a fascinating footnote to history. For this plot that almost succeeded they were detained at American General Headquarters at Chaumont for weeks. They were questioned about possible violations of the neutrality of Holland, violation of Army regulations

---

[1] By T. H. Alexander, from the *Reader's Digest*, December 1937, pp. 34–8, copyright 1937 by The Reader's Digest Association, Inc.; condensed from the *Saturday Evening Post* for October 23, 1937, copyright 1937 by The Curtis Publishing Co. Original title: "They Tried to Kidnap the Kaiser."

273

by visiting unauthorized regions, unauthorized use of Army automobiles, and about the theft of a certain ash tray from the Kaiser's library. Although the taking of the ash tray is officially a mystery, the ash tray is now in the United States. It is the figure of a German policedog with a long-stemmed pipe in his mouth, and bears the German imperial coat of arms and under it the initials W. I.—Wilhelm Imperator. These eight men went to capture an emperor; what they got was an ash tray.

It was on December 31, 1918, that the expedition got under way, led by Colonel Luke Lea. They had not gone 30 kilometers when their Winton car broke down. The tires were worn out and the car had no brakes, so, whenever the party coasted down a snow-covered hill at breakneck speed, they did so at imminent peril of their lives. Fortunately, just at the moment of breakdown, an American Army truck passed and one of the men was sent back with it to secure another car. In the meantime, the Winton was patched up.

Both cars now headed for Liége, where they found that they could not get passports for Holland without weeks of delay. Then Colonel Lea remembered that, as a Democratic member of the United States Senate, he had been well acquainted with Brand Whitlock, then United States Minister to Belgium. So they made a beeline to Brussels.

Mr. Whitlock asked the party to make out applications for American passports, which they did, stating that they wished to travel in Holland on personal business, but in uniform. Colonel Lea made it clear to the legation secretary that their object was an unofficial "journalistic investigation" (at that time he owned and published two Nashville newspapers). But the passports as issued stated that the Americans were on official business, and referred to Colonel Lea as "United States Senator Luke Lea."

Colonel Lea had been the youngest member ever to sit in the United States Senate, with the exception of Henry Clay, but he had been defeated for re-election. He explained that he had not been a member of the Senate for almost two years. The legation official, however, had the American view of titles and said: "Once a Senator, always a Senator. It's perfectly all right."

Nonetheless, they insisted upon properly-drawn passports. Then the embarrassed clerk explained that there were no more blank passport forms in the legation. Reluctantly accepting the passports, the Tennesseans went to the Dutch Legation, got *visas* there and also a *laissez-passer* giving them authority to travel, uniformed and by car, in Holland. This authorization was in Dutch, which none of the party could read, but as later translated it requested "the Custom and Excise Officers in Holland to give all facilities permitted by existing regulations to the most Honorable Senator Colonel Luke Lea, who is proceeding to Holland and return by motor-car on official duty for the U. S. Government." Little wonder it proved an open sesame!

The next morning, January 5, 1919, they were on their way with their two cars and entered Holland at 7 A.M., the Dutch soldiers being most obsequious when shown the *laissez-passer*. Just at dusk they were stopped by a washed-out bridge across a small tributary of the Rhine, but after a long search they found a detour to a ferryboat. The ferryman, though he finally took them across, was suspicious of the strange uniforms, and refused to wait for their return or even be on call during the night.

Here was a serious blow. Their plan had been to put the Kaiser in one of the cars, by force if necessary, and take him back to Paris, as a gift to President Wilson at the Peace Conference. But with all the luck in the world in taking the Kaiser by surprise, they would almost certainly be apprehended at the ferry.

For the first time several members of the party learned definitely of the purpose of the trip. They all insisted on going on, in the hope of being able to persuade the Kaiser to go with them voluntarily. It seems absurd, 18 years afterward, to learn that men were so fatuous as to believe that the Kaiser, who hated the French intensely, might agree to stand trial in the French capital, when he had been afraid to face his own people.

The party, proceeding, arrived at their destination, the castle in Amerongen, at about eight o'clock. They knocked loudly at the heavy gates and a small panel opened. The sentry's mouth dropped open when he saw they were Americans. Ordered to take them to the officer of the day, he opened the gate without a word and conducted them inside the house to a large, pleasant library where a wood fire was burning.

Shortly a tall, handsome and visibly agitated young man entered. This was Count von Bentinck, the son of the Kaiser's host. He asked the purpose of the visit. "I can reveal the object of our visit only to the Kaiser," replied Colonel Lea. The young count then excused himself, and members of the party could hear him talking in an adjoining room to someone whom he addressed as "Your Majesty," who replied briefly in guttural German. The count also talked over a telephone in the Dutch language.

During his brief absence from the library a German butler who resembled an army sergeant entered with cigars and ice water. A member of the party thereupon deplored, eloquently, the European superstition that Americans drink only ice water, and presently the butler returned with champagne.

The young count re-entered the room, to state that His Majesty would not see them unless the object of their visit was clearly stated.

Colonel Lea reiterated that he would divulge this only to the Kaiser. A new personage now entered, and was introduced as the burgomaster of Amerongen. To the great relief of the party, he addressed them in faultless English. He, too, asked the object of their visit, and the Americans again refused to divulge it.

Count and burgomaster then went into a huddle in the next room and the telephone was used again. Returning, they announced that His Majesty now positively refused to see them unless they stated the object of their visit. Colonel Lea then resorted for the first time to the *laissez-passer*. It created a profound impression, and the count said:

"You are here then on official business of the American government?"

"Oh, no," said Colonel Lea. "We are here on a journalistic investigation, as our application for this *laissez-passer* stated at Brussels."

"What do you mean by 'journalistic investigation'? Is it a technical term in the American Army, or are you newspaper reporters?"

"The phrase speaks for itself," said Colonel Lea, and he refused to elaborate.

The count and burgomaster retired for another conference, and were gone perhaps 30 minutes. Returning with apologies, they said that the Kaiser was unwilling to refuse to meet them, but asked their word of honor that they represented either President Wilson or General Pershing, or "even Colonel E. M. House."

This assurance the Americans refused to give and the conversation kept on aimlessly for more than an hour, until the Americans became convinced that it was the purpose of their hosts to detain them, yet not permit them to see the Kaiser.

Had they glanced out the window they might have guessed the reason for the delay. The men who had been left in charge of the cars outside had no doubts about it. For an excited Dutch army officer had gathered 150 to 200 troops outside the castle. He had issued several rounds of ammunition, and turned on two search-lights which revealed machine guns mounted on the castle walls. The Americans remember these soldiers as resembling veterans of the German armies. They surrounded the cars, and a group of curious Hollanders, sensing an impending drama, formed a circle around the soldiers.

The Americans in the cars stood the glare of the assembled Dutch and the hostile stares of the Kaiser's guard for hours. Finally, at eleven o'clock, the American officers appeared in the doorway, followed by Count von Bentinck and the burgomaster. The burgomaster wanted to know, just as the Americans were leaving, whether it was customary in the United States to pay such late calls, and the officers solemnly assured him that it was the usual thing.

The Americans bowed themselves out of this hopeless situation, shook hands with the burgomaster and the young count, and got in their cars. They fully expected that an effort would be made to detain them. Indeed, a few minutes after they had gone, upon the discovery of the loss of the Kaiser's treasured ash tray, an alarm was given by telephone; but the Americans, despite a long delay at the ferry, slipped across the border and were soon back with their regiment.

For the next week the press was filled with sensational accounts of the escapade. The Dutch instituted an investigation, but it seemed distinctly perfunctory. Not so at American Army headquarters, where questioning of the eight men was prolonged and insistent.

Colonel Lea stressed the information he had obtained, the most valuable of which, he said, was that the Kaiser was neither ill nor insane; that he was yet recognized by his associates as the Emperor of Germany, and that he had a military establishment with him in exile.

One of the serious charges was that the party had used Army automobiles, but this was dropped after the defense proposed calling a host of officers, including General Pershing, who was said to have used an Army car to go to Nice on a vacation. The officials perked up, however, when Sergeant Reilly innocently remarked that he had brought back an ash tray from the trip. At once the sergeant was sent under guard to his quarters to produce the ash tray. He brought it to the investigators with an Irish twinkle in his eyes—it was a German-made ash tray for the tourist trade, sold at ten francs per dozen!

After weeks of investigation, the idea of a court-martial was abandoned, but Colonel Lea received an official reprimand. The members of the party were ordered back to their regiment, which shortly sailed for the United States.

In 1921, at a reunion of the 30th Division in Nashville, the guest of honor was General Pershing. Someone asked him, rather timidly, what he thought of the attempt to kidnap the Kaiser. The old soldier's eyes twinkled. "Why," he said, "I'd have given a year's pay to have been with those boys in Holland." [1]

It was only incidentally to Luke Lea's exploit that the press had a wonderful time, but exploits equally bizarre have often been staged by American circulation managers. The risk to life and limb might be very genuine. One of the most remarkable stunts of this sort was the one described by Emile Gauvreau; he does not say that he inspired it, but he was certainly managing editor of the New York *Graphic* when it was perpetrated. This is his account.[2]

---

[1] Colonel Luke Lea died November 18, 1945, aged sixty-six.

[2] Taken from *My Last Million Readers*, by Emile Gauvreau, published and copyright by E. P. Dutton & Co., Inc., New York. Copyright 1941. Pp. 126–7.

Santa in Central Park

The last Christmas promotion party for our readers was an occasion I was to remember. The *Graphic* distributed toys to the poor from the bandstand in Central Park and had obtained permission from Mayor Jimmy Walker to land an audacious Santa Claus in an airplane in the sheep meadows, a short distance away, where thousands of children had been attracted to the scene. In clear weather the venture would have been hazardous, but the sky became overcast in the afternoon, and soon the Park was swept by an icy, howling wind. Three hours went by while the children set up a clamor for the delayed Santa, whose part was to be played by Will Mahoney, a popular Broadway comedian. He was to be flown from Long Island by a barnstorming aviator known as Swanee Taylor, who would have attempted a rocket flight to the moon for any imaginative editor ready to put up the money for it. After two dangerous forced landings on the way, Taylor, who believed his reputation was at stake, actually brought Mahoney down in the Park, following some desperate maneuvering five hundred feet above us. As the screaming children crowded about the plane, Mahoney, a mass of icicles, rose angrily in his red suit in the open cockpit, yanked off what was left of his white whiskers and wig, and shouted:

"To hell with Santa Claus! I'll never ride in these damned things again!"

A ride for a bride[1]

When the story of bloodshed at Bunker Hill reached Bohemia Hall, in Cecil County, Maryland, Albert De Courcy left his brother Ernest to support the dignity of the house and make patriotic speeches, while he went to the front, conscious that Helen Carmichael, his affianced wife, was watching, in pride and sadness, the departure of his company. Letters came and went, as they always do, until rumor came of a sore defeat to the colonials at Long Island; then the letters ceased.

It was a year later when a ragged soldier, who had stopped at the hall for supper, told of Albert's heroism in covering the retreat of

---

[1] From Charles M. Skinner: *Myths and Legends of Our Own Land* (Philadelphia and London: J. B. Lippincott Co.; 1896), Vol. II, pp. 64–7.

Washington. The gallant young officer had been shot, he said, as he attempted to swim the morasses of Gowanus. But this soldier was in error. Albert had been vexatiously bogged on the edge of the creek. While floundering in the mud a half-dozen sturdy red-coats had lugged him out and he was packed off to the prison-ships anchored in the Wallabout. In these dread hulks, amid darkness and miasma, living on scanty, unwholesome food, compelled to see his comrades die by dozens every day and to be flung ashore where the tide lapped away the sand thrown over them, De Courcy wished that death instead of capture had been his lot, for, next to his love, he prized his liberty.

One day he was told off, with a handful of others, for transfer to a stockade on the Delaware, and how his heart beat when he learned that the new prison was within twenty miles of home! His flow of spirits returned, and his new jailors liked him for his frankness and laughed at his honest expletives against the king. He had the liberty of the inclosure, and was not long in finding where the wall was low, the ditch narrow, and the abatis decayed—knowledge that came useful to him sooner than he expected, for one day a captured horse was led in that made straight for him with a whinny and rubbed his nose against his breast.

"Why!" he cried, "it's Cecil! My horse, gentlemen—or was. Not a better hunter in Maryland!"

"Yes," answered one of the officers. "We've just taken him from your brother. He's been stirring trouble with his speeches and has got to be quieted. But we'll have him today, for he's to be married, and a scouting party is on the road to nab him at the altar."

"Married! My brother! What! Ernest, the lawyer, the orator? Ho, ho! Ah, but it's rather hard to break off a match in that style!"

"Hard for him, may be; but they say the lady feels no great love for him. He made it seem like a duty to her, after her lover died."

"How's that? Her own—what's her name?"

"Helen—Helen Carmichael, or something like that."

Field and sky swam before De Courcy's eyes for a moment; then he resumed, in a calm voice, and with a pale, set face, "Well, you're making an unhappy wedding-day for him. If he had Cecil here he would outride you all. Ah, when I was in practice I could ride this horse and snatch a pebble from the ground without losing pace!"

"Could you do it now?"

"I'm afraid long lodging in your prison-ships has stiffened my joints, but I'd venture at a handkerchief."

"Then try," said the commandant.

De Courcy mounted into the saddle heavily, crossed the grounds at a canter, and dropped a handkerchief on the grass. Then, taking a few turns for practice, he started at a gallop and swept around like the

279

wind. His seat was so firm, his air so noble, his mastery of the steed so complete, that a cheer of admiration went up. He seemed to fall head-long from the saddle, but was up again in a moment, waving the handkerchief gayly in farewell—for he kept straight on toward the weak place in the wall. A couple of musket-balls hummed by his ears: it was neck or nothing now! A tremendous leap! Then a ringing cry told the astonished soldiers that he had reached the road in safety. Through wood and thicket and field he dashed as if the fiend were after him, and never once did he cease to urge his steed till he reached the turnpike, and saw ahead the scouting party on its way to arrest his brother.

Turning into a path that led to the rear of the little church they were so dangerously near, he plied hands and heels afresh, and in a few moments a wedding party was startled by the apparition of a black horse all in a foam, ridden by a gaunt man, in torn garments, that burst in at the open chancel door. The bridegroom cowered, for he knew his brother. The bride gazed in amazement. " 'Tis the dead come to life!" cried one. De Courcy had little time for words. He rode forward to the altar, swung Helen up behind him, and exclaimed, "Save yourselves! The British are coming! To horse, every one, and make for the manor!" There were shrieks and fainting—and perhaps a little cursing, even if it was in church—and when the squadron rode up most of the company were in full flight. Ernest was taken, and next morning held his brother's place on the prison-list, while, as arrange-ments had been made for a wedding, there was one, and a happy one, for Albert was the bridegroom.

Brady's leap [1]

In the region where so many places commemorate, by their names, his daring deeds, tradition preserves his fame, and from father to son the stories are handed down. But many such accounts have slept in the memories of men, and have perhaps passed away with that elder generation to which the name of Brady was a household word. Upon some, or at least one, of the more marvelous tales, our modern wise-acres, finding no record save the uncertain one of man's memory, have sought to throw discredit. The fact that the point where the Cuyahoga rushes through a narrow fissure in the rocks, its current contracted to a width of less than thirty feet, still bears the name of Brady's Leap, is

---

[1] From D. M. Kelsey: *Our Pioneer Heroes and Their Daring Deeds* (Philadelphia and St. Louis: Scammell & Co.; 1885), pp. 189–91.

to them worth nothing. But Brady's own lips had told the tale, and those who had heard it from him were not inclined to disbelieve it.

With a party of twenty followers, he had set out on a scouting expedition to the neighborhood of Sandusky, but was waylaid by a large force of Indians at a small lake, now called by his name, in what is now Portage County, Ohio. From the sharp engagement that followed, only two white men escaped with their lives, Brady being one. Such was his first acquaintance with this lake, the story being proven by the excavations made on the southern shore by his friends, who found there a number of skulls and a sword—the relics of the fight.

His famous leap across the Cuyahoga was made, according to some authorities, a short time after this; according to others, when he escaped from the Indians by throwing the child toward the fire. It was probably after the date of most of his adventures, as will be evident when we come to consider the result.

Hotly pursued from Sandusky, a distance of about a hundred miles, he found on reaching the Cuyahoga, that his enemies hemmed him in. To go backward was impossible—and how could one man bridge that chasm, more than twenty-five feet wide? But there is no other way of escape from the yelling fiends, and summoning all his courage, with one mighty leap he bounds over the yawning gulf. Convulsively his hands clutch at the bushes growing on the bluff he had gained; but they give way; down, down, he slips almost his own height; but the iron nerves do not fail him, the sinewy hands grasp still other supports, and he continues his flight. The savages stand on the other bank, for a moment, motionless with astonishment; quickly recovering themselves, three or four fire at him, hitting him in the leg.

Notwithstanding his wound, Brady continued to run. The Indians left the steep cliff, and crossed the river at the Standing Stone, where the more gently sloping banks enabled them to approach the water. Finding them still in hot pursuit, Brady bent his way towards the lake now bearing his name, and plunged into its waters. The savages were gaining rapidly on him, and his wound so impeded his flight that he knew concealment was necessary. Striking out, then, towards a part of the lake that was covered with the broad leaves and white blossoms of the waterlily, the hollow, flexible stems of these attracted his attention, and he found, by experimenting, that he could breathe through one of these, and thus keep his head under water.

The Indians followed his bloody trail to the water's edge, and finding it end there, were at a loss. Examining carefully the shores of the lake, they concluded that he had not emerged; that, exhausted by his wound, he had been accidentally drowned, or had preferred that death to a bloodier one at the hands of his enemies. All the remainder of the day, and part of the night they spent in searching for him, dead or

281

alive, but finally gave it up, and returned to make a more careful survey of the spot where he had cleared the river at a bound. As soon as he felt it safe to do so, Brady left the water, and succeeded in making his escape to the settlement.

Returning to the river, the Indians carefully inspected the spot, measuring by their eye the distance as accurately as they could; and arrived at a very singular conviction: none of them, they felt assured, could leap it; since it was impossible to them, it would be ridiculous to suppose a white man could do it; the evidence of their eyes, of course, could not be disregarded, but they reconciled the fact and its impossibility by the sage conclusion: "He no man, he no jump across the river; he wild-turkey, he fly."

And so convinced were they of this, that they carved upon the rock to which he had leaped, the rude representation of a wild-turkey's foot. This token of an exhibition of physical power beyond the belief of even eye-witnesses remained there until the summer of 1856, when, as the rock was to be quarried, Judge Moses Hampton, of Pittsburgh, obtained permission to cut it out. The distance has been several times measured, the measurements varying from twenty-five to twenty-seven and a half feet, the steep cliffs on either side rising to a height of some thirty feet above the surface of the water.

Survival[1]

O ur men in the South Pacific fight nature, when they are pitted against her, with a greater fierceness than they could ever expend on a human enemy. Lieutenant John F. Kennedy, the ex-Ambassador's son and lately a P T skipper in the Solomons, came through town the other day and told me the story of his survival in the South Pacific. I asked Kennedy if I might write the story down. He asked me if I wouldn't talk first with some of his crew, so I went up to the Motor Torpedo Boat Training Centre at Melville, Rhode Island, and there, under the curving iron of a Quonset hut, three enlisted men named Johnston, McMahon, and McGuire filled in the gaps.

It seems that Kennedy's P T, the 109, was out one night with a squadron patrolling Blackett Strait, in mid-Solomons. Blackett Strait is a patch of water bounded on the northeast by the volcano called Kolombangara, on the west by the island of Vella Lavella, on the

---

[1] By John Hersey, in *The New Yorker*, June 17, 1944, pp. 27–38. Permission The New Yorker, Copyright 1944, The F-R Publishing Corporation. This is an entirely factual narrative.

south by the island of Gizo and a string of coral-fringed islets, and on the east by the bulk of New Georgia. The boats were working about forty miles away from their base on the island of Rendova, on the south side of New Georgia. They had entered Blackett Strait, as was their habit, through Ferguson Passage, between the coral islets and New Georgia.

The night was a starless black and Japanese destroyers were around. It was about two-thirty. The 109, with three officers and ten enlisted men aboard, was leading three boats on a sweep for a target. An officer named George Ross was up on the bow, magnifying the void with binoculars. Kennedy was at the wheel and he saw Ross turn and point into the darkness. The man in the forward machine-gun turret shouted, "Ship at two o'clock!" Kennedy saw a shape and spun the wheel to turn for an attack, but the 109 answered sluggishly. She was running slowly on only one of her three engines, so as to make a minimum wake and avoid detection from the air. The shape became a Japanese destroyer, cutting through the night at forty knots and heading straight for the 109. The thirteen men on the P T hardly had time to brace themselves. Those who saw the Japanese ship coming were paralyzed by fear in a curious way: they could move their hands but not their feet. Kennedy whirled the wheel to the left, but again the 109 did not respond. Ross went through the gallant but futile motions of slamming a shell into the breach of the 37-millimetre anti-tank gun which had been temporarily mounted that very day, wheels and all, on the foredeck. The urge to bolt and dive over the side was terribly strong, but still no one was able to move; all hands froze to their battle stations. Then the Japanese crashed into the 109 and cut her right in two. The sharp enemy forefoot struck the P T on the starboard side about fifteen feet from the bow and crunched diagonally across with a racking noise. The P T's wooden hull hardly even delayed the destroyer. Kennedy was thrown hard to the left in the cockpit, and he thought, "This is how it feels to be killed." In a moment he found himself on his back on the deck, looking up at the destroyer as it passed through his boat. There was another loud noise and a huge flash of yellow-red light, and the destroyer glowed. Its peculiar, raked, inverted-Y stack stood out in the brilliant light and, later, in Kennedy's memory.

There was only one man below decks at the moment of collision. That was McMahon, engineer. He had no idea what was up. He was just reaching forward to slam the starboard engine into gear when a ship came into his engine room. He was lifted from the narrow passage between two of the engines and thrown painfully against the starboard bulkhead aft of the boat's auxiliary generator. He landed in a sitting position. A tremendous burst of flame came back at him from the day room, where some of the gas tanks were. He put his hands over his face, drew his legs up tight, and waited to die. But he felt water hit him after the fire, and he was sucked far downward as his half of the P T sank. He began to struggle upward through the water. He had held his breath since the impact, so his lungs were tight and they hurt. He looked up through the water. Over his head he saw a yellow glow—gasoline burning on the water. He broke the surface and was in fire again. He splashed hard to keep a little island of water around him.

Johnston, another engineer, had been asleep on deck when the collision came. It lifted him and dropped him overboard. He saw the flame and the destroyer for a moment. Then a huge propeller pounded by near him and the awful turbulence of the destroyer's wake took him down, turned him over and over, held him down, shook him, and drubbed on his ribs. He hung on and came up in water that was like a river rapids. The next day his body turned black and blue from the beating.

Kennedy's half of the P T stayed afloat. The bulkheads were sealed, so the undamaged watertight compartments up forward kept the half hull floating. The destroyer rushed off into the dark. There was an awful quiet: only the sound of gasoline burning.

Kennedy shouted, "Who's aboard?"

Feeble answers came from three of the enlisted men, McGuire, Mauer, and Albert; and from one of the officers, Thom.

Kennedy saw the fire only ten feet from the boat. He thought it might reach her and explode the remaining gas tanks, so he shouted, "Over the side!"

The five men slid into the water. But the wake of the destroyer swept the fire away from the P T, so after a few minutes, Kennedy and the others crawled back aboard. Kennedy shouted for survivors in the water. One by one they answered: Ross, the third officer; Harris, McMahon, Johnston, Zinsser, Starkey, enlisted men. Two did not answer: Kirksey and Marney, enlisted men. Since the last bombing at base, Kirksey had been sure he would die. He had huddled at his battle station by the fantail gun, with his kapok life jacket tied tight up to his cheeks. No one knows what happened to him or to Marney.

Harris shouted from the darkness, "Mr. Kennedy! Mr. Kennedy! McMahon is badly hurt." Kennedy took his shoes, his shirt, and his sidearms off, told Mauer to blink a light so that the men in the water would know where the half hull was, then dived in and swam toward the voice. The survivors were widely scattered. McMahon and Harris were a hundred yards away.

When Kennedy reached McMahon, he asked, "How are you, Mac?"

McMahon said, "I'm all right. I'm kind of burnt."

Kennedy shouted out, "How are all the others?"

Harris said softly, "I hurt my leg."

Kennedy, who had been on the Harvard swimming team five years before, took McMahon in tow and headed for the P T. A gentle breeze kept blowing the boat away from the swimmers. It took forty-five minutes to make what had been an easy hundred yards. On the way in, Harris said, "I can't go any farther." Kennedy, of the Boston Kennedys, said to Harris, of the same home town, "For a guy from Boston, you're certainly putting up a great exhibition out here, Harris." Harris made it all right and didn't complain any more. Then Kennedy swam from man to man, to see how they were doing. All who had survived the crash were able to stay afloat, since they were wearing life preservers—kapok jackets shaped like overstuffed vests, aviators' yellow Mae Wests, or air-filled belts like small inner tubes. But those who couldn't swim had to be towed back to the wreckage by those who could. One of the men screamed for help. When Ross reached him he found that the screaming man had two life jackets on. Johnston was treading water in a film of gasoline which did not catch fire. The fumes filled his lungs and he fainted. Thom towed him in. The others got in under their own power. It was now after 5 A.M., but still dark. It had taken nearly three hours to get everyone aboard.

The men stretched out on the tilted deck of the P. T. Johnston, McMahon, and Ross collapsed into sleep. The men talked about how wonderful it was to be alive and speculated upon when the other PT's would come back to rescue them. Mauer kept blinking the light to point their way. But the other boats had no idea of coming back. They had seen a collision, a sheet of flame, and a slow burning on the water. When the skipper of one of the boats saw the sight, he put his hands over his face and sobbed, "My God! My God!" He and the others turned away. Back at the base, after a couple of days, the squadron held services for the souls of the thirteen men, and one of the officers wrote his mother, "George Ross lost his life for a cause that he believed in stronger than any one of us, because he was an idealist in the purest sense. Jack Kennedy, the Ambassador's son, was on the same boat and also lost his life. The man that said the cream of a nation is lost in war can never be accused of making an overstatement of a very cruel fact. . . ."

When day broke, the men on the remains of the 109 stirred and looked around. To the northeast, three miles off, they saw the monumental cone of Kolombangara; there, the men knew, ten thousand Japanese swarmed. To the west, five miles away, they saw Vella Lavella; more Japs. To the south, only a mile or so away, they actually could see a Japanese camp on Gizo. Kennedy ordered his men to keep as low as possible, so that no moving silhouettes would show against the sky. The listing hulk was gurgling and gradually settling. Kennedy said, "What do you want to do if the Japs come out? Fight or surrender?" One said, "Fight with what?" So they took an inventory of their armament. The 37-millimetre gun had flopped over the side and was hanging there by a chain. They had one tommy gun, six 45-calibre automatics, and one .38. Not much.

"Well," said Kennedy, "what do you want to do?"

One said, "Anything you say, Mr. Kennedy. You're the boss."

Kennedy said, "There's nothing in the book about a situation like this. Seems to me we're not a military organization any more. Let's just talk this over."

They talked it over, and pretty soon they argued, and Kennedy could see that they would never survive in anarchy. So he took command again.

It was vital that McMahon and Johnston should have room to lie down. McMahon's face, neck, hands, wrists, and feet were horribly burned. Johnston was pale and he coughed continually. There was scarcely space for everyone, so Kennedy ordered the other men into the water to make room, and went in himself. All morning they clung to the hulk and talked about how incredible it was that no one had come to rescue them. All morning they watched for the plane which they thought would be looking for them. They cursed war in general and P T's in particular. At about ten o'clock the hulk heaved a moist sigh and turned turtle. McMahon and Johnston had to hang on as best they could. It was clear that the remains of the 109 would soon sink. When the sun had passed the meridian, Kennedy said, "We will swim to that small island," pointing to one of a group three miles to the southeast. "We have less chance of making it than some of these other islands here, but there'll be less chance of Japs, too." Those who could not swim well grouped themselves around a long two-by-six timber with which carpenters had braced the 37-millimetre cannon on deck and which had been knocked overboard by the force of the collision. They tied several pairs of shoes to the timber, as well as the ship's lantern, wrapped in a life jacket to keep it afloat. Thom took charge of this unwieldy group. Kennedy took McMahon in tow again. He cut loose one end of a long strap on McMahon's Mae West and took the end in his teeth. He swam breast stroke, pulling the helpless McMahon along on his back. It took over five hours to reach the island. Water lapped into Kennedy's mouth through his clenched teeth, and he swallowed a lot. The salt water cut into McMahon's awful burns, but he did not complain. Every few minutes, when Kennedy stopped to rest, taking the strap out of his mouth and holding it in his hand, McMahon would simply say, "How far do we have to go?"

Kennedy would reply, "We're going good." Then he would ask, "How do you feel, Mac?"

McMahon always answered, "I'm O.K., Mr. Kennedy. How about you?"

In spite of his burden, Kennedy beat the other men to the reef that surrounded the island. He left McMahon on the reef, and told him to keep low, so as not to be spotted by Japs. Kennedy went ahead and explored the island. It was only a hundred yards in diameter; coconuts on the trees but none on the ground; no visible Japs. Just as the others reached the island, one of them spotted a Japanese barge chugging along close to shore. They all lay low. The barge went on. Johnston, who was very pale and weak and who was still coughing a lot, said, "They wouldn't come here. What'd they be walking around here for? It's too small." Kennedy lay in some bushes, exhausted by his effort, his stomach heavy with the water he had swallowed. He had been in the sea, except for short intervals on the hulk, for fifteen and a half hours. Now he started thinking. Every night for several nights the P T's had cut through Ferguson Passage on their way to action. Ferguson Passage was just beyond the next little island. Maybe . . .

He stood up. He took one of the pairs of shoes. He put one of the rubber life belts around his waist. He hung the .38 around his neck on a lanyard. He took his pants off. He picked up the ship's lantern, a heavy battery affair ten inches by ten inches, still wrapped in the kapok jacket. He said, "If I find a boat, I'll flash the lantern twice. The password will be 'Roger', the answer will be 'Willco.' " He walked toward the water. After fifteen paces he was dizzy, but in the water he felt all right.

It was early evening. It took half an hour to swim to the reef around the next island. Just as he planted his feet on the reef, which lay about four feet under the surface, he saw the shape of a very big fish in the clear water. He flashed the light on it and splashed hard. The fish went away. Kennedy remembered what one of his men had said a few days before, "These barracuda will come up under a swimming man and eat his testicles." He had many occasions to think of that remark in the next few hours.

Now it was dark. Kennedy blundered along the uneven reef in water up to his waist. Sometimes he would reach forward with his leg and cut one of his shins or ankles on sharp coral. Other times he would step forward onto emptiness. He made his way like a slow-motion drunk, hugging the lantern. At about nine o'clock he came to the end of the reef, alongside Ferguson Passage. He took his shoes off and tied them to the life jacket, then struck out into open water. He swam about an hour, until he felt he was far enough out to intercept the P T's. Treading water, he listened for the muffled roar of motors, getting chilled, waiting, holding the lamp. Once he looked west and saw flares and the false gaiety of an action. The lights were far beyond the little islands, even beyond Gizo, ten miles away. Kennedy realized that the P T boats had chosen, for the first night in many, to go around Gizo instead of through Ferguson Passage. There was no hope. He started back. He made the same painful promenade of the reef and struck out for the tiny island where his friends were. But this swim was different. He was very tired and now the current was running fast, carrying him to the right. He saw that he could not make the island, so he flashed the light one and shouted, "Roger! Roger!" to identify himself.

On the beach the men were hopefully vigilant. They saw the light and heard the shouts. They were very happy, because they thought that Kennedy had found a P T. They walked out onto the reef, sometimes up to their waists in water, and waited. It was very painful for those who had no shoes. The men shouted, but not much, because they were afraid of Japanese.

One said, "There's another flash."

A few minutes later a second said, "There's a light over there."

A third said, "We're seeing things in this dark."

They waited a long time, but they saw nothing but phosphorescence and heard nothing but the sound of waves. They went back, very discouraged.

One said despairingly, "We're going to die."

Johnston said, "Aw, shut up. You can't die. Only the good die young."

Kennedy had drifted right by the little island. He thought he had never known such deep trouble, but something he did shows that unconsciously he had not given up hope. He dropped his shoes, but he held onto the heavy lantern, his symbol of contact with his fellows. He stopped trying to swim. He seemed to stop caring. His body drifted through the wet hours, and he was very cold. His mind was a jumble. A few hours before he had wanted desperately to get to the base at Rendova. Now he only wanted to get back to the little island he had left that night, but he didn't try to get there; he just wanted to. His mind seemed to float away from his body. Darkness and time took the place of a mind in his skull. For a long time he slept, or was crazy, or floated in a chill trance.

The currents of the Solomon Islands are queer. The tide shoves and sucks through the islands and makes the currents curl in odd patterns. It was a fateful pattern into which Jack Kennedy drifted. He drifted in it all night. His mind was blank, but his fist was tightly clenched on the kapok around the lantern. The current moved in a huge circle—west past Gizo, then north and east past Kolombangara, then south into Ferguson Passage. Early in the morning the sky turned from black to gray, and so did Kennedy's mind. Light came to both at about six. Kennedy looked around and saw that he was exactly where he had been the night before when he saw the flares beyond Gizo. For a second time, he started home. He thought for a while that he had lost his mind and that he only imagined that he was repeating his attempt to reach the island. But the chill of the water was real enough, the lantern was real, his progress was measurable. He made the reef, crossed the lagoon, and got to the first island. He lay on the beach awhile. He found that his lantern did not work any more, so he left it and started back to the next island, where his men were. This time the trip along the reef was awful. He had discarded his shoes, and every step on the coral was painful. This time the swim across the gap where the current had caught him the night before seemed endless. But the current had changed; he made the island. He crawled up on the beach. He was vomiting when his men came up to him. He said, "Ross, you try it tonight." Then he passed out.

Ross, seeing Kennedy so sick, did not look forward to the execution of the order. He distracted himself by complaining about his hunger. There were a few coconuts on the trees, but the men were too weak to climb up for them. One of the men thought of sea food, stirred his tired body, and found a snail on the beach. He said, "If we were desperate, we could eat these." Ross said, "Desperate, hell. Give me that. I'll eat that." He took it in his hand and looked at it. The snail put its head out and looked at him. Ross was startled, but he shelled the snail and ate it, making faces because it was bitter.

In the afternoon Ross swam across to the next island. He took a pistol to signal with, and he spent the night watching Ferguson Passage from the reef around the island. Nothing came through. Kennedy slept badly that night; he was cold and sick.

The next morning everyone felt wretched. Planes which the men were unable to identify flew overhead and there were dogfights. That meant Japs as well as friends, so the men dragged themselves into the bushes and lay low. Some prayed. Johnston said, "You guys make me sore. You didn't spend ten cents in church in ten years, then all of a sudden you're in trouble and you see the light." Kennedy felt a little better now. When Ross came back, Kennedy decided that the group should move to another, larger island to the southeast, where there seemed to be more coconut trees and where the party would be nearer Ferguson Passage. Again Kennedy took McMahon in tow with the strap in his teeth, and the nine others grouped themselves around the timber.

This swim took three hours. The nine around the timber were caught by the current and barely made the far tip of the island.

Kennedy found walking the quarter mile across to them much harder than the three hour swim. The cuts on his bare feet were festered and looked like small balloons. The men were suffering most from thirst, and they broke open some coconuts lying on the ground and avidly drank the milk. Kennedy and McMahon, the first to drink, were sickened, and Thom told the others to drink sparingly. In the middle of the night it rained, and someone suggested moving into the underbrush and licking water off the leaves. Ross and McMahon kept contact at first by touching feet as they licked. Somehow they got separated, and, being uncertain whether there were any Japs on the island, they became frightened. McMahon, trying to make his way back to the beach, bumped into someone and froze. It turned out to be Johnston, licking leaves on his own. In the morning the group saw that all the leaves were covered with droppings. Bitterly, they named the place Bird Island.

On this fourth day, the men were low. Even Johnston had changed his mind about praying. McGuire had a rosary around his neck, and Johnston said, "McGuire, give that necklace a working over." McGuire said quietly, "Yes, I'll take care of all you fellows." Kennedy was still unwilling to admit that things were hopeless. He asked Ross if he would swim with him to an island called Nauru, to the southeast and even nearer Ferguson Passage. They were very weak indeed by now, but after an hour's swim they made it.

They walked painfully across Nauru, to the Ferguson Passage side, where they saw a Japanese barge aground on the reef. There were two men by the barge—possibly Japs. They apparently spotted Kennedy and Ross, for they got into a dugout canoe and hurriedly paddled to the other side of the island. Kennedy and Ross moved up the beach. They came upon an unopened rope-bound box, and back in the trees, a little shelter containing a keg of water, a Japanese gas mask, and a crude wooden fetish shaped like a fish. There were Japanese hardtack and candy in the box and the two had a wary feast. Down by the water they found a one-man canoe. They hid from imagined Japs all day. When night fell, Kennedy left Ross and took the canoe, with some hardtack and a can of water from the keg, out into Ferguson Passage. But no P T's came, so he paddled to Bird Island. The men there told him that the two men he had spotted by the barge that morning were natives, who had paddled to Bird Island. The natives had said that there were Japs on Nauru, and the men had given Kennedy and Ross up for lost. Then the natives had gone away. Kennedy gave out small rations of crackers and water, and the men went to sleep. During the night, one man, who kept himself awake until the rest were asleep, drank all the water in the can Kennedy had brought back. In the morning the others figured out that he was the guilty one. They swore at him and found it hard to forgive him.

Before dawn, Kennedy started out in the canoe to rejoin Ross on Nauru, but when day broke a wind arose and the canoe was swamped. Some natives appeared from nowhere in a canoe, rescued Kennedy, and took him to Nauru. There they showed him where a two-man canoe was cached. Kennedy picked up a coconut with a smooth shell and scratched a message on it with a jackknife: "Eleven Alive Native Knows Posit and Reefs Nauru Island Kennedy." Then he said to the natives, "Rendova, Rendova."

One of the natives seemed to understand. They took the coconut and paddled off.

Ross and Kennedy lay in a sickly daze all day. Towards evening it rained and they crawled under a bush. When it got dark, conscience took hold of Kennedy and he persuaded Ross to go out into Ferguson Passage with him in the two-man canoe. Ross argued against it. Kennedy insisted. The two started out in the canoe. They had shaped paddles from the boards of the Japanese box, and they took a coconut shell to bail with. As they got out into the Passage, the wind rose again and the water became choppy. The canoe began to fill. Ross bailed and Kennedy kept the bow into the wind. The waves grew until they were five or six feet high. Kennedy shouted, "Better turn round and go back!" As soon as the canoe was broadside to the waves, the water poured in and the dugout was swamped. The two clung to it, Kennedy at the bow, Ross at the stern. The tide carried them southward toward the open sea, so they kicked and tugged the canoe, aiming northwest. They struggled that way for two hours, not knowing whether they would hit the small island or drift into the endless open.

The weather got worse; rain poured down and they couldn't see more than ten feet. Kennedy shouted, "Sorry I got you out here, Barney!" Ross shouted back, "This would be a great time to say I told you so, but I won't!"

Soon the two could see a white line ahead and could hear a frightening roar—waves crashing on a reef. They had got out of the tidal current and were approaching the island all right, but now they realized that the wind and the waves were carrying them toward the reef. But it was too late to do anything, now that their canoe was swamped, except hang on and wait.

When they were near the reef, a wave broke Kennedy's hold, ripped him away from the canoe, turned him head over heels, and spun him in a violent rush. His ears roared and his eyes pinwheeled, and for the third time since the collision, he thought he was dying. Somehow he was not thrown against the coral but floated into a kind of eddy. Sud-

291

denly he felt the reef under his feet. Steadying himself so that he would not be swept off it, he shouted, "Barney!" There was no reply. Kennedy thought of how he had insisted on going out in the canoe, and he screamed, "Barney!" This time Ross answered. He, too, had been thrown on the reef. He had not been as lucky as Kennedy; his right arm and shoulder had been cruelly lacerated by the coral, and his feet, which were already infected from earlier wounds, were cut some more.

The procession of Kennedy and Ross from reef to beach was a crazy one. Ross's feet hurt so much that Kennedy would hold one paddle on the bottom while Ross put a foot on it, then the other paddle forward for another step, then the first paddle forward again, until they reached sand. They fell on the beach and slept.

Kennedy and Ross were wakened early in the morning by a noise. They looked up and saw four husky natives. One walked up to them and said in an excellent English accent, "I have a letter for you, sir." Kennedy tore the note open. It said, "On His Majesty's Service. To the Senior Officer, Nauru Island. I have just learned of your presence on Nauru Island. I am in command of a New Zealand infantry patrol operating in conjunction with U. S. Army troops on New Georgia. I strongly advise that you come with these natives to me. Meanwhile I shall be in radio communication with your authorities at Rendova, and we can finalize plans to collect balance of your party. Lt. Wincote. P. S. Will warn aviation of your crossing Ferguson Passage."

Everyone shook hands and the four natives took Ross and Kennedy in their war canoe across to Bird Island to tell the others the good news. There the natives broke out a spirit stove and cooked a feast of yams and C ration. Then they built a leanto for McMahon, whose burns had begun to rot and stink, and for Ross, whose arm had swelled to the size of a thigh because of the coral cuts. The natives put Kennedy in the bottom of their canoe and covered him with sacking and palm fronds, in case Japanese planes should buzz them. The long trip was fun for the natives. They stopped once to try to grab a turtle, and laughed at the sport they were having. Thirty Japanese planes went over low toward Rendova, and the natives waved and shouted gaily. They rowed with a strange rhythm, pounding paddles on the gunwales between strokes. At last they reached a censored place. Lieutenant Wincote came to the water's edge and said formally, "How do you do. Leftenant Wincote."

Kennedy said, "Hello. I'm Kennedy."

Wincote said, "Come up to my tent and have a cup of tea."

In the middle of the night, after several radio conversations between Wincote's outfit and the P T base, Kennedy sat in the war canoe waiting at an arranged rendezvous for a P T. The moon went down at eleven-twenty. Shortly afterward Kennedy heard the signal he was waiting for—four shots. Kennedy fired four answering shots.

A voice shouted to him, "Hey, Jack!"

Kennedy said, "Where the hell you been?"

The voice said, "We got some food for you."

Kennedy said bitterly, "No, thanks, I just had a coconut."

A moment later a P T came alongside. Kennedy jumped onto it and hugged the men aboard—his friends. In the American tradition, Kennedy held under his arm a couple of souvenirs: one of the improvised paddles and the Japanese gas mask.

With the help of the natives, the P T made its way to Bird Island. A skiff went in and picked up the men. In the deep of the night, the P T and its happy cargo roared back toward base. The squadron medic had sent some brandy along to revive the weakened men. Johnston felt the need of a little revival. In fact, he felt he needed quite a bit of revival. After taking care of that, he retired topside and sat with his arms around a couple of roly-poly mission-trained natives. And in the fresh breeze on the way home they sang together a hymn all three happened to know:

> Jesus loves me, this I know,
> For the Bible tells me so;
> Little ones to Him belong,
> They are weak, but He is strong.
> Yes, Jesus loves me; yes, Jesus loves me. . . .

It is hard to say whether America's true tales of the sea or her false ones are the more remarkable. Seafaring men are notorious tellers of tall tales, in all ages and lands, but the true stories that they know need no embellishment. Of the next group of stories, two may be false or exaggerated; the other three are nothing but the truth.

Thrilling adventure[1]

We heard the other day a story related by an old sailor, Captain Jacob—, which made a great impression on us, and which we wish we could repeat with the unction and nautical phraseology of the worthy narrator.

It occurred during the last war. The captain, who was a native of Plymouth, was running on to the coast in a schooner loaded with flour. He had nearly reached his destination, when he was overhauled by the enemy's frigates, who ordered him peremptorily to heave a line aboard. There was no resisting the command, for the schooner was without arms, and the tender full of marines and sailors armed to the teeth with pistols, muskets and cutlasses. The captain had a light but fair breeze aloft, his sails drew, and he was driving near a reef, the entrance to which he was perfectly familiar with, and once inside which, he was sure of making port, undisturbed by the tender.

In this view he ordered one of his men forward with the line, and in a clear stentorian voice, perfectly audible on board the tender, sang out: "Heave your line aboard!" then he added, *sotto voce,* so as to be heard only by his men, *"Heave it short!"*

The Yankee sailor caught the hint, and "hove" according to directions. The end of the line fell splashing in the water.

High above the execrations of the English officer commanding the tender, rose the roar of the indignant Yankee skipper:

"Is that the way to heave a line, you lubberly son of a land-crab? Heave the line ship-shape, you lubber, or I'll cut your liver out! *Heave it short!"*

Again the line fell short, and the English officer and Yankee captain

[1] From Porter's *Spirit of the Times,* April 22, 1848.

vied with each other in showering imprecations and invectives on the head of the blundering "land-lubber." Meanwhile the breeze was freshening, and the schooner drawing nearer to the reef.

Again and again the order to heave was given, with the same undertone addition, and with the same result. The Englishman began to smell a rat, and just as the Yankee skipper threw himself flat on his deck, and made his men follow his example, the report of a dozen muskets was heard, and a shower of bullets came whizzing through the rigging.

"Let them fire and be darned!" said the Yankee—"I'll show them a clean pair of heels."

And taking his tiller between his heels, as he lay upon the deck, he run the schooner cleverly inside the reef.

They were soon out of gun shot from the baffled tender. Up went the stars and stripes, with a hearty cheer from the mariners, and an old one-eyed sea-dog pulled out a fife, and gave them Yankee Doodle in strains as melodious as the triumphant notes of a porker that has escaped the butcher's knife. Captain Jacob saved his bacon and his flour, too.

—Yankee Blade

Slitly Stove

The editor of the *Yankee Blade*[1] termed the story just quoted a thrilling one and wished that he could have told it with the "unction" of a seafaring man. Actually seafaring Americans, especially the New Englanders among them, often showed themselves masters of a dispassionate style. The mate of the ship *Niagara* wrote a typically phlegmatic account of an exciting accident in his log in June 1853, as follows:[2]

All these 24 hours calm pleasant weather. Ship close in by the ice plenty of whales in the ice all four boats in the ice a Whaling, at 6 P.M. the Starboard and Waist boats struck one whale, at the same time the Captain was nocked out of his boat by the second Iron and taken under the Ice for several minutes but by Good Luck we succeeded in Saving him although badly bruzed and took him to the ship. Lost two lines and got the boats Slitly Stove. At three A.M. the Larboard boat lowered and struck the Whale run under the Ice and cut line in a few minutes the Whale come out of the ice and went on and struck again he ran under the ice and the iron drew. So Ends these twenty-four hours.

---

[1] From which the *Spirit of the Times* extracted the story.
[2] From William H. Tripp: *There Goes Flukes* (New Bedford: Reynolds Printing; 1938), p. 111.

The reader of this entry might well wish for the captain's own account of this day's work. It is extant, though never printed hitherto, and it is only slightly more emotional than the mate's record. The captain describes his eventful day thus:[1]

At noon struck a whale with the Starboard boat and parted. . . . At six P.M. the Starboard and Waist boat fastened to another at the same time and each put out a drag. Not having unbent my second Iron when the knot that bent my two lines together went out of the boat it caught the bowline in my short warp and took the second iron out of the boat and me with it carrying me some distance under the ice and bruising me against it as the whale was going quick. After getting clear of the line I came up under a long piece of ice and was nearly suffocated before I could get out. When the Men hauled me onto the Ice I was speechless but my sense of Hearing and my seeing was perfect. When I was taken out of the boat the Men cut the two lines, so we lost 400 fathoms of line. Spoke the Neptune of N. London. Lat. 60.58 Long. 173.00

An interesting story of a whaleboat lost from a ship is that told by Captain Roland F. Coffin in *An Old Sailor's Yarn*.

Queer fare [2]

Coffin was in the captain's boat, and the captain held on to a whale that ran away all one night. They killed the whale in the morning, "waifed" it, and then started to sail back and find the ship.

"We missed the ship some way. Arter runnin' till noon the next day and seein' nothin' of her, the old man made up his mind that we had run by her; that she was a-workin' up to windward to look for us, and had reached so far over our track as to be out of our sight when we passed her. 'So,' says he, ' 'tain't no use to run off any further, and 'tain't no use pullin' to windward, and the best thing we can do is jist to lay still, and she'll cruise about till she finds us.'

"Well, we laid still for twenty-four hours longer, and then our grub was very near all used up, and things was a-lookin' bad for us; so we set sail and concluded we'd reach back and forth on a wind, and we done so . . . till near six o'clock, when just as we was a-goin' round one of the chaps who had stood up for to git a good look sings out 'Land ho!' Up we all jumped in a jiffy, and there, sure enough, about two p'ints on the lee bow, was a small island.

"They landed on the island at daylight the next morning. It was one

---

[1] From MS. Private Journal of Benjamin Clough, Master of Ship *Niagara*, off Cape St. Thaddeus, June 2, 1853 (in the possession of the editor).

[2] From John R. Spears: *The Story of the New England Whalers* (New York: The Macmillan Co.; 1908), pp. 265–72.

of the coral reefs common to certain parts of the Pacific, and one not found on the charts.

"What we wanted jist then more than anythin' else was somethin' for to drink. We hadn't had no water for nearly twenty-four hours. You may jist imagine, then, how glad we was when one of the party by the name of Tom Bunker—he belonged to Nantucket—sung out, 'Here's a spring!' You see, sir, there was six of us all told, and the old man had made us separate as far apart as we could and yet be within hail, and so go across the island for to survey it like and try for to find wood and water. At Tom's hail, however, we all come to at once and ranged up to him, and sure enough, here was a little spring of beautiful clear water. If you want to know what first-class tipple is you must try spring water arter you've been in a boat twenty-four hours without any. Tom told us that afore he come up with the spring he seen the whole ground alive with some kind of creepin' animal, but what they was he couldn't tell. Well, we didn't hyst that in exactly, but we thought that maybe Tom's bein' so long on the water without anythin' for to drink had made him kind of loony, and so he imagined he seen animals when he hadn't. 'What's funny about this here island,' says the old man, 'is that there ain't no birds onto it. I've landed on plenty of islands afore which didn't have no natives onto 'em, and there was always thousands of birds; and here, exceptin' some gulls a-flyin' over the reef, we ain't seen a bird.'

" 'Talkin' about inhabitants,' says one of the chaps, just then, 'what do you call that thing yonder?' We looked where he p'inted and there, sure enough, was a native. He appeared for to be kind of frightened of us, and kept at a respectful distance, and as we advanced he retreated. So the old man, he says, 'You stay here, my lads, and I'll go for'ard alone, and then maybe it won't be so much afeerd.' So we sits down and the old man he goes ahead, puttin' his hands onto his breast, and a-makin' all sort of motions for to show that he didn't mean no harm; and finally the savage seemed to understand, and stopped still for to let our old man come up. But it seemed, as he told us arterward, when he got within hailin' distance, all of a sudden the native, as we had took it to be, runned toward him, and with a kind of a yell like jist tumbled down all into a bunch at his feet. Well, we heerd the yell the critter gave, and we rushed up to where the old man was, and if I ever see a man flabbergasted completely, it was that old man. 'Boys,' says he, 'that ain't no native; it's a woman and a white woman at that; and how on earth she got here beats me entirely.'

"Well, she soon come around to herself, and if ever you see a critter delighted for to see anybody that there critter was delighted for to see us. And the first words she said when she come to was: 'It ain't no dream; you are real. Thank God, I am saved!'

" 'Well, as to that, marm,' says our old man, 'of course we'll do any thin' for you that's in our power; but whether you be saved or not, there's different opinions about, but there ain't no doubt of the fact that we are lost.'

The lone woman was the wife of the captain of a whale ship that had been lost with all hands except her on the reef. She had been washed ashore and then had managed to save enough from the wreck to make herself comfortable so far as living was concerned, and there she had remained for five years.

"Well, it was a good job for us, anyway. When we got to her hut she says to our old man, 'Now you and your men sit down here behind the house, and I'll go to work for to cook you a breakfast. Of course I didn't expect company, and so I heven't got none ready at present; but there's plenty here and I won't be long a-gittin' of it.' Well, she takes a stick that looked somethin' like a boat's tiller and away she went into the grove of cocoanuts, and we seen her runnin' back and forth a-strikin' at somethin' on the ground, but whatever it was we didn't know, and to tell the truth we didn't care. Fact was we was all pretty well tuckered out, and gittin' where all things was comfortable and a good breakfast promised us, we jist give up and stretched down onto the grass and went to sleep. The old man sot the example, and I heerd him a-borin' pump-log afore I dropped off. I was woke up by one of the finest smells of cookin' I ever smelt, and it fetched me right up onto my feet to onct, and I went along to where the woman had her fire—jist some stones with a fire built onto 'em,—and found that what I smelt come from a big sasspan which she had over the fire. 'Wait a few minits,' says she, 'it's almost done; and if you don't say it's a good stew, then call me a bad cook.' The smell had waked up the rest of the chaps by this time, and we was all ready for our meal when she dished it up. Well, sir, I never eat anything like that stew in all my born days. I s'pose it was because I was hungry, partly, but then it really was extremely nice as she made it, for we had it often after that when we wasn't so sharp set.

"The woman she looked on quite delighted for to see us eat, and a-fillin' each chap's dish as fast as it was empty; but arter she had helped us all around for the sixth time . . . says she, 'I'll bet you don't any of you know what you've been eatin'.'

" 'Well, marm,' says our skipper, 'that 'ere was jist the question I was a-goin' for to ask you; this here's a powerful good stew, and shows that you're a first class cook,—but that of course you would be, comin' from Nantucket,—but I hain't seen no birds onto the island, and I can't jist judge from the taste what sort of an animal you've made it of.'

" 'Well,' says she, 'that there was a rat stew, and rats is now about the only livin' thing there is upon the island except ourselves, and I begun to think that if they increased much more they'd eat me as they have everythin' else.'

The rats had come from the wrecked ship, "the numerous eggs in the birds' nests provin' a great temptation," and they had driven the birds from the reef. They had then begun to clear the cocoanut trees, and the lost sailors found themselves face to face with the problem of controlling the increase of the rats under penalty of starvation. But while they were working at the problem in sailor fashion—"we had rat to eat all ways, roast rat, broiled rat, fried rat, rat fricassee, and rat stew"— the ship to which they belonged arrived off the island and took them away, leaving the rats in full control.

Sailing blind[1]

September, October, November, and most of December—for almost four months the *Puritan* matched her stout planking with stormy seas on the homeward voyage. The North Atlantic in December held severe weather—gales, intense cold, and snow storms. It was almost the middle of December before the *Putnam's* sounding line told the officers that the ship was off Nantucket.

On Dec. 25 the ship was moving along in thick snow, with no observations for two days. Captain Bowditch was on deck now, standing continuous watch, he and his officers staring off into the curtain of white that shut them off from a view of everything except the seas smashing at the ship. According to the calculations Bowditch had made after his sight of the sun two days before, he was near the outer harbor of Salem. The officers had little to say about the ship's position. The responsibility was all Bowditch's. It was his ship, and, for all practical purposes, his snow storm.

As it grew dark and the ship continued under way, not only the officers but the crew began to be uneasy. The *Putnam* was off dangerous shores. Hidden behind the snow were rocks that could shatter timbers and scatter cargo, masts, and rigging in the surf. Salem Harbor's channels were outlined with rocks. One ledge in the harbor had been given the name of Bowditch, after a great-grandsire who had wrecked his vessel on it.

The *Putnam* went on, the officers straining their eyes ahead and the members of the crew watching the little navigator aft who held the safety of the ship in his hands. The snow fastened onto the tops of the

---

[1] From Robert Elton Berry: *Yankee Stargazer: The Life of Nathaniel Bowditch* (New York: Whittlesey House, McGraw-Hill Book Co.; 1941), pp. 138–40.

yards, whitened sails and sheets, piled in the corners of the decks, coated the clothing of the men on watch.

In holding to his course, in sailing blind toward his home port, Bowditch was doing something that no other seasoned mariner would have done. All up and down the coast other ships ready to make port were standing off and on, waiting for the snow to stop. Going into harbor was too dangerous.

Other masters, if they had attempted to go into port in this snow storm, would have been risking the lives of their crews and their vessels. Bowditch had something additional to lose. He had set himself up as an authority on navigation. If he should put his ship on the rocks, for years afterwards when his book was mentioned seamen would nod and recall that he had wrecked an Indiaman in a foolhardy attempt to make port in a snow storm.

"Our old man goes ahead as if it was noonday!" one of the crew said as the *Putnam* headed in for the rock harbor. It didn't take much imagination to envision men and wreckage washing back and forth in the surf, black spots in the semidarkness.

Regardless of the risk Bowditch was taking, the fact remains that he knew where his ship was. He had, in addition, one lucky break. At the entrance to the harbor the snow lifted momentarily—just long enough to confirm the position of the ship. During seconds when there was a rift in the wall of snow Bowditch and his officers were able to see the light on Baker's Island. The one glimpse was enough. The *Putnam* went on in, to dock at the foot of the town of Salem, following a channel through the rocks that Bowditches had been following for generations—a channel that hugged the Marblehead shore, that led around Peach's Point and past shoals called Kettlebottom, Endeavors, Triangles, and Great and Little Aqua Vitae.

The *Putnam* docked at 9 o'clock on Christmas Day, and Bowditch, in a hurry to be ashore, scrawled the last entry in the ship's log:

"Arrived at Salem Dec. 25, in the evening."

He left it for other seamen to tell the story of his making port in the storm, and the stories grew in the telling as they went up and down the coast to add to the Bowditch legend. One of the most common exaggerations was that the little navigator had sailed into harbor without even a glimpse of a landmark.

Saving the *Sharon*

This true story of how a boy of nineteen recaptured a New Bedford whaler from mutineers was familiar to American seamen a century ago and has often been told, in print and otherwise. The present version, written by the chief participant shortly after the event, has never been printed and differs considerably from most of those hitherto published.

The most accurate account hitherto published was entitled "Wonderful Exploit of Benjamin Clough" and was reprinted by *Littell's Living Age* in March 1845 from an unidentified newspaper. It is the progenitor of all other printed accounts, so far as can be learned, but these have gradually wandered from their original; it was accurate, and they are increasingly less so. Some of the more interesting differences will be noted later. The *Living Age* account is a little fuller than that which follows; it says, for instance, that Benjamin Clough, the hero of the exploit, was in the water an hour and a half, and that after he summoned the mate and crew on board, half an hour elapsed before they ventured to return. Clough's own account omits these striking details; he was disinclined to emphasize his hardships and courage. In fact Captain Clough (as he was for the rest of his life) seldom spoke of this exploit. His son, Benjamin Clough, told the present editor (who is *his* son) that this was because some of those on board the *Sharon* who did not make a very good showing were nevertheless neighbors of Captain Clough and on pleasant enough terms with him. He would not have cared to remind them of some features of the story. As a matter of fact, he sealed his own manuscript account, and it remained sealed for more than half a century, and was locked away for nearly as long. I see no reason why the faded record should not now be printed, verbatim. It takes the form of a continuation of Clough's "Journal of a Whaling Voyage kept on board the Ship Sharon." (It was fastened with sealing wax between the two pages of the journal that followed the entries for November 1, 1842.)

Saturday, November 5, 1842.[1]
This day commences with light variable winds. At nine A.M. raised sperm whales and lowered the larboard and waist boats, leaving the Captain,

---

[1] All printed accounts give the date as Sunday, November 6. But the unofficial log-book gives the date as Saturday, November 5, and Clough wrote to his father that that was the date.

Steward, and three Kanakas[1] on board to keep ship. I went off to steer the larboard boat. We struck a whale and turned him up and continued to chase other whales until we observed the flag at the main topgallant head at half-mast. We then pulled for the ship. When we got within hailing distance we saw the steward at the mast-head and he informed us that the Kanakas had killed the Captain and got possession of the ship, having the cutting spades, harpoons, hammers, and other weapons ready to destroy the crews of the boats as soon as they should come alongside. Mr. Smith[2] then told the Steward to cut the halliards and let the sails run down, which he did. We then pulled up toward the ship, when they commenced heaving bone belaying pins, hammers, and wood into the boat, having ready to use as soon as the boat should come near enough, one of them keeping to each boat when they approached the ship and the other one at the wheel, and we saw that we could not approach to board her without the loss of lives. We then concluded to wait until dark. When it began to grow dark we pulled out ahead of the ship. I took the boat knife in my mouth as a weapon against sharks as there was a great number around and dropped silently overboard and swam for the head of the ship. When I got to the head of the ship I saw one of the Kanakas standing between the night-heads pounding on a tin pan, but he did not see me. I then dropped alongside of the ship. When I came to the stern I went up the rudder and into the cabin window, took off my clothes, got two cutlasses and put them into the forward cabin. I then got some powder and balls and muskets and commenced loading the muskets. I could hear the natives talking and see them walking around the quarter deck collecting wood and other missiles to heave at the boats. I had got two of my muskets loaded and the powder into the third one and standing the muskets up at the foot of the companionway stepped into the after cabin to get more balls. I heard someone coming down. I stepped to the door to look and just as I got to the door one of the natives had just got to the bottom of the stairs and knocked the musket down. It being darker in the after cabin there at the foot of the stairs I could see him but not he me. I stepped out and got hold of a cutlass and made a thrust at him but it being dark I wounded him but slightly in the side, when he gave a shout and rushed for me and got hold of me, I being at the door of the after cabin. I stepped back into the cabin and succeeded in throwing [him] onto the cabin floor, both of us having hold of the cutlass. In the meantime, wounding me in the hands in several places he then began to call lustily for the others to come to his help. I then wounded him as much as I could and thinking he was about dead I got up to see if the others were a-coming, having lost hold of the cutlass. But he jumped [up] immediately and having hold of the cutlass began to lay about him manfully by the sound which it made against the furniture and against my flesh, but he soon gave it up and I heard him breathe very hard for a number of times and then I heard him no more. I then took a musket and stepped to the foot of the stairs and saw one of the natives standing at the head of the companionway with a long cutting spade in his hands shoved about half way down the stairs. I put the musket up and shot him and as the gun went off the spade came down and struck me on the thick part of my arm above the elbow. I heard the native fall on deck and groan twice and then I heard no more from him. I then stepped back into the

---

[1] Islanders. They came from what is now the Gilbert group. It was earlier called the Kingsmill group, but when my father told me the story he called it Molino del Rey.

[2] The mate.

cabin bleeding very freely from my wounds. In a few moments I heard the other native coming aft and he came to the companionway and looked down, having a short-handled spade, but seeing one of the natives dead and not seeing the other he went forward again. I then called the boats to come on board, which they did, and got a light and came down into the cabin and saw the native lying on the transom with a boat-knife in one hand that I left on the transom when I came into the window and a cutlass in the other. Mr. Smith then took a musket and shot him dead and he was dragged on deck, both cabin floors being covered with blood where he and I had bled. The other Kanaka lay dead by the side of the companionway. They were both taken along to the waist and threw overboard. Captain Norris lay dead on deck abreast of the after part of the main rigging, having a deep gash in his side, his head nearly severed from his body and being shockingly mangled by the hogs and pieces of his scul lying about the decks. He was taken carried aft and laid on the turning lathe. My wounds were then dressed being about a dozen and some of them pretty deep but mostly about the arms and right hand. In the mean time a strict search was made after other Kanaka but he could not be found and the watch was set, the watch keeping a sharp lookout with arms in their hands. At daylight the next morning all hands were called and commenced fitting the rigging, it being calm. At eight commenced to sew the captain up, at eight one half he was taken along to the waist, a chapter read in the bible and a prayer in the prayer-book and [the] body launched into the deep. Our hogs seven in number were knocked in the head and thrown overboard after sail was made and the blood washed from the ship. A search was made for the other Kanaka and he was soon found on the Larboard between the fore and main hatchways and after some resistance he was got on deck and handcuffs put on to him and chained to a ringbolt. It appears by his account that when he came aft and saw the other native dead he went and jumped overboard and swam away from the ship, it being calm, and after the boats were hoisted up he got hold of the eyebolt in the rudder and hung by it until things got still on deck and then came and got on deck by the bobstays and went down into the fore-hold &c.

[If this ending seems abrupt, it should be remembered that the writer was partially disabled. Three months later he penned, with some difficulty, a letter to his father in which he relates his exploit in the same matter-of-fact fashion, but concludes as follows:]

The native was put in irons and the ship headed for Sidney. There we arrived 22nd of Dec., 1842. We delivered our native up to the American Consul. We left the 6th of Jan., the mate, Thomas H. Smith taking command and I am second mate. My wounds got healed up about the time we went into Sidney. We now have about 500 Blls of sperm oil on board. But how long we shall be out is more than I can say. I have enjoyed very good health since we left Sidney except my right hand which is so that I can hardly hold a pen. We have got a good crew on board and I am in hopes that we shall do something as we are on good ground. I have not time to write more as I am holding paper in my hand. Give my respects to all enquiring friends, etc.

B. Clough.

It is pleasant to add that when the young man (he had been only nineteen at the time of his adventure) reached New Bedford, the owners gave him command of a ship, thus making him the youngest master that ever sailed from that port, and the insurance companies, also grateful, gave him a gold watch, a chronometer, a sextant, and a marine glass, all suitably inscribed.

This story was a plain one, and plainly told by its hero; so far as I have heard any oral versions, they, too, were unadorned. When writers took it up, slight changes took place, and then more radical ones. A few recent alterations are worth tracing here, for they furnish a graphic view of fact on its way into fiction.

Stanley Rogers, an excellent story-teller, published in London in the 1920's[1] a book called *Ships and Sailors*. In Chapter v, which deals in part with the *Sharon*, he appears to follow the good old *Littell's Living Age* account, but in touching it up, he errs. Knowing (possibly) but one Ascension Island,[2] and reading that the *Sharon* put in at Ascension, he assumes that this was in the Atlantic, and locates his story there. Wrong island! It was in the Pacific, as he would have realized had he only noticed the latitude and longitude as given in the *Living Age*. He then copied the steward's name as Jose dos Rios; it was des Reis. This is not very material, certainly, but it does enable us to distinguish a later account as drawn from Rogers. Finally, making a natural guess, he says: "During the passage [home] Clough remained an invalid." Actually Clough became second mate (equivalent to first, as Mate Smith was now acting captain) January 6, 1843, two months after the mutiny, and remained in this office for the rest of the voyage.

Rogers's errors are easily forgiven, but his version has been too readily accepted and too casually "improved." In 1937 Irvin Anthony, in *Revolt at Sea*,[3] gave a chapter to the *Sharon*. That he rewrote Rogers is indicated by his transfer of the events from their proper ocean to the Atlantic, and by his reference to "Jose dos Rios." Having noted Rogers's correct statement that the *Sharon* sailed from Fairhaven, he tells us that "Clough was a loyal son of the town." Perhaps it does not matter today, but Clough was a loyal son of Monmouth, Maine. (He never lived in Fairhaven.) The nearest land at the time of the mutiny, says Anthony, was "a choice between Ascension and Saint Helena"; since he has got himself into the wrong ocean, this error is natural. At a critical moment in the story we are treated to some elegant description. Clough "began to undress. The rest lolled upon the thwarts, looking curiously at his white body so dim in the darkness. Once stripped—" and so on. Pretty, but Clough did not strip until he had boarded the *Sharon*.

---

[1] And in Boston (Little, Brown & Co.), in 1928.
[2] Pardonable. The *Encyclopædia Britannica* knows but one, and that the Atlantic one.
[3] New York: G. P. Putnam's Sons.

At the end of his fight, we are told, "Clough was unconscious." (Rogers had said that he was "half-fainting," which is likely enough.) Far from unconscious, Clough actually hailed the crew and gave them directions about boarding. And finally, according to Mr. Anthony, Clough "lay in blankets and mopped his gruel down. It had been a close shave, but he regained his health and landed in Fairhaven a discharged patient." Hardly that; he had actively assisted in command and navigation for months.

In *Mutiny at Sea*, by Robert L. Hadfield,[1] a chapter called "The Hero of the Sharon" begins by telling us that "the broad rollers of the South Atlantic were a deep blue"; wrong ocean again. Clough shortly appears, with "a flow of oaths that could outshine the captain's." So far as I know my grandfather's manners—and I have consulted people who remembered him—Clough never swore at all. We are then told that Clough "liked the master and had little use for the mate." Mr. Hadfield could only guess; as it happens, he guessed grotesquely wrong on one of these points, and not exactly right on the other. He supplies a good deal of conversation; it seems well invented, but of course there is no way of knowing how far it resembles what was actually said. Clough, of course, strips, and finds the water cold. (This was Atlantic water, unlike that in the real story.) After the fight he is unable to call to the mate and gets the boy to do so. Plausible, but the facts were otherwise. All in all, the chapter makes good reading. It is well invented, but invention is invention, fact fact.

Believing the unvarnished truth quite good enough, I have printed it partly in the hope of checking the decorative versions. It seems to me that these are getting a little out of hand.

---

[1] New York: E. P. Dutton & Co.; 1938.

Perhaps it is true that the biggest American lies are told in the West. Again, perhaps it isn't. All that can safely be said is that the humor of understatement has never flourished in the American West, though Mark Twain occasionally employed it. The East has, of course, become industrialized, and its population heterogeneous. But find yourself a New England Yankee (and there are plenty: witness John Gould's book, for example), and you will have found a man who can hold his own in any lying match.

Ballads have in general been avoided in this collection, because by their rhyme and otherwise they twist a story out of its best form and (for rhyme's sweet sake) introduce extrinsic detail. But the anonymous verse "I wish I could tell a lie" had to be admitted.

Western liars[1]

An authentic liar knows what he is lying about, knows that his listeners—unless they are tenderfeet, greenhorns—know also, and hence makes no pretense of fooling either himself or them. At his best he is as grave as a historian of the Roman Empire; yet what he is after is neither credulity nor the establishment of truth. He does not take himself too seriously, but he does regard himself as an artist and yearns for recognition of his art. He may lie with satiric intent; he may lie merely to make the time pass pleasantly; he may lie in order to take the wind out of some egotistic fellow of his own tribe or to take in some greener; again, without any purpose at all and directed only by his own ebullient and companion-loving nature, he may "stretch the blanket" merely because, like the redoubtable Tom Ochiltree, he had "rather lie on credit than tell truth for cash." His generous nature revolts at the monotony of everyday facts and overflows with desire to make his company joyful.

Certainly the telling of "windies" flourished in the Old World long before America was discovered; nevertheless the tall tale both in subject matter and in manner of telling has been peculiar to the frontiers of America, whether in the backwoods of the Old South, in the mining

---

[1] From Mody C. Boatright: *Tall Tales from Texas* (Dallas: The Southwest Press; 1934), "A Preface on Authentic Liars," by J. Frank Dobie, pp. vii–ix.

camps of the Far West, amid the logging camps presided over by Paul Bunyan, or on the range lands stretching from the Gulf of Mexico to the Canadian line. Very likely the Pilgrim Fathers did not indulge much in the art of yarning, and the stately Cavaliers pretty much left that sort of entertainment to the poor—"poor but honest"—settlers. As to whether the "decay in the art of lying" that Oscar Wilde observed in literary fiction has blighted that to be heard around camp fires and on the galleries of ranch houses, we need not here inquire. The "big uns" that Mody Boatright has gathered together in this book are not altogether out of the past.

They express a way that range folk talked and they express also a way in which these folk cartooned objects familiar to them like rattlesnakes, sand storms, jack rabbits, the expanding and contracting powers of rawhide, the suddenness of Texas northers, "killings" according to a code that clearly distinguished a killing from a murder, and other things. They are, in short, authentic both as to the characters represented and the subjects discoursed upon.

When in the old days two cow outfits met upon the range, and there was "ample time," as Andy Adams would say, they sometimes arranged what was known as an "auguring match." Each outfit would pit its prime yarn-spinner against the other and there followed a contest not only of invention but of endurance. John Palliser in *The Solitary Hunter; or, Sporting Adventures of the Prairies* (London, 1856) relates how after an all-night talking contest between a Missourian and a Kentuckian, the "umpire at a quarter past five" found the Kentucky man fast asleep, his opponent "whispering in his ear, sitting up close beside him." What the contestants talked about, Palliser does not say, but there is ample testimony to prove that the "auguring matches" on the range had as precedent among the backwoodsmen of the South who were to push out upon the ranges a kind of round table talk in which each talker sought to cap the tall tales of his fellow with one a little taller.

For genuine artists a solitary opponent is sufficient; art is substantive. In *Piney Woods Tavern; or, Sam Slick in Texas* (Philadelphia, 1858), by Samuel A. Hammett, the narrator in traveling from the Brazos to the Trinity rivers found the San Jacinto "a roarin' and a hummin' it. . . . Free soil movements was a goin' on, and trees a-tumbling' in all along the banks."

I see thar war no help for it [the narrator goes on]. So I took my feet outen the stirrups, threw my saddle-bags over my shoulder, and in me and the mar went.

We war in a awful tight place for a time, but we soon landed safe. I'd jest got my critter tied out, and a fire started to dry myself with when I see a chap come ridin' up the hill on a smart chunk of a poney. . . .

"Hoopee! stranger"—sings out my beauty—"How d'ye? Kept your fireworks dry, eh? How in thunder did ye get over?"

"Oh!" says I, "mighty easy. Ye see, stranger, I'm powerful on a pirogue; so I waited till I see a big log a-driftin' nigh the shore, when I fastened to it, set my critter a-straddle on it, got into the saddle, paddled over with my saddle-bags, and steered with the mare's tail."

"Ye didn't, though, by Ned!" says he, "did ye?"

"Mighty apt to"—says I—"but arter ye've sucked all that in and got yer breath agin, let's know how *you* crossed?"

"Oh!" says he, settin' his pig's eyes on me, "I've been a-ridin' all day with a consarned ager, and orful dry, and afeard to drink at the prairie water holes; so when I got to the river I jest went in fer a big drink, swallered half a mile of water, and come over dry shod."

"Stranger," says I, "ye'r just one huckleberry above my persimmon. Light and take some red-eye. I thought ye looked green, but I were barkin' up the wrong tree."

Story-telling in Texas was so popular that at times it interfered with religion. The pioneer Baptist preacher, Z. N. Morrell, relates in his autobiographic *Flowers and Fruits in the Wilderness* (Dallas, 1886) that on one occasion while he was preaching in a log cabin in East Texas his sermon was drowned by the voices of men outside "telling anecdotes." After an ineffectual reprimand, the preacher finally told his interrupters that if they would give him a chance he would tell an anecdote and that then, if it was not better than any of theirs, he would "take down his sign and listen to them." They agreed to the challenge. The anecdote he proceeded to relate about Sam Houston and the battle of San Jacinto won him the right to keep on talking without interruption. The triumph was but a repetition of David Crockett's election to Congress through his b'ar stories.

An anecdote is not by any means necessarily a windy, but people who cultivate the art of oral narration will sooner or later indulge in exaggerative invention. Some candidate for the Ph.D. degree should write a thesis on the interrelationship of the anecdote, the tall tale, and the short short story in America. What is probably the most widely known story that the nation has produced, "The Celebrated Jumping Frog of Calaveras County," is all three—and it is mostly just a yarn in which the frontier character, Jim Smiley, character being the essence of good anecdote, is more important than the frog.

Maine liars[1]

All real Maine people are natural-born liars, which is not at all so hideous a distinction as being a trained liar—the kind better known elsewhere. My wife hadn't got used to this when Henry Jorgen came up to brood solace with me over the continued wet weather. Instead of commenting prosaically that we'd had enough rain for anyone with normal desires, Henry, who lives twenty miles from the ocean, said, "Got a sea serpent in my pasture."

My wife was just about to insinuate a doubting remark, but I knew Henry was merely emphasizing his displeasure at the weather, so I beat her to it and said, "A big one?"

"Not awful big," said Henry without a trace of humor in his voice, "but pretty-colored. He's green and orange, with butter-colored spots." He said the serpent came up in the orchard at low tide and dug oysters, and then we talked about other things and had a pleasant visit.

This sort of simile, this method of making a basic fact memorable, has nothing to do with injunctions against false witness. Henry, and people like him, has never been known to utter an untruth. He lies because it's the most artistic way he knows of to tell the truth. So long as kindred ears hear his remarks, and the usual trade discount is taken, he is merely indulging in a literary pastime—sort of an intellectual exercise like fitting a complete thought into the structure of a sonnet—except that we folks don't wind up in such a welter of mental fatigue as is suggested by most sonnets.

Instead, good and wholesome lying brightens our lives, and we probably derive a comfort from it that is unknown to strangers. I think my wife is getting used to it. When Jerry Turner was doing a lot of bragging about his hens, she tried to take him down a peg one day by asking, "I hear your hens lay eggs as big as grapefruit."

Jerry looked her straight in the eye and said, "No, that ain't so—but my pigeons do."

---

[1] From *Farmer Takes a Wife* by John Gould (New York: William Morrow & Co.; 1945), pp. 83–4. Copyright 1945 by John Gould; by permission of William Morrow & Co., Inc.

Old Man Montgomery[1]

Old Man Montgomery would go out into the hills for months, and all he would take for grub was a gunnysack full of white bread. When the dogs killed a lion he would cut out a chunk and eat that, and keep on until he met some old-timer who was qualified to appreciate his stories.

"He had camped down on Jim Yost and, while Jim was listening to a story that it took two hours to tell, he made up one of his own. Montgomery's stories were all about trailing mountain lions and the hand-to-hand fights he had with them, and Jim went on from there.

" 'I trailed a lion one time,' he said, 'until he wore off all his claws and had to den up in the rocks, but of course I went right in after him. Just as I turned the last corner a big rattlesnake raised his head and looked me in the eye, but I grabbed him by the neck, jumped in after the lion and, using the snake for a whip, I chased him clear out of there and across the plains to the San Pedro River.

" 'Well, did you catch him?' says Montgomery, who didn't believe in spoiling a good story; and Jim Yost shook his head.

" 'When he got to the river,' he said, 'it was bone dry, but before I could start across a big cloudburst came down—a wall of water fifty feet high, sweeping everything before it—so of course I had to let him go!'

" 'That man is a dadburned liar,' says Montgomery, 'But I heard a bigger one than that. A feller was bragging about a rattlesnake he'd seen that was a hundred yards long and had rattles that looked like a string of box cars.

" 'Isn't that so, Bud?' he asked his pardner.

" 'Well, I don't know,' Bud says. 'It started to go down a hole before I got there and I only saw the last twenty-five feet.'

"I knew a Cousin Jack that was always telling about how deep the mines were in the old country, and another miner says:

" 'We have deep mines in this country, too. Out on the Mojave Desert I come to this camp, and you could see the top of the hoist twenty miles away. When I got close I saw a big cable running up to the wheel, but I couldn't see the engineer. He was down behind the drum, which was turning around real fast, asleep. I went down and woke him up and asked him when the cage would be up.

" 'Let's see,' he says. 'What day is this?'

---

[1] Taken from *Old California Cowboys*, by Dane Coolidge, published and copyright by E. P. Dutton & Co., Inc., New York. Copyright 1939. Pp. 80-2.

" 'Tuesday,' I says.

" 'It'll be up at three-thirty, Thursday,' he says, and went to sleep again."

"At the West"[1]

M uch attention has been paid to the rearing of poultry at the West, and the method now in use of hatching chickens I consider far superior to the Egyptian one of hatching them in ovens. It is simply to fill a barrel with eggs, head it up, and set a hen upon the bung.

"Out West"[2]

O ut West" saw logs were being stolen. A huge one was watched all night by two men. "When daylight broke, to their surprise, the gents had been there and stolen the log, and left the two watchmen straddling the bark, unconscious of the thief."

Mississippi water[3]

A Kentucky roarer declares that since he has signed the teetotal pledge he has drank Mississippi water by the gallon. "Talk to me of a man eating a peck of dirt in a lifetime," said he, "why, I have only been swallowing the sediment for a month, and am already chuck full of sand-bars, snags, rafts, islands and sunken flat-boats, and never was healthier in my life."

---

[1] From Porter's *Spirit of the Times,* February 26, 1848.

[2] From Porter's *Spirit of the Times,* June 10, 1848.

[3] From Porter's *Spirit of the Times,* August 5, 1848.

The toughest game-cock on record[1]

Whilst travelling recently in Virginia, I became acquainted with a "rale Down-Easter" who had come "all the way from Varmount," and who flourished under the distinguished appellation of "Colonel Phil." One of nature's "queer lumps of clay" is Phil; he is, undeniably, great at anything and everything, "cock fighting" especially.

"I once had a Cock," said he, "that could jist rip the rag off all natur. I fout him agin evrything in Varginny, and whipt 'em all teu; arterwards I gin 'em all a heel and whaled 'em all over agin, leastwise, them that I hadn't killed afore. So the boys got a kind'a skeert, and d— a bird would they pit agin him, so I jist turned him in among the hens, and kept him fur the good he *had* done.

"Wall, I guess I kept him about five years, till the old feller got to be stun blind and bald headed, and times got to be allscrougin hard in old Varginny; perwisions was all-fired high, and money sneaken scase, and then my young'uns had got most unkimmon powerful appetites, so I begun to think about killin' the old cock. It pulled right stret agin the grain, I tell ye now, but I had to deu it, *and* deu it I did. I kasoused him inteu a bucket of bilin' water, and—deu you believe? why it tuck teu of my young'uns and a big pair uv pinchers a hull day to git the critter's feathers out!

" 'How shall I cook him, Phil?' ses my wife.

" 'Wall, I guess you mout as well put him in the oven,' ses I. So she kind'a basted him all over with possum fat, put him in a big dish with about half a bushel of sweet potaters, and baked him *brown!*" Here Phil stuck his hands into the pockets of his pants, e'en to his elbows—shrugged his shoulders, drew a long breath, and

"I kinder guess," said he, " 'twas tater and *smell* for dinner, *that* day, anyhow, fur of all the d—eternal tough poultry I ever heerd on, that cock was a leetle mite the hardest!

"I tuck him out into the kitchin, and carved him up with the *axe;* a swetten job I had on it, teu. Put him inteu a steupan, and kind'a parbiled him till the next day;—but 'twas no airthly use; the more he biled the tougher he got—my young uns all got to cryin' with the jaws ache, and the old woman she squirmed her head around and squealed right out!"

" 'What on airth's the matter?' sez I.

" 'Thar's a *bone* in my throat,' sez she.

---

[1] From Porter's *Spirit of the Times*, April 29, 1848.

"Now I knowed *that* was a lie, for the jaws of human natur never could a got to a bone in *that* chicken, so I thought I'd jist look and see what ail'd her—and you may jist spread me all over with molasses, and then lick me off, if there warn't about teu inches of the sharp eend of a *gaff* that had come out of the old cock, a stickin' stret across her throat! That a kind a made me mad, so I kasoused him into the iron pot, and biled agin like h—! I had a young possum in the house that I'd killed the day afore, so after the old cock had biled about six hours, steady, I made a pie on 'em, both together, and *baked him agin!*

"That pie did *look* almighty nice, now I tell you; *my* mouth a kind'a itched and twitched at the corners like, when I looked at it, and the young uns jumped round fur rale joy. D—n you, old boy, thinks I, as we sot down to dinner, I've weakened ye some, this time, anyhow.

" 'Give me the middle piece, Phil,' sez my wife.

" 'Sartain, Prude,' sez I; and with that I stuck the knife inteu it, when—

" 'Tuk! Tuk! Tuk! Tuckarooh!'

" 'Jist you stop your foolin', young Zeph,' sez I; the boy could give a righteous imitation of a chicken, and I swon I thought it *was* him; 'jist you stop yer foolin',' sez I, 'or I'll tarn ye away from the table.'

" 'It wasn't me, fa—'

" 'Shet up,' sez I; 'shet up and mind your manners,' and with that I stuck the knife in agin, and tuck a nice round piece right out uv the centre. I swow, if there wan't jist about then the darndest, and most etarnal spittin' *and* splutterin', till evry bit uv possum was jerked clear out uv the pie, and then the d— old *Rooster poked his head out uv the crust and crowed!*"

Colonel Phil says that the cock was an imported one, and, "considering what a h—ll of a job he had to cut his spurs," must have been ancient when he first got him. Now, the supposition is, that when Horatio said

> "But even then the morning cock crew loud;
> And at the sound it shrunk in haste away,"

he must have had reference to that same old cock.

Yours, Mr. Spirit,

Dick Dashall.

Playing possum[1]

[In the Deep Delta country of Louisiana men used to gather in the evening to sing and tell stories. Dr. H. L. Ballowe] a gallant bachelor, then as now [1944], was a leading participant. "I could sing like a nightingale, with a voice rich, clear and true." Somewhere in the program, Dr. Ballowe remembers, when the fumes of the wine had stimulated the imagination, and before drowsiness stilled the tongue, someone suggested the telling of "big lies." These were the Paul Bunyan tales of the Delta. The story-tellers vied to see who could concoct the most grotesque and the most whopping; Dr. Ballowe won considerable repute. One of his best, in dialect, went this way:

"I trap' all day. When I get back to camp, I am blow' out an' hongry. At the camp I ax my wife what he have cook. 'Not much, vieux,' he say. 'I pick up a few swimp an' crab. With these, I have make a gombo.' 'A gombo, chére, is very lill' for a man fatigue' like me. For what you don' kill a chicken?' My wife say 'We have only one lef' an' he lay egg every day. It would be mortal sin to kill a beas' like that.'

"At the same secon' I hear 'qua-ak! qua-ak!' I run, throw open the door, an' what I see? A big rat-de-bois have grab our las' hen by the neck. 'Yas, ahn?' I holler, an' give him a coup de baton what put his feet in the air. 'Look,' I tell my wife, 'le Bon Dieu est bon, oui. I will skin the possum. Zebe in the next camp, he will give me bottle wine for the hide. You will cook the meat. With gombo, wine an' it, an' bread and café, we will eat good.' My wife find two-three potato, an' everything come good.

"Befo' we start to eat, with the wine ope' on the table an' that gombo in the bowl, she ope' the do' of the stove to look how ev'ything is go. Maybe you not believe it, but there was the rat-de-bois stand up in that pan! He have eat the potato an' drink the grease. Now he jomp out the stove, he pass between my wife leg, an' on the table. He turn over the gombo, knock over the wine, then he run out the back door, me behin' 'im. Outside was the poor hen still on the groun, his neck all twis', his eye making comme-ci, comme-ça. That rat grab him as he pass an' run away in the grass. That was not all, no. Tha night he go to Zebe' camp an' take his skin from the stretching board an' put it back on. Now that was some*thing*, ahn?"

---

[1] From Harnett T. Kane: *Deep Delta Country* (New York: Duell, Sloan & Pearce; 1944), pp. 247–8.

"I wish I could tell a lie"

I am indebted to Susan Bacon Keith of Santa Barbara, California, for the following ballad, and for the accompanying note by Isaac H. Jones.)

As children we heard this yarn from J. Allen Boone who heard it from an old sea captain, in Newport, R. I. I do not know that it has ever been printed, in fact I never came across any one who had heard it. So I have no idea who wrote it.

Isaac H. Jones, M.D.

I stood one day by a breezy bay
 A watchin' the ships sail by,
When a tired tar said—with a shake of his head
 "I wish I could tell a lie.

I've seed some sights that would jigger your lights
 And have jiggered me own—in sooth,
But I ain't worth a darn at spinnin' a yarn
 That wanders away from the Truth.

We was off on the brig—the Rig—A Gig,
 A mile and a half to sea,
When Captain Snook with a troubled look
 He comes and he says to me—

'Hey! Bos'n Smith, make haste forthwith
 An' hemstitch the for'ard sail;
Accordion pleat the dory sheet
 For there's goin' to be a gale.'

I straightway did as the Captain bid
 And no sooner the job was thru,
Than a North wind—Whoof! bounded over the roof,
 An' sufferin' lights she blew!

She blowed the tars clean off the spars,
 The spars clean off the mast,
While anchors 'n sails, 'n pails 'n nails
 Went by on the wings of the blast.

And before we could look—she blowed the cook
 Straight out o' the galley bin,
While pots 'n pans and Kettles 'n cans
 Went rattlin' after him.

She blowed the fire from the galley stove,
 The coal from the galley bin,

315

Then she whizzed a pace past the Captain's face
An' blowed the beard off his chin.

'Now whizzle me dead' the Captain said
An' the words blowed out of his mouth
'We're lost I fear, if the wind don't veer
An' blow a while from the South!'

An' whizzle me dead—no sooner he said
Them words that blowed from his mouth,
Then the wind veered 'round with a hurricane sound
And blowed straight in from the South.

An' we opened our eyes with wild surprise
With never a word to say,
For in changing her tack, the wind blowed back
The things that she'd blowed away.

She blowed the tars back onto the spars,
The spars back onto the mast
Back came the sails, an' the pails an' the nails
That into the ship stuck fast.

An' before we could look—she blowed the cook
Back into the galley coop;
Back came the pans an' the kettles an' cans,
Without even spillin' the soup.

She blowed the fire back into the stove
Where it burned in its proper place,
An' we all of us cheered as she blowed the beard
Back onto the Captain's face.

There's more of my tale—said the Mariner hale,
That would jigger your lights in sooth,
But I ain't worth a darn at spinnin' a yarn
That wanders away from the truth."

6. NEWSPAPERDOM: STRANGE
INVENTIONS

Few American newspapers exist without at least one wag on the staff, a circumstance agreeable to the public, but often disturbing enough to editors and proprietors. These latter sometimes strive to make the best of the matter by shifting their more facetious reporters to police or shipping news, or sports, for in these departments a degree of levity is considered permissible. But genius will not forever be restrained. Strange items appear, or get caught and thrown out (along with the reporter, sometimes) by anxious editors. The power of the press is great, and the temptation to use it for utter mystification or sheer deception must have occurred to many a prudent wage-slave. What happens to those who succumb may be read in the story "Paris interlude."

Happily, some newspapermen are allowed to invent what they will— just so long as the public is given to understand that it is all in fun. Hence the hen that lays square eggs, and a thousand other unexpected little items, including no small proportion of the so-called "human-interest stories." Some typical inventions are subjoined—typical, be it said, in that they are like nothing at all to be found in the orderly world of reasonable fact. Americans do this sort of thing best; it could almost be said that they are the only newspapermen who do it at all. Such, perhaps, is an incidental benefit of freedom of the press. Or maybe it's the air.

The fabulous Lester Green[1]

What's a man to do when he writes pure nature-faking stories that everyone believes? That's what happens when Lester Green, the sage of Prospect, Connecticut, produces, through mysterious cross-breeding, on his Kowless farm, a creature as fabulous as that hardy perennial, the summer sea serpent.

The late Lou Stone, whose Winsted fables were recalled recently in *Newspaperman,* always insisted that his tales were not fake, but rather, truth, flavoured with imagination. Lester Green, on the other

---

[1] By Mollie Cullen, from the Waterbury, Connecticut, *Republican;* reprinted from *Newspaperman,* July 1944.

317

hand, makes up his yarns out of whole cloth, or rather, whole flora and fauna, and immediately he receives frantic orders for batches of eggs which will hatch out strange furred or feathered friends, or salesmen call upon him and beg to manufacture one of his new gadgets which are more wondrous than anything that can be expected in the post-war era. Lester has all his orders pasted in a scrap book and he looks at them dreamily sometimes, figuring out the millions he would be worth if he could produce the goods.

There was, for instance, the quick-ripening tomato he produced by crossing a tomato with a red pepper. As a result the red pepper provided warmth for the tomato plant which could be planted in February and kept frost-free. When a western farmer wrote for seeds of this horticultural phenomenon Lester had to write and tell him that he had given up the idea. It seems that the red pepper ingredient in the plant made the tomato shrivel up and burn when the hot weather came.

He could have been the apple and cider king of the world if he had been able to fill another order which came from a big glue firm in Canada. Lester hit upon an idea to prevent orchard losses from wind-fall apples. He sprayed glue on the fruit early in the season and the apples stuck tightly on the trees through high winds, rain and sleet. The glue kept the fruit in a state of firm and rosy preservation.

When the glue salesman made the trip from Boston to the little town of Prospect, he had a hard time finding Lester Green, because, in a way, there ain't no sech person. The gentleman farmer of Kowless Farm is really C. Louis Mortison, whose cartoons signed "Mort" are known all over New England. Lester Green, the jolly witty Yankee farmer, was his first invention. Mr. Mortison had to assume family responsibilities at an early age, when his father died, leaving him, at 14, the family wage earner. He always wanted to be a cartoonist and spent every minute away from his factory bench drawing, planning, and hoping. Finally he was able to go to an art school in the west but he worked so hard keeping himself alive while studying that his health broke down and an outdoor job, preferably in the country, was advised. So he went back to Prospect, where he lived as a boy, and started a chicken farm. He kept on drawing in his spare moments and eventually sold his first cartoon to the Waterbury Republican. He sold eggs to the staff, too, and occasionally another drawing. His keen and humorous observations on politics and small town affairs of Prospect gave the state editor the idea that here was a good correspondent, so "Mort" joined the staff. Since a country correspondent in a small town has to bear the slings and arrows of outraged townfolk no matter what he writes, "Mort" decided to put his observations in the mouth of

Lester Green. It was months before Prospect readers knew his real identity. Some of them don't know yet.

The nature faking stories started with a true account of a farmer's wagon which lost a wheel on a Prospect hill. The wheel rolled downhill with increasing velocity and crashed into a chestnut tree, shaking several burrs from the tree. Lester Green wrote the item as it happened, then feeling skittish because the hens were laying well that day, he added that the chestnut burrs popped open, shooting out the nice smooth chestnuts. All the farmer had to do was to pick them up. The state desk featured the item and Lester Green decided then and there that fiction is stranger than truth and he'd give it the works.

His first yarn, which was picked up by the AP and sent all over the country, concerned a brood of furbearing chicks. A hen with a setting of eggs had been caught unaware when Lester flooded a small meadow. Cold weather came suddenly and when Lester was cutting ice, he found the hen and the eggs trapped in a square block. He chipped the ice from around the eggs and set the eggs on the stove. Soon the chicks began to emerge, but instead of pin feathers, they were wearing fur coats, provided by nature to keep them warm in an unfamiliar climate. A farmer in northern Canada wrote Lester offering him any price for some of the chicks, but, unfortunately, they died before they could be shipped. "They smothered to death wearing fur coats in the brooder," Lester said.

Lester Green's mail box in the Prospect postoffice was stuffed to bursting the day after the story about his permanent wave fluid hit print. One day while butchering, he discovered a minute gland in a pig's tail which was responsible for its curl. He extracted the fluid, diluted it with alcohol and rubbed it on Mrs. Green's hair which immediately became a mass of curls. The public response to that little bit of fantasy would make anyone's hair curl.

Two engineers hurried from Waterbury to Prospect after reading about a chimney fire in the Green farmhouse. Lester rushed to the roof with a bucket of sand which he threw down the chimney. At the same time Mrs. Green grabbed a box of what she thought was salt and threw it on the fire in the kitchen stove. But it wasn't salt; it was washing soda. The fumes of the soda went up as the sand came down, the chemicals fused, and when the fire was out the Greens possessed a chimney lined with hard glass. The engineers had a lot of difficulty finding Lester Green's house and, after tramping miles through the underbrush of Prospect hills, went back to Waterbury muttering about glass houses.

Speaking of salesmen, Lester has hit up an idea of keeping them from bothering him when he's drawing or cross-breeding. He installed a parking meter in front of his house and any salesman who wants to sell him something, has to deposit a nickel for every 15 minutes of salestalk. Usually when it's all over, they owe the Prospect sage more than he paid for the gadget.

The Lester Green yarns have become nationally famous. Hardly a day passes without the genial creator receiving clippings from far-off places recounting some of his tall tales. But the story that got the greatest amount of publicity and was the subject of editorials and cartoons in several papers in the hunt sections of the country had to do with Lester's dog. He trained the dog to run from, rather than at, foxes. Thus, when a fox appeared, the dog started running for home with Reynard in hot pursuit. Lester waited with a gun, and got the fox. He had a silver fox cape for Mrs. Green in less time than it took to load the rifle. Hunters all over the country thought this was a good idea as did animal lovers, so Lester proceeded to revolutionize rabbit hunting. Watching a bunny pecking at his tobacco plants one day, he lured a flock of rabbits about him, and taught them to chew. There wasn't a dead rabbit in Prospect that season because the animals hid behind the hedges and when a hunter came near, they let fly a mouthful of tobacco juice plumb into his eyes.

Today, "Mort's" cartoons are appearing daily in the Waterbury Republican, The Waterbury American, and also in The Sunday Republican, as well as in various periodicals. He is busy on illustrations for War Bond drives and other wartime projects, but he's still crossbreeding and inventing.

Last winter, he figured out a way of preventing the rear end from colliding with the icy sidewalk. He built a shoe with a hollow sole and filled the sole with sand. He cut an opening in the sole for the big toe. Every time he came to an icy spot, he wiggled his toe and a trickle of sand smoothed the way before him. He received a number of calls for a hollow fish hook when the trout season opened. The hollow in the hook was filled with dry ice. When the trout nibbled at the bait attached to the hook, he froze to it. Lester tried the hook out on a trout and was astonished when he pulled in the fish, to find it wearing a complete set of false teeth. The day after this story appeared, an old lady appeared at the Kowless farm entry and demanded the teeth which she insisted she had lost in that very brook when she leaned over to study her reflection. Lester told her that, unfortunately, the teeth couldn't be pried from the fish hook and he would hate to see her going around town looking like a baited trout. She left minus the teeth.

Last summer he experimented with bees and mosquitoes. He crossed a bee with a lightning bug so that the bee could see at night and gather more honey. He crossed a mosquito with a lightning bug so that the summer boarders at Kowless could see the wily mosquitoes and get away before the kill.

"Now," says Lester, lighting another in his chain of cigars, "I am at work on something which will revolutionize the communications system. I am crossing a carrier pigeon with a parrot. The resulting bird will then talk his messages and there will be no need of unwrapping the band from his leg. I will then cross the bird with an owl so that it can see at night."

The typographical howitzer[1]

Thomas P. Brown, former newspaper man now engaged in publicity work in San Francisco, sends the Gazette the following story. He says, "This is a famous short story written by Sam P. Davis, noted Nevada journalist, author and historian, and brother of the famous Robert H. (Bob) Davis of the *New York Sun*, who died last year. This story is to be found in his volume of *Short Stories*, published by the Golden Era Company, San Francisco, 1886. In the preface of this book, which was dated at Carson City, Nevada, November 25, 1885, Sam Davis says:

" 'This book had its origin, not in any deliberate design, but is merely a collection of short stories and few fugitive poems, contributed at irregular intervals to the columns of various newspapers and periodicals, the author at the time—upon the principle that "sufficient to the day is the evil thereof"—not expecting to rake them together in their present form. Under the circumstances, the necessity of an extended preface is not apparent.'

(Brown continues) "Far be it from me, after having quoted a preface written by the author of 'The First Piano in Camp,' and of those undying verses entitled 'The Sage Bush,' to attempt a preface of my own, and yet I am impelled to say a few words to friends in and out of the newspaper world before they revel in the immortal humor of 'The Typographical Howitzer' which Sam Davis penned some sixty years ago.

" 'The Typographical Howitzer' is one of the best known western stories ever printed. It has gone the rounds of the press repeatedly. It is a classic which is new every time one reads it. It makes one appreciate anew the value of enduring writing. And it makes one rejoice that Sam Davis knew Mark Twain and Dan de Quille and was a part of Nevada and of the West during those stirring, romantic years of a fast receding heroic past.

---

[1] From *Ghost Town News*, Buena Park, California, December 1943.

"May I add that it was my privilege to have known Sam Davis in his later years when I was a newspaper correspondent at Sacramento, California. When Sam Davis would drop into my office, copy for the wire would be held in abeyance, and visiting newspaper men would forget assignments, while we were regaled by anecdotes related by the veteran editor of the Carson City *Appeal*.

"And now here's the story."—

THE TYPOGRAPHICAL HOWITZER

By Sam Davis

It was nearly twenty years ago when Dan de Quille and Mark Twain attempted to start a paper in Mendocino County. They took the type and material of their recently defunct newspaper establishment in San Francisco, and loading the stuff on a big wagon, struck out into the country to retrieve their fortune. They packed their type just as it stood in the forms, tied up the articles with stout cords by a process well known to printers, and packing them closely in boxes, vowed to establish a newspaper somewhere which would be the leading exponent of politics and history for the Pacific Coast. Had not an unfortunate circumstance taken place it is evident that the newspaper which they contemplated founding would have been alive today. Their journey over the mountains was utterly uneventful until they reached Simpson's Station, a spot well known to old travelers on that route. Here they met a party of emigrants making for Lower California, and the latter had with them a small mountain howitzer which they had brought with them across the plains.

Twain took a great fancy to this gun, and offered fifty dollars for it, with two kegs of powder. The emigrants were glad enough to part with it, as they concluded the time for its use had passed. Dan thought the purchase of the artillery and military supplies was a reckless piece of extravagance, and said as much, but Mark replied:

"When we start our paper we must fire a salute. A newspaper office with artillery has a big bulge on the business. No well-regulated office in California should be without a howitzer. If a man comes in for a retraction we can blow him into the next county. The howitzer goes."

This silenced the argument, and the next day the two journalists took the road with their printing outfit and artillery.

The next night they camped in a mountain ravine, fifteen miles from Simpson's, and after building the usual campfire, fell asleep. About eleven o'clock the horses wakened them by prancing about, and the two journalists were led to the conclusion that a party of Indians was making arrangements for a night attack. In the clear moonlight human forms could be distinguished about half a mile away at the foot of the ravine. The idea of encountering Indians had never entered the heads of the two fortune-seekers, and they had no arms. Suddenly Twain brightened:

"The howitzer?"

"We've got nothing but powder," said Dan.

"Well, powder'll scare 'em; and we'll load her up."

The piece was immediately loaded with a good big charge, and the two men felt quite certain that the Indians, hearing the roar of the gun, would beat an unconditional retreat. The piece was hardly loaded and placed in position when about forty of the red-skins came charging up the ravine.

Twain seized a brand from the campfire and was about to lay it on the touch-hole, when Dan yelled "Hold on!" as he rammed something into the mouth of the piece and remarked:

"Turn 'er loose."

The roar of the howitzer echoed through the lonely forest, and the savages, with frantic cries of pain, reeled down the ravine in wild confusion.

"What in h— did you put in?" asked Mark.

"A column of solid nonpareil and a couple of sticks of your spring poetry."

"The poetry did the business, Dan. Get one of your geological articles ready for the next charge, and I guess it'll let the red devils out for the present campaign."

The savages again advanced. Mark attended to the powder, and Dan assorted the shot, so to speak.

"Jeems Pipe's song, 'My Mountain Home.'"

"Good for three Indians—sock 'er in."

"An acrostic by John B. Ridge, in long primer."

"It'll paralyze 'em."

"Frank Pixley on the Constitution—half a column of leaded brevier."

"If it hits 'em, the day is won."

"Your leader on 'Law and Order.'"

"Save it as a last resort."

Dan pulled the type out of the boxes and stuffed column after column in the howitzer's mouth as the savages came charging on. Another round from the gun, and the redskins rolled over and over each other like boulders swept by a mountain cloud-burst. Mark, in an ecstasy of delight, pulled an American flag out of his effects, nailed it to the tail-board of the wagon, and was about to make a speech, when the dusky figures of the foes were once more seen moving to the attack.

The piece was again loaded, and this time with a double charge. Mark's leader on "Law and Order"; the puff of an auction house, by

Fred McCrellish, "as a sickener," Dan said; Frank Gross' verses on "The Rebel Yell"; an agricultural article by Sam Seabaugh, showing the chemical properties of corn-juice as an educational lever; a maiden poetic effort by Oliver Harper, and some verses by Col. Cremony and Frank Soule, completed the load.

"That poetry reaching 'em first will throw 'em into confusion, and my editorial coming upon the heels of the rest will result in a lasting demoralization. It will be like the last cavalry charge of the French troopers at the battle of Austerlitz."

For the third and last time the faithful howitzer belched its typographical compliments to the advancing foe. The havoc was terrible. There was a wild yell from a score of savage throats, and the low groans of the dying floated up the ravine on the gentle wind. The two men walked over the field of slaughter and counted fifty-six aboriginals lying in heaps. The bodies were horribly mutilated with nonpareil, bourgeois, "caps" misery dashes, and unassorted pi.

"My leader cooked that man's goose," said Mark, pointing to a savage hanging over the limb of a cedar.

"My geological article did the business for him," rejoined Dan, nodding carelessly at an Indian whose head was laying twenty yards away.

"The pen is mightier than the sword."

"You bet. Hurrah for Faust and Gutenburg!"

"Is there any type left?"

"Not a pound."

Ten days later the two journalistic tramps reached Virginia City, weary, discouraged, and footsore, and secured places on the ENTERPRISE.

A few days ago Dan received the following from his former partner:

Hartford, Connecticut,
January 1, 1880.

Dear Dan:—

I send you the congratulations of the New Year. Do you recollect the time we exterminated the tribe of unlettered (?) savages in Mendocino County? If you can spare the time I wish you would make a pilgrimage to that historic spot, gather the ghostly relics together, and plant a tablet (not too expensive) to the memory of the departed. Have a shooting-stick lying across a long bow with our monogram and coat-of-arms entwined, and some appropriate epitaph carved on the stone; an extract from Carl Schurtz's views on the "Peace Policy" might do. Enclosed is a dollar and a half for your incidental expenses; you can deadhead traveling expenses.

Yours,
Mark Twain.

324

P. S.—Send a thigh-bone of the fallen chief by next express.

M. T.

Dan will attend to the matter in the spring. The old howitzer used on the occasion is still in his possession.

From *Brewery Gulch Gazette*, Bisbee, Arizona.

The electric bulldog[1]

THE ELECTRIC BULLDOG, a new and improved electronic version of the Frankenstein-Apprenti-Sorcier myth as it has been re-created back in, I believe Cincinnati, or maybe it was Cleveland. It was Ohio, anyway, and this is it:

There was a technical expert of some kind who lived in whichever of the places it was, and he had been working out a variety of new uses for the photo-electric cell for some local industrial plant. For one reason and another, the requirements of the plant didn't give him as much scope to spread out in as his imagination required, so he began tinkering with it around home, and, to show what he could really do when the hobbles were taken off, he confected a small sensitized platform on his front porch from which a little railroad track led through a trap door in the wall into his bedroom. The platform was marked off plainly, and the paper boy had orders to drop the morning paper in it. When the paper was dropped, the trap door opened, a cast-iron bulldog rolled out along the track and picked it up, and rolled back inside and deposited it at the master's bedside. On being patted on the head, the faithful animal wagged its tail, rolled out of sight under the bed, and was through for the day. No feeding, no defleaing, no fighting other dogs, no barking at night, no nothing. Just pure service, and nothing to pay for it except a few cents a month for the electricity.

Well, it worked, and people gawped at it and stood lined up along the curb to watch while the paper boy touched the magic spring of a morning, and then they got to dropping things on their own account—bread-wrappers, old shoes, anything at all, just to see the bulldog roll out and perform, and since it was piling up a big light bill and wearing the contraption out for nothing, the inventor turned it off and went on to more practical things and forgot all about it. During spring housecleaning, somebody apparently turned it on again. He didn't know it at the time. He found it out one night when, returning home from

---

[1] From "Hesperiana," by H. L. D., in the *Rocky Mountain Herald*, Denver, Colorado, May 12, 1945. H. L. D. is the novelist H. L. Davis, author of *Honey in the Horn*.

somewhere with some light-hearted friends and turning to call a gay farewell to them from the porch, he stuck his foot into the area that had been designed for the paper. Before he had time to finish the farewell, the trap-door opened, the bulldog rolled purposefully out behind him, grabbed him by the ankle, threw him flat on his face, and started back inside, dragging him.

There was not light enough for his friends to see what the trouble was. For a minute or two they weren't quite sure there was any. It might, they thought, be merely another of his gags. He was always pulling them. Then the bulldog hauled his leg in through the trap-door, leaving a sort of corolla of torn pants-leg and epidermis frilled around it, until he was in clear up to his crotch. That wouldn't go through. The dog set itself for a fresh start and almost split him lengthwise trying to force him. He screamed for help, and his friends began to realize vaguely what was happening. They rushed up onto the porch and laid hold on him to pull him loose. There were four of them against one electric bulldog, but the bulldog made them dig. First they gained an inch; then he made it back, and a couple more with it; then they strung out tandem and took a death grip on the inventor, who was stretched a foot beyond his normal stature and cracking in the middle, and laid in on one desperate and concerted surge. The house gave, the track gave, the bulldog gave, and the inventor screamed bloody murder. Then all the fuses blew out, and they reeled back into the street, still clutching him, and fell in a heap on top of him.

He was in bed for three weeks thereafter as a result of his injuries, but that isn't the ending that the Ohio story-telling convention leaves it with. In some states it would be, with possibly the addition of a moral about tinkering with buzz-saws, or something on that dark and Sophoclean order. Where the Ohio narrative comes to rest is on the visit of the attending physician, which took place the following morning. The physician was pretty savage about being called out to minister to a patient who was, obviously, the victim of his own idiocy, and took occasion, on leaving, to offer a number of sarcastic remarks on the mentality of a man who would be so asinine as to stick his foot into a place that everybody else in town knew about, had seen work, and had sense enough to stay clear of. He departed, mentioning that if such a thing happened again the inventor could do his own doctoring. There was a painful silence in the sick chamber for a few moments, followed by a crash and a scream from the porch. Then the trap-door opened and in came the bulldog, its jaws firmly clenched on the doctor's leg.

The albino crow[1]

Bruce Barton ought to know about this.

Four years ago, Mr. Barton was one of the Gentlemen from New York in the House of Representatives. More specifically, he was the Gentleman from Manhattan's silk stocking district.

When Mr. Barton decided to stand for the United States Senate against upstate James Mead, whose followers clanged about the hustings in a miniature caboose to call sentimental attention to their man's affection for the railroads, I was concerning myself with the behavior of politicians for the Binghamton Press.

That was a choice year for the aspiring political reporter. The war was boiling up. The politicians were calling upon the faithful of New York north of the Bronx to recognize this and that true prophet. The general result was gratifying to anyone with a hungry typewriter.

Then I gave The Hon. Mr. Barton the bird. It was a high point of my journalistic career.

My paper was going down the middle of the road in that Barton-Mead campaign. A kind word was dropped here, a smile there. When Mr. Barton hit town, he was unaware blissfully of the neighborly gesture in store for him.

It was four o'clock that afternoon when the city editor called me to his desk, looked me over with a sigh and opened the three-star to page three. There in the middle of the page was a two-column cut of a discouraged-looking guy holding what appeared to be a beat-up white guinea hen who had stunted her growth with too many cigarettes.

"Look," said the CE, passing his hand over his brow, "I don't want any arguments. Just listen. After I finish, I'm getting out of here. Don't talk." I opened my mouth prepared to say briskly, "Okay, chief," when he interrupted me. "Quiet," he said.

"This," he continued, jabbing the picture with his finger, "is a crow. An albino crow. It is the only albino crow in existence so far as we are concerned. The chances of catching an albino crow are something like one in 10 billion. Quiet. I am told it is an omen, a sign from the blue. A good omen. One of our readers, a simple tiller of the soil, captured it outside of town. As you can see, we have run a story on it."

He paused with that far-away-and-gone look in his eye, shook his head as though clearing it and vouchsafed:

"Bruce Barton is about due in town. You are to meet the Congressman and arrange to get a picture of him before his speech. Make the

[1] By Tom Cawley, from *Newspaperman*, July 1944.

appointment for 7:05. At 7 P.M., you will meet this good farmer with the albino crow in the lobby of the Arlington Hotel. You will take the crow to Mr. Barton, place it in his hands, get the picture and return the fowl to the farmer with a gratuity of $2. Your cutlines will say that Mr. Barton has a good omen, or words to that effect. Quiet, please."

The city editor had finished. He turned and stared at the nearby office that housed the Big Boss, a hunted look in his eye. He shook his head again and left, his steps halting. He never even said goodnight. He left me alone with my thoughts and a foreboding or two.

I bulwarked myself with a bowl of chili across the alley, repaired to the hotel and timed my arrival nicely with that of the Barton party. I wasn't feeling very well, but I pulled myself together, put on my best Wickett-of-the-Times manner and accosted Mr. Barton, saying:

"Mr. B., I want to get your picture with, uh . . . with . . ." I bogged down miserably.

"Fine, fine, son," beamed the ruddy-faced advertising dynamo. "Come up to the room in a couple of minutes." He bustled off.

One of those guys who always gets stuck with the details in a campaign caravan—like knowing how to get hotel reservations and automobiles and cracked ice after 1 A.M.—was lurking by a potted palm and I grabbed him. I implored him to stall Mr. Barton until I could get up there with a photographer.

The lensman arrived on the scene, barging noisily into the lobby and looking down his nose at the mere mortals in his path.

"Okay, okay," he said. "Where's the bird? Where's Barton? Let's get going. You'd think this was a weekly."

"Bird?" echoed the detail man, weakly. "What bird?"

"Relax," I said, shaking all over. I was feeling worse. The boss' secretary walked in, looking pale.

"He's here," she murmured.

"Who?" I asked foolishly.

"The bird guy."

I found him. Circling the man, who looked scared, I came up on his flank.

"Where is it?" I asked.

He looked around furtively; whispered conspiratorially, "Here," and flicked his jacket open and shut much in the manner of a B-picture detective.

"It'll smother," I said.

"Never mind," he said.

I pushed him toward the elevator. The photographer, the boss' secretary and the confused detail man brought up a disordered rear.

The farmer stopped short of the elevator. "Uh, look," he volunteered. "He's dead."

I staggered. "Who? Barton?"

"The bird," he said. "He died this afternoon. But you people told me to bring it in and here it is."

I cut him short as he prepared to pull the remains out, waved everyone away from me and walked blindly to a telephone booth. I called the city editor at his home.

"The damned bird is dead," I reported bitterly. "The guy's here with a very dead albino crow. If you ask me, it's a good omen. Where do you want the body hid? And what do I do now?"

There was a threatening silence on the wire. Then it came.

"I wash my hands of the whole affair," said the master of my editorial soul. "All I know is you're supposed to get the Congressman with that bird in his hand. I'm not telling you what to do or what not to do, but as far as I'm concerned, I never heard from you." His laugh was mocking, if not unhinged slightly, as he hung up.

I returned to the scene and herded everybody moodily into the elevator car. We avoided the man with the sordid bulge in his honest denim. The car stopped at the candidate's floor and we emerged into the dim corridor. The farmer suddenly thrust a bundle of greyish-white feathers into my hands. The celebrated albino regarded me coldly, with no passion in his cadaver's eyes. His bill was curled into a sculptured sneer. I sneered back. I even pinched him. I pushed the Barton buzzer.

The smartest idea I'd had all evening struck me. I decided to cut and run, but then it was too late. Mr. Barton opened the door and greeted us with genial cries and hospitable utterances.

"Come in, come in," said he. I died twice on the way across the room.

"Congressman," I quailed, "This is an albino crow. One in 10 billion. Good omen. Good old omen. Good crow. Good luck. Make a picture. Fine art. Ha, ha. Just hold it, Mr. Barton. Bird in the hand, eh, Mr. Barton? Ha, ha. Now watch the birdie. Ha, ha."

A good guy, Mr. B. lifted old Rigor Mortis from my perspiring clutch and began to stroke the feathers. I shudddered.

"A quiet little thing," he said, "isn't she?" He looked more closely and began to swivel our feathered chum's head around. The bulb flashed and I charged across the room croaking: "Great stuff. Fine feature stuff." I snatched the bird, shovel-passed it to the boss' secretary, who handed it and the dough to the open-mouthed farmer.

"Out," I muttered savagely.

The following afternoon, one of the most touching tableaux in modern politics greeted our readers. It was a large cut illustrating the candidate's views on the state of the nation, the Democrats and so forth. The picture was a curly-haired, kindly man tenderly holding a pretty bird, the only one in captivity, absolutely. The cutlines were gems, banging away at that Good Omen.

Mr. Barton lost the election.

The cry-baby shark[1]

Editors, Vineyard Gazette:

I wish you would please send me a copy of The Fisherman, published by your paper, as a friend of mine told me you had an amusing article about a disabled whale. I wonder if it was a brother to the "cry baby shark" they found floating off Long Island some years ago.

Here's your story:

Capt. Elijah Brown, a coasting trade captain, while sailing from New York to Providence, sighted this cry baby shark floating motionless off East Hampton, L. I. As he got closer to it he found it was dead. He decided it would be worth while to tow the great fish to the beach, along the sandy shore, away from the town. He ran a kedge anchor out, so it would not drift away, and went ashore and reported his find to an old friend of his by the name of Capt. Bill Tucker, an old time whaler of East Hampton.

Capt. Bill and Elijah found the shark to be sixty-five feet long, twenty-two feet beam, and fifteen feet deep, just about big enough to go through Shinnecock Canal before they put in the locks. Capt. Bill went up to his house, got some saws, axes and large knives to open up the fish to see what it died of—it looked like dropsy.

With the aid of several fishermen, Capt. Bill cut a hole in the side of the great monster, and entering the body of the shark, he found a large barrel of oil, which no doubt had caused its death. The old whaler said no doubt the barrel fell off some passing steamer, and the oil was seeping from the bung, and apparently the shark had tasted the liquid when he was hungry and swallowed the barrel, which could not be digested.

It had evidently caused the marine monster great pain, as its eyes, the old whaler told us, showed traces of continuous tears. That was why he named it the cry baby shark. The captain opened the giant's mouth and propped up the roof with a couple of telephone poles, so the natives were able to walk inside without stooping and look around.

Before moving picture and camera men were able to get to the beach, Capt. Bill that night had a local house mover move the carcass

[1] From the *Vineyard Gazette*, December 1, 1944.

up in the village where his son Henry had just completed the foundation for an eight car garage. So Capt. Bill had it set in the foundation and, with slight alterations, it made Bill's son one of the finest garages in the village and saved him a large lumber bill.

So, if you are ever down on the eastern end of Long Island, stop at the Cry Baby Shark Garage—they'll give you service with a tear.

EDWIN R. CHAMBERS,
The Long Island Raconteur.
PATCHOGUE, LONG ISLAND, N. Y.

P.S. If you have some good fish stories, please send them along.

E. R. C.

Human hibernation[1]

E lbert S. Stevens, a long-time resident of Bridgewater Corners (near Coolidge's place at Plymouth), had an old scrap-book in which he found a clipping purporting to give an eyewitness account of a human hibernation experiment in a "remote mountain village near Montpelier" (almost in my own back yard). The date of the old clipping and the paper from which it was taken are unknown, as is the author of the tale; but the clipping describes the adventures of an unnamed traveler who inadvertently became an eyewitness of an "operation," as he described it, in which half a dozen members of the snowbound hamlet submitted to being drugged and frozen and put aside until spring.

The *Rutland Herald,* reprinting the clipping from the Stevens scrapbook, quotes the rest (May 24, 1939):

"A Strange Tale—by A. M. I am an old man now and have seen some strange sights in the course of a roving life in foreign lands as well as in this country, but none so strange as one I found recorded in an old diary kept by my Uncle William that came into my possession a few years ago at his decease.

"The events described took place in a mountain town some twenty miles from Montpelier, the capital of Vermont. I have been to the place on the mountain and seen the old log house where the events I found recorded in the diary took place and seen and talked with an old man who vouched for the truth of the story and that his father was one of the parties operated on.

---

[1] Reprinted from *Winter in Vermont* by Charles Edward Crane (New York: Alfred A. Knopf; 1941), pp. 85–9, by permission of Alfred A. Knopf, Inc. Copyright 1941 by Alfred A. Knopf, Inc.

331

"The account runs in this wise—Jan. 7—I went on the mountain today and witnessed what to me was a horrible sight. It seems that the dwellers there who are unable either from age or other reasons to contribute to the support of their families are disposed of in the winter in a manner that will shock the one who reads this diary unless that person lives in that vicinity.

"I will describe what I saw. Six persons, four men and two women, the man a cripple about thirty years old, the other five past the age of usefulness, lay on the earthy floor of the cabin drugged into insensibility, while members of the families were gathered about them in apparent indifference. In a short time the unconscious bodies were inspected by several old people who said, 'They are ready.' They were then stripped of all their clothing except a single garment. Then the bodies were carried outside and laid on logs exposed to the bitter cold mountain air, the operation having been delayed several days for suitable weather.

"It was night when the bodies were carried out and the full moon occasionally obscured by flying clouds, shone on their upturned, ghastly faces and a horrible fascination kept me by the bodies as long as I could endure the severe cold. Soon I could stand the cold no longer and went inside, where I found the friends in cheerful conversation. In about an hour I went out and looked at the bodies. They were fast freezing.

"Again I went inside where the men were smoking their clay pipes but silence had fallen on them. Perhaps they were thinking of the time when their time would come to be carried out, for in the same way, one by one they at last lay down on the floor and went to sleep. I could not shut out the sight of their freezing bodies outside, neither could I bear to be in darkness, but I piled on the wood in the cavernous fireplace and seated on a shingle block passed the dreary night.

"January 8—Day came at length but did not dissipate the terror that filled me. The frozen bodies became visibly white on the snow that lay in huge drifts about them. The women gathered about the fire and soon commenced preparing breakfast. The men awoke and conversation again commencing, affairs assumed a more cheerful aspect.

"After breakfast the men lighted their pipes and some of them took a yoke of oxen and went off toward the forest, while others proceeded to nail together boards making a box about ten feet long and half as high and wide. When this was completed they placed about two feet of straw in the bottom. Then they laid three frozen bodies in the straw. Then the faces and upper parts of the bodies were covered with a cloth; then more straw was put in the box and the other three bodies placed on top, and covered the same as the first ones, with cloth and straw.

"Boards were then firmly nailed on top to protect the bodies from being injured by carnivorous animals that made their home on these mountains. By this time the men who went off with the ox team returned with a huge load of spruce and hemlock boughs which they unloaded at the foot of a steep ledge, came to the house and loaded the box containing the bodies on the sled and drew it to the foot of the ledge near the load of boughs.

"These were soon piled on and around the box and it was left to be covered with snow which I was told would lay in drifts twenty feet deep over this rude tomb. 'We shall want our men to plant our corn next Spring,' said a youngish-looking woman, the wife of one of the frozen men, 'and if you want to see them resuscitated, you come here about the tenth of next May.'

"With this agreement I left the mountaineers, living and frozen, to their fate and returned to my home in Boston where it was weeks before I was fairly myself, as my thoughts would return to that mountain with its awful sepulchre.

"Turning the leaves of the diary, the old man recounts, he came to the following entry: May 10—I arrived here at ten A.M. after riding about four hours over muddy, unsettled roads. The weather here is warm and pleasant, most of the snow is gone except here and there there are drifts in the fence corners and hollows. But nature is not yet dressed in green.

"I found the same parties here I left last January ready to disinter the bodies of their friends. I had no expectation of finding any life there, but a feeling that I could not resist impelled me to come and see.

"We repaired at once to the well remembered spot at the ledge. The snow had melted from the top of the brush, but still lay deep around the bottom of the pile. The men commenced work at once, some shoveling, and others tearing away the brush. Soon the box was visible. The cover was taken off, the layers of straw removed and the bodies, frozen and apparently lifeless, lifted out and laid on the snow.

"Large troughs made out of hemlock logs were placed nearby filled with tepid water, into which the bodies were placed separately with the head slightly raised. Boiling water was then poured into the trough from kettles hung on poles nearby until the water was as hot as I could hold my hand in. Hemlock boughs had been put in the boiling water in such quantities that they had given the water the color of wine.

"After lying in the bath about an hour, color began to return to the bodies, when all hands began rubbing and chafing them. This continued about an hour when a slight twitching of the muscles of the face and limbs, followed by audible gasps showed that life was not quenched and that vitality was returning.

"Spirits were then given in small quantities and allowed to trickle down their throats. Soon they could swallow and more was given them when their eyes opened and they began to talk, and finally sat up in their bath-tubs.

"They were taken out and assisted to the house where after a hearty meal they seemed as well as ever, and in no wise injured, but rather refreshed, by their long sleep of four months. Truly, truth is stranger than fiction."

The last sentence of this story may be the only true one in it, but this weird tale got around the country, and the mayor of Montpelier turned over to me some inquiries that came from readers in distant states, wanting to locate definitely the town described and to get further details, all of which I have been unable to obtain. I broadcast the absurd yarn by radio and observed varying degrees of gullibility on the part of those who listened. The fact, of course, that human hibernation is given scientific support by the experiments reported to the American medical association gave the story the only leg it had to stand on, and that was tottery indeed.

Strange items from Skiff's Island

Joseph Chase Allen, of the *Vineyard Gazette*, a continuous inventor of improbabilities, sometimes dates his communications from his Skiff's Island office. Since Skiff's Island is under water most of the time, this heading might serve as a warning—if any were needed. In a typical *Gazette* page (January 12, 1945, as it happens) the Wheelhouse Loafer (for this is Allen's favorite pseudonym) recounts a visit to the Vineyard Haven boatyard, a call on Orin Norton, the village blacksmith at Edgartown, and sundry other matters, and then opens the Skiff's Island mail and answers his correspondents. Some of these are real, as are the shipyard people and the blacksmith, but—

However, we quote:

Because of the many and varied tasks which confront the gang, they switch jobs according to wind and weather in order to lose no single minute. They have tools and material laid ready in a dozen places, and if the wind pipes nor'west, they have timbers to raise to take advantage of the breeze. If she hauls southeast and rains, then they get inside of a shed and plank up the side of a brig, and so on, very efficient all around.

On this day, however, the weather was nothing very definite. There was little wind, little rain, little sun and little cold. So here we found the gang hard at work on the lousiest job of all. "It is like this," explained Albert, looking disgusted, "we have stems, sternposts, hunks of keel, and bucketsful of thole-pin holes, all collected from the wreckage. We are supposed to sort these out and build boats around them, in the restoration program! I maintain that it is a staggering burden to place upon the faculties of any man to hand him a pair of row-lock cleats or a breast-hook and tell him to restore the boat that they used to belong to!"

"If there is any sympathy being handed out, I claim my share!" says Cap'n Gus Bunker. "It falls to my lot to unkink and re-coil all the odds and ends of waterline and boot-tops, scattered from hell to breakfast all over the beaches! If I can't find the boats that they came from, and stick 'em back on again, my day is counted as a failure and Albert has to plan something that they will fit! I have collected more than 17,000 fathoms of boot-top and waterline to date, all of it unclaimed so far. I wouldn't care so much, if it was mine, but some of this is kinked so that I just hate to be associated with it in any way!"

"It is a matter to be thankful for," says Cap'n Joe Andrews, "That the property of my department is not apt to float. While it is true that my duties are just as exacting as ever, I am not required to fit the ballast out of Number 1 ship, into the bilges of Number 4. There was one lead keel that drifted ashore, and I was expected to make suitable disposal of it. But I sawed it up and made inside ballast of it, so that it served its purpose and there was no great problem."

. . . .

Orin Norton, the village blacksmith of Edgartown, was under his spreading chestnut tree as usual, blacksmithing a watch-spring, or something of the sort. There was nothing unusual in Orin making a watch-spring, but when he told us that it was made from a sliver that he had sliced off the wheel of a steam-roller, we marvelled. "Hell's bells," says Orin, "there's really nothing to it! I had to have a piece of good metal, and this had the shape already hove into it!" Orin can blacksmith anything, by Judas! Last week he blacksmithed a lug on to the tail-end of a breeze of wind so that when it swoops through the shop and into his airtight[1] it will haul the door shut after it and not chill the shop all to the devil!"

. . . .

So to the broaching of the Skiff's Island mail and the diffusion of knowledge in bulk form, for the benefit of the millions of Gazette readers.

Sioux City, N. Dak. Wheelhouse Loafer, Sir: Just what happens to water stored in casks? I have read all sorts of loathsome things regarding the appearance of life in the drinking water aboard ships. T. C.

Answer. Nobody actually knows what minute forms of life are swallowed in every sip of water. But all hands of experience know that they will grow and develop if the water is stored, particularly in wood. On lengthy voyages in sailing ships, lizards with six pairs of legs, alligators, and other reptiles, as large as six feet over all, have appeared in the water casks, all developed from invisible life-germs that were bailed up in the water.

. . . .

Bellows Falls, Vt. Dear Wheelhouse Loafer, What is the tradition about the law of gravity being upset at sea? A. L.

Answer. Why it isn't upset exactly, but it is altered in a manner of speaking. Ashore, for example, you put water in a bucket to keep it from splashing about. Well, at sea, you put the bucket into the water to effect the same purpose.

---

[1] Wood-stove.

Cornfield, Kans. Dear Wheelhouse Loafer: Does a storm wind reach a higher velocity on the ocean than on the land? And can you give me any illustration of this fact? I. O.

Answer. The bare mathematics of the problem should be sufficient to show you that the wind is bound to attain a higher velocity at sea. There are no hills, mountains or other immovable objects to break or alter its force. Nothing appears before it that is not flexible and yielding to a considerable degree. The actual force, however, cannot be well or clearly determined except under proper and perhaps unusual conditions, of which we are glad to cite one, as follows.

The principle is very ancient indeed, that, with reference to a sail, or other object which holds wind, if a hole or perhaps several of them are let into the object, it will stand greater strain. You will frequently observe banners stretched across streets, thus provided with openings to prevent the fabric from tearing under wind pressure.

Now, one Cap'n Ira Marchant, master of the whaling brig Four Brothers, was a very scientific man, and sailing on a voyage in the early Eighties, he had provided his craft with specially designed storm-sails, with the idea of saving on canvas. His main-tops'l, under which he would normally lay in time of storm, was rigged with a vent in the bunt, which could be opened to any size to relieve the pressure; this in addition to the three sets of reef-points and, of course, the clew-lines which allowed for goose-winging the sail.

Somewhere to the s'uth'ard of the West Indies, the Four Brothers struck what was probably a hurricane, and the old man hove her to, close-reefed his main-tops'l, set a corner of the foretop-m'st-stays'l, and reckoned he could ride out anything. The wind increasing, he ordered the vent in the tops'l to be started, which was done, a rip-cord opening a slit estimated at six inches in width and about as long.

The brig rode it out without mishap, but about the time the storm started to die out, all hands were astounded to see the forem'st topple and crash over the side, leaving a stump about eighteen feet high. When, later, they were able to examine the break, they discovered that the wind blowing through that vent in the tops'l had apparently assumed the consistency of solid matter, and had actually bored or cut the forem'st nearly through, leaving a scarf like that of a very fine rasp!

Paris interlude[1]

O f the many more or less remarkable individuals who have been employed in the editorial department of the *Paris American* during that daily newspaper's thirty years of life in France, unquestionably one of the most interesting is John Hagen. He created a legend which, in a sense, is highly revelatory of the Paris of his time. Each new office

[1] By Edgar Calmer, from *Story*, Vol. IV, No. 19 (February 1934), pp. 56–62. Copyright, 1934, by Story Magazine, Inc. Edgar Calmer is an American journalist, former staff member of the Paris edition of the *New York Herald Tribune*.

generation (and they are frequent) is inclined to preserve the memory of Hagen a little more reverently than the preceding one. Probably the reason is that as John Hagen's figure recedes into the past his personality and his exploits seem to become more and more fabulous, until the younger men around the City Room today are accustomed to regard him as a sort of Gargantua belonging in the infancy of history, living out his adventures in the days when Paris was Paris and not the other end of the longest gangway in the world.

John Hagen was a reporter on the *Paris American* for two weeks in the year 1925. His origins and immediate past were unknown to the men he worked with and at the end of that brief period, his saga completed, John Hagen disappeared amid circumstances fatally similar to those which attended his arrival.

Paris, they say, changes little, yet time passes quickly. Two years after Hagen vanished there was not a man left on the paper who had been there to witness this reporter's career. As Scott McKendrick told the story to me, one evening in August, Hagen's contributions to American history in Paris have been handed down by word of mouth through an organization which has never changed too quickly to preserve them. A man falls heir to them by tradition, along with a number of other sensational anecdotes, all of them the exclusive property of this newspaper—which, it may be pointed out to begin with, is by its odd location and the nature of the exterior conditions within which it operates, one of the most curious institutions of its kind extant.

They tell of John Hagen fourteen stories which taken together make something more of an epic than an idyll. They tell of his hiring, which considering everything, was accomplished without much difficulty. On a mild day in May a taxi drove up to the door of the *Paris American* and four young men got out, bearing between them Hagen's prostrate but conscious body. He was carried thus supine through twenty yards of outer offices to the sanctum of the managing editor, where the four young men stood Hagen upright while he was formally engaged. Hagen, who had been drinking, then fell back easily into the arms of his companions and was similarly borne to the street.

The incident was not remarkable, since a busy summer was expected and the *Paris American,* a small paper, had lost suddenly its four best men through an automobile accident, a drinking party, and the birth of a child. That year, though never since, any American who could hold a copy-pencil in his hand was being sought after throughout the summer.

Mr. Hagen, the new reporter, was heard from no more that day. Late the following afternoon the city editor received a telephone call from the barber shop on the upper Champs-Elysees stating that a gentleman had passed out in the chair while having his hair cut and had just previously left word that the *Paris American* was to be notified in case anything happened to him.

The city editor was an old Hearst man and he personally took a taxi to see that Mr. Hagen got home safely and to bed.

Though John Hagen did little reporting and less writing for the *Paris American* during his incumbency, he succeeded in getting himself on the front page of the rival local newspaper as a result of his activities the next day. Moved by an obscure fidelity to his countrymen, he ventured to intervene in a private American quarrel going on in a celebrated cabaret in Montmartre at about three o'clock in the morning and was beaten up, first by the celebrated proprietor and afterwards successively by three waiters and the leader of the colored orchestra.

The evening of the fourth day of John Hagen's career as a Continental newspaperman was a beautiful evening and members of the editorial staff of the *Journal de Paris,* a French daily, were taking their apéritifs on a café terrace near the Bourse. It so happened that when they were halfway through their first drinks and discussing as French journalists do, everything except the day's news, a taxi drove by rapidly and John Hagen fell out of it. The Parisian journalists did not know Mr. Hagen but immediately decided he must be an American newspaperman. Very courteously they helped him to a seat on the terrace, ordered him a drink and invited him to dinner.

Hagen had a connoisseur's taste in firearms of many kinds and was especially interested in big pistols. None of his associates knew this however until the following night, when the reporter made his first appearance of the day at the *Paris American* by holding up the composing room with two large Colt revolvers. He had lined up the staff and relieved them of about three hundred francs when he inadvertently passed out cold on the floor while stuffing the bills into his pocket. The guns were confiscated and John Hagen was taken home to bed.

They tell of him how on the sixth day he was sent to interview one of the most celebrated musicians in the world, a curly-haired, sad-eyed man whose name is as familiar to most people as their own. Hagen talked for a while with the violin virtuoso at his Paris hotel and after asking a long list of grave questions, which the musician, a serious man, as gravely answered, the reporter concluded by saying: "Now then, if you don't mind my asking. I want to get it straight. Just what instrument do you play, Mister?"

No one was more surprised than the city editor of the *Paris American* the next day when about six in the evening John Hagen walked rapidly into the office declaring he had a big story and sat down at a typewriter in a corner of the room. The office, though busy, awaited the story with interest. For nearly an hour Hagen banged at the typewriter, his head gradually sinking towards his lap. At five minutes of seven he straightened up and with a triumphant gesture tore a sheet of paper from the machine. Then he passed out.

The entire story had been written on one line of the paper, the writer having neglected to release the rubber cylinder.

It was thereupon decided that the new reporter, Mr. Hagen, had better try his hand at desk work. Accordingly the next day a small delegation called at his hotel, awoke him, treated him to breakfast and gained the city room with him by three o'clock in the afternoon. Mr. Hagen was ordered to write headlines. He did so expertly with the first dozen heads he had to write that the city editor left the rest of them for the copy-readers on the night shift. One of these fellows, a man with a sense of humor, let one of the more decorous heads through. As a result the paper bore a double-column head on the front page the next morning which read:

COURT RULES 6,000 FRANCS PER MONTH
ENOUGH TO KEEP TWO DANCERS IN PARIS.
. . . .

Mr. Hagen was then retired as a headwriter and given one day to make good as a reporter again. He celebrated the occasion by digging up one of the best local stories of the year and then exchanging so many drinks with his informants that he wandered into the office of the rival American newspaper by mistake and wrote the story there. The men in the office already knew Hagen, by sight or reputation, and let him alone. The reporter wrote the article with his eyes shut but the facts were in it nevertheless. Later he was escorted to his hotel and carefully put to bed.

Fortunately for John Hagen this incident did not come to the ears of his superiors for some time. In the meantime he was registered a failure as a street man and assigned to the cable desk. He spent the tenth day of his career with the *Paris American* showing the rest of the office his skill in padding out short telegraphic messages so that they became subjects of more than usual interest. In fact, two of the stories Mr. Hagen, the desk specialist, sent to the composing room that night were later looked for in the cables and not found there at all.

One told of a special Memorial Day ceremony participated in by the President of the United States and the first lady of the land, in which the couple climbed to the roof of the White House in Washington and stood at salute before an electrically-illuminated American flag while a septet of trombonists from the Marine Band played Beethoven's "Creation."

The other, dated Salt Lake City, Utah, read: "Albert C. Grizzold, a member of the local House of David, was seriously injured today in the laundry in which he was working when his beard caught in a clothes-wringer. He was removed to Municipal Hospital."

From the eleventh day onward John Hagen began noticeably to weaken. Not that the mere few days of steady drunkenness while he was employed as a newspaperman in Paris could affect his naturally strong constitution. It was more a matter of a few years. And the crash, when it came, was sudden. The first evidence that Mr. Hagen was nearing the end was offered by Mr. Hagen himself. He made a surprisingly early entrance at the office but stayed only long enough to whisper into the ear of each of his colleagues that he was being shadowed by a horrid little man, no taller than a dwarf, who had followed him from bar to bar for three days and was even then waiting for him in the *bistro* across the street—confident, with his horrid grin, that Hagen would return.

The following afternoon John Hagen telephoned his city editor to make an engagement for that evening in a well known drink emporium in midtown. The city editor accepted because he liked Hagen and hoped to straighten him out eventually. An hour later, thinking himself somebody else, Hagen again telephoned his city editor, this time to warn that John Hagen was an exceptionally dangerous man and that the rendezvous agreed on was only for the purpose of Shanghai-ing the editor.

"There are gunmen on every corner of Paris tonight," said the mysterious voice—which, however, the city editor had no difficulty in recognizing. "I advise you not to stir from your office," the voice said.

Mr. Hagen's city editor was a patient man but he figured he had gone about as far as he intended to go with Mr. Hagen. He offered his reporter one more assignment, a comparatively simple one. The understanding was that if Mr. Hagen failed to show up with the story he was through.

It so happened that Paris at the time had a royal visitor, a man who is [1] probably the world's most celebrated bachelor. This personality was to make a formal visit to a French boys' orphanage near the city that afternoon and John Hagen was assigned to cover that visit. At about ten o'clock in the evening the reporter returned to his desk. He had actually covered the story. And he decided to fix it up swell.

A remarkable series of incidents then occurred. Men who know the conditions under which an American newspaper was brought out in Paris in those days will, perhaps, not be surprised at what happened. Mr. Hagen, the new reporter, wrote his article and handed it over to a copyreader who was a little too drunk to be able to read anything but not quite drunk enough to be unable to write a head for it which,

---

[1] Was, in 1934. (Editor's note.)

while meaning anything, meant nothing, and made sense. The night news editor was off duty for a few minutes so the copy went to the composing room without approval. Finally, the first edition being late, the proof desk ran over the galley forms rapidly and failed to notice the several lines of print in John Hagen's contribution with which a horrified world was confronted just a few hours later.

These lines, buried at the bottom of a column on an inside page, brought to a close the story about the royal bachelor's formal visit to the orphanage and read as follows:

> As His Highness concluded his inspection tour of the building he paused to pat the head of a little René Mathieu, 9, the youngest inmate of the establishment.
> "And what is your name, young man?" His Highness inquired in perfect French and with the smile which is known throughout the world.
> "None of your God-damned business," replied the youngster. Whereupon His Highness, with that grace and skill which have endeared him to a million subjects, raised his riding crop and with one blow dashed the lad's brains out.

A merciful curtain may as well be drawn over the consequences of what came to be known forever thereafter as Hagen's story. The *Paris American* despite this and other reverses, still survives. And John Hagen was dismissed the same day his first and last article was published. Four men alighted from a taxi on the fourteenth afternoon bearing his supine form between them, carried him thus to the managing editor's office, stood him upright before the desk while he was fired, then bore him down to the waiting taxi, took him home, and put him to bed.

One or two old *Paris American* men claim the Hagen saga has an epilogue. According to McKendrick, it should not be included in the definitive version. I give it here because it seems quite as good as the rest of the story and because the rest of the story is certainly almost too good to be altogether true. Three days after Hagen was seen for the last time, the city room received a wire from a large liner, in mid-ocean on its way to New York. Hagen had evidently fixed the wireless operator. It read:

ON THIS BOAT WITHOUT TICKET CAPTAIN DOESN'T KNOW IT YET. CAN YOU HELP WIRE INTENTIONS—HAGEN.

The city room held a little conference and then wired back:

INTENTIONS HONORABLE

Mr. Hagen has not been heard from since.

De Quincey started it, of course; started, that is, the practice of treating murders as entertainment. Or had the *Newgate Calendar,* despite its professed didacticism, done the same thing? At all events, we in America have carried the technique still further, and pushed any qualms quite into the background. No wonder that Dali, an amateur of the horrible, asked the late Edmund Pearson,[1] who had been happily discoursing on the Borden case: "Was there any cannibalism in it?" There is no cannibalism in the two murders discussed below.

Belle of Indiana[2]

Had it not been for an unfortunate hired man and a fire, Belle Brynhilde Poulsatter Sorenson Gunness might have been in business to this day; and a very profitable and interesting line it must have been. She was an extremely retiring and uncommunicative person and until fire destroyed her home near La Porte, Indiana, on April 28, 1908, she was practically unknown except to a circle of what one shudders to call her intimates.

Belle first appeared in La Porte in 1901. She was then the Widow Sorenson, relict of Mads Sorenson who died in 1900 leaving her with two children and eight thousand dollars in life insurance. From sale of the Sorenson home in Illinois the widow received another five thousand dollars. Thus she was financially well fixed when she bought a forty-eight-acre farm about a mile out of La Porte and moved there with two children of her own and another youngster, Jennie Olson, daughter of one Antone Olson.

The Widow Sorenson was forty-two years old in 1901. Neighbors describe her as "rugged," which would seem wholly inadequate. She was five feet seven inches tall and weighed two hundred pounds, most of which was pure brawn. When her household effects arrived at the farm, the truckers were amazed at the ease with which she juggled

---

[1] So I heard Mr. Pearson say. He fully appreciated this tribute to his own narrative powers.

[2] From Stewart Holbrook: *Murder Out Yonder* (New York: The Macmillan Company; 1944), pp. 126–44. By permission of The Macmillan Company, publishers.

heavy trunks, boxes, and crates. One of them, who may have been drinking that day, swore that he saw the woman pick the big upright piano clean off the floor of the porch, lug it unaided into the front room, and set it down as gently as she would have handled a basket of eggs. "Ay like music in home," Belle had beamed.

"Weigh three hunnert pound, easy," the awed trucker said later, referring to the piano.

In spite of her retiring disposition, neighbors soon learned that the Widow Sorenson was an accomplished farmer who could pitch hay and milk cows and who did her own butchering of hogs and calves, the meat of which she sold in La Porte. She wasn't a widow long. How they first met isn't clear; but in April of 1902 she married Peter Gunness, a Norwegian who seemed to be a jolly, honest person and became well liked by neighboring farmers. But Peter wasn't long for the world. In December, after only seven months of wedded bliss, he was killed when, as Mrs. Gunness explained the matter, he was struck on the head by a sausage grinder that fell from a shelf.

It is of course idle to speculate on whether or not the shelf had been jiggled. The La Porte coroner was called and, although later he admitted that the sausage-grinder affair "looked a little queer," he found officially that Peter Gunness, God rest his soul, had been the victim of an accident.

The Widow Gunness, who henceforth was known as Belle Gunness, was no doubt glad of the four-thousand-dollar life insurance policy which the oddly animated sausage machine had liquidated. But she continued to live modestly, even frugally, and it soon became apparent that in spite of her forty-three years Belle was in an interesting condition. A son whom she named Philip was born in 1903. In addition, her brood included Daughters Lucy and Myrtle by her previous marriage and the Jennie Olson she was caring for.

Although it was not known until later—tragically later—Belle Gunness was addicted to the use of matrimonial journals. That is, she advertised in them—listing, as was the custom, her desire for a good husband and being not too coy regarding her own personality and qualifications. What Belle wanted, it seemed, was a man of Scandinavian birth, preferably Norwegian, who was kind and honest and who would help a lovable and hard-working widow to lift the mortgage on her little farm. The "kind and honest" part of the desired man's qualifications might be winked at, one gathers; but the mortgage-lifting end of the deal was nothing short of imperative. "Triflers," Belle's advertisement said coldly, "need not apply."

A photograph of Belle Gunness at this period shows a squat, powerfully built woman in a long plain dress with puff sleeves, a Gibson Girl hair-do, and an exceedingly dull and heavy face. Looking at the photograph, one is hard put to explain the undoubted attraction the woman exercised on a large number of men. To term the woman in this photograph "plain" is mere flattery. But either this picture is a gross libel on Belle or her personal charm was such that no photograph could catch and hold it.

Shortly after the death of Mr. Gunness, Belle engaged a hired man to work around her place; but she herself was still active in butchering pigs, of which she had many, and in caring for the garden. The hired men changed from time to time, some of them very suddenly indeed; but none of them entered Belle's life very deeply until the next to last one, of which more later.

In 1906 a Mr. John Moo arrived at Belle's farm from Elbow Lake, Minnesota. He was a husky, good-looking man of about fifty years of age, well dressed by country-town standards, and a native of Norway. His object was matrimony, and he had been fetched by one of Belle's advertisements, in the wedding bells periodicals. With him John Moo brought one thousand dollars to "pay off the mortgage" on his intended's farm.

John was introduced to callers and neighbors as Cousin John, and for almost a week he was seen about the house every day. Then, one day, he wasn't there. That was thirty-five years ago. John Moo hasn't been seen since.

Hard on the heels of the disappearing Moo came George Anderson of Tarkio, a village in the northwestern corner of Missouri. George, like both Peter Gunness and John Moo, was a native of Norway. Living in Missouri must have given him some of the skepticism for which that state is famous; George Anderson did not bring very much money with him to Belle's place.

He was mighty glad he hadn't. Long afterward he related why.

Attracted by Belle's description of herself in one of the marriage papers, Anderson had made the long trip to La Porte with the intention of matrimony. After the usual amenities—and by now Belle must have been getting pretty good at amenities—the woman brought up the little matter of raising the mortgage. Really charmed by the husky Belle, George was seriously considering returning home to get what might be termed the entrance fee and then marrying the woman.

Early on his visit to the farm, however, he suddenly awoke in the middle of the night. "All in a cold sweat," he recalled. Bending over him and peering intently into his face was Belle herself, a lighted candle in her hand. What she intended to do, if anything, George Anderson never found out. He was so startled at the odd expression in the eyes and on the usually phlegmatic face of his intended bride that he let go a yell. Belle ran out of the room. So did George. He put on his clothes and got the hell out of there as fast as he could go, and

344

kept going until he reached the La Porte railroad station, on foot, where he got a train for Tarkio, Missouri.

After Anderson's departure there *may* have been a lull, a sort of brief hiatus, between the arrivals of men with matrimonial intentions. Again, there may have been no break at all. It is difficult to say. In any case, Belle was not idle. She changed her advertising copy in the wedding-bell journals, and she also engaged a new hired man—a rather dim-witted young French-Canadian by name of Ray L'Amphere, who presently anglicized his name into plain Lamphere. What his relations with Belle were, other than as hired man, are not positively known; but probably they were rather interesting, as events were soon to indicate.

Either just before or just after Lamphere came to live and work at the farm, young Jennie Olson, the sixteen-year-old girl who had been put in Belle's care by the child's father, Antone Olson, disappeared. Possibly "disappeared" is too strong a word to use at this point, for Belle explained everything to neighbors. Jennie "had gone to California," she said, and was at school there. It is certainly a fact that Jennie went somewhere in midsummer of 1906. That was thirty-five years ago. She hasn't been seen since.

During the lull in the mortgage-raising, Belle began to be something of a mystery woman in the neighborhood. Hack drivers of La Porte told of delivering trunks to the Gunness farm at night. One of the drivers was Clyde Sturgis. One night he drove out there with a big heavy trunk which was well bound with rope. Sturgis, always a helpful man, unloaded the trunk and started to cut the rope with his jack-knife. Belle was at him in a fury. "What are you trying to do!" she fairly screamed. "I'll take care of this trunk." And with that she picked it up off the porch like a box of marshmallows and lugged it inside.

Added to the business of the mysterious trunks, which doubtless became more mysterious every time it was retold, was that neighbors noted Belle kept the shutters on her house tightly drawn, both day and night, for a long period. And farmers going by late at night often saw Belle herself on the prowl, around her barn or in a small yard some fifty by seventy-five feet which Belle had recently enclosed with an *eight-foot* fence of stout and fine wire mesh. Entrance to this yard was by a rugged gate of tough oak which rumor said was always locked and to which Belle alone had the key.

The cellar of the house, too, was always kept locked except at hog-butchering season. At these times a stray neighbor or two had happened to call when Belle was in the cellar, her sleeves rolled up, wielding knife and cleaver like the best man Mr. Swift or Mr. Armour ever had. The cellar was admirably rigged for such work. It contained a long heavy table of hardwood, twelve inches thick, and a large tub for scalding purposes. In the ceiling over the tub was a hook and pulley. Leather strips along the wall held a professional assortment of fine butcher's implements.

The lull in the stream of callers—if lull there was—came to an end in April of 1907. In that merry spring month Mr. Ole Budsberg, a native of Norway but long a citizen of Iola in Waupaca County, Wisconsin, packed his extension suitcase and took a train of steamcars for La Porte. Belle met him at the station in her own buggy. The loving couple had long since exchanged photographs, as is the happy custom in mail-order matrimonial circles, and they had no trouble recognizing each other.

Mr. Ole Budsberg was a middle-aged man, the father of several grown sons. He had done very well with certain logging jobs in the white pine of Wisconsin and had saved his money. With him to La Porte he brought two thousand dollars in cash. This was, as one might guess, for the purpose of raising that apparently immutable mortgage on the forty-eight acres of the Widow Gunness.

Mr. Budsberg arrived on the farm late in April of 1907. That is thirty-four years ago and he hasn't been seen since.

2

Nineteen hundred and seven had been a rather slow year at the farm, but 1908 opened very auspiciously indeed when Mr. Andrew K. Helgelein arrived at the place in January and was made welcome by the charming chatelaine of what soon was to be known as Abattoir Acres. Mr. Helgelein was a native of Norway, but for years past he had been living near Aberdeen, South Dakota, where he successfully raised wheat.

Mr. Helgelein came with the most honorable intentions of matrimony. In his big wallet he carried no less than three thousand dollars in cash, with which to—but never mind. What had fetched him was obviously a series of letters, the last one of which happily has survived to give a good sample of Belle's literary style and general technique. It was written in Belle's own clear hand on January 13, 1908, and was inadvertently but fortunately left at his South Dakota home by Mr. Helgelein when he started for La Porte. Wrote the Belle of Indiana:

To the Dearest Friend in the World: No woman in the world is happier than I am. I know that you are now to come to me and be my own. I can tell from your letters that you are the man I want. It does not take one long to tell when to like a person, and you I like better than anyone in the world, I know.

Think how we will enjoy each other's company. You, the sweetest man in the whole world. We will be all alone with each other. Can you conceive of anything nicer? I think of you constantly. When I hear your name mentioned, and this is when one of the dear children speaks of you or I hear myself humming it with the words of an old love song, it is beautiful music to my ears.

My heart beats in wild rapture for you. My Andrew, I love you. Come prepared to stay forever.

And, by God, he did. That was thirty-three years ago and he hasn't been seen since.

Now affairs at the farm departed from their usual humdrum quiet. Ray Lamphere, the hired man, had a frightful quarrel with Belle. He, like many another poor man, had fallen in love with her and he was jealous of the latest star boarder, Helgelein. In a terrible temper he packed up his belongings and left. In La Porte he told friends that Belle owed him back wages. He said he knew enough about Belle to make her pay him not only his wages but to keep his mouth shut, too.

Lamphere must have done a deal of talking, for it got to Belle's ears. She promptly had him arrested on complaint that he was insane and a menace to the public. He was given what passed in those days for a sanity hearing, and was found sane. He made a call on Belle at the farm. They argued heatedly about something. She had him arrested again, for trespass.

Lamphere was a man who could take it. He paid a fine for trespass and he remained in the neighborhood. It is even thought that he called on Belle again. He also continued to make various veiled threats about her, and once mentioned to Farmer William Slater that "Helgelein won't bother me no more. We fixed him for keeps."

Trouble also assailed Belle from another quarter. She got a letter from Mr. Asle Helgelein, a substantial citizen of Mansfield, South Dakota, who wanted to know what had become of his brother Andrew. Belle wrote in reply that Andrew had gone away, doubtless on a visit to his native Norway. To this whimsey Asle Helgelein answered that he was positive that his brother had done no such thing.

Now we get a real sample of how Belle met a challenge of this sort. She sat right down and wrote Asle that she wished he would come to La Porte to aid her in a search for Andrew. She intimated, too, that searches of this kind cost money. If Asle replied to this invitation it is not of record.

For once in her life Belle Gunness was worried. Or so she seemed to M. E. Leliter, prominent attorney of La Porte, to whom the woman came on April 27, 1908. She told him she was mortally in fear of Ray Lamphere, the ex-hired man. He had threatened to kill her, she said. He had promised to burn her house around her ears. In view of these things hanging over her she wanted to make her will. It is significant, perhaps, that she did not ask for police protection from Lamphere.

347

Attorney Leliter drew up a will and she signed it. It left her estate to her two children by the late Mr. Sorenson and her one child by the late Mr. Gunness. In case the children did not survive her, the estate was to go to a Norwegian children's home, a sort of orphanage, in Chicago.

Leaving Mr. Leliter's office, Belle proceeded to the La Porte bank—where she paid off a five-hundred-dollar note. Then she returned to the farm.

Early next morning farmers on the McClung Road saw the Gunness home in flames. It burned to the ground. Only the hired man, one Joe Maxon, escaped, and he said he barely made it. Noise of the flames licking at his room had awakened him, he said, and he jumped out his second-story window in his underwear. He vowed that just before jumping he had shouted loudly to wake Mrs. Gunness and the children, but had received no reply. They had been in the house when he went to bed.

When the embers had cooled slightly, searchers found four bodies. Three were readily identified as those of Lucy and Myrtle Sorenson, Belle's daughters, and of Philip Gunness, her son. The other corpse was the headless body of a woman. All four were found on a mattress in the cellar. On top of them were the charred remains of the pride of Belle's parlor, the fine upright piano.

Sheriff Albert H. Smutzer was called. He viewed the scene and arrested Ray Lamphere, the farm hand who had been doing so much talking about Mrs. Gunness. Immediately upon his arrest and without so much as one question asked him, Lamphere asked one of his own. "Did Widow Gunness and the kids get out?" he inquired.

But Lamphere denied any knowledge of how the fire started, even when he was confronted by John Solyam, a neighbor's boy, who identified Lamphere as the man he had seen running away from the Gunness place just before the flames were noticed. "You wouldn't look me in the eye and say that," Lamphere asserted.

"Yes, I will," the lad said, and continued, "You found me hiding behind the bushes and you told me you'd kill me if I didn't get out of there."

Lamphere was indicted for murder; and a charge of arson was left, as you might say, hanging over him, just in case the other charge wasn't sufficient. The victim named in the murder charge was of course Mrs. Gunness. But, and the doubts began piling up one on top of the other, *was* the headless body that of Mrs. Gunness?

Swan Nicholson, neighboring farmer who had known Mrs. Gunness over a period of six years, viewed the headless corpse and said, without qualification, no, it wasn't that of the hefty widow. It wasn't tall enough, it wasn't big enough, and, well, it just didn't look like her at all. C. Christofferson, another farmer who had often called at the mystery place to do plowing and other work, was as positive as Nicholson had been. No, he said, that body had never been Belle. And so said Mrs. Austin Cutler, an old acquaintance.

From Chicago came Mrs. Nellie Olander and Mr. Sigurd Olson, sister and brother of the Jennie Olson who had lived with Belle and had "gone to California" not long before. Mrs. Olander and Mr. Olson told authorities they had known Belle ever since they could remember and that the headless body was of someone else, not Belle.

A tragic visitor at this time was Antone Olson, father of the missing girl. He came from Chicago to view the charred bodies. Jennie's was not among them. Mr. Olson told police he had planned to visit the Gunness home on the following Sunday to see if Jennie was all right. He said he had dreamed a few nights before that the Gunness home had been burned to the ground and Jennie was in the fire. It had worried him.

Physicians measured the charred remains of the headless woman. Making proper allowances for the missing head and neck, they concluded that the corpse was that of a woman five feet three inches tall and weighing about one hundred and fifty pounds. Belle, as those who knew her agreed, had not been a hair under five feet seven and weighed at least one hundred and eighty-five pounds, possibly more. Swan Nicholson was quite definite. The Widow Gunness, he said with sober assurance, weighed two hundred pounds if she weighed an ounce.

Clerks in La Porte stores who had sold Mrs. Gunness various articles of wearing apparel were interviewed for their knowledge of clothing sizes. These figures were compared with estimates of acquaintances. Physicians had meanwhile made careful measurements of the corpse. The two sets of measurements, one real, the other estimated, indicated that the body found in the cellar must be that of someone other than Belle. This is how they compared:

	Victim (inches)	Mrs. Gunness (inches)
Biceps	9	17
Bust	36	46
Waist	26	37
Thigh	25	30
Hips	40	54
Calf	12½	14
Wrist	6	9

Despite these discrepancies, and admitting they would like to have more definite proof, police authorities said the headless corpse was that of Belle Gunness. Three rings on the left hand were considered additional proof. One was set with diamonds and had no markings. A plain gold band was engraved "M.S. to J.S. Aug. 22 '94"; another gold band was marked "P.G. to J.S. 3–5–'95." It was reasonable to believe that these rings had to do with Belle's first marriage, to Mads Sorenson, and her second, to Peter Gunness. Because of the condition of the flesh it was impossible to say if these rings had been on these fingers for a long time.

Presently, as in all such cases of doubt, there came forward those witnesses who are apparently present, in swarming numbers, when any skulduggery has come to light. Half a dozen persons volunteered the information that they had seen Mrs. Gunness driving a woman to the farm on the night of the fire. Descriptions of this mysterious party varied from "slim" to "fairly stout." All agreed she had been a dark woman.

What the harassed authorities needed was a head for the corpse, or at least a skull. Search of the barns and outbuildings and of the near-by swamp revealed nothing in the form of a head. The sheriff was prepared to call it a day—to let the whole confusing matter rest as it was and to go ahead with the prosecution of the farm hand, Lamphere, for murder of Mrs. Gunness. Doubtless that is exactly what would have happened had it not been for the appearance on the scene of Asle Helgelein of Mansfield, South Dakota. This was the brother of Andrew, the man Belle had reported to Asle as on his happy way to Norway. Asle had not known of the Gunness fire until his arrival at La Porte. He had come simply to find his brother.

Asle went to Sheriff Smutzer with his suspicions that Andrew had somehow been done in by this woman he had come to marry. The sheriff didn't seem very interested, but Asle was persistent and the sheriff finally agreed to make another inspection of the premises. In the high-fenced yard, the gate to which had to be broken by police, were noted several soft depressions in the ground. Joe Maxon, Belle's latest hired man, the one who barely had escaped from the burning house, told officers that Belle once had him wheel dirt into the yard to level the partly filled holes. Contained rubbish, Belle had said. At the urging of Asle Helgelein deputies took shovels and started digging.

The first layers under the soft earth were indeed rubbish—old cans, bottles, and so forth—but suddenly a digger let out an exclamation. He came up with a good fat gunny sack. In it was a body well hacked but still in fair condition, everything considered. Helgelein looked closely at the remains. "That's Andy," he said.

The deputies now dug with a right good will. Before sundown that day, which was May 3, 1908, they had uncovered the remains of at least four bodies. One of these was identified as that of Jennie Olson, the girl who "had gone to California." One of the others was a tall man with a dark moustache. The two others were of children.

Next day the yard yielded four more bodies. On the third day only one body was found. That made a total of ten in the yard. If the four in the cellar were added, the grand total was fourteen—an impressive number for so small a farm.

When he was informed of the bodies found in the yard, Lamphere, the ex-hired man, screamed in his cell. "Bodies, murder, Helgelein!" was his curious cry. "My God, that woman! Now I know what was going on!"

Not all the bodies could be identified, but positive identifications were made of those of Jennie Olson, Andrew Helgelein, John Moo, and Ole Budsberg. For reasons that need not be gone into here, three other bodies were presently presumed to be those of one Olaf Lindblom and one Eric Gerhalt, both Norwegians who had come, separately, to visit Belle, and that of a hired man whose name was never known.

The remains of several *other* bodies were mere fragments—fingers and other small bones for which comparative skulls and trunks were missing. As physicians attempted to sort the hundreds of spare parts, the heavy table and the vat in the Gunness cellar took on a possible new meaning that made strong men shudder. Had that vat been used for purposes other than the scalding of hogs? One couldn't know, but police and physicians now looked at the several cleavers found in the ashes with new interest.

With Belle's private boneyard apparently exhausted, police felt that the investigation was completed—finished. They hadn't reckoned with the growing public rumor about that headless corpse and its possible connection with the mystery woman seen with Belle in her buggy on the night of the fire. New witnesses came forward. They had seen this same dark woman get off the evening train from Chicago. Belle had met her at the La Porte depot. They had driven out the McClung road together, toward the farm.

Maybe so; but Joe Maxon, Belle's final hired man, had seen no strange woman that night, although he admitted it was possible one could have been in the house without his knowledge. "It sure was a queer place," he allowed in what was a fair attempt at understatement.

No matter what Joe Maxon said, local opinion had it settled that the headless corpse was that of a woman the crafty Belle had imported to the farm for just such a purpose. Belle herself was safe somewhere, elsewhere. So the story grew and solidified.

Dr. Ira P. Norton, La Porte dentist, had been very busy at the time of the Gunness fire and had not then connected the fire with a former patient. With the Gunness farm and its odd harvest now on the front pages of the nation's press, Dr. Norton recalled that he had done some dental work for the late Mrs. Gunness. He told the police he could easily identify his own work, which was a bridge of gold and porcelain.

Police doubted Dr. Norton would have anything to work on. They said a fire hot enough to consume a head would also consume, or at least melt, both gold and porcelain. Not so, said Dr. Norton. The gold caps would not fuse under 1800 degrees Fahrenheit. The porcelain would not disintegrate at less than 2000 degrees. "That would call for a blowpipe flame," the dentist said.

The next problem was how to sift the ashes and debris of a large house and find a few small teeth—even if they existed, which the police seemed to doubt. Louis Schultz, a public-spirited citizen of La Porte, heard of the quandary and went to the officers with a suggestion. He was an old sourdough, he said, not long since returned from the Yukon, and if he had a little lumber and some encouragement he would build a regular gold-mine sluice box right there on Belle's place. With plenty of running water handy he would sluice every jeasley bit of stuff in the ruins of the house, and if there was any gold to be found in the claim he damned well would find it.

This Louis Schultz was plainly God-given. The sluice was built in Belle's front yard; water was piped from the barn; and old Klondike Louis, the ninety-eighter, went to work on the strangest mining job of his career, while thousands cheered.

The thousands who cheered Louis at his work came not only from La Porte and surrounding towns but from Chicago, where the daily papers were whooping up the biggest story of the year and one of the best horror stories of all time. Klondike Louis, indeed, was a sensation. With his sluice box roped off and scores of extra deputies needed to handle the huge crowds, he shoveled tons of debris and washed it down over the riffles before the largest audience a sourdough ever had. At that time newsreels were in infancy and seem not to have caught the epic event; but newspaper photographers were all over the place, catching Louis in pose after pose.

Bets were made on the outcome. Chicago bookies formed pools on the day and hour Louis would strike pay dirt in the Belle Gunness Mine. Vendors of popcorn and tonic circulated in the crowd, which on its peak day was estimated to be six thousand persons. On May 19, after four days of hard work, Klondike Louis struck the vein. Washed out from the muck and debris of the house was a piece of dental bridge-work containing two lower bicuspids capped with gold, and four porcelain teeth between them.

Dr. Norton looked closely. "My work, positively," he said. "Those are Mrs. Gunness' teeth."

3

In November, Ray Lamphere, the ex-farm hand, went on trial in La Porte for the murder of Mrs. Gunness. He was ably defended by Wirt Worden and was acquitted. Tried for arson, he was convicted. Obviously the jury did not believe Mrs. Gunness was dead. Lamphere was sent to prison at Michigan City, where he died in 1909.

Before his death Lamphere told a long and sometimes disconnected story of his affairs with Mrs. Gunness to a trusty at the prison by name of Harry Myers, and after Lamphere's death Myers retold it to prison officials. High lights of this account were that Belle did *not* die in the fire. Despite the evidence of the dental work, the body was that of a woman Belle had lured from Illinois on the promise of housework, then killed and beheaded to preclude identification. The head had been destroyed by use of quicklime, "in a hole dug in the swamp."

Lamphere painted a horrible picture of the female monster on the prowl. With the stand-in woman butchered, Belle went methodically to work on her own children, killing them one after another with practiced hand, then piled the four bodies onto the mattress after dressing the woman in some old clothes that would readily be recognized as Belle's clothing.

In all, Lamphere said, Belle had lured forty-two men to her house. Only one had escaped, presumably the alert George Anderson of Tarkio, Missouri, who had awakened to find Belle standing over his bed peering into his face so intently.

From her dupes Belle had got amounts of cash varying from one thousand dollars to thirty-two thousand dollars each, Lamphere said. Usually she drugged their coffee, then bashed in their heads while they were in a stupor. She then dissected the bodies on the big table in the cellar, tied the parts into neat bundles, and buried them in the locked yard. On occasion she varied the monotony—by putting the bodies into the hog-scalding vat and adding generous amounts of quicklime.

Lamphere admitted to Myers that he had helped Belle bury "several bodies" but denied that he ever had a part in the killing. Jennie Olson had been killed because "she knew too much." It was the same with Belle's own children. The other unidentified children had been put in Belle's care by mothers or fathers of broken homes.

As for the late Peter Gunness, alleged victim of the bounding sausage grinder, Belle had killed him with an axe.

Not all of the dying Lamphere's story made sense. No doubt it was also grossly exaggerated. Some of it was sheer fantasy. And he was oddly silent regarding his own relations with Mrs. Gunness. But on the subject of the headless corpse he was positive; it was not Belle. She was safely away.

And that is the opinion today of many oldsters around La Porte, who believe that Belle, who left only a small amount in her bank account, had killed the unknown woman, fired the house, and left for other parts.

On a somewhat different plane Belle lives on just as Ambrose Bierce, the old journalist, did for many years in spite of his probable death in Mexico in 1916. As recently as 1931 Belle was "seen" in a Mississippi town. In the same year the body of a woman found in Los Angeles was thought to be hers. It wasn't. For more than twenty years the sheriff's office at La Porte received an average of two queries a month about Belle—Belle the Hoosier Monster, the Queen of the Abattoir, the Female Bluebeard. During the past decade the queries have been fewer, but they continue.

Belle Gunness, in fact, seems assured of an enduring place in the folklore of the region. I base this guess on the fact that she is the subject of at least one ballad, and when a person or an event gets into song it is not likely to be forgotten as soon as one not in ballad. The literary or musical merit of the ballad has nothing at all to do with its lasting qualities, as witness the doggerel about Jesse James, Jim Fisk, Floyd Collins, and other folk heroes.

The ballad about Belle I heard sung to the air of "Love, O Careless Love," and the verses I have been able to unearth are as follows:

> Belle Gunness lived in In-di-an;
> She always, always had a man;
> Ten at least went in her door—
> And were never, never seen no more.
>
> Now all these men were Norsker folk
> Who came to Belle from Minn-e-sote;
> They liked their coffee, and their gin:
> They got it—plus a mickey finn.
>
> And now with cleaver poised so sure
> Belle neatly cut their jug-u-lur (sic);
> She put them in a bath of lime,
> And left them there for quite some time.
>
> There's red upon the Hoosier moon
> For Belle was strong and full of doom;
> And think of all them Norska men
> Who'll never see St. Paul again.

One of the last direct links between Belle Gunness and the present day is an old, old woman confined in the Longcliff Hospital for the Insane at Logansport, Indiana. She has been a patient there for a good many years and is one of the characters of the institution. She worked at Belle's place for several months and is not averse to talking about it.

354

The favorite question asked this old woman is "What did Belle Gunness do with all those men?" And the invariable reply, accompanied by a truly horrible leer, is "She fed 'em to the hawgs."

On the subject of Belle being alive or dead the old crone is noncommittal. "Who knows?" she says.

If Belle still lives, as many believe, she is eighty-two years old in 1941. That's getting on, as they say; but should I happen on a farmhouse in some back-country place and the proprietor is a husky old woman who kills her own hogs, I'll be on my way—no matter the road or the weather.

The middle man

It was nearly one o'clock in the morning when Harry Wesson got on a subway train at Times Square, bound for Washington Heights. He was sleepy, and barely able to note, without being much interested, that the car was nearly empty, and that an elderly lady across the aisle was staring at him with apparent disapproval. Why? He had had a few drinks, it was true. But—

This vague line of thought was broken at the next stop, when three men came in arm-in-arm; if Wesson had looked dissipated, as he suspected he did, these men looked drunk, and the old lady transferred her unfavorable attention to them. For this, or some other reason, they sat down beside her. Two of them stared at Wesson; the man in the middle seemed too drunk to stare at anyone. His companions talked across him, but they seemed to be speaking some foreign language. Wesson could not understand a word, but he felt that they were talking about him. Odd—but it didn't matter.

At Fifty-ninth Street several people got out; nobody got on, and Wesson noticed that he, the old lady, and the three men were alone in the car. The old lady now appeared fidgety, and the drunk had passed out. The other two continued their unintelligible conversation, and again it seemed to Wesson that they were talking about him. As the train slowed down at Seventy-second Street the old lady rose decisively and marched toward the door, brushing against Wesson.

"You follow me, young man!" she muttered. "Mind that, now!"

Somewhat dazed, Wesson obeyed. On the platform, as the train moved away, he said, annoyed: "What can I do for you, madam?"

The old lady snorted.

"Young man, I should think I've done something for you. Didn't you see that the middle man was dead?"

This story, in essence, has drifted about New York for decades, not changing very much, though sometimes Wesson is a young girl, the old lady an old gentleman, and so on. The underlying mystery is never solved. A few years ago the late Alexander Woollcott told it (with a young girl and an old gentleman in the cast) in the *New Yorker*. Three weeks later (March 15, 1930) he had something interesting to report to *New Yorker* readers. This is his postscript:[1]

"You have not traced the story of the girl and the dead man in the subway back far enough," writes my precious leader, Edmund Pearson, who is shortly to be recalled to Harvard to occupy the Chair of Murder. "In its earlier version it was (pardon me) a better yarn. Finley Peter Dunne *fils*, who thinks that you and I are the two nicest old gentlemen in New York, with the longest memories, and that we used to walk down Broadway in the mellow twilights of 1815, chanting glees with Washington Irving and Fitz-Greene Halleck—Mr. Dunne, I say, would be shocked that you did not recall the grimmer story which came out in *The Bookman* about 1902 [2] when, under the editorship of Harry Thurston Peck and Arthur Maurice, that was a most readable magazine—as it is now again in 1930.

"This story was a corker. There was the old, horse-drawn 'bus, toiling slowly down Fifth Avenue in a blinding snowstorm. Everything silent, since the snow was already five or six inches deep. The middle-aged couple lived in Washington Square and had been at the theatre—way up town, say at Thirty-eighth or Fortieth Street. They enter an empty 'bus—you remember those 'buses in the days when *Life* was constantly caricaturing them and their lean horses. They had straw on the floor; a driver on the box; a smoky oil lantern at the front; a tin box in which you put your fare; and a door which the driver opened with a string when you signalled that you wished to get out.

"The 'bus, with the man and his wife, goes slowly through the snow down as far as—well, Twenty-second Street—when three other passengers get on, two young fellows supporting a third, whose heels drag. They address him as Jim, and tell him to buck up. But Jim is far gone in liquor; or, as they said in the sprightly 80's, he has a jag. He can do nothing for himself. A few streets below, one of them again tells Jim to buck up, slaps him on the back and gets out. A little later, the other one repeats the advice to Jim, and he, too, gets out. Jim is still silent; still sullen; and still slumped in the seat. Then the man leans forward and takes a look at Jim. Instantly he gets up, pulls the cord, and says to his wife: 'We get out here.' And out he gets, followed by his indignant and scolding wife. They stand in the drifting snow, near the corner of Fourteenth Street, and the wife wishes to know if her husband is crazy. Seven blocks still to go, and get her out in this blizzard—what does he mean? Her husband says: 'Did you see that young man?' No, she didn't. What has that to do with it? 'Well, I did, and his throat was cut from ear to ear.' "

---

[1] From the *New Yorker*, March 15, 1930, p. 34.
[2] This editor cannot find it in the *Bookman* for 1902—or 1901, or 1903.

BOOK IV

FROM ANOTHER WORLD

FROM ANOTHER WORLD: *Coincidence,*

clairvoyance, ghosts.

THE editor of this collection does not believe in ghosts, but he does believe in ghost stories. Clairvoyance, another manner of communication with other worlds, is even less convincing, he thinks, but to be as fair as possible he has included here the best documented story he knows of a piece of American soothsaying. (Yet the tale is a migrant, and without names and places it is told, often with the prophecy congealed into the neat form: "You have no future.")

"How," say the believers, "do you then explain this sequence of prophecy and fulfillment?"

I would explain it as pure coincidence. On this point I think Cicero's remark leaves nothing more to be said. That realist, in his treatise on divination, remarked that no soothsayer is so unlucky that none of his prophecies ever come true.

Ghosts are another matter. If a ghost story is really artfully told, who would be so austere as to refuse to suspend his disbelief? But American ghost stories are not our best yarns. Perhaps we are not old enough as an inhabited land. We have no donjons and no ancestral curses, centuries old. Haunted houses, yes, but their stories are too often short and vague. James's "The Turn of the Screw" and Mrs. Wharton's ghost stories are excellent, but they are art products, they have no native flavor of America. Peter Rugg and Hudson's Catskill crew are American legends now, but they were born in an ink-bottle. The late H. P. Lovecraft[1] created ghosts, but to most readers these appear synthetic.

A few choice ghosts we do possess, and those included here will, it is hoped, make the reader uneasy, especially if read the proper way, alone at midnight.

---

[1] See, for instance, H. P. Lovecraft: *Beyond the Wall of Sleep* (Sauk City, Wisconsin: Arkham House; 1943).

1. COINCIDENCE, PREMONITION, PROPHECY

Coincidences, of which life is of course full, lead the superstitious to strange conclusions, and the more remarkable the coincidence, the stranger the conclusion. Mr. Henry Hough, being a New England Yankee, is able to take in his stride the strange coincidence that he recounts; he does not even talk about the finger of fate, and this forbearance gives his anecdote a pleasing matter-of-factness.

Mrs. Lehr's account of the veridical fortune-teller is remarkable in a different way. She gives real names, though no date, and she speaks as a first-hand witness; she heard the prophecy before the event. This is very unusual; most American versions of this story vouch for it as something that happened to a cousin, an aunt, a distant relative, a person of undisputed veracity, and so forth and so on. But try to get in touch with the original sponsors! They have moved away, they are dead, the story-teller is out of touch with them—in short, you draw a blank every time.

Mrs. Lehr's story is still told in Newport, but no one else has told it as circumstantially as she. To one who wishes to believe it, and to believe in fortune-telling, it is quite unanswerable.

In a world of chances [1]

There was the time when a visiting criminal broke the safe on the principal steamboat wharf of the island and stole the cash receipts of the Labor Day weekend (the peak of transportation business), amounting in total to $7,150.91. It seemed doubtful whether the miscreant or miscreants could be apprehended. But by one of those pleasant circumstances of country life, which so often turns up a novel aspect for prosaic patterns, there was a fragment of romance in the background. This romance was slight and of a sentimentality suitable to the time of year—summer—and the place—a resort by the sea. A boy employed as ticket seller for the steamboat company had changed a five dollar bill for a girl who was spending the season as waitress in

[1] From: *Country Editor*, by Henry Beetle Hough, copyright 1940, reprinted by permission of Doubleday & Company, Inc.; pp. 164–6.

a hotel, and as it was summer and the two were young, he had written on the bill, "Keep this. H." This bill was then a talisman, and the boy kept it in the office safe, planning to redeem it through an exchange with another bill before the season ended. It did not occur to the safecracker or his associates that any of the company funds might be hot in this particular way. The chance which followed was as unlikely a thing as ever took place in a world of chances. A man named Fowler who turned out to be an associate of the criminal—of the chief criminal, that is—tried to pass the marked bill on one of the steamboats at a time when the romantic ticket seller was a passenger. The boy was leaving for his winter home, and in another day, another two hours, he would have been out of the way for good. But on this fateful trip he stood in the saloon on the main deck and heard the purser at the window speak of a mark on a bill. Curiosity moved him to take a look at the bill, and the rest was a job to the liking of the police. In a short time the man Fowler had turned informer, and Archie Drew was locked up in our jail.

For the following story the narrator, Mrs. Lehr, gives no date. Mr. Vinson Walsh, Senator Walsh's son, did die in an automobile accident at Newport, on August 19, 1905. A mystery-reader, an acquaintance of mine, on hearing the story promptly declared that the accident must have been faked. "It was a murder," she proclaimed, "and the fortune-teller was in cahoots with the murderer. Anybody can see that." It is possible that in time the reading of mystery and murder fiction will add another dimension to American story-telling. Mr. James Thurber has already produced a new solution of the murder in *Macbeth*, based strictly upon the conventions of our detective fiction.[1]

Something original[2]

Mamie Fish[3] gave a party for the members of the New York Yacht Club which had put into Newport on its August cruise. She was very anxious to have something rather original, so she and I went to Narragansett Pier to hire the crystal-gazer there who had a great reputation. When the day of the party arrived he was attired in some mar-

---

[1] See James Thurber: *My World and Welcome to It* (New York: Harcourt, Brace & Co.; 1942), pp. 33ff.

[2] From *King Lehr and the Gilded Age*, Copyright, 1935, by Elizabeth Drexel Lehr, published by J. B. Lippincott Company, pp. 233–5.

[3] Mrs. Stuyvesant Fish.

vellous flowing robes which Mamie had presented to him, and installed in a room which she had had specially decorated in Oriental style for the occasion. There was a lot of laughter as everyone compared notes on his predictions; all the guests wanted to consult him, even the sceptics. Only the young son of Senator Walsh was disappointed. . . . "The fellow would not tell me anything at all," he complained to Mamie. . . . "He stared into that crystal of his until I thought he had gone to sleep, then he said he could see nothing for me, and that it was no use going on trying. . . . I told him he was not much of a fortune-teller if that was all he could do. . . ."

At the end of the party Mrs. Fish and I went over to the seer who was packing up his table and crystal with a most brisk and business-like air. Mamie told him his performance had been a great success. . . . "Oh, by the way," she added, "you don't seem to be able to see the future for everyone. One of my guests told me you could tell him nothing. . . ." The man nodded. . . . "Was it a young gentleman about nineteen or twenty?" "Yes."

"Well, Madam, you would not have liked me to tell what I did see. I saw no future for him, because there is none to see. His life is finished. He is going to die within the next few hours."

Mrs. Fish started in surprise. . . . "That young Walsh boy! Nonsense, it is impossible. Why, he is in perfect health. Do you mean he is going to die violently? . . ." The man nodded. . . .

"That young gentleman will die because it is his time to die. It is his destiny. I could not avert it. By this time tomorrow he will be dead."

Mamie laughed incredulously, but I was rather relieved the next day when we all went to lunch at the Clam Bake Club to see the Walsh boy at the table, looking the picture of health and high spirits. Mrs. Fish whispered, "It just shows that one should not pay any attention to the rubbish those fortune-tellers try to make you believe. . . . He said 'a few hours' and it's more than a few hours now, and the boy is perfectly well."

Alas! We rejoiced too soon. Evelyn Walsh and her brother were to drive home in their new sports car, taking a number of friends with them. We watched them all pack into the seats; their laughter came back to us on the wind as they started off.

An hour later a man drove up to the Club, white-faced and shaking. . . . "There has been a frightful motor accident along the road. . . . Senator Walsh's son has been killed. . . ."

2. HAUNTED HOUSES

America needs more and better haunted houses. But a house should stand vacant a long time if a ghost is really to settle down in it, and America has been increasingly short of houses since World War I. Families since the beginning of World War II, and especially since its conclusion, have had to "double up," often in houses that should have been torn down long since. "No vacancy" has become a ubiquitous sign in our cities. But, no vacancy, no ghost. It is true that any empty house may be called "haunted," but creaks and tappings and even strange lights are a dime a dozen, in the estimation of a ghost-connoisseur.

One American has invented a fine series of ghosts and haunted houses, but these are only pictorial. If someone will now invent stories which will match the drawings of Chas. Addams [1] (or the acting of Boris Karloff), the American ghost will really be getting somewhere.

Room for one more [2]

When an intelligent comely girl of twenty-odd summers was invited for the first time to the Carolina estate of some distant relatives, their lovely plantation fulfilled her fondest expectations. She was given a room in the west wing, and prepared to retire for the night in a glow of satisfaction. Her room was drenched with the light of a full moon.

Just as she was climbing into her bed, she was startled by the sound of horses' hooves on the gravel roadway. Curious, she walked to the window and saw, to her astonishment, a magnificent old coach pull up to an abrupt stop directly below her. The coachman jumped from his perch, looked up and pointed a long, bony finger at her. He was hideous. His face was chalk-white. A deep scar ran the length of his left cheek. His nose was beaked. As he pointed at her, he droned in sepulchral tones, "There is room for one more!" Then, as she recoiled

---

[1] See, for instance, his album of drawings, *Drawn and Quartered* (New York: Random House; 1942).

[2] Reprinted from Bennett Cerf: *Try and Stop Me*, by permission of Simon and Schuster, Inc. Copyright, 1944, by Bennett Cerf. Pp. 277-9.

in terror, the coach, the horses and the ominous coachman disappeared completely.

The girl slept little, but the next day she was able to convince herself that she had merely had a nightmare.

The next night, however, the horrible experience was repeated. The same coach drove up the roadway. The same coachman pointed at her and intoned, "There is room for one more!" Then, as before, the entire equipage disappeared.

The girl, now panic-stricken, could scarcely wait for morning. She trumped up some excuse to her hosts and left immediately for home.

Upon arrival, she taxied to her doctor from the station and told him her story in tremulous tones. The doctor persuaded her that she had been the victim of a peculiar hallucination, laughed at her terror, and dismissed her in a state of infinite relief. As she rang for the elevator, its door swung open before her.

The elevator was very crowded, but she was about to squeeze her way inside—when a familiar voice rang in her ear. "There is room for one more!" it called. In terror, she stared at the operator. He was the coachman who had pointed at her! She saw his chalk-white face, the livid scar, the beaked nose! She drew back and screamed . . . the elevator door banged shut.

A moment later the building shook with a terrible crash. The elevator that had gone on without her broke loose from its cables and plunged eighteen stories to the ground. Everybody in it, of course, was crushed to a pulp.

We didn't go back [1]

Southwest of Winslow near the Chavez Hills and the Pass was located an old stage station. Here when the first stages was running a through route, a family had stayed overnight and had been slaughtered by the Apaches—men, women, and children. Never since then had anyone stayed overnight in the place, and it had long ago been abandoned.

But it was well located for a stopping place, as water were handy, and good grass. We cowboys would pull up there, water and unsaddle our horses and put our beds down for the night in one of the old rooms. Pretty soon we would hear horses' hoofs and the sound of wheels and the creak of old springs. When the sounds got close a voice would

---

[1] From Jesse James Benton: *Cow by the Tail* (Boston: Houghton Mifflin Co.; 1943), pp. 172–4. Used by permission of the publishers, Houghton Mifflin Company.

holler, "Whoa!" and the hoofs and wheels would stop, and then the voice would say, "Hello in there." We boys would throw the front door open, but not a soul was there, no horses, no wagon, no stage, nothing. Then our hair would sort of stand up on our heads and usually we would saddle up and leave there on a high gallop.

Well, one night I pulled in there with Gus and two other cowboys. It were in the fall, turned dark about seven o'clock. We was feeling a little shaky, but we lit a candle and played poker for a while. About eight-thirty, sure enough, here come the galloping horses. Then the wheels slid a little and a voice called, "Whoa!" Just as he hollered, "Hello in there," one of the boys blew out the candle and jumped for the door. The moon was in the first half, so we could see pretty well. But not a living thing were near. We pushed out together and ran around the place, making a circle three hundred yards around it—not a soul! Not a mark or track anywheres.

After some chinning we decided to stick it out. But we moved outside to a tree about one hundred yards away from the house. Everything stayed quiet, and we were feeling mighty brave. Finally we laid down and was just getting to sleep when inside the house some dogs begun to bark. Sounded like two or three of them. We sat up, pulled on our boots, and walked over nearer to the house. Just then the barking turned to growling, and we heard many blood-curdling screams of women and children, the curses of rough men, chains clanking. Screaming and cursing grew louder than ever, mixed with the growling of dogs. Suddenly all was dead quiet. Not a sound.

While the racket lasted we had been froze in our tracks, but the dead silence got us. Everyone of us made a bee line for his horse, slung on the saddles and blankets and rode two-three miles before we ever said a word. Then we each had to tell what we had heard, and we all agreed that the noise come out of the house and also that no living people or dogs was anywhere near there.

We didn't go back.

We told a lot of other fellers about it, and some said they had heard and seen the same and wouldn't go near that place for no amount of money. However, one cowboy, George Perry by name, laughed loud and long and made all kinds of fun of us, said he sure would bet us fifty dollars he could go alone and stay there all night. We covered that bet pronto. He had heard so much about that haunted station from us and others that he decided he would make no failure. When we got to the stage station he went inside and fixed his bed comfortable and then took a chain he had brought along and fastened himself by his leg to a supporting post in the building. He locked the chain with a padlock and throwed the key into the far corner of the room. *"Hasta luego,* boys," he said. We told him we would be back early next morning, and he laid down for what he told us would be a good night's rest.

Next morning when we boys went back you never seen such a sight as he was. His eyes were bloodshot; he was wild-looking, with hair all mussed up; and he had worn a path all back and forth in front of the post he was chained to, like a chained bear would do. He said he hoped he died before he had to spend another night like that. He had sure heard everything we boys told him about, and more besides— not one time but three different times. Said he would have given ten year of his life to get hold of that key and run out of that house. Never seen a man so glad to get out of a place after we unlocked him.

All this were back in the eighties. In 1921 I met some folks in Douglas who had been making a automobile trip through Arizona, seeing the Grand Canyon, Petrified Forest, Meteor Crater. They told me they had camped out on the trip, said they had no trouble camping at all, except one night when they stopped about thirty miles southwest of Winslow. They said they had just got comfortable in their blankets when they begun to hear something growling and fighting. They thought it were bears, got up in a hurry, and put their beds in their car.

They said while they was packing up, they heard all kinds of noises coming from a place near-by where there was a bunch of trees and bushes. After they started on, the road went over a little hill, and looking back at the grove they saw in the moonlight what they thought was the outlines or ruins of a little house. Then they crossed a creek. Well, I knew by their description it were what was left of the old stage station so I told them of my early-day adventures at that place. We agreed the old ghosts of that dead family was still there, hanging around the place.

Such ghosts as that of Hamlet's father, troubled spirits who can not rest until their mission is accomplished, were known even to the ancient Greeks and Romans. A more disturbing type is the visitant whose mission is never to be accomplished. The Wandering Jew is the type. This is not an American ghost, unless it is to be recognized in Peter Rugg. Of Peter many people confidently speak who have never heard of his creator, for, reversing the usual process, Peter was literature first, and legend afterward.

Comparatively few readers know (or remember) that Rip Van Winkle and the ghosts of Hudson's crew appeared first in Irving's pages. He did not collect the story; he invented it.

Peter Rugg[1]

(From Jonathan Dunwell of New York to Mr. Herman Krauff.)

Sir:—Agreeably to my promise, I now relate to you all the particulars of the lost man and child which I have been able to collect. It is entirely owing to the human interest you seemed to take in the report that I have pursued the inquiry to the following result.

You may remember that business called me to Boston in the summer of 1820. I sailed in the packet to Providence; and when I arrived there, I learned that every seat in the stage was engaged. I was thus obliged either to wait a few hours, or accept a seat with the driver, who civilly offered me that accommodation. Accordingly I took my seat by his side, and soon found him intelligent and communicative. When we had travelled about ten miles, the horses suddenly threw their ears on their necks as flat as a hare's. Said the driver, "Have you a surtout with you?"

"No," said I; "why do you ask?"

"You will want one soon," said he. "Do you observe the ears of all the horses?"

"Yes; and was just about to ask the reason."

"They see the storm-breeder, and we shall see him soon."

---

[1] By William Austin, from Samuel Adams Drake: *A Book of New England Legends* (Boston: Roberts Brothers; 1884), pp. 90–105.

At this moment there was not a cloud visible in the firmament; soon after a small speck appeared in the road.

"There," said my companion, "comes the storm-breeder; he always leaves a Scotch mist behind him. By many a wet jacket do I remember him. I suppose the poor fellow suffers much himself—much more than is known to the world."

Presently a man with a child beside him, with a large black horse and a weather-beaten chair, once built for a chaise-body, passed in great haste, apparently at the rate of twelve miles an hour. He seemed to grasp the reins of his horse with firmness, and appeared to anticipate his speed. He seemed dejected, and looked anxiously at the passengers, particularly at the stage-driver and myself. In a moment after he passed us, the horses' ears were up, and bent themselves forward so that they nearly met.

"Who is that man?" said I; "he seems in great trouble."

"Nobody knows who he is; but his person and the child are familiar to me. I have met him more than a hundred times, and have been so often asked the way to Boston by that man, even when he was travelling directly from that town, that of late I have refused any communication with him; and that is the reason he gave me such a fixed look."

"But does he never stop anywhere?"

"I have never known him to stop anywhere longer than to inquire the way to Boston. And let him be where he may, he will tell you he cannot stay a moment, for he must reach Boston that night."

We were now ascending a high hill in Walpole; and as we had a fair view of the heavens, I was rather disposed to jeer the driver for thinking of his surtout, as not a cloud as big as a marble could be discerned.

"Do you look," said he, "in the direction whence the man came; that is the place to look. The storm never meets him, it follows him."

We presently approached another hill; and when at the height the driver pointed out in an eastern direction a little black speck about as big as a hat,—"There," said he, "is the seed storm; we may possibly reach Polley's before it reaches us, but the wanderer and his child will go to Providence through rain, thunder, and lightning."

And now the horses, as though taught by instinct, hastened with increased speed. The little black cloud came on rolling over the turnpike, and doubled and trebled itself in all directions. The appearance of this cloud attracted the notice of all the passengers; for after it had spread itself to a great bulk, it suddenly became more limited in circumference, grew more compact, dark and consolidated. And now the successive flashes of chain lightning caused the whole cloud to appear like a sort of irregular network, and displayed a thousand fantastic images. The driver bespoke my attention to a remarkable configuration in the cloud; he said every flash of lightning near its centre discovered

368

to him distinctly the form of a man sitting in an open carriage drawn by a black horse. But in truth I saw no such thing. The man's fancy was doubtless at fault. It is a common thing for the imagination to paint for the senses, both in the visible and invisible world.

In the mean time the distant thunder gave notice of a shower at hand; and just as we reached Polley's tavern the rain poured down in torrents. It was soon over, the cloud passing in the direction of the turnpike toward Providence. In a few moments after, a respectable-looking man in a chaise stopped at the door. The man and child in the chair having excited some little sympathy among the passengers, the gentleman was asked if he had observed them. He said he had met them; that the man seemed bewildered, and inquired the way to Boston; that he was driving at great speed, as though he expected to outstrip the tempest; that the moment he had passed them, a thunder-clap broke directly over the man's head, and seemed to envelop both man and child, horse and carriage. "I stopped," said the gentleman, "supposing the lightning had struck him; but the horse only seemed to loom up and increase his speed; and as well as I could judge, he travelled just as fast as the thundercloud."

While this man was speaking, a pedlar with a cart of tin merchandise came up all dripping; and on being questioned, he said he had met that man and carriage, within a fortnight, in four different states; that each time he had inquired the way to Boston, and that a thunder-shower, like the present, had each time deluged his wagon and his wares, setting his tin pots, etc., afloat, so that he had determined to get marine insurance done for the future. But that which excited his surprise most was the strange conduct of his horse; for that long before he could distinguish the man in the chair, his own horse stood still in the road, and flung back his ears. "In short," said the pedlar, "I wish never to see that man and horse again; they do not look to me as though they belonged to this world."

This was all I could learn at that time; and the occurrence soon after would have become with me "like one of those things that had never happened," had I not, as I stood recently on the doorstep of Bennett's Hotel in Hartford, heard a man say, "There goes Peter Rugg and his child! He looks wet and weary, and farther from Boston than ever." I was satisfied it was the same man I had seen more than three years before; for whoever has once seen Peter Rugg can never after be deceived as to his identity.

"Peter Rugg!" said I; "and who is Peter Rugg?"

"That," said the stranger, "is more than anyone can tell exactly. He is a famous traveller, held in light esteem by all inn-holders, for he never stops to eat, drink, or sleep. I wonder why the Government does not employ him to carry the mail."

"Ay," said a bystander, "that is a thought bright only on one side. How long would it take in that case to send a letter to Boston?—for Peter has already, to my knowledge, been more than twenty years travelling to that place."

"But," said I, "does the man never stop anywhere? Does he never converse with anyone? I saw the same man more than three years since near Providence, and I heard a strange story about him. Pray, sir, give me some account of this man."

"Sir," said the stranger, "those who know the most respecting that man say the least. I have heard it asserted that Heaven sometimes sets a mark on a man either for judgment or a trial. Under which Peter Rugg now labors, I cannot say; therefore I am rather inclined to pity than to judge."

"You speak like a humane man," said I; "and if you have known him so long, I pray you will give me some account of him. Has his appearance much altered in that time?"

"Why, yes; he looks as though he never ate, drank, or slept; and his child looks older than himself; and he looks like time broken off from eternity, and anxious to gain a resting-place."

"And how does his horse look?" said I.

"As for his horse, he looks fatter and gayer, and shows more animation and courage, than he did twenty years ago. The last time Rugg spoke to me he inquired how far it was to Boston. I told him just one hundred miles.

" 'Why,' said he, 'how can you deceive me so? It is cruel to mislead a traveller. I have lost my way; pray direct me the nearest way to Boston.'

"I repeated, it was one hundred miles.

" 'How can you say so?' said he; 'I was told last evening it was but fifty, and I have travelled all night.'

" 'But,' said I, 'you are now travelling from Boston. You must turn back.'

" 'Alas!' said he, 'it is all turn back! Boston shifts with the wind and plays all around the compass. One man tells me it is to the east, another to the west; and the guide-posts, too, they all point the wrong way.'

" 'But will you not stop and rest?' said I; 'you seem wet and weary.'

" 'Yes,' said he; 'it has been foul weather since I left home.'

" 'Stop, then, and refresh yourself.'

" 'I must not stop; I must reach home tonight, if possible; though I think you must be mistaken in the distance to Boston.'

"He then gave the reins to his horse, which he restrained with difficulty, and disappeared in a moment. A few days afterward I met the man a little this side of Claremont, winding around the hills in Unity, at the rate, I believe, of twelve miles an hour."

"Is Peter Rugg his real name, or has he accidentally gained that name?"

"I know not, but presume he will not deny his name; you can ask him—for see, he has turned his horse, and is passing this way."

In a moment a dark-colored, high-spirited horse approached, and would have passed without stopping; but I had resolved to speak to Peter Rugg, or whoever the man might be. Accordingly I stepped into the street, and as the horse approached, I made a feint of stopping him. The man immediately reined in his horse. "Sir," said I, "may I be so bold as to inquire if you are not Mr. Rugg?—for I think I have seen you before."

"My name is Peter Rugg," said he: "I have unfortunately lost my way. I am wet and weary, and will take it kindly of you to direct me to Boston."

"You live in Boston, do you?—and in what street?"

"In Middle Street."

"When did you leave Boston?"

"I cannot tell precisely; it seems a considerable time."

"But how did you and your child become so wet? It has not rained here today."

"It has just rained a heavy shower up the river. But I shall not reach Boston tonight if I tarry. Would you advise me to take the old road or the turnpike?"

"Why, the old road is one hundred and seventeen miles, and the turnpike is ninety-seven."

"How can you say so? You impose on me! It is wrong to trifle with a traveller. You know it is but forty miles from Newburyport to Boston."

"But this is not Newburyport; this is Hartford."

"Do not deceive me, sir. Is not this town Newburyport, and the river that I have been following the Merrimac?"

"No, sir; this is Hartford, and the river the Connecticut."

He wrung his hands and looked incredulous.

"Have the rivers, too, changed their courses, as the cities have changed places? But see! the clouds are gathering in the south, and we shall have a rainy night. Ah, that fatal oath!"

He would tarry no longer. His impatient horse leaped off, his hind flanks rising like wings; he seemed to devour all before him and to scorn all behind.

I had now, as I thought, discovered a clew to the history of Peter Rugg, and I determined, the next time my business called me to Boston, to make a further inquiry. Soon after, I was enabled to collect the following particulars from Mrs. Croft, an aged lady in Middle Street, who has resided in Boston during the last twenty years. Her narration is this:

371

The last summer, a person, just at twilight, stopped at the door of the late Mrs. Rugg. Mrs. Croft, on coming to the door, perceived a stranger, with a child by his side, in an old weather-beaten carriage, with a black horse. The stranger asked for Mrs. Rugg, and was informed that Mrs. Rugg had died in a good old age more than twenty years before that time.

The stranger replied, "How can you deceive me so? Do ask Mrs. Rugg to step to the door."

"Sir, I assure you Mrs. Rugg has not lived here these nineteen years; no one lives here but myself, and my name is Betsey Croft."

The stranger paused, and looked up and down the street, and said: "Though the painting is rather faded, this looks like my house."

"Yes," said the child; "that is the stone before the door that I used to sit on to eat my bread and milk."

"But," said the stranger, "it seems to be on the wrong side of the street. Indeed everything here seems to be misplaced. The streets are all changed, the people are all changed, the town seems changed; and what is strangest of all, Catherine Rugg has deserted her husband and child. Pray," continued the stranger, "has John Foy come home from sea? He went a long voyage; he is my kinsman. If I could see him, he could give me some account of Mrs. Rugg."

"Sir," said Mrs. Croft, "I never heard of John Foy. Where did he live?"

"Just above here, in Orange Tree Lane."

"There is no such place in this neighborhood."

"What do you tell me? Are the streets gone? Orange Tree Lane is at the head of Hanover Street, near Pemberton's Hill."

"There is no such lane now."

"Madam! you cannot be serious. But you doubtless know my brother, William Rugg. He lives in Royal Exchange Lane, near King Street."

"I know of no such lane, and I am sure there is no such street as King Street in this town."

"No such street as King Street! Why, woman, you mock me! You may as well tell me there is no King George! However, madam, you see I am wet and weary; I must find a resting-place. I will go to Hart's tavern, near the market."

"Which market, sir?—for you seem perplexed; we have several markets."

"You know there is but one market,—near the Town dock."

"Oh, the old market; but no such person has kept there these twenty years."

Here the stranger seemed disconcerted, and uttered to himself quite audibly: "Strange mistake! How much this looks like Boston! It certainly has a great resemblance to it; but I perceive my mistake now. Some other Mrs. Rugg, some other Middle Street."

"Then," said he, "madam, can you direct me to Boston?"

"Why, this is Boston, the city of Boston. I know of no other Boston."

"City of Boston it may be; but it is not the Boston where I live. I recollect now, I came over a bridge instead of a ferry. Pray what bridge is that I just came over?"

"It is Charles River Bridge."

"I perceive my mistake; there is a ferry between Boston and Charlestown; there is no bridge. Ah, I perceive my mistake. If I were in Boston my horse would carry me directly to my own door. But my horse shows by his impatience that he is in a strange place. Absurd, that I should have mistaken this place for the old town of Boston! It is a much finer city than the town of Boston. It has been built long since Boston. I fancy it must lie at a distance from this city, as the good woman seems ignorant of it."

At these words his horse began to chafe and strike the pavement with his fore-feet. The stranger seemed a little bewildered, and said, "No home tonight"; and giving the reins to his horse, passed up the street, and I saw him no more.

It was evident that the generation to which Peter Rugg belonged had passed away.

This was all the account of Peter Rugg I could obtain from Mrs. Croft; but she directed me to an elderly man, Mr. James Felt, who lived near her, and who had kept a record of the principal occurrences for the last fifty years. At my request she sent for him; and after I had related to him the object of my inquiry, Mr. Felt told me he had known Rugg in his youth; that his disappearance had caused some surprise; but as it sometimes happens that men run away, sometimes to be rid of others, and sometimes to be rid of themselves; and Rugg took his child with him, and his own horse and chair; and as it did not appear that any creditors made a stir,—the occurrence soon mingled itself in the stream of oblivion, and Rugg and his child, horse and chair, were soon forgotten.

"It is true," said Mr. Felt, "sundry stories grew out of Rugg's affair, —whether true or false I cannot tell; but stranger things have happened in my day, without even a newspaper notice."

"Sir," said I, "Peter Rugg is now living; I have lately seen Peter Rugg and his child, horse and chair. Therefore I pray you to relate to me all you know or have ever heard of him."

"Why, my friend," said James Felt, "that Peter Rugg is now a living man, I will not deny; but that you have seen Peter Rugg and his child is impossible, if you mean a small child; for Jenny Rugg, if

373

living, must be at least—let me see—Boston Massacre, 1770—Jenny Rugg was about ten years of age. Why, sir, Jenny Rugg, if living must be more than sixty years old. That Peter Rugg is living, is highly probable, as he was only ten years older than myself, and I was only eighty last March; and I am as likely to live twenty years longer as any man."

Here I perceived that Mr. Felt was in his dotage; and I despaired of gaining any intelligence from him on which I could depend.

I took my leave of Mrs. Croft, and proceeded to my lodgings at the Marlborough Hotel.

If Peter Rugg, thought I, has been travelling since the Boston Massacre, there is no reason why he should not travel to the end of time. If the present generation know little of him, the next will know less; and Peter and his child will have no hold on this world.

In the course of the evening I related my adventure in Middle Street.

"Ha!" said one of the company, smiling, "do you really think you have seen Peter Rugg? I have heard my grandfather speak of him as though he seriously believed his own story."

"Sir," said I, "pray let us compare your grandfather's story of Mr. Rugg with my own."

"Peter Rugg, sir, if my grandfather was worthy of credit, once lived in Middle Street, in this city. He was a man in comfortable circumstances, had a wife and one daughter, and was generally esteemed for his sober life and manners. But, unhappily, his temper at times was altogether ungovernable; and then his language was terrible. In these fits of passion, if a door stood in his way, he would never do less than kick a panel through. He would sometimes throw his heels over his head and come down on his feet, uttering oaths in a circle; and thus in a rage he was the first who performed a somerset, and did what others have since learned to do for merriment and money. Once Rugg was seen to bite a tenpenny nail in halves. In those days everybody, both men and boys, wore wigs; and Peter, at these moments of violent passion, would become so profane that his wig would rise up from his head. Some said it was on account of his terrible language; others accounted for it in a more philosophical way, and said it was caused by the expansion of his scalp,—as violent passion, we know, will swell the veins and expand the head. While these fits were on him Rugg had no respect for heaven or earth. Except this infirmity, all agreed that Rugg was a good sort of man; for when his fits were over, nobody was so ready to commend a placid temper as Peter.

"It was late in autumn, one morning, that Rugg, in his own chair, with a fine large bay horse, took his daughter and proceeded to Con-

374

cord. On his return a violent storm overtook him. At dark he stopped at Menotomy, now West Cambridge, at the door of a Mr. Cutter, a friend of his, who urged him to tarry the night. On Rugg's declining to stop, Mr. Cutter urged him vehemently. 'Why, Mr. Rugg,' said Cutter, 'the storm is overwhelming you: the night is exceeding dark: your little daughter will perish: you are in an open chair, and the tempest is increasing.' *'Let the storm increase,'* said Rugg, with a fearful oath, *'I will see home tonight, in spite of the last tempest, or may I never see home!'* At these words he gave his whip to his high-spirited horse, and disappeared in a moment. But Peter Rugg did not reach home that night or the next; nor, when he became a missing man, could he ever be traced beyond Mr. Cutter's in Menotomy.

"For a long while after, on every dark and stormy night, the wife of Peter Rugg would fancy she heard the crack of a whip, and the fleet tread of a horse, and the rattling of a carriage passing her door. The neighbors, too, heard the same noises; and some said they knew it was Rugg's horse, the tread on the pavement was perfectly familiar to them. This occurred so repeatedly, that at length the neighbors watched with lanterns, and saw the real Peter Rugg, with his own horse and chair, and child sitting beside him, pass directly before his own door, his head turned toward his house, and himself making every effort to stop his horse, but in vain.

"The next day the friends of Mrs. Rugg exerted themselves to find her husband and child. They inquired at every public-house and stable in town; but it did not appear that Rugg made any stay in Boston. No one, after Rugg had passed his own door, could give any account of him; though it was asserted by some that the clatter of Rugg's horse and carriage shook the houses on both sides of the streets. And this is credible, if indeed Rugg's horse and carriage did pass on that night. For at this day, in many of the streets, a loaded truck or team in passing will shake the houses like an earthquake. However, Rugg's neighbors never afterward watched; some of them treated it all as a delusion, and thought no more of it. Others, of a different opinion, shook their heads and said nothing.

"Thus Rugg and his child, horse and chair, were soon forgotten, and probably many in the neighborhood never heard a word on the subject.

"There was, indeed, a rumor that Rugg afterwards was seen in Connecticut, between Suffield and Hartford, passing through the country with headlong speed. This gave occasion to Rugg's friends to make further inquiry. But the more they inquired, the more they were baffled. If they heard of Rugg one day in Connecticut, the next they heard of him winding round the hills of New Hampshire; and soon after, a man in a chair with a small child, exactly answering the description of Peter Rugg, would be seen in Rhode Island inquiring the road to Boston.

"But that which chiefly gave a color of mystery to the story of Peter Rugg was the affair at Charlestown Bridge. The toll-gatherer asserted that sometimes on the darkest and most stormy nights, when no object could be discerned, about the time Rugg was missing, a horse and wheel carriage, with a noise equal to a troop, would at midnight, in utter contempt of the rates of toll, pass over the bridge. This occurred so frequently, that the toll-gatherer resolved to attempt a discovery. Soon after, at the usual time, apparently the same horse and carriage approached the bridge from Charlestown Square. The toll-gatherer, prepared, took his stand as near the middle of the bridge as he dared, with a large three-legged stool in his hand. As the appearance passed, he threw the stool at the horse, but heard nothing, except the noise of the stool skipping across the bridge. The toll-gatherer, on the next day, asserted that the stool went directly through the body of the horse; and he persisted in that belief ever after. Whether Rugg, or whoever the person was, ever passed the bridge again, the toll-gatherer would never tell; and when questioned, seemed anxious to waive the subject. And thus, Peter Rugg and his child, horse and carriage, remain a mystery to this day."

This, sir, is all that I could learn of Peter Rugg in Boston.

Was it quite fair of Washington Irving to deceive his ingenuous correspondent, in 1858? Perhaps it was; perhaps Irving felt that anyone who believed in Diedrich Knickerbocker might be allowed to believe anything. At all events, his letter [1] is a masterpiece of double meaning.

Sunnyside, Feb. 5, 1858.

Dear Sir:

I can give you no other information concerning the localities of the story of Rip Van Winkle, than is to be gathered from the manuscript of Mr. Knickerbocker, published in the Sketch Book. Perhaps he left them purposely in doubt. I would advise you to defer to the opinion of the "very old gentleman" with whom you say you had an argument on the subject. I think it probable he is as accurately informed as any one on the matter.

Respectfully, your obedient servant,

Washington Irving.

---

[1] From Pierre M. Irving: *Life and Letters of Washington Irving* (New York: G. P. Putnam & Son; 1867), Vol. III, p. 54.

Rip Van Winkle[1]

W hoever has made a voyage up the Hudson must remember the Kaatskill mountains. They are a dismembered branch of the great Appalachian family, and are seen away to the west of the river, swelling up to a noble height, and lording it over the surrounding country. Every change of season, every change of weather, indeed, every hour of the day, produces some change in the magical hues and shapes of these mountains, and they are regarded by all the good wives, far and near, as perfect barometers. When the weather is fair and settled, they are clothed in blue and purple, and print their bold outlines on the clear evening sky; but sometimes, when the rest of the landscape is cloudless, they will gather a hood of gray vapors about their summits, which, in the last rays of the setting sun, will glow and light up like a crown of glory.

At the foot of these fairy mountains, the voyager may have described the light smoke curling up from a village, whose shingle-roofs gleam among the trees, just where the blue tints of the upland melt away into the fresh green of the nearer landscape. It is a little village, of great antiquity, having been founded by some of the Dutch colonists in the early times of the province, just about the beginning of the government of the good Peter Stuyvesant, (may he rest in peace!) and there were some of the houses of the original settlers standing within a few years, built of small yellow bricks brought from Holland, having latticed windows and gable fronts, surmounted with weathercocks.

In that same village, and in one of these very houses (which, to tell the precise truth, was sadly time-worn and weather-beaten), there lived, many years since, while the country was yet a province of Great Britain, a simple, good-natured fellow, of the name of Rip Van Winkle. He was a descendant of the Van Winkles who figured so gallantly in the chivalrous days of Peter Stuyvesant, and accompanied him to the siege of Fort Christina. He inherited, however, but little of the martial character of his ancestors. I have observed that he was a simple, good-natured man; he was, moreover, a kind neighbor, and an obedient hen-pecked husband. Indeed, to the latter circumstance might be owing that meekness of spirit which gained him such universal popularity; for those men are most apt to be obsequious and conciliating abroad, who are under the discipline of shrews at home. Their tempers, doubtless, are rendered pliant and malleable in the fiery furnace of domestic

---

[1] From (Washington Irving:) *The Sketchbook of Geoffrey Crayon, Gent.* (New York: G. P. Putnam & Son; 1868), pp. 53–80.

tribulation; and a curtain-lecture is worth all the sermons in the world for teaching the virtues of patience and long-suffering. A termagant wife may, therefore, in some respects, be considered a tolerable blessing; and if so, Rip Van Winkle was thrice blessed.

Certain it is, that he was a great favorite among all the good wives of the village, who, as usual with the amiable sex, took his part in all family squabbles; and never failed, whenever they talked those matters over in their evening gossipings, to lay all the blame on Dame Van Winkle. The children of the village, too, would shout with joy whenever he approached. He assisted at their sports, made their playthings, taught them to fly kites and shoot marbles, and told them long stories of ghosts, witches, and Indians. Whenever he went dodging about the village, he was surrounded by a troop of them, hanging on his skirts, clambering on his back, and playing a thousand tricks on him with impunity; and not a dog would bark at him throughout the neighborhood.

The great error in Rip's composition was an insuperable aversion to all kinds of profitable labor. It could not be from the want of assiduity or perseverance; for he would sit on a wet rock, with a rod as long and heavy as a Tartar's lance, and fish all day without a murmur, even though he should not be encouraged by a single nibble. He would carry a fowling-piece on his shoulder for hours together, trudging through woods and swamps, and up hill and down dale, to shoot a few squirrels or wild pigeons. He would never refuse to assist a neighbor in even the roughest toil, and was a foremost man at all country frolics for husking Indian corn, or building stone fences; the women of the village, too, used to employ him to run their errands, and do such little odd jobs as their less obliging husbands would not do for them. In a word, Rip was ready to attend to everybody's business but his own; but as to doing family duty, and keeping his farm in order, he found it impossible.

In fact, he declared it was of no use to work on his farm; it was the most pestilent little piece of ground in the whole country; everything about it went wrong, and would go wrong, in spite of him. His fences were continually falling to pieces; his cow would either go astray, or get among the cabbages; weeds were sure to grow quicker in his fields than anywhere else; the rain always made a point of setting in just as he had some out-door work to do; so that, though his patrimonial estate had dwindled away under his management, acre by acre, until there was little more left than a mere patch of Indian corn and potatoes, yet it was the worst conditioned farm in the neighborhood.

His children, too, were as ragged and wild as if they belonged to nobody. His son Rip, an urchin begotten in his own likeness, promised to inherit the habits, with the old clothes, of his father. He was generally seen trooping like a colt at his mother's heels, equipped in a pair of his father's cast-off galligaskins, which he had much ado to hold up with one hand, as a fine lady does her train in bad weather.

Rip Van Winkle, however, was one of those happy mortals, of foolish, well-oiled dispositions, who take the world easy, eat white bread or brown, whichever can be got with least thought or trouble, and would rather starve on a penny than work for a pound. If left to himself, he would have whistled life away in perfect contentment; but his wife kept continually dinning in his ears about his idleness, his carelessness, and the ruin he was bringing on his family. Morning, noon, and night, her tongue was incessantly going, and everything he said or did was sure to produce a torrent of household eloquence. Rip had but one way of replying to all lectures of the kind, and that, by frequent use, had grown into a habit. He shrugged his shoulders, shook his head, cast up his eyes, but said nothing. This, however, always provoked a fresh volley from his wife; so that he was fain to draw off his forces, and take to the outside of the house—the only side which, in truth, belongs to a hen-pecked husband.

Rip's sole domestic adherent was his dog Wolf, who was as much hen-pecked as his master; for Dame Van Winkle regarded them as companions in idleness, and even looked upon Wolf with an evil eye, as the cause of his master's going so oft astray. True it is, in all points of spirit befitting an honorable dog, he was as courageous an animal as ever scoured the woods; but what courage can withstand the everduring and all-besetting terrors of a woman's tongue? The moment Wolf entered the house his crest fell, his tail drooped to the ground, or curled between his legs, he sneaked about with a gallows air, casting many a sidelong glance at Dame Van Winkle, and at the least flourish of a broomstick or ladle he would fly to the door with yelping precipitation.

Times grew worse and worse with Rip Van Winkle as years of matrimony rolled on; a tart temper never mellows with age, and a sharp tongue is the only edged tool that grows keener with constant use. For a long while he used to console himself, when driven from home, by frequenting a kind of perpetual club of the sages, philosophers, and other idle personages of the village, which held its sessions on a bench before a small inn, designated by a rubicund portrait of His Majesty George the Third. Here they used to sit in the shade through a long, lazy summer's day, talking listlessly over village gossip, or telling endless sleepy stories about nothing. But it would have been worth any statesman's money to have heard the profound discussions that sometimes took place, when by chance an old newspaper fell into their hands from some passing traveller. How solemnly they would listen to the contents, as drawled out by Derrick Van Bummel, the schoolmaster, a dapper, learned little man, who was not to be daunted by the most gigantic word in the dictionary; and how sagely they would deliberate upon public events some months after they had taken place.

The opinions of this junto were completely controlled by Nicholas Vedder, a patriarch of the village, and landlord of the inn, at the door of which he took his seat from morning till night, just moving sufficiently to avoid the sun and keep in the shade of a large tree; so that the neighbors could tell the hour by his movements as accurately as by a sun-dial. It is true that he was rarely heard to speak, but smoked his pipe incessantly. His adherents, however, (for every great man has his adherents), perfectly understood him, and knew how to gather his opinions. When anything that was read or related displeased him, he was observed to smoke his pipe vehemently, and to send forth short, frequent, and angry puffs; but when pleased, he would inhale the smoke slowly and tranquilly, and emit it in light and placid clouds; and sometimes, taking the pipe from his mouth, and letting the fragrant vapor curl about his nose, would gravely nod his head in token of perfect approbation.

From even this stronghold the unlucky Rip was at length routed by his termagant wife, who would suddenly break in upon the tranquility of the assemblage and call the members all to naught; nor was that august personage, Nicholas Vedder himself, sacred from the daring tongue of this terrible virago, who charged him outright with encouraging her husband in habits of idleness.

Poor Rip was at last reduced almost to despair; and his only alternative, to escape from the labor of the farm and clamor of his wife, was to take gun in hand and stroll away into the woods. Here he would sometimes seat himself at the foot of a tree, and share the contents of his wallet with Wolf, with whom he sympathized as a fellow-sufferer in persecution. "Poor Wolf," he would say, "thy mistress leads thee a dog's life of it; but never mind, my lad, whilst I live thou shalt never want a friend to stand by thee!" Wolf would wag his tail, look wistfully into his master's face; and if dogs can feel pity, I verily believe he reciprocated the sentiment with all his heart.

In a long ramble of the kind on a fine autumnal day, Rip had unconsciously scrambled to one of the highest parts of the Kaatskill mountains. He was after his favorite sport of squirrel-shooting, and the still solitudes had echoed and reëchoed with the reports of his gun. Panting and fatigued, he threw himself, late in the afternoon, on a green knoll, covered with mountain herbage, that crowned the brow of a precipice. From an opening between the trees he could overlook all the lower country for many a mile of rich woodland. He saw at a distance the lordly Hudson, far, far below him, moving on its silent but majestic course, with the reflection of a purple cloud, or the sail of a lagging bark, here and there sleeping on its glassy bosom, and at last losing itself in the blue highlands.

On the other side he looked down into a deep mountain glen, wild, lonely, and shagged, the bottom filled with fragments from the impending cliffs, and scarcely lighted by the reflected rays of the setting sun. For some time Rip lay musing on this scene; evening was gradually advancing; the mountains began to throw their long blue shadows over the valleys; he saw that it would be dark long before he could reach the village, and he heaved a heavy sigh when he thought of encountering the terrors of Dame Van Winkle.

As he was about to descend, he heard a voice from a distance, hallooing, "Rip Van Winkle! Rip Van Winkle!" He looked round, but could see nothing but a crow winging its solitary flight across the mountain. He thought his fancy must have deceived him, and turned again to descend, when he heard the same cry ring through the still evening air: "Rip Van Winkle! Rip Van Winkle!"—at the same time Wolf bristled up his back, and giving a low growl, skulked to his master's side, looking fearfully down into the glen. Rip now felt a vague apprehension stealing over him; he looked anxiously in the same direction, and perceived a strange figure slowly toiling up the rocks, and bending under the weight of something he carried on his back. He was surprised to see any human being in this lonely and unfrequented place; but supposing it to be some one of the neighborhood in need of his assistance, he hastened down to yield it.

On nearer approach he was still more surprised at the singularity of the stranger's appearance. He was a short, square-built old fellow, with thick bushy hair, and a grizzled beard. His dress was of the antique Dutch fashion,—a cloth jerkin strapped round the waist— several pair of breeches, the outer one of ample volume, decorated with rows of buttons down the sides, and bunches at the knees. He bore on his shoulder a stout keg, that seemed full of liquor, and made signs for Rip to approach and assist him with the load. Though rather shy and distrustful of this new acquaintance, Rip complied with his usual alacrity; and mutually relieving one another, they clambered a narrow gully, apparently the dry bed of a mountain torrent. As they ascended, Rip every now and then heard long, rolling peals, like distant thunder, that seemed to issue out of a deep ravine, or rather cleft, between lofty rocks, toward which their rugged path conducted. He paused for an instant, but supposing it to be the muttering of one of those transient thunder-showers which often take place in mountain heights he proceeded. Passing through the ravine, they came to a hollow like a small amphitheatre, surrounded by perpendicular precipices, over the brinks of which impending trees shot their branches, so that you only caught glimpses of the azure sky and the bright evening cloud. During the whole time Rip and his companion had labored on in silence; for though the former marvelled greatly what could be the object of carrying a keg of liquor up this wild mountain, yet there was something strange and incomprehensible about the unknown, that inspired awe and checked curiosity.

On entering the amphitheatre, new objects of wonder presented themselves. On a level spot in the centre was a company of odd-looking personages playing at ninepins. They were dressed in a quaint, outlandish fashion; some wore short doublets, others jerkins, with long knives in their belts and most of them had enormous breeches, of similar style with that of the guide's. Their visages, too, were peculiar: one had a large beard, broad face, and small piggish eyes; the face of another seemed to consist entirely of nose, and was surmounted by a white sugar-loaf hat, set off with a red cock's tail. They all had beards, of various shapes and colors. There was one who seemed to be the commander. He was a stout old gentleman, with a weather-beaten countenance; he wore a laced doublet, broad belt and hanger, high crowned hat and feather, red stockings, and high-heeled shoes with roses in them. The whole group reminded Rip of the figures in an old Flemish painting, in the parlor of Dominie Van Shaick, the village parson, and which had been brought over from Holland at the time of the settlement.

What seemed particularly odd to Rip was, that, though these folks were evidently amusing themselves, yet they maintained the gravest faces, the most mysterious silence, and were, withal, the most melancholy party of pleasure he had ever witnessed. Nothing interrupted the stillness of the scene but the noise of the balls, which, whenever they rolled, echoed along the mountains like rumbling peals of thunder.

As Rip and his companion approached them, they suddenly desisted from their play, and stared at him with such fixed, statue-like gaze, and such strange, uncouth, lack-lustre countenances, that his heart turned within him, and his knees smote together. His companion now emptied the contents of the keg into large flagons, and made signs to him to wait upon the company. He obeyed with fear and trembling; they quaffed the liquor in profound silence, and then returned to their game.

By degrees Rip's awe and apprehension subsided. He even ventured, when no eye was fixed upon him, to taste the beverage, which he found had much of the flavor of excellent Hollands. He was naturally a thirsty soul, and was soon tempted to repeat the draught. One taste provoked another; and he reiterated his visits to the flagon so often that at length his senses were overpowered, his eyes swam in his head, his head gradually declined, and he fell into a deep sleep.

On waking, he found himself on the green knoll whence he had first seen the old man of the glen. He rubbed his eyes—it was a bright sunny morning. The birds were hopping and twittering among the bushes, and the eagle was wheeling aloft, and breasting the pure morning breeze. "Surely," thought Rip, "I have not slept here all night." He recalled the occurrences before he fell asleep. The strange man with a keg of liquor—the mountain ravine—the wild retreat among the rocks—the woebegone party at ninepins—the flagon—"Oh! that flagon! that wicked flagon!" thought Rip,—"what excuse shall I make to Dame Van Winkle?"

He looked round for his gun, but in place of the clean, well-oiled fowling-piece, he found an old firelock lying by him, the barrel incrusted with rust, the lock falling off, and the stock worm-eaten. He now suspected that the grave roisters of the mountain had put a trick upon him, and having dosed him with liquor, had robbed him of his gun. Wolf, too, had disappeared, but he might have strayed away after a squirrel or partridge. He whistled after him, and shouted his name, but all in vain; the echoes repeated his whistle and shout, but no dog was to be seen.

He determined to revisit the scene of the last evening's gambol, and if he met with any of the party, to demand his dog and gun. As he rose to walk, he found himself stiff in the joints, and wanting in his usual activity. "These mountain beds do not agree with me," thought Rip, "and if this frolic should lay me up with a fit of rheumatism, I shall have a blessed time with Dame Van Winkle." With some difficulty he got down into the glen: he found the gully up which he and his companion had ascended the preceding evening; but to his astonishment a mountain stream was now foaming down it, leaping from rock to rock, and filling the glen with babbling murmurs. He, however, made shift to scramble up its sides, working his toilsome way through thickets of birch, sassafras, and witch-hazel, and sometimes tripped up or entangled by the wild grape-vines that twisted their coils or tendrils from tree to tree, and spread a kind of network in his path.

At length he reached to where the ravine had opened through the cliffs to the amphitheatre; but no traces of such opening remained. The rocks presented a high, impenetrable wall, over which the torrent came tumbling in a sheet of feathery foam, and fell into a broad deep basin, black from the shadows of the surrounding forest. Here, then, poor Rip was brought to a stand. He again called and whistled after his dog; he was only answered by the cawing of a flock of idle crows, sporting high in air about a dry tree that overhung a sunny precipice; and who, secure in their elevation, seemed to look down and scoff at the poor man's perplexities. What was to be done? the morning was passing away, and Rip felt famished for want of his breakfast. He grieved to give up his dog and gun; he dreaded to meet his wife; but it would not do to starve among the mountains. He shook his head, shouldered the rusty firelock, and, with a heart full of trouble and anxiety, turned his steps homeward.

As he approached the village he met a number of people, but none whom he knew, which somewhat surprised him, for he had thought himself acquainted with every one in the country round. Their dress, too, was of a different fashion from that to which he was accustomed. They all stared at him with equal marks of surprise, and whenever they cast their eyes upon him, invariably stroked their chins. The constant recurrence of this gesture induced Rip, involuntarily, to do the same, when, to his astonishment, he found his beard had grown a foot long!

He had now entered the skirts of the village. A troop of strange children ran at his heels, hooting after him, and pointing at his gray beard. The dogs, too, not one of which he recognized for an old acquaintance, barked at him as he passed. The very village was altered; it was larger and more populous. There were rows of houses which he had never seen before, and those which had been his familiar haunts had disappeared. Strange names were over the doors—strange faces at the windows—everything was strange. His mind now misgave him; he began to doubt whether both he and the world around him were not bewitched. Surely this was his native village, which he had left but the day before. There stood the Kaatskill mountains—there ran the silver Hudson at a distance—there was every hill and dale precisely as it had always been. Rip was sorely perplexed. "That flagon last night," thought he, "has addled my poor head sadly!"

It was with some difficulty that he found his way to his own house, which he approached with silent awe, expecting every moment to hear the shrill voice of Dame Van Winkle. He found the house gone to decay—the roof fallen in, the windows shattered, and the doors off the hinges. A half-starved dog that looked like Wolf was skulking about it. Rip called him by name, but the cur snarled, showed his teeth, and passed on. This was an unkind cut indeed. "My very dog," sighed poor Rip, "has forgotten me!"

He entered the house, which, to tell the truth, Dame Van Winkle had always kept in neat order. It was empty, forlorn, and apparently abandoned. The desolateness overcame all his connubial fears—he called loudly for his wife and children—the lonely chambers rang for a moment with his voice, and then all again was silent.

He now hurried forth, and hastened to his old resort, the village inn—but it too was gone. A large rickety wooden building stood in its place, with great gaping windows, some of them broken and mended with old hats and petticoats, and over the door was painted, "The Union Hotel, by Jonathan Doolittle." Instead of the great tree that used to shelter the quiet little Dutch inn of yore, there now was reared a tall naked pole, with something on top that looked like a red nightcap, and from it was fluttering a flag, on which was a singular assemblage of stars and stripes;—all this was strange and incomprehensible. He recognized on the sign, however, the ruby face of King George, under which he had smoked so many a peaceful pipe; but even this was singularly metamorphosed. The red coat was changed for one of blue and buff, a sword was held in the hand instead of a sceptre, the head was decorated with a cocked hat, and underneath was painted in large characters, GENERAL WASHINGTON.

There was, as usual, a crowd of folk about the door, but none that Rip recollected. The very character of the people seemed changed. There was a busy, bustling, disputatious tone about it, instead of the accustomed phlegm and drowsy tranquility. He looked in vain for the sage Nicholas Vedder, with his broad face, double chin, and fair long pipe, uttering clouds of tobacco-smoke instead of idle speeches; or Van Bummel, the schoolmaster, doling forth the contents of an ancient newspaper. In place of these, a lean, bilious-looking fellow, with his pockets full of hand-bills, was haranguing vehemently about rights of citizens—liberty—Bunker's Hill—heroes of seventy-six—and other words, which were a perfect Babylonish jargon to the bewildered Van Winkle.

The appearance of Rip, with his long, grizzled beard, his rusty fowling-piece, his uncouth dress, and an army of women and children at his heels, soon attracted the attention of the tavern-politicians. They crowded around him, eyeing him from head to foot with great curiosity. The orator bustled up to him, and, drawing him partly aside, inquired "On which side he voted?" Rip stared in vacant stupidity. Another short but busy little fellow pulled him by the arm, and, rising on tiptoe, inquired in his ear, "Whether he was Federal or Democrat?" Rip was equally at a loss to comprehend the question; when a knowing, self-important old gentleman, in a sharp cocked hat, made his way through the crowd, putting them to the right and left with his elbows as he passed, and planting himself before Van Winkle, with one arm akimbo, the other resting on his cane, his keen eyes and sharp hat penetrating, as it were, into his very soul, demanded in an austere tone, "What brought him to the election with a gun on his shoulder, and a mob at heels; and whether he meant to breed a riot in the village?"—"Alas! gentlemen," cried Rip, somewhat dismayed, "I am a poor quiet man, a native of the place, and a loyal subject of the King, God bless him!"

Here a general shout burst from the by-standers—"A tory! a tory! a spy! a refugee! hustle him! away with him!" It was with great difficulty that the self-important man in the cocked hat restored order; and, having assumed a tenfold austerity of brow, demanded again of the unknown culprit, what he came there for, and whom he was seeking? The poor man humbly assured him that he meant no harm, but merely came there in search of some of his neighbors, who used to keep about the tavern.

"Well—who are they?—name them."

Rip bethought himself a moment, and inquired, "Where's Nicholas Vedder?"

There was silence for a little while, when an old man replied, in a thin piping voice, "Nicholas Vedder! Why, he is dead and gone these eighteen years! There was a wooden tombstone in the churchyard that used to tell all about him, but that's rotten and gone too."

"Where's Brom Dutcher?"

"Oh, he went off to the army in the beginning of the war; some say he was killed at the storming of Stony Point—others say he was drowned in a squall at the foot of Antony's Nose. I don't know—he never came back again."

"Where's Van Bummel, the schoolmaster?"

"He went off to the wars, too, was a great militia general, and is now in congress."

Rip's heart died away at hearing of these sad changes in his home and friends, and finding himself thus alone in the world. Every answer puzzled him too, by treating of such enormous lapses of time, and of matters which he could not understand: war—congress—Stony Point— he had no courage to ask after any more friends, but cried out in despair, "Does nobody here know Rip Van Winkle?"

"Oh, Rip Van Winkle!" exclaimed two or three, "oh, to be sure! that's Rip Van Winkle yonder, leaning against the tree."

Rip looked, and beheld a precise counterpart of himself, as he went up the mountain; apparently as lazy, and certainly as ragged. The poor fellow was now completely confounded. He doubted his own identity, and whether he was himself or another man. In the midst of his bewilderment, the man in the cocked hat demanded who he was, and what was his name.

"God knows," exclaimed he, at his wits' end; "I'm not myself—I'm somebody else—that's me yonder—no—that's somebody else got into my shoes—I was myself last night, but I fell asleep on the mountain, and they've changed my gun, and everything's changed, and I'm changed, and I can't tell what's my name, or who I am!"

The by-standers began now to look at each other, nod, wink significantly, and tap their fingers against their foreheads. There was a whisper, also, about securing the gun, and keeping the old fellow from doing mischief, at the very suggestion of which the self-important man in the cocked hat retired with some precipitation. At this critical moment a fresh, comely woman pressed through the throng to get a peep at the gray-bearded man. She had a chubby child in her arms, which frightened at his looks, began to cry. "Hush, Rip," cried she, "hush, you little fool; the old man won't hurt you." The name of the child, the air of the mother, the tone of her voice, all awakened a train of recollections in his mind. "What is your name, my good woman?" asked he.

"Judith Gardenier."

"And your father's name?"

"Ah, poor man, Rip Van Winkle was his name, but it's twenty years since he went away from home with his gun, and never has been heard of since,—his dog came home without him; but whether he shot himself, or was carried away by the Indians, nobody can tell. I was then but a little girl."

Rip had but one question more to ask; but he put it with a faltering voice:

"Where's your mother?"

"Oh, she too had died but a short time since; she broke a blood-vessel in a fit of passion at a New England peddler."

There was a drop of comfort, at least, in this intelligence. The honest man could contain himself no longer. He caught his daughter and her child in his arms. "I am your father!" cried he—"Young Rip Van Winkle once—old Rip Van Winkle now!—Does nobody know poor Rip Van Winkle?"

All stood amazed, until an old woman, tottering out from among the crowd, put her hand to her brow, and peering under it in his face for a moment, exclaimed, "Sure enough! it is Rip Van Winkle—it is himself! Welcome home again, old neighbor. Why, where have you been these twenty long years?"

Rip's story was soon told, for the whole twenty years had been to him but as one night. The neighbors stared when they heard it; some were seen to wink at each other, and put their tongues in their cheeks: and the self-important man in the cocked hat, who, when the alarm was over, had returned to the field, screwed down the corners of his mouth, and shook his head—upon which there was a general shaking of the head throughout the assemblage.

It was determined, however, to take the opinion of old Peter Vanderdonk, who was seen slowly advancing up the road. He was a descendant of the historian of that name, who wrote one of the earliest accounts of the province. Peter was the most ancient inhabitant of the village, and well versed in all the wonderful events and traditions of the neighborhood. He recollected Rip at once, and corroborated his story in the most satisfactory manner. He assured the company that it was a fact, handed down from his ancestor the historian, that the

Kaatskill mountains had always been haunted by strange beings. That it was affirmed that the great Hendrick Hudson, the first discoverer of the river and country, kept a kind of vigil there every twenty years, with his crew of the Half-moon; being permitted in this way to revisit the scenes of his enterprise, and keep a guardian eye upon the river and the great city called by his name. That his father had once seen them in their old Dutch dresses playing at ninepins in a hollow of the mountain; and that he himself had heard, one summer afternoon, the sound of their balls, like distant peals of thunder.

To make a long story short, the company broke up and returned to the more important concerns of the election. Rip's daughter took him home to live with her; she had a snug, well-furnished house, and a stout, cheery farmer for a husband, whom Rip recollected for one of the urchins that used to climb upon his back. As to Rip's son and heir, who was the ditto of himself, seen leaning against the tree, he was employed to work on the farm; but evinced an hereditary disposition to attend to anything else but his business.

Rip now resumed his old walks and habits; he soon found many of his former cronies, though all rather the worse for the wear and tear of time; and preferred making friends among the rising generation, with whom he soon grew into great favor.

Having nothing to do at home, and being arrived at that happy age when a man can be idle with impunity, he took his place once more on the bench at the inn-door, and was reverenced as one of the patriarchs of the village, and a chronicler of the old times "before the war." It was some time before he could get into the regular track of gossip, or could be made to comprehend the strange events that had taken place during his torpor. How that there had been a revolutionary war,—that the country had thrown off the yoke of old England,—and that, instead of being a subject of his Majesty George the Third, he was now a free citizen of the United States. Rip, in fact, was no politician; the changes of states and empires made but little impression on him; but there was one species of despotism under which he had long groaned, and that was—petticoat government. Happily that was at an end; he had got his neck out of the yoke of matrimony, and could go in and out whenever he pleased, without dreading the tyranny of Dame Van Winkle. Whenever her name was mentioned, however, he shook his head, shrugged his shoulders, and cast up his eyes; which might pass either for an expression of resignation to his fate, or joy at his deliverance.

He used to tell the story to every stranger that arrived at Mr. Doolittle's hotel. He was observed, at first, to vary on some points every time he told it, which was, doubtless, owing to his having so recently awaked. It at last settled down precisely to the tale I have related, and not a man, woman, or child in the neighborhood but knew it by heart. Some always pretended to doubt the reality of it, and insisted that Rip had been out of his head, and that this was the one point on which he always remained flighty. The old Dutch inhabitants, however, almost universally gave it full credit. Even to this day, they never hear a thunder-storm of a summer afternoon about the Kaatskill, but they say Hendrick Hudson and his crew are at their game of ninepins; and it is a common wish of all hen-pecked husbands in the neighborhood, when life hangs heavy on their hands, that they might have a quieting draught out of Rip Van Winkle's flagon.

NOTE

The foregoing Tale, one would suspect, had been suggested to Mr. Knickerbocker by a little German superstition about the Emperor Frederick *der Rothbart,* and the Kypphäuser mountain: the subjoined note, however, which he had appended to the tale, shows that it is an absolute fact, narrated with his usual fidelity.

"The story of Rip Van Winkle may seem incredible to many, but nevertheless I give it my full belief, for I know the vicinity of our old Dutch settlements to have been very subject to marvellous events and appearances. Indeed, I have heard many stranger stories than this, in the villages along the Hudson; all of which were too well authenticated to admit of a doubt. I have even talked with Rip Van Winkle myself, who, when last I saw him, was a very venerable old man, and so perfectly rational and consistent on every other point, that I think no conscientious person could refuse to take this into the bargain; nay, I have seen a certificate on the subject taken before a country justice and signed with a cross, in the justice's own handwriting. The story, therefore, is beyond the possibility of doubt.

D. K."

POSTSCRIPT

The following are the travelling notes from a memorandum book of Mr. Knickerbocker.

The Kaatsberg or Catskill Mountains, have always been a region full of fable. The Indians considered them the abode of spirits, who influenced the weather, spreading sunshine or clouds over the landscape, and sending good or bad hunting seasons. They were ruled by an old squaw spirit, said to be their mother. She dwelt on the highest peak of the Catskills, and had charge of the doors of the day and night to open and shut them at the proper hour. She hung up the new moons in the skies, and cut up the old ones into stars. In times of drought, if properly propitiated, she would spin light summer clouds out of cobwebs and morning dew, and send them off from the crest of the mountain, flake after flake, like flakes of carded cotton, to float in the air; until dissolved by the heat of the sun, they would fall in gentle showers, causing the grass to spring, the fruits to ripen, and the corn to grow an inch an hour. If displeased, however, she would brew up clouds black as ink, sitting in the midst of them like a bottle-bellied spider in the midst of its web; and when these clouds broke, woe betide the valleys!

In old times, say the Indian traditions, there was a kind of Manitou or Spirit, who kept about the wildest recesses of the Catskill Mountains, and took a mischievous pleasure in wreaking all kinds of evils and vexations upon the red men. Sometimes he would assume the form of a bear, a panther, or a deer, lead the bewildered hunter a weary chase through tangled forests and among ragged rocks; and then spring off with a loud ho! ho! leaving him aghast on the brink of a bristling precipice or raging torrent.

The favorite abode of this Manitou is still shown. It is a great rock or cliff on the loneliest part of the mountains, and, from the flowering vines which clamber about it, and the wild flowers which abound in its neighborhood, is known by the name of the Garden Rock. Near the foot of it is a small lake, the haunt of the solitary bittern, with water-snakes basking in the sun on the leaves of the pond-lilies which lie on the surface. This place was held in great awe by the Indians, insomuch that the boldest hunter would not pursue his game within its precincts. Once upon a time, however, a hunter who had lost his way, penetrated to the Garden Rock, where he beheld a number of gourds placed in the crotches of trees. One of these he seized and made off with it, but in the hurry of his retreat he let it fall among the rocks, when a great stream gushed forth, which washed him away and swept him down precipices, where he was dashed to pieces, and the stream made its way to the Hudson, and continues to flow to the present day; being the identical stream known by the name of Kaaters-kill.

4. GHOSTS: MISSION ACCOMPLISHED

Having already confessed my skeptical bent, I may as well here say that I take an extreme view about ghosts, and think all that have ever been or are ever seen are but vain imaginings. Yet I cannot but admire the judicious language of John Warner Barber, who pays an only slightly ambiguous tribute to the sponsors of ghosts in introducing the strange story of Mr. Joseph Beacon.

I have been murdered[1]

The following, which is given in Mather's Magnalia, appears to be well authenticated. Whatever may be our belief respecting appearances or premonitions of this kind, volumes might be filled with similar relations, equally unaccountable, given by persons whose testimony would be received as truth on every other subject.

"It was on the second of May, in the year 1687, that a most ingenious, accomplish'd and well-dispos'd young gentleman, Mr. Joseph Beacon by name, about 5 a-clock in the morning, as he lay, whether sleeping or waking, he could not say, (but judg'd the latter of them) had a view of his brother then at London, although he was now himself at our Boston, distanc'd from him a thousand leagues. This, his brother appear'd to him in the morning, (I say) about 5 a-clock, at Boston, having on him a Bengale gown which he usually wore, with a napkin ty'd about his head: his countenance was very pale, ghastly, deadly, and he had a bloody wound on one side of his forehead.— Brother! says the affrighted Joseph. Brother! answer'd the apparition. Said Joseph, what's the matter, brother! How came you here! The apparition reply'd, brother, I have been most barbarously and inhumanly murder'd by a debauch'd fellow, to whom I never did any harm in my life. Whereupon he gave a particular description of the murderer; adding, brother, this fellow changing his name, is attempting to come over unto New-England, in Foy or Wild: I would pray you on the first arrival of either of these, to get an order from the governour to seize the person whom I have now describ'd; and then

[1] From John W. Barber: *New England, New York, New Jersey, and Pennsylvania* (Portland, 1848), pp. 500–1.

do you indict him for the murder of me, your brother. I'll stand by you and prove the indictment. And so he vanish'd. Mr. Beacon was extreamely astonish'd at what he had seen and heard; and the people of the family not only observ'd an extraordinary alteration upon him for the week following, but have also given me under their hands a full testimony that he then gave them a full account of this apparition. All this while, Mr. Beacon had no advice of anything amiss attending his brother then in England; but about the latter end of the June following, he understood by the common ways of communication, that the April before, his brother going in haste by night to call a coach for a lady, met a fellow then in drink with his doxy in his hand. Some way or other the fellow thought himself affronted in the hasty passage of this Beacon, and immediately ran in to the fireside of a neighbouring tavern, from whence he fetch'd out a fire-fork, wherewith he grievously wounded Beacon on the skull, even in that very part where the apparition shew'd his wound. Of this wound he languished until he dy'd, on the 2nd of May, about 5 of the clock in the morning, at London. The murderer, it seems, was endeavouring an escape, as the apparition affirm'd; but the friends of the deceased Beacon seiz'd him; and prosecuting him at law, he found the help of such friends, as brought him off without the loss of his life: since which, there has no more been heard of the business."

Ask me no questions[1]

William Briggs was congratulating himself as he rode his roan mare home on a moonlight October night. "There's not a better mare to be had for the money in Queen Anne's County," he meditated, "nor in the whole of Maryland for that matter."

Then he fell to thinking about his good friend, Thomas Harris, who had died two weeks before. He had bought the mare that day from James Harris, Thomas' brother, who was administering his estate. James was a good friend of his, too, and he certainly had given him a bargain in that mare.

Briggs and Thomas Harris had been soldiers together in the Revolutionary War, and had been intimate friends for many years. Thomas had died after a sudden and brief illness and Briggs had been alone with him when the end came. Thomas had made his mistakes, but he was a good fellow—always he could be depended upon to keep his word, he reflected.

[1] From Ida Clyde Clarke: *Men Who Wouldn't Stay Dead* (New York: Bernard Ackerman; 1945), pp. 107–13.

The roan mare was going along in the moonlight at a good steady pace, and, as he was getting sleepy, Briggs was glad that home was less than a mile farther on. They were alongside the graveyard, and that was scarcely a mile from his house.

He thought the tombstones looked awfully white and tall, but maybe it was because the moonlight was so bright. He thought of Thomas' grave, and he hoped James would put up a tombstone for him. There'd be money enough. Thomas was well fixed, what with the land he owned and the livestock and everything. Yes, James ought to put up a tombstone for Thomas.

Suddenly the horse jumped—half-way across the road, it seemed to Briggs—and neighed loudly. He jerked the bridle, but the mare pranced around in a semicircle and stopped against the graveyard fence.

To his amazement Briggs saw Thomas Harris standing there on the other side of the fence, looking at him. He wore the sky-blue coat he had last worn when alive, and he looked as he always did when he was in the flesh, except for the sad, weary look in his bleary eyes. For a full minute he stood there, looking at rider and horse, and then he appeared to melt into the moonlight. The horse shivered and Briggs stared. He was cold and speechless with terror. He had waited for Harris to speak, but the tall, sad man had only stood there, looking at him.

He had difficulty in getting the mare to move, and then she persisted in going around in circles for some minutes. Finally he got her headed toward home, and he urged her to her best pace. That mile seemed ten, but at last he drove up to his barn, and unsaddling the mare as quickly as he could, he let her go where she would. He was glad to get out of that queer moonlight and into the comfortable bed beside his sleeping wife.

He was perfectly sure he'd seen the ghost of Thomas Harris, but he decided not to say anything about it. It was just one of those things that would make a lot of talk, and nobody could do anything about it. So he kept quiet.

Next morning as he was eating his breakfast in the big, warm kitchen, his wife started right in talking about Thomas Harris.

"Did you hear anything at the court-house yesterday about Thomas' will?" she asked.

"No, there's nothing to hear," he replied. "James is administrator. He's in charge of everything."

"Well, I'm thinkin' about Thomas' four illegitimate children—what they are goin' to get. Thomas always provided for them well—I'll say that for Thomas—and I hope he fixed it in his will so they'll get something. He's got no wife or regular children to leave it to, and

James and Mary have no children, and they're well fixed—they don't need Thomas' money. The children should have it."

A few days later Briggs went to town again, and when he returned he volunteered to his wife some first-hand information about Thomas Harris' will.

"Well, there's trouble brewing about Thomas' illegitimate children," he told her.

Mrs. Briggs wiped her hands on her apron and dropped into a rocking-chair. She was all curiosity.

"As near as I can get it," her husband said, "Thomas fixed it in his will that James was to sell that piece of land on the Chester River now and divide the purchase price among the four children, and when they come of age they'll get the rest of his estate."

"I knew it—I knew it," his wife interrupted, "I just knew for sure Thomas would provide for the children."

"But wait. Let me tell you. James sold the land, but when the lawyers drew up the papers they found that Thomas was not seized in fee but in tail of the land."

"And what does that mean, for heaven's sake?"

"Well, that's the way the law reads. What it means is that Thomas had no legal right to devise the land and the children can't inherit any of his property because they are illegitimate. They can't inherit anything. James is the natural heir, he gets it all."

The news of this legal entanglement was soon talked about all over Queen Anne's County.

The day after he reported the situation to his wife, Briggs was ploughing in his corn field about three miles from the graveyard, when —all of a sudden—the ghost of Thomas again appeared to him—this time in broad daylight.

He was so frightened that his manner attracted the attention of John Bailey, who was ploughing near by, and he ran to see what ailed Briggs.

"What's the matter?" Bailey asked.

As it was plain that Bailey had not seen the ghost, Briggs decided not to say anything about it, and he managed to finish his day's work and get home. But the memory of the shadowy figure in the sky-blue coat, and the sad, appealing face of his friend haunted him day and night.

A few nights later, when he was in bed with his wife, he distinctly heard Thomas Harris groan, just as he had groaned the moment before his death. Mrs. Briggs heard the groans, too, and she got up and searched the house carefully in an effort to solve the mystery. Briggs did not get up. He knew that the ghost of Thomas was abroad again, and he thought it best to keep still. But his wife wouldn't be quiet.

"You've dreampt something," he told her. Finally she went to sleep.

Next night as he was lying awake—for he had been unable to sleep now for some time—he saw a strange shadow appear on the wall. As he watched it, the form of Thomas emerged. Suddenly he felt a great weight upon him which overpowered him, and it was hours before he could shake off the terrible feeling of weight and oppression.

At last he was drifting into unconsciousness, being thoroughly exhausted, when he was sure that something struck him a severe blow blow just over the eyes. His wife, and two young men who were sleeping in the next room that night, were awakened by the sound of the blows, and they got up very much frightened.

It was then that he told of his experiences with the ghost. Next morning his eyes were black and his head was sore and swollen.

From that night on the ghost appeared to him frequently and on one occasion it walked with him a distance of five hundred yards and talked to him. He declared that the voice was low and hollow, and not like the voice of Thomas, and that at times he had difficulty in understanding the words.

"Ask me no questions," the ghost admonished him.

But Briggs persisted. "Why don't you go to your brother James," he asked, "and give him your message?"

Again the hollow voice said, "Ask me no questions."

The ghost instructed him to ask James if he remembered a conversation he had with him on the east side of the haystacks on the day before he was stricken with his fatal illness. In that conversation, Thomas had told his brother—according to the ghostly voice—that he wanted the land sold and the purchase money divided among the four children. Then, when they came of age, he was to divide the remainder of the estate among them.

As that was the third time Briggs had seen the ghost that day, he decided to tell James. He went to him immediately and told him the whole strange story.

James said he remembered the conversation with his brother on the east side of the haystacks, and that he would carry out his brother's wishes. He was perfectly sure that Briggs had seen the ghost of his brother, as no one else alive, except himself, knew of the conversation.

"I've done wrong by Thomas," he admitted, "but I'll make everything right. I sold the land and took the money. The lawyers told me that the children have no legal right to any of Thomas' estate because they're illegitimate—that I get everything by law, because I am the natural heir. But I did promise Thomas—when he talked that day by the haystacks—that I would give everything to his children. William, next time you see the ghost, you tell him I do remember that conversation and I will give the money to his children as I promised I would."

That evening Briggs was again visited by the ghost, but when he repeated what James had said, the spectre vanished, apparently satisfied.

It so happened that James died before he could fulfill his promise to the ghost and carry out his brother's wishes. His widow, Mary, was left in charge of the estate. And Mary was of a different mind.

In due time, the four illegitimate children of Thomas Harris, on the strength of the ghost's message as delivered to William Briggs and relayed to James Harris, brought suit against the widow, Mary Harris, for the purchase price of the tract of land in question.

Because of the conspicuous part played by the ghost, the case was one of the most sensational ones in the legal annals of Queen Anne's County. There was a brilliant array of counsels on both sides. The Honorable James Tilghman was the presiding judge. His Excellency Robert Wright—later Governor of Maryland—and the Honorable Joseph N. Nicholson were counsel for the plaintiffs, and John Scott and Richard T. Earle, eminent lawyers of the day, represented the defendant.

After the grounds of the controversy had been stated with great solemnity by counsel on both sides, the witness, William Briggs, was produced and sworn in to testify on behalf of the plaintiffs. Judge, jury, counsel and spectators listened amid intense excitement to this remarkable testimony.

The case of the plaintiffs rested entirely on the testimony of the ghost.

The court-room was crowded and the excitement ran high as the trial opened. When Briggs was called to the witness stand a dead silence fell over the room. He was known to be a man of character, of brave, undaunted spirit. He had been a good soldier in the Revolutionary War, and he was perfectly disinterested and unconnected with the parties concerned. What William Briggs said the people of Queen Anne's County would believe.

The lawyers on both sides questioned him closely, for all were eager to get every detail concerning the appearance of the ghost. He told everything up to a certain point. He said that when he walked and talked with the ghost of Thomas he told him some things that were confidential. "I promised never to speak of them," he said, "and I intend to keep that promise."

In vain the lawyers questioned and urged him. Finally he claimed the protection of the Court, saying he had told everything the ghost had said that had any bearing on the case, and that nothing short of the loss of his life would induce him to divulge the ghost's secrets.

John Bailey was called to the stand, and testified as to the truth of certain of Briggs' testimony. He had not seen the ghost, but he saw Briggs standing as if in deep conversation with some person—though no person was there.

There was really nothing for the Court to decide. The law was plain. Illegitimate children had no claims on the estates of their parents. There was no prolonged legal argument. The purpose of the trial was mainly to get the facts, under sworn testimony, as to the appearance of the ghost of Thomas Harris to William Briggs. This object was accomplished.

Everybody knew perfectly well, law or no law, that Mary Harris would never withhold from Thomas Harris' children the proceeds of his estate, after William Briggs' testimony. There was not a lawyer in Queen Anne's County who would have dared advise her to do so. Had there been any doubt on that score the testimony of Briggs dispelled that doubt. No one was willing to take any chances on incurring the displeasure of the ghost.

So, in due time, Thomas' children received the money through the Orphans' Court of Queen Anne's County, the money having been paid in from James Harris' estate.

NOTE. Mrs. Clarke explains that she obtained her facts from a rare pamphlet, printed in Baltimore in 1807, with the title: *Authentic account of the appearance of a ghost in Queen Anne's County, Maryland; proved in said County Court,* etc.

Fiddler's dram[1]

Talk about your fiddlers—why, in yonder's times we *had* fiddlers around here! None of your modern-age make-shifters that whip all the tunes till a body can't tell "Rabbit in the Pea Patch" from "Bull Amongst the Yearlings." Nor in them days they didn't make the fiddle sound like a jug full of hungry mosquitoes, neither! No siree! They just made the sweetest music this direction from heaven.

And in all yonder time I verily know there never was a finer hand to fiddle than Ples Haslock. He fiddled for all the square dances and play-parties anywheres around. No gathering of whatever kind amounted to much unless Ples was there, with his long solemn face and them light blue far-shot eyes, patting his foot and ripping away on his fiddle and calling the figgers.

> "Gents, hands in your pockets, back to the wall,
> Take a chaw tobaccer and balance all!

---

[1] By James R. Aswell, from the Tennessee Writers Project: *God Bless the Devil* (Chapel Hill: University of North Carolina Press; 1940), pp. 106–16.

> Ladies, do-se-do with the gents you know,
> Swing your corner and-a here we go!"

He wasn't no old billygoat fiddler with crazy ways and a cracked voice. He was right young and by nature handsome. All the girls sighed, but Ples just didn't deal in women. He said, "Give me my fiddle and a place to pat my foot and they's nothing else in creation I crave." His daddy had got an old fiddlebox in a bunch of junk he'd traded from an Irish Gypsy for a nag is how Ples got started fiddling. He made his own strings out of catamount guts and the bow from the tail hairs of mare colts. Then he teached his self to fiddle till he laid it plumb over any of the old heads.

Since his daddy died, Ples lived at home by his self over near Post Oak, but he was a man that just didn't stay home much. He liked to ramble and visit around. Wheresoever he went, he was twice as welcome as anybody. He had word of all the latest things and happenings and he could keep a family spell-charmed to the midwarp of the night telling tales he made out of his head. He'd make the young-uns elder-shoot flutes and cornstalk fiddles, and, when asked to, he'd get out his own old fiddle and make it talk—I *mean* talk! You'd swear to hear it that there was a live mockingbird singing in that fiddlebox or a buzzing cow-fly or maybe a little peeping chicken. He could take and mock cats fighting or old gossip women gabbing till folks fell in the floor laughing. And he could fiddle the old tunes to where the meanest man in the county would break under and cry all down his face.

Nothing was too good for Ples Haslock when he visited around. He was welcomed by high and low as long as he wanted to stay and they begged him to stop longer when he fancied to go.

They had fiddling contests then, but it got so there wasn't a heap of contest to them. Everybody come to know that Ples Haslock was going to win hands down. He always walked off with the gallon jimmyjohn of fine oak-chartered drinking whiskey they give for the prize. Why, it come to the point where they had to give another jug for second prize or they'd never had nobody in the contest but Ples. The other fiddlers only tried to outbeat each other. None of them had any show at all against Ples and they purely all knowed it.

So what happened one time but the wall of the jail at Dukedom fell out and the county court didn't have no money in the poke to fix it. When the squires figgered to get up a fiddling contest to raise the money, everybody says, "We'll have to send over to Post Oak and tell Ples Haslock and notify him."

Coot Kersey was the best fiddler near and around Dukedom and Coot says, "He may can't come this time. I hear he's a sick man. Down with heart dropsy is what I hear."

398

"Don't you *hope* so, Coot?" they says, and laughed him to a fair dead-stand.

The County Court Clerk says, "I've got to drive my rig over to Post Oak on business tomorrow. I'll tell Ples and notify him."

So the County Court Clerk dropped his hitching block in front of Ples Haslock's the next day and called, "Heyo! You to home, Ples?"

Nobody answered him, so he walked through the weeds to the house, a one-room shack that looked like a good strong puff of air would blow it over. The clapboards was dropping off and the shingles curled up every which way like the feathers of an old Dominecker hen.

When the County Court Clerk climbed the shaky steps to the porch, Ples woke up inside and said, "Who's there?"

"Just me," says the County Court Clerk and give out his name.

"Well, come right in!" says Ples. "Ain't seen you since I don't rightly know when. How're you folks living at Dukedom?"

"Pretty fair, Ples. Can't complain."

The room was one big clutteration of old clothes, pots and pans, and junk, and Ples was setting up in a mess of dirty comforts on his bed at the far end.

Everything else might be knocking around just anywheres it lit, but Ples didn't care a whet so long as his fiddle was safe. He never let go of that fiddle—had it now beside him in bed, running his fingers over it like you'd pet a child. It give the County Court Clerk a shock to see how like death Ples looked, green-faced and shrunk, with big brown liver splotches on his face and hands. He had gone down mightily, but his eyes was just as blue-bright as ever. His nose looked natural. It always had been big and bony.

County Court Clerk said, "How're you feeling, Ples?"

"Well," says he, "I could say I was down in the back. I could say I don't know what I'd do if it wasn't for them kind people that neighbor me round. I could say it and I *do* say it. Three times a day some good neighbor woman brings me some nice something to eat and sets a spell talking. The menfolks come over at night and see that I ain't fell out of bed to my harm. Between times, I just lay around and play my fiddle."

"I heard you was ailing," says the County Court Clerk.

"It's for a fact," says Ples. "Heart dropsy runs in the Haslock line. Here of late I've been having night flotations too. But seems like I'm coming around some. Aim to be up and on my feet soon."

The County Court Clerk was of two minds whether to tell him about the contest but now he figgered it wouldn't do no harm. So he come out about the jail wall and the contest and notified Ples that it would be held at the Dukedom school two weeks come a Monday.

Minute he heard that, Ples peartened up mightily. "I'll be there!" he says. "When the roll is called at Dukedom, Ples Haslock will be there certain sure!"

So the County Court Clerk visited a while and then had to be on his way. "We'll be looking for you, Ples," he says.

"Get your fiddler's dram ready," says Ples, "for I virtuously aim to win it."

Well, the night of the contest most everybody in the county come to Dukedom in their Sunday best and tramped into the schoolhouse and settled in their seats. Everybody was in a looking-forward mood. You know how them gatherings are. A heap of shouting and high joking back and forth. Old gossip-trots running from one group to another with the latest. Young bloods standing around talking loud and the girls giggling and sneaking looks at them. Little mustards running up and down the aisles, snatching things from each other, having rooster-fights at the back of the hall, and raising a general rumpus. Little girls setting with their folks and sticking out their tongues at the boys when nobody was looking. Babies crying, people coughing, and the lye soap smell pretty strong.

The crowd was getting restless. Little boys, and some not so little, begun whistling and banging desks for things to get started.

Old Judge Huley Dunlap was the chairman of the committee and he come out on the stage and give out that the contest was fixing to start. Then he put on his glasses and read off the names of the fiddlers, seven in all.

When he got through, everybody commenced yelling, "How about Ples Haslock?"

"Well," says Judge Dunlap, "we hoped he could make it, but till yet he ain't showed up. He's been laid up in bed lately and I reckon he couldn't stand the trip over here from Post Oak. Anybody that wants to can get their admission back at the door."

Some folks grumbled but everybody stayed set and things quieted down.

So the seven fiddlers come out on the stage and taken seats and the contest was ready to break out.

Everybody knowed that five of the seven fiddlers might as well not have got in the contest. They was plain everyday set-in-a-rocker-and-scratch-aways. The contest was between Coot Kersey and Old Rob Reddin, number six and seven. With Ples Haslock down and out, Coot and Old Rob was the best fiddlers you could find anywhere around and about in the county. Everybody figgered Old Rob was the likely one, not because his fiddling was fancier than Coot's but because of the crazy way he carried on.

The five sorry fiddlers sawed away and got through without nobody paying attention in special. Coot and Old Rob would do the real fiddling and they come last.

There was a big laugh when Coot's turn come. Everybody always felt like laughing when they saw Coot. The way his head bobbed up and down on his long red wrinkled neck with every step he took, the way his chin ran back and his nose beaked out, and the way a long tag of his hair kept wattling down to the bridge of his nose put everybody in mind of an old turkey gobbler. Coot gobbled when he talked, too.

But one thing sure—Coot could make a fiddle sing. He was the dead serious kind of fiddler. Had to have his fiddle set just right across his knees before he'd commence, but let him get started and he sure fiddled. His piece was "Leather Britches." He went at it like a boy killing snakes, whipping and scraping away and stamping his foot till he'd worked up a pouring sweat. When he'd finished, he was as limp as an old rag. He drawed down a powerful claphand from the listeners.

The gathering set up smart when it come Old Rob Reddin's turn and he hobbled to the front of the stage. Folks started grinning before he'd done a thing. Old Rob was as funny to look at as Coot Kersey, but not because he put you in mind of no bird or animal. He was a lard-fat little man and when he walked his stomach wabbled in front of him. He'd never been heard to open his mouth without some real funny humor-saying rolling out. If ever by accident he was to have a mournful spell and say anything serious, people would've laughed at him just the same. Seeing Old Rob meant laughing like falling in the creek meant getting wet.

So old Rob he plumped his self down in the fiddler's chair. He laid his fiddle on his lap and winked at his wife that was setting down front. All on a sudden he yelled, "Hold to your seats, folks! I'm driving wild!"

He give the gathering time to stop howling. Then he lit in fiddling "Hell Turned Loose in Georgia." The way he carried on, a body'd thought he was having some sort of fit if they hadn't knowed better. When he drawed a high note he'd open his mouth wide, run his eyebrows to his hair-line, and shoot his neck up. On low ones he'd bend almost to the floor. Every once in so often he'd throw his bow into the air. While it was coming down he'd bawl out things like *"Eating* hogeye!" and "I *love* chitlins!" and "Ladies, where *was* your man last Saturday night?"

Everybody was still shouting and stamping and whistling when Old Rob come down off the platform. No need to hold the jimmyjohn over the different fiddlers' heads to see who'd get the most applauding. A deaf and dumb blind man could easy see Old Rob had that contest.

Like everybody, the judges was so taken up with watching Old Rob cut capers because he'd won that they didn't see Ples Haslock till he'd already started playing. The first anybody knowed he was anywheres about was when a fiddle begun on the stage.

The crowd looked to see who it was, and there sat Ples in the chair with his fiddle across his knees, his bow weaving over the strings, and his foot patting steady. Yes, there he set with his eyes shut and his head nodding in time with his foot.

It was a dumbfounder, all right. For just a minute the gathering thought maybe they was seeing things. But there he was, Ples Haslock, all drawed and pale from sickness, fiddling in the contest just a snatch before it was too late.

The minute folks seen it *was* Ples, the hall got as still as time in a grave.

It was about nine o'clock when Ples started in and he fiddles over an hour. It was straight honest fiddling—none of your stunts on the strings like Coot Kersey, none of that loud fool-blabber that was Old Rob Reddin's stock in trade.

Folks there had heard fiddlers that could make them laugh and fiddlers that could make them cry, but Ples this night didn't do neither one. When you listened to him you nearly forgot who you was. You just set limp in your seat while your mind tried to remember something cloudy and away far off, something you'd never really seen or done.

Ples played "Poor Wayfaring Stranger" and "The Two Sisters" and "The Elfin Knight" and a dozen or more.

When Ples Haslock did stop, it verily did look like the crowd was going to tear the whole place down and scatter the pieces. They heaved to their feet and whooped, whistled, screamed, and bellered and hammered on the desks. Kept it up while Judge Huey Dunlap handed Ples the jimmyjohn of fine red drinking whiskey and said, "I hereby present and award to Ples Haslock this prize which may he enjoy it as much as the good people of Dukedom done his fiddling." Leastways they seen Judge Dunlap's mouth flapping and knowed he was saying something like that.

Well, Ples stood up, holding his fiddle and his bow under his left arm and heisting the jimmyjohn with a crooked finger of his right hand. He flipped that jimmyjohn over his shoulder, jerked the corncob out of the mouth of it with his teeth, and taken a long pull, his fiddler's dram.

Right then come a crash. For the chair, the jimmyjohn and Ples and his fiddle all landed in a heap on the floor.

Man, woman and child run up onto the stage. But Judge Huey

Dunlap made them stand back. "Get a doctor!" he says. "This man is done for, or near it. I can't feel no heart-beat at all."

So they hushed down and stood looking at Ples where he laid there on the stage.

"Think of it!" they says. "Poor Ples coming thirty miles to Dukedom with the last life in him just to win this contest!"

"He sure was a man that liked to fiddle!"

"Would you look at his clothes," says somebody. "All covered with clay, they are. From the looks of it, he must walked all the way and through the swamp at that."

They kept saying, "It's the beat of all ever happened in Dukedom!"

Before long the doctor comes hustling in and knelt down and examined over Ples. He said, "How'd he get in here?"

So they told him. Judge Dunlap says, "He just keeled over dead before our eyes, poor man."

"Keeled over, my granny!" says the doctor. "This here man has been dead for forty-eight hours at the very least. And from the clay he's got on his clothes, I'd say buried, too."

The first story in this group is definitely an oral migrant,[1] the second a laboratory piece, so well written, however, that it does sound "folksy."

I have heard of the first of these ghosts on Cape Cod, and have been solemnly assured of its appearance on Benefit Street, in Providence, Rhode Island. But in which house on that street? That, alas, the informant could not say.

He floated in[2]

Two ladies from the faculty of a famous New England college for women decided to spend one of their vacations in an automobile tour to California and back. They traveled westward by way of the Petrified Forest and the Grand Canyon, and headed for home by the Salt Lake City route. They were two normal, unimaginative women, enjoying to the full a tour of their native country.

Late one evening, they were driving through the flat and monotonous fields of Kansas, intent upon reaching a hostel some thirty miles distant, when their car broke down. They were the kind of drivers who know nothing whatever about motors. They had no choice but to wait for some good Samaritan to come driving along and help them—and it soon became obvious that no other car was likely to come that way until the next morning.

It was then that one of the ladies noticed a two-story, unpainted farmhouse, set back some distance from the road. They approached it gingerly, wary of watch-dogs, and knocked timidly on the front door. Nobody answered. The impression grew on them that the house was uninhabited. When they discovered that the door was unlocked, they entered, calling loudly, and flashing their pocket searchlight in every corner. They found the living room and kitchen in good order, but an undisturbed layer of dust indicated that no human being had been in them for days.

The ladies blessed their luck, and decided to spend the night in the

---

[1] For other migrants, see pp. 627–8, below.

[2] Reprinted from Bennett Cerf: *Try and Stop Me* by permission of Simon and Schuster, Inc. Copyright, 1944, by Bennett Cerf. Pp. 271–3.

living room. The couch was fairly comfortable, and they bundled themselves up in robes which they fetched from the stalled automobile. There were dry logs in the fireplace; the ladies soon had a roaring fire going, and, in the light of the flickering embers, went peacefully to sleep.

Some hours later, one of the ladies awoke with the distinct feeling that somebody had entered the house. Her friend jumped up at precisely the same moment. A chill seemed to run through the room, followed by the unmistakable scent of the salt sea, although the nearest ocean front was over a thousand miles away. Then a young man walked into the room! Rather he *floated* in, because they heard no footsteps. He was dressed in boots and oilskins; sea-spray glistened on his rough stubble of reddish beard. He moved to the dying fire, shivering violently, and knelt down before it.

One of the women screamed. The figure turned slowly, gave a sort of mournful sigh, and slowly dissolved into nothingness. The terrified women clutched each other desperately, and lay there until the morning sun poured through the dusty window panes. "I saw it; I know I did!" said one of them. "Of course you did; I saw it too," the other reassured her, and then pointed dramatically to the fireplace. Before it was a small puddle of brackish water, and a piece of slimy green weed.

The ladies made for the open air, but the bolder of the two snatched up the piece of weed before they bolted, and held it gingerly at arm's length. When it dried, she placed it carefully in her bag.

Eventually a car rattled along the highway, and the driver cheerfully consented to tow the ladies to the nearest garage. While the mechanic tinkered with the engine, the ladies asked him about the deserted house some miles back on the road. "That must have been the Newton place," he said with no special show of interest. "Been empty nigh on to two years now. When Old Man Newton died, he left it lock, stock and barrel to his son Tom, who said he didn't like farming, and lit out one day for the East. Spoke of taking to the sea, like his great-grandfather did. Ain't none of us seen hide nor hair of him since that day!"

When the ladies returned to their college, they took the green weed, which still seemed clammy and damp, to the head of the botany department. He readily confirmed their suspicions. "It's seaweed, all right," he told them. "Furthermore, it's a kind that's only found on dead bodies!" The ship news reporter of the *Evening Sun* reported that a Thomas Newton had sailed as first-class seaman on a freighter called the *Robert B. Anthony* on April 14, 1937. It had gone down with all hands aboard in a storm off the Greenland coast six weeks thereafter.

405

Who fell from aloft?[1]

Quick's ever I see her I knowed she was Yankee-built fast enough, though there 'twas painted on her stern plain's daylight, 'Falls of Ettrick,' Sunderland; but come to once git aboard, and 'twa'n't only a short time 'fore I'd bated dollars to doughnuts she was the ole Gertrude Spurshoe. They'd turned to and changed her over into a full ship rig, and painted her all up diff'rent, and besides that she was nigh buried out o' sight un'neath a tormented great deckload of deals; but still there was quite a few things I twigged pooty quick, so's there wa'n't no doubt in my mind but what she was the ole Gerty for sure.

"There wa'n't ary one of the crew knowed the fust blame' thing about her, mind ye, but soon's ever the chance showed up, I took and sounded the mate on the subjic', and he 'lowed right off 'twas jest how I thought.

"Wal, o' course I was nach'ally kind of pleased like to git aboard the ole packet ag'in so fashion, being's how I see her built and launched, and had made r'ally my fust deep-water v'yage in her, let alone bein' so ter'ble well acquainted along o' ole Cap'n Spurshoe ever sence I knowed enough to go. And besides all that, 's I say, she was a grand good, dry, comfort'ble ole creetur to go into, take it most any kind of chance, but ye see it did appear so sort of sing'lar like the way I'd fell in along on her ag'in, that 'twas nach'al I should make some consid'ble amount of talk about it forrard amongst the rest-part o' the crew.

"They was a tol'ble clever class o' fellers that trip, take 'em by and large, but there was one hard-looking ticket amongst 'em that come aboard crazy drunk, and kep' so long after everybody else had sobered off. When he did finally git hisself straightened out, he turned to in good shape, and 'peared to be a proper sailor man, but still there was allus suppn' about the cut o' the feller's jib I couldn't go nohow. Seem's though he wa'n't the leastways anxious to chum in 'long of nobody, and it's dinged sure nobody didn't hanker for no truck 'long of him. To look at the cuss, nine out o' ten would sot him down for a reg'lar-built Dago, without no efs nor ands about it, but the steward he 'lowed the feller had shipped under the name o' McLaren, and had give out he was a Novy Scoshy Scotchman. Anyways, McLaren is how he was called aboard the vessel, though most any pore fool would known that wa'n't his right name, not by a jugful.

"Wal, as I was sayin', I'd been in the way o' making more or less

[1] From George S. Wasson: *Captain Simeon's Store* (Boston: Houghton, Mifflin Co.; 1903), pp. 106–28. Used by permission of the publishers, Houghton Mifflin Company.

talk about this 'ere ship Falls of Ettrick being the ole Yankee barque Gerty Spurshoe, but this yaller-mugged Portogee Novy Scoshy-man he seldom ever sot round 'long o' the rest-part on us, without 'twas jest to bolt his grub same's a dog, and git out ag'in, so seem's though he'd never heern none of this talk till one time it come round that somebody happened to blart it right out afore him about my being a towny of ole Cap'n Spurshoe's, and goin' into the vessel when she was a Yankee barque, in room o' being an English timber drogher.

"Wal, sir, that blame' Dago he sot there shovelling down his vittles jest scand'lous, same's usual, but quick's ever he heern this talk he sort of choked up like, and bedide now, ef he didn't jest turn consid'ble white round the gills! The cuss tried his dingdest to pass it off, though, but I took good notice he was all of a tremble the whole length on him, and after this 'ere, seem's though he acted even queer'n whatever he had afore. He'd allus try to sneak off all soul alone by hisself ef 'twas anyways so's he could work it, and come to that, his actions the whole time was for all the world same's though he cal'lated folks was allus a-watchin' and huntin' of him like.

"But I know I ketched him time and ag'in giving me his ugly black looks, jest eggsac'ly same's though he was fairly itchin' for a chance to knife me in the back, ye know, and 'twa'n't jest only me that twigged it neither, for ole steward he come one time and gimme warning to allus keep a good sharp eye to wind'ard for that feller. Ole steward he 'lowed how he'd been shipmates 'long o' them Dagoes so's to know 'em root and branch—a bloody sight better'n what he wanted to, s' he; and he 'lowed this one had a bad gredge ag'in me for suppn' or other, though what under the living canopy he was down on me for in pertikler I couldn't noways make out to fathom. I never so much as even see him that I knowed on afore coming aboard the ship, and sence then, I'd took oath him and me hadn't had no kind of truck together no way or t'other.

"Come to keep turning of it over, though, I couldn't seem to rec'lect seeing of him gimme none o' them cut-throat looks of his'n till after the time he overheern the talk about my being acquainted 'long o' the vessel the way I was. Wal, I bothered my head some consid'ble little for a spell tryin' to put this and that together, but I couldn't never appear to make no great sight o' headway.

" 'Twas plain enough that finding out that night about the ship's being the ole Gertrude was the biggest kind o' s'prise-party to him, and 'twas jest so plain he didn't love me none the better for claimin' to know so much about her. Them two things I could see all clear through enough, but whenever I'd git that fur, I'd be sure to fetch up all standing, and so bimeby the thing pooty much dropped out o' mind altogether.

"Mister Dago he kep' on skulkin' round same's ever, but never once opened his face to me, nor to nobody else, for that matter, and we'd made out to wiggle the ole craft somewheres nigh half acrost the big pond, when along in the aft'noon one day she up and shet in thick o' fog on us; and ef ever she *was* thick o' fog, that 'ere was the time, too; —one of them proper ole black, dreepin' fogs, ye know, jest as thick's so much ma'sh mud, so's you couldn't begin to see nowheres nigh the length o' the vessel. 'Twould bunch up in great big drops on every nameable thing you'd lay hand to, and I rec'lect plain as can be the stiddy dreepin', dreepin', it kep' up off'n the spars and rigging, same's so much rain in the summer time.

"And soon's ever it come night-time, wal, bedide now, but didn't it everlastingly make out to be some black, though! It couldn't been no blacker'n what it was that night, noways they could rigged it,—jest only a reg'lar out and out dungeon o' fog it was, that would soak up a light so's thirty foot off you'd scursely know she was lit at all!

"The ole man, I know, he was chock full of trouble, frettin' and stewin' around, him and the mate, together, about keeping an extra sharp lookout there forrard, and all that, though Lord knows for all the good a lookout was sich a chance as that, he might full better be turned in with a blanket hauled over his head. What mod'rit little air o' wind there was that day had been out here to the south'ard and east'ard, but she kep' petering out after sundown, and I know when it come our watch there wa'n't so much as a breath from nowheres,—jest a perfec' stark dead calm she was, so's the ship had lost every mite of steerageway, and fell off in the trough o' the sea.

"There was one o' them long-drawed ole seas a-running, so's the creetur she jest laid there wallering right in the trough, a-rollin' and rollin' away, oh, ter'ble slow and lonesome like, with the sails aloft givin' out little easy flaps every time she fetched up, and sending down a spatter of them big drops atop o' the deckload.

"Wal, I was standing somewheres about 'midships, I know, and this 'ere Novy Scoshy Dago, it was his trick at the wheel, ye un'stand. The second mate he was aft there too, somewheres, and the rest part o' the watch was scattered round one place and another. There didn't appear to be ary man on deck talkin' a word, neither. Someways it made out to be so cussed still and black that night, seem's though all our tails was sort o' down like, though prob'ly nobody wouldn't owned up to it then.

"All to once, whacko! there come the ongodliest ole thump right on deck chock aft there, so's the ship jarred the whole length on her, and most the very same secont that set-fired Dago let go a screech outen him, I swan, fit to turn the blood cold in your veins!

"Then the secont mate he up and commenced yellin' somebody had

408

fell from aloft, and all hands on us made a break aft. The ole man he turned to and fetched a light outen the cabin quick's ever he could, and sir, laying right there on the quarter-deck, jest forrard o' the wheel, betwixt it and the after end of the house, was a heap of suppin' dressed in oilskins, and a big pool o' blood dreeblin' out from un'neath on't.

"McLaren he'd fell forrard in a dead faint acrost his wheel, with his arms hanging down limp and swingin' every time the rudder kicked on a sea and give it a spoke or two one way or t'other. Seems's ef I could see him there this minute, doubled over the wheel that way for all the world same's ef he was stoopin' down so's to git a close squint at this 'ere thing on deck in front on him! Wal now, you, ef there wa'n't the devil's own shindy aboard that ship! The ole man he took his lamp right off and tried to find out who it was that had fell, though so fur's known, there wa'n't nobody aloft anyways; no airthly call for it, ye know. They took and kind o' straightened the thing out so's to git a look at the face on't, and we all see he was a big black-looking devil, but sir, there wa'n't ary soul aboard knowed who 'twas, not ef they was to swing for it! Nary one o' the ship's company wa'n't missing, that was a blame' sure thing, and you can bate them fellers commenced to git nerved up in good shape over the business! McLaren had been lugged below, and soon's ever he come to hisself we tried to git suppn' outen him about it; but seems's though the feller had flew right off'n his nut complete, and allst in the world he'd do was to jabber away stiddy mostly in some dod-blasted outlandish lingo or other, and keep rollin' them big wild-lookin' eyes of his'n fit to beat creation.

"Wal, the boys all the time was gittin' more and more worked up, ye see, and commencin' to take on the very wust way. Every mother's son on 'em 'lowed how the ole man had ought to turn to and heave the dod-blowed thing to hell over-board quick's ever he could; but he kep' a-hanging back like, a-backin' and fillin', and trying to quiet 'em down someways. For one thing, I know he would have it the feller was a stowaway; but, setfire! he knowed better all the time'n to talk such stuff as that to us! The ship's hold was stowed chock-a-block full of lumber jest as solid as ever you could pack it, and there wa'n't no place else for ary living soul to take and hide hisself away for a fortni't going on three weeks, same's he must done. And 'lowin' there *was* some feller made out to stow hisself away aboard, what in the name o' reason should possess him to turn to and go aloft a dirty black night same's that was?

"No sir-ee, sir! The ole man he couldn't make out to shove no sich guff's that down our throats, not much he couldn't! There wa'n't ary one on us cal'lated to turn in ag'in with that dev'lish thing in oil-skins laying aboard the ship, and I guess ef the truth was known, both mates felt about the same's we done. Anyways, they held a number of confabs along o' the ole man, and fin'lly seems's though he come to see it wa'n't no good buckin' ag'in the whole on us, so-fashion.

"Bedide now, you! I won't un'take to say but what there'd been a risin' aboard that hooker ef he hadn't give in jest as he did. You take the common run of hands before the mast, ye know, and they'll most gin'ally put up with a sight o' crowding most ways, but sure's you live now, I tell ye the ole man's head was level when he turned to and give us lief to take and heave the thing over the side that same night.

"But come to git right down to it, though everybody wanted to be red o' the hell-fired thing the wust ole way, still there wa'n't ary man into the whole ship's company that darst to up and tech of it. The mate he tried orderin' and coaxin' this one and that one, but he couldn't stir nobody to make ary move, when all to once be dinged ef that 'ere luny McLaren didn't fetch a spring up on deck and yells fit to stund ye like, 'I've handled him once, and I can ag'in!' s' he.

"They pooty nigh stripped the feller naked, trying to fetch him to below there, ye know, and I'm tellin' of ye he did look some desp'rate the time he give that tiger-leap and grappled along o' the thing on deck there! Up he picked it same's ef it wa'n't no heft at all, and whisked athwartship to the rail afore ever we'd r'ally took it in, and was jest in the very act of ending it up so's to give it a header, when, true's ever I'm settin' here, that 'ere hell-fired thing fetched a twist, wropped two big long arms clean round McLaren, and the pair on 'em div' over the rail together! My soul and body, you, but that's the honest truth, and jest as they done so, up come the dog-gonedest sounding laugh ever was heern yet, I'll gu'rantee!

"Wal, sir, there was hell to pay and no pitch hot, now don't you go thinkin' there wa'n't! The ole man and the mates was yelling to launch a bo't, and to heave 'em a cork-jacket, and to do this and that and I dunno what not, but now sure's ever you live, there wa'n't none o' that crowd would step foot into no bo't, not that night they wouldn't! The ole man he swore how McLaren had fell overboard, or else jumped over of his own accord; but there! we all see for ourselves jest how it was, and I cal'late there wa'n't ary man but what wouldn't stood keel-hauling sooner'n took chances into a bo't after them two jest that pertikler night. There was a pair o' life preservers hove after 'em, and some of the crowd made out to pry over a stick or two o' timber from offen the deckload, though of course they only done so jest by way of saying they done *suppn'*, for everybody knowed well nothin' in God's world wouldn't be no good.

"Wal, for a consid'ble spell there wa'n't much else talked aboard that packet, now I tell ye, but bimeby the thing kind o' blowed over like, same's them things doos, ye know, in time. I left the ship there to Liverpool, and the very fust time I was to home here, I made it a p'int to jest go right up and see ole Cap'n Spurshoe. I'd been mullin' of the thing over to myself pooty much all the time, ye see, trying to git the true bearings some ways or 'nother, so I took and walked up to the ole sir's place there, and put it to him plain and fair, was every ary cuttin' scrape, or great shakes of a row aboard the Gertrude after I'd left her.

" 'No,' says the ole sir right away. 'No,' s'he, 'there never was no cuttin' nor no trouble at all, to speak on, without,' s'he, 'without it was the last trip ever I made in her,' s'he, 'there was a Portogee, or some sich outlandish-man, took a tumble from off'n the mizzen-tops'l yard one night, and killed hisself deado, and what's more,' s'he, 'they allus mistrusted most damn'ly how there was foul play mixed up into it.'

"Seem's though there was these two outlandish-men shipped aboard the Gertrude for the run to Havre from Mobile with cotton—one big one, and one kind o' mejum-sized feller. Seem's though there was bad blood betwixt 'em from the fust, and the big one he was allus and forever picking on the other feller like, and thumpin' of him round, so's the small one was heern more'n once to make his threats how he'd git a come-uppance someways.

"Seem's though them two was aloft on the mizzen-tops'l yard this 'ere wet, dirty night, and some o' the boys was knowin' to it they'd had an extry lively falling out that very same aft'noon. Wal, sir, the big one he fin'll come down a-flyin' and struck the quarter-deck same's a thousand o' brick,—killed hisself deader'n forty herring,—and his partner give out how the foot-rope had parted un'neath the pair on 'em, and how he like to have fell hisself; but, mind ye, every soul that see that piece of rigging, 'lowed how she had been cut clean and clip with a knife, in room o' parting, so's they didn't make no bones about laying the job right plumb to this 'ere Dago, and got the cuss fairly skeered of his life afore ever they made port.

"Ole sir, there, he 'lowed how he was like to have clapped the feller in irons and give him up soon's ever they got in, but seem's though they was ter'ble short-handed that trip, so's he kep' letting the thing go, and the bloody cut-throat made out to give 'em the slip afore ever the ship was docked there to Havre. Ole sir he turned to that time I see him, and overhauled his chist of logbooks so's to show me the exact entry where the big Dago was killed that way.

"So there you have the whole bus'niss complete. I couldn't seem to read the whole thing jest right at the fust send-off, but same time I wa'n't so tormented numb but what I could see through a millstone quick's ever the hole showed up good and plain."

6. UNCONVENTIONAL GHOSTS

Lovers of Dickens may remember one of the interpolated tales in Pickwick Papers [1] in which the ghost of a chair gives some good advice. He was a British ghost; his American counterpart is not quite so vocal, but does get a message across. The phantom doe of the next yarn is not much like any non-American ghost, any more than the dialect in which the story is told is like any outside of early Vermont. (Good judges agree that the late Rowland E. Robinson was a very accurate transcriber of local speech.)

The haunted chair [2]

When we moved to Schenectady, we hired a house awful cheap 'cause 'twas said to be spooked, and the neighbors said nobody wouldn't live in it. But we didn't care, 'cause we didn't take no stock in spooks. But as I'm a-setting here, things happened that changed our feelings on the subject.

We had just went to bed the first night, dog-tired with riding in a lumber wagon all the day from Schoharie to Schenectady. We hadn't had time to shut our eyes 'fore we hearn, thumpety-thump, thumpety-thump, coming down the attic stairs. I kivered up my head with the bedding, but I couldn't shut out the sounds. Thumpety-thump, thumpety-thump—I could hear it just as plain as day. Past the door the thing thumpety-thumped, and down the stairs, thumpety-thump, thumpety-thump, and right on through the kitchen, and down the cellar steps, making the ungodliest racket you ever hearn tell. 'Twas more than pop and the boys could stand, so they up and follered after to see what in Sam Hill was up. When we girls hearn them pattering down in their bare feet, we got up and follered after.

When all of us had got down the cellar steps, we seen that chair that had made all the racket, with one of its legs p'inting to a spot in the cellar bottom. We all just stood and gawped till Ike, who was always terrible daring, said he believed the chair was trying to tell us suthin'

---

[1] In Chapter xiv, "The Bagman's Story."

[2] From Emelyn Elizabeth Gardner: *Folklore from the Schoharie Hills, New York* (Ann Arbor: University of Michigan Press; 1937), p. 96.

about the place 'twas pi'nting at. So he went and got a shovel and dug
like he kin. And Ike certainly kin make the dirt fly when he wants to.
He didn't have to dig far 'fore his shovel struck suthin' hard. Then he
did dig! And pretty soon we could see the edge of a box a-sticking out.
He didn't just know whether he'd better go on or not, but we all
hollered to him to hurry up and unkiver the rest of the box. And the
chair was so excited it jumped up and down like it had went plumb
crazy.

When he got the box unkivered so as they could, pop and the boys
pried off the lid. And as I'm a-telling you, there was the body of a man
all smooched with blood. 'Twas as plain as the nose on your face that
he'd been murdered, and the chair wanted folks to know it.

It didn't take us long to fill up that hole and git out of that house,
bag and baggage, 'cause of course, we, being strangers in Schenectady,
everybody would think we'd murdered somebody and come there to
hide the body. The chair was awful mad 'bout our gitting out, and
thumpety-thumped up the cellar steps lots louder'n it had come down
'em; then up the next stairs and on up to the attic. We thought it
would thump all the plastering down on our heads, 'fore it got through;
it thumpety-thumped so all over the attic.

Nobody asked us why we was a-moving out so soon, 'cause nobody
ever stayed more'n one night, and most not that long. But I kin tell you
we was thankful enough to git back to Schoharie, where chairs stays
where they's put, and don't go raring and rampaging 'round, scaring
folks out of their wits, p'inting out murders and goodness know what!

The phantom doe[1]

W al, boys, 'f I must I must, I s'pose," said Lisha, pulling hard at
his pipe between words, "but I hain't no gret at tellin' stories.
Ye see"—after some silent back-tracking of memory—" 'twas baout Noer
Chase; he was the fust one in taown 't hed a pleasure waggin, 'n' they
uster call it Noer's Ark. He'd been sellick man three fo' years 'n' sot in
the leegislatur' onct—cousin t' Jerushy, tew—'n' orter been in better
business 'n' goin' crustin',[2] but he went, 'n' more'n onct. So one March
the' was the alfiredest crust, 'n' he hedn't nothin' to du much, 'n' says
he,'I guess I'll hassome fun,' says he. So he got him a club, an' put on
his snowshoes an' put 'er fer a basin up in the maountin where he

---

[1] From Rowland E. Robinson: *Uncle Lisha's Shop* (New York: Forest and Stream
Publishing Co.; 1887), pp. 126–9.
[2] Hunting deer trapped by crusted snow.

413

knowed the' was some deer a-yardin'. I know the ezack spot, an' so du you, Samwill. Right out where the east branch o' Stunny Brook heads. He got Amos Jones tu go 'long with him, 'n' they got there an' faound the deer, twenty on 'em or more, a-yardin' 'raound in the little spruces, 'n' all poorer 'n wood. Wal, they schattered 'em aout an' went at 'em. Amos he seen Noer knock down ten on 'em and cut the' thruts, 'n' then he telled 'im for tu stop, f' that was 'nough. But Noer he laughed 'n' said he was jes' beginnin' tu hassome fun; 'n' then he put arter a doe that was heavy with fa'n, 'n' as he run up 'longside on her, she stumbled in the crust her laigs all a-bleedin', an' rolled up 'er eyes turrible piti-ful tow-wards him, and gin a beseechin' kind of a blaat. An' Amos he hollered auot tu Noer t' let 'er 'lone, but Noer he on'y laughed 'n' said haow t' he was goin' ter kill tew tu one shot, 'n' he gin 'er a lick on the head with his club 'fore Amos co'ld git tu him. . . .

"Amos didn't hardly never cuss, but I s'pose he ripped aout then 'n' gin it tu Noer hot 'n' heavy, 'n' said he was a good min' tu sarve him 's he'd sarved the doe; 'n' jes' then he happened tu see that Noer was standin' 'long side o' the doe, right onderneath an onlucky tree, 'n' then he said he knowed suthin' 'ould happen tu 'im, 'n' tol' 'im so. But Noer on'y laughed at 'im, 'n' called 'im a sup'stitious chickin-hearted ol' granny, an' took aout his knife tu cut the doe's thrut. Amos couldn't stan' it tu see no more sech murderin', 'n' so he cleared aout and went hum. Wal, Noer finished the doe, 'n' then took arter a-yullin' buck next. The buck started daown the maountin, 'n' bein' putty light he skinned it 'long putty good jog, so's 't Noer couldn't ketch up with 'im 's easy 's he hed with t'other ones. So Noer 'gin to git mad, 'n' doubled his jumps, 'n' went tearin' daown hill lickerty split, 'n' hed mos' ketched up tu the deer, when the toe of his snowshoe ketched int' the limb of a blowed-daown tree, an' he fell, kerlummux! 'n' struck his laig on another limb on't an' broke his laig. . . .

"His laig pained him onmassyfully, 'n' like 'nough he hurt his head tew, for he went inter a swound, I s'pose, an' he lay quite a spell 'fore he come tu, 'n' 'twas mos' night. Fust thing, he tried tu git up; but he couldn't make it aout till he got holt of a-saplin' an' pulled hisself up, an' then he couldn't take a step. An' while he stood there a-considerin', that 'ere doe appeared right afore him, lookin' at him jest as she did when he run her daown! He said, 'Shoo!' but she didn't stir a mite, and then he reached daown an' picked up his club an' hove it at 'er, 'n' he said it went through her jes' 's if she'd ben a puff o' smoke, an' it went a-scootin' over the crust twenty rods daown the hill, 'n' she never stirred! He tried to walk agin, but he couldn't step a step, an' then he goddaown on all fours an' crawled's well's he could tow-wards the clearin's, an' that ere doe kep' allers jes' so fur ahead on him, allers lookin' at him jes' as she did afore he knocked her in the head. An' when it begin tu grow duskish the' was a wolf set up a-yowlin' behind him as he snailed along a-groanin' an' a-sweatin' like a man a-mowin', an' not goin' more'n a rod in five minutes, 'n' then tew more wolves jined in a-yowlin' so clus tu him 't his toes tickled, 'n' when he looked over his shoulder he could see the dum'd critters a-shoolin' 'long arter him like black shadders, 'n' every naow 'n' then sittin' up on their rumps an' yowlin' for more tu jine 'em. An' all the time that 'ere doe kep' jes' so fur ahead on him, allers a-lookin' at 'im jes' so mournful. Bimebye arter dark, he got tu the clearin', an' he couldn't go no furder, so he sot his back agin a tree 'n' sot there an' hollered with his club in his hand, for he'd picked it up in his crawlin', an' there he sot, 'n' there the wolves sot, and right betwixt 'em stood the doe, which the wolves never took no more notice on her 'n' of a shadder. Arter a while— seemed 's 'ough 't was a week t' Noer,—someb'dy hearn the rumpus, wolves a-yowlin' an' man a-hollerin', an' Aar'n Gove an' Moses Hanson 'n' mongst 'em rallied aout an' went up, an' faound him an' fetched 'im hum. They got a darkter an' sot his laig, but he was sick for three months, 'n' many a time, they said, he seen that 'ere doe a'lookin' in't the winder 'n' hearn the wolves a-yowlin' raound the haouse, but the' could none o' the rest on 'em see her nor hear the wolves. Bimebye he got better, an' so's 't he could git aout raound. An' then his son, the on'y one 't he had, went off t' the fur West a-trappin' an' a-tradin' fer furs an' skins, an' got killed by Injins, an' then his oldes' darter run away with a wuthless, drinkin' goo'-for-nothin' creetur; an' his other darter married an Irishmun, an', wust of all, so Noer said, Amos Jones come up to see him, and said, 'I tol' yer so!' Then Noer got wus an' run int' the comsumption, 'n' arter lingerin' an' lingerin', he died."

415

7. FAKE GHOST

The ghosts that practical jokers [1] create are mostly but a very low-class spook, but they have earned a place in American mythology. The Centerville Ghost is above average, especially in the effects he produced. Man made him, and therefore let him pass for a ghost.

The Centerville ghost [2]

Mining camps have always had the reputation of being places of spirits—liquid, ghost, gay—or name your own variety. But, in the spring of 1901, the copper camp was confronted with an entirely different type of spirit, one that was purportedly supernatural and which was reported to have transferred its habitat in unearthly realms to the streets and byways of the suburb of Centerville, a short half mile north of the business district. The entire population of Centerville, together with most of the population of Butte, was frightened half to death before the spectre ceased its midnight prowling.

It was on a Sunday night, March 6, 1901, that the ghost made its first public appearance. As the hour reached midnight, two youthful residents of the little town, homeward bound on Main Street, were astounded to see, what they later described as "a shrouded apparition, partially concealed by a luminous sort of haze, with two balls of fire for eyes, and emitting a pungent, sulphur-like odor." The spectre was traveling from the direction of the West Greyrock Mine, and continued its progress until within six feet of the terrified youths, when it suddenly stopped, threw its head back, and in the manner of a wolf, poured forth "a long, piercing, soul-tearing scream," and, as suddenly as it came, disappeared as if into the ground in a cloud of phosphorescent vapor.

Upon recovering the use of their legs, the thoroughly frightened young men lost little time in making tracks for their respective homes. There, with labored breath, they told of their fearsome experience.

---

[1] Pp. 665–73, below, chronicle some non-ghostly activities of American jokers.

[2] From *Copper Camp: Stories of the World's Greatest Mining Town Butte, Montana.* By the Writers' Project of Montana, published by Hastings House, Publishers, Inc., 1943, pp. 67–71.

Fake Ghost

The next morning the ghost was the sole topic of conversation in Centerville.

Over back fences, from house to house—which, because of the steepness of Butte hill, were practically on top of each other anyhow—the story traveled. Each teller enlarged on the details until by nightfall there were over a dozen different stories being told with a score of persons saying that they had personally come in contact with the weird apparition.

The news quickly reached the city, but the skeptical newspapers would have none of it. Not until several nights had passed, and the unearthly visitor had been reported to have made its appearance in widely separated localities of the little town on succeeding evenings, did the newspapers see fit to send reporters to investigate the rumored visitations.

The newshawks learned plenty. Scores of Centerville residents told of personally meeting up with the awesome spook. On the same evening of the reporter's visit, the ghost had been followed by a dozen young men to an abandoned shack on East Summit Street, below the Mountain Con Mine, where it again disappeared. Two of the bravest youths remained on guard at the shack to await its reappearance. Their companions, returning hours later found both boys lying in the shack in an unconscious condition. Upon being revived, they told the strange story of being attacked by the monster, who, they claimed, grasped them with its grimy talons and proceeded to give them a thorough trouncing. They stubbornly clung to this story despite the fact that their bodies bore no visible marks to substantiate the tale.

The newsmen had heard enough. The following morning's papers carried bold-face headlines telling of the marauding apparition and continued with a lurid story describing the ghost's nightly depredations. Their story, sent out over the Associated Press wires, was carried by most of the papers of the nation. Residents of Centerville remained behind locked doors, and the good wives of the little community saw to it that the lights burned throughout the night.

Still the prowling wraith continued its nocturnal ramblings. A Centerville Miss, whose veracity was unquestioned, told a story of being held prisoner in a small alleyway by the luminous figure, who, she stated, had tied her up with pieces of rope and smoked innumerable cigarettes while he stood watch over her. Finally, she told, the apparition apparently tiring of her worldly company, released her and once again disappeared, taking the ropes that held her bound along with him.

On the night of Friday 13 (an excellent night for a spook hunt), the Butte newspapers assigned two armed reporters to the scene. The reporters drafted the services of two Centerville Irishmen, Mike Col-

lane and Jack Murphy, who were armed with double-barreled shotguns. The four decided to trail the phantom to its lair, and once and
for all to put a finish to its ramblings.

A page-one story with headlines told the residents of the copper
camp the next morning of the eerie adventures of the quartet. It
seems that in their plans to track down the apparition the two reporters were to proceed up a seldom-used pathway at the foot of an
old mine dump a few hundred feet from the railway tracks. Collane
and Murphy were to take the B. A. & P. railway tracks running east.
As the latter pair, with cocked shotguns, cautiously approached a
string of empty ore cars on the tracks the spectre suddenly appeared
before them. This time the ghost had the appearance of a dark figure,
very tall and clothed in what appeared to be a long ulster.

As the story read, Murphy, the braver of the two, commanded,
"Halt! Are you a man or a ghost?" Receiving no reply, he let go with
both barrels, the ghost slowly dissolving before his terrified eyes. His
partner, Collane, petrified with fright, had not fired his gun. The two
newspaper men, hearing the shot, hurried to the scene and learned
of the encounter from the trembling lips of the Irishmen. So frightened
were they, the story related, that both had to receive medical attention, Murphy remaining in bed for several days recovering from his
terrible experience.

That the reporters gave entire credence to the story is shown by the
final paragraph of their account:

"If the apparition or ghost, or whatever the object which was encountered on the railroad tracks last night, is not supernatural, it is
certainly one of the most puzzling things which has ever come up for
discussion in Butte. There is no question that the appearance of the
object was a creation in the mind of the men who went in search of
it, and if it had been a man it could not have survived the shots which
were taken at it from a distance of less than ten feet by a good marksman."

For several days the ghost was page-one news and the talk of the
camp. Centerville was paralyzed with fright. Business on the little
main street was at a standstill after sundown. Residents dared not to
venture forth after dark, and the men on nightshift coming home
from mines in that vicinity gave the spook's domain a wide berth.

On the night of Sunday, March 15, a posse of close to two hundred
men was formed to end forever the prowling of the spectre. Armed
with clubs, pitchforks, knives and guns of all descriptions, the small
army was deployed into squads of from six to a dozen men. Every
nook and cranny in Centerville was visited.

Oddly enough, the phantom did not make its appearance on that
evening, or, for that matter, any further evenings. Self-preservation,

418

evidently the first law of ghosts as well as humans, presumably kept it at home. There would certainly have been a showdown of man versus spook, if it had dared to face any of the determined armed force abroad that evening.

However, two Walkerville residents claimed to have encountered the apparition that same night in the neighborhood of the old Lexington Mill, a mile distant from Centerville. Their story appeared in the following morning's Butte *Miner*:

"The two men stated that they talked to the ghost and that it replied to some of their questions. The spectre was asked why it appeared to disturb people at such unseemly hours and it replied that it was full of trouble and had lots of trouble ahead of it. It had such a heavy burden to carry that it could not rest and it sought the freedom and quiet of the night to help restore its calm. It stated further that after Thursday night, it would appear no more, but would retire to the realm in which it belonged, never again to trouble the earthly."

The ghost's final message reassured the residents of Centerville and Butte and they once more dared forth at night without fear of meeting with the spirit.

It was a matter of thirty years before the secret of the Centerville ghost was exposed. Meanwhile, many residents of the hill city believed implicitly that the spook was indeed a supernatural being, and that at some time it might return. During this time it was used as a threat to make naughty children behave.

In 1930 at a political gathering in Hibernian Hall in Centerville, an exposé of the affair was made. Joe Duffy, Butte laundryman, for years noted for his pranks, held the answer.

As Duffy told it that evening, it seems that he and two friends (who, incidentally, were newspapermen, one on the morning and the other on the evening paper) framed the deal.

Duffy started the rumor around Centerville and played it up for several days. As the story traveled, each teller embellished the tale with fanciful additions of his own. At this point, the two reporters stepped in with stories in their individual papers. The rest, according to Joe Duffy, was merely "the power of suggestion." There never had been an actual ghost or anyone masquerading as such.

As to the two Irishmen, who in company with the newswriters had encountered the spectre on the railroad tracks, Duffy claimed they were but a couple of Centerville saloon hangers-on just getting over a terrific "bender" and had been experiencing hallucinations of one kind or another for over a week. The guns provided for them had been thoughtfully loaded with blanks.

419

BOOK V

TALL TALES OF AMERICA

BOOK V

TALL TALES OF AMERICA

TALL TALES OF AMERICA: *The familiar*

ones and some less familiar

THE humor of exaggeration did not originate in the United States. Rabelais and Munchausen were not Arkansans; but it is true that fantastic lies have always seemed to please Americans. No doubt this has been particularly true of the West and the Southwest, but the tall tale is not exclusively theirs. Our literary historians need a little admonition on this point. So convinced, for example, was Constance Rourke that "windies" must belong in the West that in her excellent book on American humor[1] she can account for a story in an *Old Farmer's Almanac* for 1836, a very tall story, only by declaring that the New England Yankee "had appropriated western tall tales in a spare gingerly fashion of his own." Now, this is pretty far off. Yankees were not, in the thirties, we may guess, borrowing their humor from the West. The story itself may have originated in New England; it is told of Ethan Allen,[2] among others.

One protesting voice against what he properly calls "a congealing error in our literary history" is that of Richard M. Dorson, who in June 1943 published in the *New England Quarterly*[3] an article entitled "Jonathan Draws the Long Bow." In this article Mr. Dorson gives a generous sampling of New England fantasy; he also reminds us[4] that "the New York *Spirit of the Times* devoted racy columns to humorous scenes in the South and West, but we have not been told that a good many of its sketches were set in New England, nor that its most distinguished competitor, the Boston *Yankee Blade,* ran predominantly to New England matter, nor that the *Blade* in turn was rivalled by other Boston literary family journals of the kind so abundant in the 1840's and '50's, *The Saturday Rambler, Union Jack, The Yankee Privateer,* and *The Portfolio,* whose titles bulge with folk humor. If Western almanacs rioted in comic fiction, so did sec-

---

[1] Constance Rourke: *American Humor, a study of the national character* (New York: Harcourt, Brace & Co.; 1931), p. 31. It tells of a man losing a powderhorn in the river. His companion dives for it—and is spied on the river-bottom pouring powder from the missing horn into his own.

[2] Stewart H. Holbrook: *Ethan Allen* (New York: The Macmillan Co.; 1940), p. 267.

[3] Vol. XVI, p. 244.

[4] Ibid., p. 245.

tional almanacs published in Boston. If the St. Louis *Reveille* and New Orleans *Picayune* are examples of regular newspapers which were prolific in popular humor, so are the Burlington *Free Press* and the Exeter *News Letter*. If Tennessee produced "Sut Lovingood," Rhode Island gave birth to *The Jonny-Cake Letters*. And quite apart from the literary period of frontier humor (1830–1860), folk story has seeped into print in New England through diverse channels of publication that still tap the unremitting flow of back-country oral narrative."

He might have added, for it is probably relevant, that the editor of the *Spirit of the Times* was a native of Vermont.

Since many tall tales of the West were woven about the deeds and supposed deeds of David Crockett, a passage which Mr. Dorson quotes from the *London Handbook of Joking*[1] is highly apposite. It is a strong suspicion of mine that much of the "filler" in the *Spirit of the Times,* recounting wild improbabilities "from the West" was written by William T. Porter himself. At all events, we may suppose that he was in sympathy with the doctrine set forth by the anonymous London writer, since he quoted it. The passage is as follows:[2]

Talk of Crockett! Why Ezekiel Nash, a genuine down-easter, could send him to eternal smash right slick off. Nash chaws chain cables for "backey," takes gunpowder for snuff, and blows his nose with a tin pocket handkerchief; he sleeps between iron sheets, which in winter are made red-hot. Instead of rats and mice, wolves and grisly bears prowl around his room at night, but he sleeps so sound he's obliged to be thrown out of the window every morning to wake him. Mother missed him when he was a baby, and found him at last seated on a hornet's nest, playing at bopeep with a couple of rattlesnakes.

As an infant, 'Zekiel was a wonder, I guess; he had razors and bayonets for toys, walked in top-boots when he was three days old, sucked hot coals, and used to rub his gums with a nutmeg-grater; they weaned him the very day he was born, and fed him on pap made of flint-stones and lignum-vitae soaked in prussic acid. His appetite, for a boy, was awful; he once eat a buffalo and three parts of a horse and then asked if tea wasn't ready. When Nash travels by rail, he gets out to walk a trifle of forty or fifty miles, and waits an hour till the train overtakes him. The engine comes up, panting and blowing, and often says with a forced laugh, "Bust my biler, 'Zekiel, but of all mortal critters, you're the biggest; I recon your father was a flash of lightning, and your mother an earthquake. Darn me, if you ain't an ornament to creation."

In selecting the next group of stories I have made no particular effort to redress the balance, though I agree with Mr. Dorson that it has been badly tilted. I have, however, not overlooked the eastern part of the United States in my survey of wonders.

---

[1] Via the *Spirit of the Times* (October 21, 1848).
[2] Ibid., p. 244.

Mr. Carl Sandburg, in a free-verse description of the thoughts, the stories, and the aspirations of Americans[1] has given a good deal of space to their yarns. A typical passage follows.

They have yarns

Of a skyscraper so tall they had to put hinges
On the two top stories so to let the moon go by,
Of one corn crop in Missouri when the roots
Went so deep and drew off so much water
The Mississippi riverbed that year was dry,
Of pancakes so thin they had only one side,
Of "a fog so thick we shingled the barn and six feet out on the fog,"
Of Pecos Pete straddling a cyclone in Texas and riding it to the west coast where "it rained out under him,"
Of the man who drove a swarm of bees across the Rocky Mountains and the Desert "and didn't lose a bee,"
Of a mountain railroad curve where the engineer in his cab can touch the caboose and spit in the conductor's eye,
Of the boy who climbed a cornstalk growing so fast he would have starved to death if they hadn't shot biscuits up to him,
Of the old man's whiskers: "When the wind was with him his whiskers arrived a day before he did,"
Of the hen laying a square egg and cackling, "Ouch!" and of hens laying eggs with the dates printed on them,
Of the ship captain's shadow: it froze to the deck one cold winter night,
Of mutineers on that same ship put to chipping rust with rubber hammers,
Of the sheep counter who was fast and accurate: "I just count their feet and divide by four,"
Of the man so tall he must climb a ladder to shave himself,
Of the runt so teeny-weeny it takes two men and a boy to see him,
Of mosquitoes: one can kill a dog, two of them a man,
Of a cyclone that sucked cookstoves out of the kitchen, up the chimney flue, and on to the next town,
Of the same cyclone picking up wagon-tracks in Nebraska and dropping them over in the Dakotas,
Of the hook-and-eye snake unlocking itself into forty pieces, each piece two inches long, then in nine seconds flat snapping itself together again,

---

[1] From *The People, Yes* by Carl Sandburg (New York: Harcourt, Brace & Co.; 1936), pp. 88–9. Copyright, 1936, by Harcourt, Brace and Company, Inc.

Of the watch swallowed by the cow—when they butchered her a year later the watch was running and had the correct time,

Of horned snakes, hoop snakes that roll themselves where they want to go, and rattlesnakes carrying bells instead of rattles on their tails,

Of the herd of cattle in California getting lost in a giant redwood tree that had hollowed out,

Of the man who killed a snake by putting its tail in its mouth so it swallowed itself,

Of railroad trains whizzing along so fast they reach the station before the whistle,

Of pigs so thin the farmer had to tie knots in their tails to keep them from crawling through the cracks in their pens,

Of Paul Bunyan's big blue ox, Babe, measuring between the eyes forty-two-ax-handles and a plug of Star tobacco exactly,

Of John Henry's hammer and the curve of its swing and his singing of it as "a rainbow round my shoulder."

"Do tell!"

"I want to know!"

During a large part of the nineteenth century America's mightiest river carried on its broad stream America's mightiest braggarts. Mark Twain has pictured them, rather affectionately than otherwise, in *Life on the Mississippi* and *Huckleberry Finn,* and lesser writers corroborate him. The next two selections were written in the forties. Though they exhibit some of the stylistic affectations of that period, which had not learned to tell a simple story simply, they do appear to represent accurate reporting.

I can lick a steamboat![1]

As soon as the steamboat was moored alongside this floating wharf, the rush to board her was tremendous. One man, dressed in a hunting shirt of coarse homespun, and a coonskin cap, with a knife, something like that which sailors wear, sticking in his girdle, was the first to get on the plank that led from the flatboat to the steamer, and in his hurry to get on board, he was pushed into the water by a gigantic fellow in a bear skin coat, a coarse wool hat, and a pair of green baize leggings. The immersion of the gentleman in the hunting shirt was altogether accidental, but it was sufficient foundation, in the estimation of the cavaliers of Arkansas, for the tournament ground to be marked off, and the trumpets to blow *"largesse"* to the knights of the coonskin cap and the green baize leggings.

As soon as the ducked man arose from the top of the mulatto colored river, he clenched one hand above his head, and hallowed, "Hold on there—you thin milk livered skunk! Hold on till I get on shore, and may I be cut up for shoe pegs if I don't make your skillet-faced phizcymahogany look like a cabbage made into sour krout!"

"See here stranger," replied the offender, "your duckin' was axesighdental; but if you want a tussel I am har—just like a fin on a catfish's back!"

"The plank was mine by seniority, as the doctors say, old cat skinner, and may I be ground up into gunpowder, if I don't light on to you like a bull bat on a gallinipper," remarked the dripping man,

---

[1] By George P. Burnham, in the *Spirit of the Times,* February 8, 1843.

as he shook himself like a Newfoundland dog, and stepped on shore.

"Stranger," said the causer of the accident, while his eye gleamed like that of an enraged panther, and his fists clenched so forcibly that his nails were driven into the palms of his hands, "perhaps you don't know that I'm the man that fought with Wash. Coffee, and dirked wild Jule Lynch?"

"May I be run on a sawyer, and may my brains fall down into my boot heels as I am walking up a stony hill, if I care if you had a rough and tumble with the devil. You pushed me off the plank and you must fight," was the peaceable reply of the wet gentleman.

"See here man," said the opponent of Wash. Coffee, as he bared his breast and pointed to a large scar that ran across three or four of his ribs, "Wild Jule done this, but I laid him up for a time—these big scratches on my face was got through my trying to hug a young bar— and this arm has been broken twice. I'm a cripple, but if you will fight, why strip and let's be at it."

In an instant a ring was made, and the two combatants, when doffed of their clothing, looked like middle aged Titans, preparing for battle. The youngest, who had fallen into the water, was about twenty-eight years of age, and his opponent was thirty-four or five. With eyes made fiery by anger, and lips quivering with intense passion, the youngest dealt his adversary a tremendous blow in the breast. Until this affront the elder man had maintained a strange coolness, and manifested a disposition rather in favor of an apology than anything else; but the instant he felt the blow his nostrils became white, and twitched like a steed's scenting battle. Closing his teeth hard together, he planted himself for the attack, and as his adversary approached him, he dealt him a fierce lick on the side of his face with his iron-bound knuckles, that laid his cheek bone as bare as though the flesh had been chopped off by an axe. Smarting with rage the other returned the compliment, and as the blood gushed in a torrent from his mouth, he turned around and spit out one or two of his teeth that were hanging by the gums, and with a "rounder" as it is technically termed, he hit the younger man a blow on the temple that laid him on the beach with a dead, heavy sound, like that of a falling tree.

"Thar, I hope he is got enough," said the elder of the two, at almost every word stopping to spit out some fragment of his broken jaw. One of his companions handed him a flask of brandy, and with a long deep drawn swallow, like that of a camel at a spring on an oasis, he gulped down enough of the fiery liquor to have made a common man mad.

"Enough," cried the other party, who had been in a like manner attended to by his friends, "yes, when I drink your heart's blood I'll cry enough, and not till then. Come on you white wired—"

428

"See here, stranger, stop thar. Don't talk of my mother. She's dead, God bless her! I'm a man from A to izzard—and you—you thin gutted wasp, I'll whip you now if I die for it!"

With a shout from the bye-standers, and passions made furious by hate and deep draughts of liquor, with a howl the combatants again went to work. Disengaging his right hand from the boa constrictor gripe of his opponent, the younger brute buried his long talon-like nails directly under the eyelids of his victim, and the orb clotted with blood hung by a few tendons on his cheek! As soon as the elder man felt the torture, his face for an instant was as white as snow, and then a deep purple hue overspread his countenance. Lifting his adversary in the air as though he had been a child, he threw him to the earth, and clutching his throat with both hands, he squeezed it until his enemy's face became almost black. Suddenly he uttered a quick sharp cry, and put his hand to his side, and when he drew it away it was covered with blood! The younger villain, while on his back, had drawn his knife and stabbed him. As the elder of the combatants staggered up, he was caught by some of his friends, and holding him in their arms, with clenched fists they muttered curses towards his inhuman opponent, who being shielded by his own particular clique, made for the river and plunged in. When about half way across, he gained a small island, and rising to his full height, he flapped his hands against his sides and crow'd like a cock.

"Ruoo-ru-oo-o! I can lick a steamboat! My finger-nails is related to a saw-mill on my mother's side, and my daddy was a double breasted catamount! I wear a hoop snake for a neck-handkerchief, and the brass buttons on my coat have all been boiled in poison! Who'll Ru-oo-ru-oo-o!!"

Driving a parson ashore[1]

A great many very *probable* stories are told of accidents and hair-breadth escapes—by sea and land. The traveller who finds himself on board a Mississippi steamer will occasionally meet a "passenger" who has shaken hands with the "grim monster," and parted company with him, at considerably less than a moment's notice!

We were a fortunate collection, on board the elegant *"Yorktown"* —upon one of her downward trips last season, and with a full river and a rapid current, were making headway at more than a twenty mile lick, down stream—on a clear day early in November.

---

[1] From Francis A. Durivage and George P. Burnham: *Stray Subjects Arrested and Bound Over* (Philadelphia: Carey & Hart; 1848), pp. 109–14.

"Drinks all round" had been the order of the evening (with a certain coterie of friends), the occupation being varied only by "cobblers for the party"—"snifters for the crowd"—or "slugs for the entire company"—until, by common consent, the "mourners" settled themselves down into comparative quiet.

Most of the passengers had disappeared for the night, and only a knot of "hard-heads" were left upon deck. These remained till daylight, amusing each other with long yarns. At early morning they had drawn some half-a-dozen listeners around them, among whom was a superstitious impostor, in rusty black, and straight hair—who was endeavouring to palm himself off for a clergyman, and who was strongly *suspected* by one of the story-tellers. The principal object of the most prominent speaker (who was a rough but good-natured Virginian) seemed to be, to impress upon the mind of this pretended Rev., the dangers and jeopardies of steam-travelling; more particularly in boats, more especially upon rivers, and more particularly on the Mississippi river! The parson had said little, but he gave his neighbours to understand that all his predilections were in favour of the "doctrine of fore-ordination."

"Whatever *is* to be, *will* be," sighed the rusty gentleman, as the Virginian concluded an account of a dreadful steam-boat accident, which occurred only a few days previously.

"You b'lieve it, do you, stranger?"

"Indeed, my friend, I do."

"P'raps you never heern tell o' that 'orful carastrophy as took place *here*-abouts, some time ago?"

"Mercy!—No."

"Last year—afo' Christmas"—

"To what?"

"To the steamer Snorter."

"No! *Where?*"

"On this very river."

"How?"

"Bu'st her biler."

"When?"

"Just about this time o' day."

"The dev—I mean, you don't *say* so!"

"Oh, yes. What *is* ter be, *will* be—and a feller can't help it."

The tabs of a dingy white neck-cloth dangled at the side of the narrator's chair, and a pair of dingier gray eyes were fixed upon the Virginian's as he proceeded.

"How *did* it happen?" asked the reverend.

"Wal. We had a fello' aboard, as was struck with a fit o' *preachin'*—and the cuss never'd sleep o' nights, but keep a hollerin' and blo'in'—

'cause he was afeered sunthin' would split afo' day—he said—we wus such a wicked set, and he'd try to hev some uv us put asho'. He was a *Jonah,* cuss him, but we fixed him afo' we got through."

"How?" asked the parson.

"How? W'y—we left him asho'!"

"Where?"

"On the river—yere."

"In the night?"

"No. *Just about this time!* We overhauled a boat as wus runnin' in the opposition (at a wood-yard below) and afo' we knew where we wus, the cap'n had got our craft under weigh agin (for the feller had started off ahead of us, in a hurry), and we wus soon neck and neck. The pitch-knots was crammed inter the furnaces, right smart, stranger, and away we went, sometimes afo' and sometimes abreast of the Snorter. Wul—we finally hove in sight of another wood-yard, whar we had to stop to take in fuel. We veered round to the sho', and made fast in a jiffy."

"Well?" said the parson, as his eyes started in their sockets.

"Wul, thar was a heap o' steam on her, and we hed made up our minds that what *'wus* to be, *would* be, and it wusn't o' no use to be skeert afo' we wus hurt; 'n so we jes naterally insisted that the other craft must be beat *any* how."

"Well?"

"Wul, wot do you suppose the cap'n did, stranger?"

"Can't say."

"He druv one end of a cro'bar into the loop over the 'scape-valve (which was bobbin' up and down, and lettin' off the extra steam) and *jes set hisself down on the other end of it!*"

"The *devil* he did!"

"The *what,* stranger?"

"I say it can't be possible!"

"But *I* say he *did,* though—and thar he sot till she blo'd up!"

"*Busted?*"

"Oh, yes! When we started from the sho'—at the first turn of the wheel on her, she bust into a thousand splinters."

"Awful!" says the parson.

"The cap'n was never heer'd on. I was standin' on the upper deck," continued the Virginian, "and the feller as wanted to preach so bad, was heavin' the pitch into the fires when she bust."

"And you never saw him more?" inquired the parson in breathless suspense.

"Oh, Yes. *As me and the smoke-pipe went up,* we met the cuss coming *down!!*"

"Well?" continued the impostor.

431

"Well, I kno'ed he wus a *Jonah*," added the Virginian, "an' ef he hadn't a bin done fer, as he wus, I'd a *licked him to death*—fer palming himself off fer a *parson*, which he wusn't!"

The gentleman with the straight hair and seedy coat turned pale upon this, and at the conclusion of the story the bell rang, below— the steam-pipe sent forth its thunder—and the boat veered round in front of another wood-yard.

"What's that?" asked the pretended parson.

"We're heavin' asho'. *This is the very yard!*"

The impostor scrambled ashore—up the steep bank—and when the last bell rung, nothing was seen of him. We left again, but no parson was in sight. We had been detained half an hour at the yard, and were now quietly making our way down stream, close to the shore—when from a bluff on the bank, a mile or so below the wood-yard, our missing parson was suddenly discovered, shaking his clenched fist most lustily at his Virginian friend, who was the first to espy him!

The only reply vouchsafed by his tormentor, to this pugnacious demonstration, was a certain twisting of his fingers in front of his phiz—while his thumb rested gently upon the tip of his nose! We continued on our course, and the last I saw of the frightened "parson," he was rushing along the river's bank at top-speed, and evincing a most religious desire to find a big stone to hurl at the head of his persecutor, who soon left him to his own reflections!

3. SOLDIERS AND SAILORS

From the beginning of recorded history to the present day, soldiers and sailors have been noted neither for the sobriety of their narrative style nor for the modesty of their first-person yarns. Least of all American soldiers and sailors. There is nothing that they can not imagine themselves accomplishing—a circumstance that has been consistently and conspicuously advantageous to the United States in time of war. Examples of military tall talk are legion, of course; I have selected two stories from World War II, of which the former is characterized by a species of modesty that transcends the wildest boasting. It has been, says Ralph Ingersoll, who narrates it, the subject of "a great many debates." No wonder. About the second story no debate is likely to arise.

What did you holler?

During the invasion of North Africa, the story goes, a young American lieutenant captured a battery of Vichy field artillery. This seems a tall tale, but the explanation is even taller. Ralph Ingersoll tells it as follows: [1]

Now it is not often in war that a battery of field artillery is captured intact and very rare indeed that this is done single-handed. So the commanding general was impressed. He and his staff considered a decoration automatic [2] and it was only as a matter of form—and to satisfy his personal curiosity—that the general sent for the lieutenant to get his story first-hand.

The lieutenant had an honest, open face. He was shy and respectful. The general was very cordial. He sat the lieutenant down, lit the young man's cigarette, and said, "Now—tell me all about it." The lieutenant fiddled with his collar, looked ill at ease, and began:

"Well, sir, I know I should not have been there, but somehow I got separated from the men and I thought the best thing I could do was to find out where all that firing was coming from. So I walked towards the noise and when I got on top of that hill—you know, sir, the one beyond the railroad—I saw that it was a battery position. The battery was firing, and when

---

[1] From Ralph Ingersoll: *The Battle Is the Pay-Off*, copyright, 1943, by Ralph Ingersoll. By permission of Harcourt, Brace and Company, Inc. Pp. 67–8.
[2] The lieutenant was not decorated.

I got close enough I saw that the soldiers were French." Here the lieutenant hesitated and began to squirm in his chair.

"Well," said the general, fascinated, "what happened then? Were you scared?"

The lieutenant said, "No, sir, but I was mighty worried. All I could think of, were your instructions about how to handle the French. You remember, sir, that your orders were not to fire on a French soldier unless we were absolutely sure that he was unfriendly. I thought, how can I tell for sure? And then I remembered that we had a countersign so that if they were friendly French they would know the reply."

"You thought," said the general very slowly, "that you had better challenge the battery that was firing, in order to be sure it was unfriendly?"

"Yes, sir," said the lieutenant brightly, "and that is what I did. I cupped my hands and hollered and when they did not have the right answer I knew I should have to make them prisoners."

"What did you holler at them?" asked the general.

The lieutenant looked perplexed. "Why, you remember the countersign for that night, sir. You must, sir. It was 'Hi Ho Silver'—and they should have answered 'Away.' So I cupped my hands and hollered 'Hi Ho Silver' at them."

"And then?" said the general.

"Oh, then they put their hands up right away—they surrendered, sir."

The Seabees [1]

Soon after joining the Navy, I was stationed at the "Seabees" paint shop, where I learned that my work was to include camouflaging and lettering. Our crew gradually became very efficient at camouflaging and went about that phase of work with great eagerness. However, this same eagerness almost landed us in the brig more than once. It all started when we camouflaged a long fence so thoroughly that three platoons of men marched right through it. Two valuable weeks were wasted while a group of carpenters searched for the broken place, and when they did find it, they had to station a man there night and day so that they wouldn't lose track of it again until it was fixed.

You can imagine every one's amazement when four new tires came rolling down the street in perfect formation, and came to a dead stop simultaneously. It wasn't until one of the "boots" tried to roll one away for his personal use that we discovered that the four tires were holding up an officer's station wagon that we had camouflaged. We hadn't had time to paint the tires, which was fortunate, because if we had the wagon would never have been found.

[1] From Sgt. Bull Davidson (editor): *Tall Tales They Tell in the Service* (New York: Thomas Y. Crowell Co.; 1943), pp. 74-5. Copyright 1943 by Thomas Y. Crowell Company.

All this was only the beginning. In our hurry to finish camouflaging the base before inspection, we painted so fast and furiously that we painted each other, and the whole crew couldn't be seen! Until we could get enough paint off to be recognized, we were charged with being AWOL for three days!

Well, sir, to top off the whole business, the inspecting Admiral couldn't find the base. He traveled all the way from New York to Florida looking for it, and if we hadn't erected a big sign at our base entrance reading HOME OF THE SEABEES, he'd still be traveling.

The American likes, possibly more than men of other nations, to be best at something—even spitting tobacco juice. As for really vicious men, a part of their warped psychology is pride in being dangerous— more dangerous than anyone else.

Terbaccer chawer[2]

I been a holdin' back and a holdin' back till I just can't stand it no longer!

All the time I was writin' my Recollections and Reflections of State-craft in the Hezrogean Era, or as it is familiarly called "The Hedge-hog Spasm," I was hankerin' to tell you about another most glorious Statesman of that period, Zebadiah Hopper.

Now, the reason I held back from telling you about Zebadiah was because he was my great-uncle—my Uncle "Zeb." You see, when one is writing something that he has every reason to believe will become a state document, parsarved for posterity in the archives of the State Library—well, he has to be a mite keerful about including his rela-tives, or he'll be accused of perverting history by horning his ancestry into the Vermont Hall of Fame, or trying to geneologic'ly hitch his-self onto the fringe of immortality. But now, in sorta "Off the Record Aftermath," I throw descretion to the winds, dogs—or hedgehogs— and come right out with bold and mixed emotions and set down for you a few excerpts from the Career of My Uncle Zeb.

In the first place, Providence didn't endow Uncle Zeb too resplend-ently in any way, and neither Fate, Life, and Fortune, none of them, delt kindly with him. Of course, Zeb riled and aggrevated 'em con-siderable by his being so derned lazy. But they no need to sot on him hard as they did. Uncle Zeb did the best he could. He striv, twitched, yanked, hauled, and cussed agin Fate but couldn't keep his head above water. And when depression, crop-control, contagious abortion, flood, corn-borer, potato-blight, oats-rust, and "lead in your maple syrup" all swooped down at once on Uncle Zeb, he got to holdin' his head

---

[1] For a special kind of American championship contest, see pp. 474–500, below.

[2] From Mark Whalon: *Rural Free Delivery: Recollections of a Rural Mailman* (Brattleboro: Stephen Daye Press; 1942), pp. 82–9.

436

under the cider faucet most of the time to numb the cruel bludgeons of Fate.

Well, we all seed Uncle was a sinkin'! Yes, the time came when Uncle threatened to "go on the town." I don't mean he wanted to throw hisself on the town, for in those days it were considered a disgrace. I use the word "threatening" in the sense of "impending." Somethin' had to be done!

We got together and decided that the best and cheapest way to rescue Uncle Zeb was to send him up to the Legislatur—fer a good long session such as most sessions 'most always is. 'Twa'n't his turn to go, but emergencies sometimes take precedence over seniority rights, even in Vermont. Of course, Zeb weren't fittin' to go exactly, but we sent him along on the theory that just one more of his stripe wouldn't make no great difference.

Nowadays when a man goes to the Legislatur he goes "with reservations." He reserves both ends of the week to spend at home. He spends the whole middle of the week in Montpelier or on the road to an' from.

In the day of Uncle Zeb, when a man went to the Legislatur he went wholehearted, lock, stock, and barrel. His folks parted with him as though he was goin' to Siberia. They knowed they wouldn't see him agin till sugarin' time—if then. All the legislaters got outside jobs for their board and clothes. Zebadiah took the first job he could get, which was washin' dishes in a restaurant at night. He couldn't make a go of it! 'Twa'n't the fact that his whiskers and chawin' terbaccer got all mixed up with his work. It were the pretty waitresses a sloshin' agin him gettin' their dishes that decided Zeb to give up the job. He saw his moral fiber being softened; this night-life of metropolitan Montpelier was disentegratin' him, so he got another job—one he was fitted for, and could stand.

Yes sir, Uncle saved his life and soul and such figments of sanity as he had by gettin' a job doin' chores and milkin' for his bed and board at a farm just this side of Hardwick. 'Twant only thirteen miles from the Capitol.

Historians tell the grand qualities of a statesman, and then at the last they crown him with the greatest attribute of all. They say, "But in spite of all this *he never lost the common touch.*"

Uncle Zeb was happy in his new job. He dog-trotted in from the farm to the Capitol every morning and walked back slow to the farm nights—heavy burdened with Affairs of State.

I've heard Uncle Zeb say often, "For genuine deep-thinking, at least for a Vermonter, thar ain't nawthin' like gettin' your head up agin a cow's flank and hearin' the milk a squishing into the pail peaceful and soothin'."

437

Some disgruntled traducin' democrats have said that Uncle got this job just because he was plain penurious. But 'tain't so! It's slander. My Uncle Zebadiah got this job so's he wouldn't lose his holt on his-self; his milkin' grip—or the *common touch*.

Shucks! How a fellow's mouth does run when he gets recountin' the great deeds of his Ancestors!

I have the temptation and desire to do belated justice to some of my other relatives by "writing them up," and some of 'em are 'most as brilliant and notorious as Uncle Zeb. But I'm going to stick to Uncle Zeb because I hain't half done him justice yet—and mebbe because I take after Uncle. Yes sir, lots of folks has told me I'm as much like Uncle Zeb as though I was bored out of his rear deck with a ship's auger.

When we sent Uncle Zeb to the Legislatur, we didn't just figger on rehabilitating him financially. We ruther hoped he'd be mentally and spiritually revivified, fired with ambition to do somethin'. In this matter I'm sorry to say we were disappointed. Uncle, on coming home, acted just like most deposed legislaters. He seemed to feel that his term at the Legislatur was not only the Apogee of his Career, but the end of all Endeavor. On arriving home, Uncle constituted himself a Court of Last Resort on all Matters in General and Nothin' in Particular. That is, Uncle Zeb settled down into what might be called a "Sedentary Judicial Life."

I don't mean to say Uncle racked his brain. I don't mean to say he even thought, or even cogitated. I guess I can best explain it by saying that Uncle "went Oriental." Yes, he spent his days in a self-induced maze of rumination, retrospection, and meditation; just lettin' vagrant mental reflexes wander through his head unhurried, unheeded, and unordered. Uncle surely did nothin' physical to disrupt the nebulous pageant that paraded through his semi-consciousness. His nearest approach to activity was whittlin' axe-helves and chawin' terbaccer. These avocations didn't disrupt the parade—they only seemed to lead it on or "drum-major it." I ain't a goin' to tell you about Uncle's axe-helves 'cause they were just ordinary and crooked like Uncle, but stern regard for truth in history compels me to speak of his terbaccer-chawin' and record the fact that in the realm of terbaccer expectoration he stands as All Time Champion.

Why, I mind one night in early spring I was over visitin' Uncle. It were one of the first of those real warm spring evenings that we Vermonters calls "Skunks Carnival"—when "skunks come up ter the window."

Yes sir, thar we sot in the gloamin' in the sittin'-room and sure enough a skunk come up to the window—which was open. Uncle and I heard him a barkin' and rustlin' under the syringa bush as he built his emplacement and got his battery into position. The air was tense! We could imagine the skunk figgerin' his azmuth and elevation. Uncle never quivered; just reached into his back pocket, drew out his plug of "Three Black Crows" and bit off a chunk. It were nerve wrackin'! The only sound was the rapid roll and crunch of Uncle's jaws! At last I heard the first of those three short sharp barks that is the skunk's equivalent for "Ready—Aim—Fire."

At the second bark, Uncle's head sunk in and shot out like a mud-turtle's. Out of his tight focused face sped a lethal charge—whizzed by me, across the room out of the window into the dark of the night and under the syringa bush—a direct hit by indirect fire! A bull's eye! Yes sir, spiked the enemy gun, silenced the battery! Uncle and I chuckled in silence as we heard the enemy trundling his artillery to the rear in defeat.

I tell the above to show the poise and finesse of Uncle and how he rose to emergencies—and to show he was far in advance of that scatter-charge blunderbuss age of terbaccer chawers who crudely found the highest expression of their art in "the drowning of a mouse at ten paces."

Uncle lived to the ripe old age of 104. Funny thing was, 'stead of drying up and shrivellin' like most real old folks do, Uncle seemed to get heavier and heavier. We often wondered about it. But when Uncle did die it was explained.

Yes sir! When I came to "lay Uncle out" (thar wa'n't none of these here morticians in those days) the mystery of Uncle's increasing girth was explained. Yes sir! When we got beneath the surface—thar was the waist bands of forty pairs of pants.

With the tears blindin' me I chiselled on his headstun:

> "It ain't no ways in human-natur
> To come unscathed through a Legislatur
> From the evils thar implanted Zeb had no chance,
> Disintegrated from inside—just like his pants!"

Goin' good[1]

I ain't a-aimin' to exaggerate none, but everybody in South Georgia knows I was the fastest runner in Bullock County, excusin' none. Every year at the Kennedy reunion—when it seemed like half of Georgia showed up—I won all the foot races. It was the same at the carnivals and County Fair; I taken all the prizes.

---

[1] Reprinted by permission of the publishers, Duell, Sloan & Pearce, Inc., from Stetson Kennedy: *Palmetto Country*, pp. 122–3. Copyright 1942 by Stetson Kennedy.

"When I was a boy me and my ten brothers used to go coon huntin' a lots. We would start out at night and hunt in the hammocks and bay-heads along the edge of the swamps. When the dogs struck trail I liked to have went crazy as a cross-eyed tadpole! I was fitten to be tied! To hear them hounds a-yowlin' through the woods made me just rarin' to take right out after them.

"My brothers would grab me, because they was afeard I'd run through the woods so fast I'd butt into a tree, or maybe get rattlesnake bit. When they grabbed me I'd fight like a wildcat. 'Don't hold me, boys!' I'd beg. Sometimes I pulled the shirt off my back, and away I'd go after the dogs.

"When I got goin' good I could leap over trees, pammetters, and briar bushes like a scairt buck deer. It didn't take me long to catch up with the dogs and pass 'em. Many a time I run ahead of the dogs and treed the coon myself. They'd skeedaddle up a tree, and I'd stand under it and holler.

"I'm gonna tell you a story you ain't gonna believe, but anybody in Bullock County will tell you it's nothin' but the Gospel Truth. When I was eighteen years old I was takin' Pa's saddle-horse out to the pasture one mornin' about sun-up. Somehow or nother I left the gate open, and Lightnin'—that was the horse's name—slipped through and lit out down the road tords Register.

"I knowed I was in for a good lickin' if Lightnin' got losted, so I taken a short cut that came out about a mile down the road. But when I come to the crossin' Lightnin' wasn't nowhere in sight, so I started to run down the road to Register to see if I could catch him. Register is thirty miles away, and I didn't get there until ten o'clock in the mornin'. I asked Uncle Josh at the General Store if he'd seen Lightnin' comin' through town, but he said he hadn't.

"I went in a bar and had me a good shot of whiskey. Toreckly I heard a rumpus, and when I looked down Main Street there was Lightnin', sweatin' and heavin' like he was about to drop! I had passed him by takin' the short cut, and had been runnin' ahead of him all the way! That afternoon I backtracked to home, and Pa never could rightly understand how come Lightnin' was so plumb tuckered out after a day in the pasture.

"I'm gettin' on in my forties now, and can't run like I used to could. But last summer our Men's Bible Class had a picnic at the beach, and when it come time to have the runnin' races a young feller started braggin' that he was a 'ten-second man' at college—meanin' he could run a hundred yards in ten seconds.

"Nobody hadn't never held a clock to my runnin', so I didn't know how fast a ten-second man was. But I challenged him to a race, the gun fired, and off we went. I have to give that young feller credit—he could nachely-born run. I didn't pull ahead of him until just before we crossed the line. I could have beat him a heap sight more if it hadn't been for my arthritis."

The wildest man of the West[1]

In the Grays Harbor County courthouse at Montesano, in western Washington, a small bronze plaque lists the names of six men and relates with sinister brevity that they met their death in futile attempts to take the celebrated outlaw John Turnow. This is the only tangible reminder of the most crafty and dangerous man ever to roam the timbered reaches of the Pacific Northwest and by far the strangest outlaw I know of.

Through some incomprehensible literary freak, Turnow has never been the subject of a paper-backed biography of the Harry Tracy–Jesse James school, and the dime novel trade thus lost a sure-fire perennial. Hence Turnow's renown is purely local where it has flourished mightily for three decades and is in no danger of dimming. Barrel-stove historians of the logging camps, some of whom saw Turnow in the flesh and others who were in at his death, keep the story alive and enhance it with the embroidery characteristic of folk tales. When winter gloom settles down over the still vast forests of the Olympic Peninsula of western Washington and stiff gales make logging operations dangerous, young loggers of 1943 who have been brought up on Tarzan and Superman sit on camp deacon seats and listen with awed respect to stories of the life and times of a human animal who combines in actuality many of the qualities of their comic strip heroes. In his own region, Turnow has long since become a folk character comparable to the mythical Paul Bunyan. And with some reason. The bare facts about Turnow were enough to build a mountain of legend.

What might be called the public life of John Turnow began on September 3, 1911, an otherwise pleasant enough autumn day in the wild Grays Harbor country of western Washington. A reddish sun beat down through the blue smoke haze of settlers' clearing fires. Here and there in the vast wilderness the toot and stutter of a logger's donkey engine could be heard. Blows of fireweed drifted like snow in the air and got into the sourdough of the few trappers and prospectors in the region. Mostly, though, the region was untracked, without roads or trails, and silent except for the occasional bickering of jays and the report of some lone hunter's rifle.

On that particular September afternoon two rifle shots occurred,

---

[1] By Stewart H. Holbrook from the *American Mercury*, December 1943.

close together. If they were heard, no one paid them heed or gave thought to the matter until it was learned that the Bauer twins, John and Will, had not returned from a bear hunt along the Satsop river. A few days later, Deputy Sheriff Colin McKenzie, one of a large searching party, found the two bodies tucked away under some brush, side by side, on the upper reaches of the Satsop. Each had been shot once, and that through the forehead.

John Turnow was at once suspected of the double murder, strange enough when you knew that Turnow was blood uncle to the twins, but not so strange if you knew about Turnow. This man was thirty-two years old in 1911. Born of a pioneer and respected family on the Turnow homestead near Satsop village, John had never, people said, been quite right in the head. From the time he began to walk he had been most peculiar. Didn't care for human companionship at all. Wanted to be alone, especially alone in the woods. By the time he was ten John was going into the timber along the Satsop and Wynooche rivers and staying all night, sometimes for several days. His family tried to curb the youth's wildness, and his response was to stay away for a month. He told his parents that he found birds and animals better companions than men. He liked to listen to what he termed the talk of crows and jays, he said, and he also heard beautiful music, "like that of organs and harps" in the winds that sifted through the tall fir and hemlock.

On his lone trips into the woods young Turnow never carried any food. Got all the food he wanted from wild things, he said—roots, birds, animals. He always carried a rifle and when he was twelve he could drill a Copenhagen snuff box at a hundred yards. At home he was moody. He did chores and other farm work under duress. He would not play with other children, not even with his brothers and sisters. I imagine he was what today would be called a retarded child.

So his parents finally sent John to a private sanitarium in Vancouver, Washington. Here he proved so hard to handle that he had to be removed and was then committed to an institution in Salem, Oregon. Though he was watched rather closely, one morning, late in 1909 nurses found his bed empty. It hadn't been slept in.

Turnow left no connecting trail, but within a few weeks of his escape from Salem—which is nearly 200 miles from the Satsop—trappers reported seeing him some twenty-five miles up the Satsop river. Turnow told two of these woodsmen that he would never be locked up again. He asked them to take a message out to his folks. "You tell them," he said in his short, gruff way, "and you tell everybody else that none of them had better come after me. I'll kill anyone who does. These are my woods. I want to be alone."

For almost two years Turnow lived on in the woods undisturbed, listening to those harps in the hemlocks, those arbor vitae organs, and communing with owls and cougars, a deranged and unlettered Thoreau without brains. His father died and word of it was taken to the son by a trapper who was on friendly or at least on speaking terms with him. John said he wouldn't go to the funeral, and he didn't; nor did he a bit later when his mother died. The estate was left to the six Turnow children and John's share, some $1,700, was put in a Montesano bank and John notified by the friendly trapper. "I don't want no money," said John. He stayed on in the woods.

Such was the status of Turnow on that September day when his nephews, the Bauer twins, were found dead. It was surmised that the twins had been sighted by Turnow and that he may have thought they were searching for him, to take him back to the hated sanitarium. And Turnow, as was later to become very evident, was a man of direct action.

II

A huge manhunt followed immediately on discovery of the murdered twins. Some 200 men ranged the Satsop and Wynooche watersheds for forty miles north and south, then spread east and west from Puget Sound to the Pacific. Here and there they found where the wild fellow had made camp, but not once was he sighted although the hunt was kept up sporadically throughout the winter of 1911–12.

Meanwhile, the usual alarms occurred: Turnow was reported to be near Port Angeles. An unknown had killed a cow near Shelton. Another unknown who, by the size of his monstrous tracks in the snow, must have been huge, was said to be in the neighborhood of Hama Hama, on Hood Canal. Any or all of these reports may have been true. Turnow was now a man six feet two inches tall and he weighed around 195 pounds, all of it bone and muscle. He knew the woods of all western Washington as other people know their living rooms—and indeed these woods were John Turnow's living room. He traveled through the timber, hunters said, swiftly and with no more noise than the soft whish of an owl. And after a fresh fall of snow, at a time when the posses were thick and numerous, he left no tracks at all, leaving one to suppose that he holed up for weeks on end like a bear; or, as some said, he took to the trees.

In fact, one Emil Swanson, a log bucker of stout back and of no imagination whatever, came into a camp one night in a condition bordering on hysteria. Not until he had downed a lusty slug of high-power lemon extract in hot water could he compose himself sufficiently to say what was the matter. When he had been about to fell a big fir, he vowed, "some kind big animal, look like man," swung out on a high branch of the tree, grabbed the limb of another tree and went sailing off to be lost in the gloom of the towering timber. "Bay Yesus," said Emil, "aye vork here no more." He got his time and went to town.

The search for Turnow ebbed and flowed throughout the winter. Then, on March 2, 1912, word came out with a prospector that Turnow had made camp at a bend of the river far up the Satsop known as The Oxbow. Colin McKenzie, the deputy sheriff who found the Bauer twins, and A. V. Elmer, deputy game warden, started in to the Oxbow country to get Turnow. They did not return.

Thirteen days later a searching party found the bodies of the two missing men. Each had been drilled once through the forehead, and an attempt made to bury them in a shallow trench dug in the form of a T. Most of the dead men's clothing had been removed. Their rifles and ammunition were gone.

The hunt for Turnow now engaged the authorities of three counties. Rewards for the man, dead or alive, totaled $5,000, and hundreds of citizens joined in the hunt. Not since the time of Harry Tracy and Dave Merrill had a man hunt of such proportions been on. The searchers used caution, too, for they knew they were pitted against a half-human animal who not only was deranged but who knew almost every acre of the large territory he had chosen for his home.

The usual alarms again occurred; the Wild Man of the Olympics, as the press now called him, was reported seen simultaneously in widely separated places. Loggers at the Simpson camps, nearly in the center of the region most favored by Turnow, took pains not to be found strolling quietly and alone through the woods. Southwest Washington, and in fact a good part of the Olympic Peninsula, had the Turnow jitters.

If you didn't know the country of John Turnow you might think it odd that more than twelve hundred men, most of them expert woodsmen, failed so much as to get sight of the wild man in a year's time of hunting. But Turnow had the craftiness of a cougar, and his domain was wide and wild. In 1912 it was pretty much virgin timber, not pines of parklike aspect, but a dense jungle of tall fir and cedar and spruce and hemlock, growing close together and with their bases set in vines and underbrush of almost tropical lushness.

Somewhere in that savage country the wild man spent the winter of 1912–13, seen by no one. Not a track of his was found. Spring came on and the man hunt continued without abating. On April 16, 1913, almost two years after the murder of the Bauer twins, and more than a year after the killing of McKenzie and Elmer, Deputy Giles Quimby sighted a small wickiup, or rude shelter of bark, in a natural clearing by a tiny lake, perhaps a mile from the scene of the last two killings. With Quimby were two trappers, Louis Blair and Charles Lathrop, who had turned man hunters with the $5,000 reward in mind. The three men were certain they had stumbled onto a hiding place of the wild man. But was Turnow there, in the hut? They withdrew to a safe distance to consider the matter; and after a brief council of war decided to approach the hunt from three directions. They began the advance, slowly, cautiously, and as quietly, or almost as quietly, as a cougar stalking a deer, their rifles cocked. It wasn't, however, quiet enough.

Deputy Quimby was moving ahead a few feet at a time, picking his every step and halting now and then to listen. He heard nothing at all until a blast of gunfire suddenly shattered the wooded silence. At the same instant he heard the crashing of brush and looked to see Louis Blair tumble headlong, blood gushing horribly from what had been his face.

Quimby's gun was at his shoulder. For a flash he saw a great head and an ugly bearded face pop out from behind a fir. Quimby fired. The head disappeared. Quimby knew the head belonged to John Turnow—but had he hit it with his shot? Quimby couldn't know— for a few moments. He listened, straining every sense to penetrate the deathly silence. Then came another shattering blast. Charles Lathrop threw up his arms, gave one agonized cry, and went tumbling to the ground. Again the great ugly head and face peered from behind the fir tree. Quimby fired instantly, again and again, until his gun was empty. He crouched down to reload. He knew he was alone now with the wild man.

With his rifle once more ready, Quimby peered around the tree he was using for protection. He saw that his tree had been chipped by bullets and knew then that Turnow had also been shooting at him, though Quimby had been too busy to notice. He looked at the tree where Turnow was hiding and could see that it had been chipped by his own bullets. But, and it was rather important to know, had one of his bullets hit Turnow?

Deputy Quimby couldn't know. He pondered. All was silent in and around the glade. That is, silent except for the worried sniffing of two hounds belonging to Blair and Lathrop. Quimby could hear the animals whining in wonder at the sudden smell and aspect of Death. But of Blair or Lathrop or Turnow, Quimby could hear nothing. For probably five minutes, which Quimby later declared to have seemed an age, the deputy waited. Then, as quietly as he could, he made his slow way through the timber and away from the lake. It had been an ambuscade, and for all he knew it might be one now. When he had got a hundred yards or so from the spot Quimby stopped to listen again. The mournful baying of the two hounds, still contemplating their late masters, was all he could hear. He now put on all speed and hurried to Camp 5 of the Simpson Logging Company, four miles distant. Here he found High Sheriff Matthews with a large posse. He led them back to the sinister little lake.

All was quiet. The posse spread out, then converged slowly toward the wickiup. Presently came a shout. "Here's the son of a bitch," a deputy called. "And he's dead, by God." At about the same time other posse members found the bodies of the two trappers. Each had been shot once, fair between the eyes.

III

John Turnow hadn't been shot through the head, but he was just as dead as the six men he had killed. There he was, the wild fellow, sprawled on his back, his big oldfashioned repeating rifle across his chest and clutched in his two hands. He was a sight that men who saw him vividly remember today, thirty years after. The huge wild man, with great matted beard and long hair, dressed in ragged garments made chiefly from gunny sacking, laid fold upon fold and filled with fir needles. On his feet was the only conventional bit of clothing he possessed, a pair of comparatively new calked boots, later identified as having belonged to the late Colin McKenzie, one of Turnow's victims.

In the little hut by the lake the posse found $6.65 in silver, a small knife, a pair of scissors and more gunny sacking of the sort the wild man had used to make his clothing. Not in the hut or anywhere else in the vicinity could the posse find so much as a scrap of food.

Reconstructing the brief, deadly battle, it was thought that Turnow, who had been accustomed to meeting *pairs* of men in the woods, and killing them, had not at first suspected the presence of a third man. It was the bullet from Quimby's gun which killed the outlaw.

Horses were brought in and Turnow and his last two victims taken out to Montesano, where an undertaker said he had never before seen the like of Turnow—all of the big man was bone and muscle. His shoulders, so the mortician reported, were like those of a gorilla; the palms of his hands were like leather. From this report, perhaps, and the added fact that it had never been possible to trail Turnow— either in snow or on bare ground—plus the experience of Emil Swanson, he who saw the strange thing among the tree tops, grew up the story, still widely believed, that the wild man often traveled through the trees, two hundred feet above the ground, like a gigantic ape. Perhaps he did. In any case, he went straight into legend, and there he remains today, half man, half ape, the Wild Man of the Olympics, intimate of bear, cougar, owls and buzzards, an unlettered, witless Thoreau who wanted to be alone and worked hard to that purpose.

The spirit of Æsop lives on in America, perversely changed into a
wild amoral humor. The step from realism to fantasy, when it concerns communication between men and animals, is a short one and
quickly taken. Sometimes the teller professes absolute belief in his
story; Morton Thompson uses this technique so effectively that we almost believe his story of Lewie the Horse. The anonymous story of
the cow-doctor may for all anyone knows be mere truth, its artless
mixture of man- and beast-doctoring as ingenuous as it seems. But
when it comes to Harold Peavey's cow, there is no doubt. Mr. Cronyn
does not believe, except in a histrionic sort of way, his own story, nor
expect us to. But he keeps near the truth, as do our great masters of
the earnest and circumstantial life. In fact, when he alleges [1] that the
cow was real, and he once owned her, I believe him. In a way.

Lewie the horse [2]

I t began the year we shipped him off to a small private school near
San Diego. It was in the backwoods, the most admirable private
school; every boy had a rifle and every boy had a horse. They ran
about wearing nothing but shorts. Their marks were amazingly high.
If they didn't study they were kept in. It is an awful thing to be kept
in. To be kept in—barefoot—while the rest of the boys were out
hysterically squilching dust between their toes, chasing quail, doctoring horses, or just playing squat tag in a cactus patch, was a penalty
so horrid and loathsome and against nature that at the end of each
year every kid was valedictorian.

Now Lewie's father was a notable horseman. Dad once had five
hotels in New York City, and he was always fretting about in one or
the other, but he never missed a day at Durland's or the Central
Park bridle path. Early in the mornings he would find the most
unmanageable horse in New York State and get on and leave the
world of cares behind him. Once or twice I went with him. He always

---

[1] In a note to his story, loc. cit., p. 365.
[2] From: *Joe the Wounded Tennis Player*, by Morton Thompson, copyright 1929,
1944, 1945, reprinted by permission of Doubleday & Company, Inc. Pp. 136–47.

forgot I was along. He would ride onto the bridle strip and, once there, his horse invariably seemed to know what was expected of him and would go nuts. At this juncture Dad would relax and start talking to himself.

"*Ho!*" he would holler. "What do you think you're doing? *Ho! C'mere!* Gonna fire that son of a bitch Howard if it's the last thing on earth I ever—*ho!* What do you think *you're* doing?"

This would go on for hours. I think he got a sort of release that way. Dad never discussed his problems with anyone but a horse, a wild, lively horse; and he probably reasoned that if the horse was lively enough he wouldn't remember what Dad had been saying and use it against him. He was a magnificent horseman. No horse ever threw him and all of them were maniacs and he balanced all his books on them.

I think it was from Dad that Lewie got sib to horses. The school's horses were purchased from a near-by Indian tribe. They cost twenty-five dollars apiece. The Indians were indifferent to what horse the school picked; they just took the twenty-five dollars and waved vaguely at the ranch. These Indian ponies roamed unbroken. Lewie got his own horse simply by going out on the range with a rope and pattering barefoot after the one he wanted, and nobody knows how he did it, but late that night he rode jauntily into the school corral, bareback, guiding the horse with the rope. I was familiar, at the end of his first year at the school, with his uncanny ability with horses. Every time I visited him he put on an exhibition for me. When he was eleven he rode a horse over a four-foot jump, bareback, standing erect. He was always in the corral. His ambition at that time was one day to have a colt. Not to buy one; to *have* one, personally.

And then one day, when he was twelve, I was down at Caliente for the races, I bumped into Lewie. The school had been given a holiday, and for a treat all the kids were taken to the track. Lewie was at the stables, his face in the stalls; I cuffed him and asked him what he was doing. He was getting ready for the next race. His brow was furrowed. It turned out that the kids were betting on the races, betting their desserts. The odds on the board meant nothing to them. They had a fairer system. Lewie got first pick; he had to give the kids three and a half to one on any horse he selected. He had to *give* odds. I smiled tolerantly. It was as good a way of teaching him the folly of gambling as any.

"How many desserts do you owe?" I asked blandly.

"Don't owe any!" he said wonderingly.

It turned out that instead of owing he was *owed* twenty-seven desserts; everybody in school was in hock to him for the remainder of the semester. He said he always picked the right horse. I asked him what animal he liked in the next race. He went over to a semicircle where they were being led around. He pushed his way through the crowd of onlookers until he was practically under the horses' feet. There, as each horse came by, he looked at it questioningly. Four of them looked right back at him, craned their necks, looked him in the eye—and made noises at him.

He came back.

"That Number Four," he said with the candor and calm of a small brother being sent to find out what time it is.

Number Four was twelve to one. He won. I got even for the day in just that one race. There were only three races left. Lewie the Horse picked the other three. Just like that. One, two, three. Four to one, six to five, and eight to one. He asked them and they told him and I bet on them. I went home delirious.

After that I wrote him long letters and made trips to his school in San Diego, trying to find out his secret. He couldn't explain it. Not in any way an adult mind could grasp.

"They tell me," he would say simply.

"How?" I'd persist.

"They just *tell* me!"

"Well, now look! Here's you and me talking, see? I tell you something—everybody can understand me—"

"Yeah. I know. They can't get over it."

"Who?"

"The horses!"

"Can't get over what?"

"You stand there wondering if they're gonna win. They tell you. And you don't believe 'em."

"Don't believe 'em?"

"No! Who do you think knows better than a horse?"

"But I don't even understand them. Hell!" I said earnestly. "I'd believe them! I don't even understand—"

"I don't know why," he'd say, patiently and virtuously. "They talk perfectly plain."

"What do they say?"

"Oh, stuff. They don't feel good, or they feel good. How they think they're gonna run, what they think of the jockey, the track, the other horses. Lotsa stuff. Gossip, mostly."

I had to see it work. My logic, that disastrous sense that teaches the difference between right and wrong to so many humans including Hitler and Chamberlain, and the fellow who sent those steers all the way from Texas to California to be milked, my logic told me that at best the kid was lying and imaginative and that at worst he actually believed what he said. The best way to break him, in either case, was

449

to make a spectacle of him. But at the last moment my heart misgave me. Lewie was a very good boy. Very quiet and sweet. I borrowed him from school and took him up to Santa Anita.

We went back to the paddock. He stood by the ring.

"Now talk to them."

The first horse went by.

"How are you going, boy?" Lewie asked.

The horse turned his head. He looked Lewie full in the eye. He made a neighing noise.

"Muh-huh-ooh-hoo-hoo-muh huh!"

The next horse came by.

"What do y'say, boy?" asked Lewie.

The horse made a different noise.

There were eight horses in that race. He talked to six of them. They talked back to him. He turned away.

"Come on," he said.

"What do you mean, 'Come on'?"

"You just want to know who's gonna win, don't you?"

"Yes. Sure. Who's going to win?"

"That Number Three."

I looked quickly at the tote board. The odds on Number Three were eight to one. I looked back at Lewie.

"How do you know?" I said suspiciously.

He reddened. He looked at me crossly. "Didn't you see me ask 'em?"

"What did they say?"

Now he was no longer bored. Now he was interested. "Number One said he was hot but he didn't like his boy. Two said absolutely no. Three said he was sore as hell and out to take everybody if he had to kick 'em over the grandstand to do it. Four didn't care one way or the other. Five had a sore back, hurting him like everything. Six said he felt good, all right, only he knew damned well Three could lick him. The other two don't count. All of them said not to pay any attention to the other two. No good."

"That's what they said?"

"Sure," he said wonderingly. "Why not?"

I stabbed a quick forefinger at him.

"Number Five's a liar then! Look at him walk! He's no sorer in the back than you are!"

Lewie the Horse looked me in the eye.

"What would he lie for?" he asked simply. "He said he's sore, he's sore."

Number Three won, going away.

Number Five broke down in the backstretch and trotted in limping.

The rest of that day was a dream. Matter-of-factly Lewie talked to the horses. Matter-of-factly they answered him back. He didn't have a form sheet. He didn't know one horse from another. He simply talked to those horses and they answered him back. It was sensational.

He picked six races out of eight. In one race the horse he picked came in second. Lewie was livid with rage. He shouted so loud that waiters came running toward us and people stood up to see what the matter was. He couldn't be silenced. He didn't even hear me.

"That dirty louse!" he screamed. "That jockey crook! That thief!" There were tears in his eyes. The jockey had pulled the horse.

Lewie never watched the horses run. He kept a pair of field glasses trained on the jockeys from the moment the race started until long after they had swept past the finish line. He watched only the jockeys.

And in the other race there were only maiden two-year-olds. He liked to talk to two-year-olds, but he said they were unreliable. They all talked big, he said, and they all meant it when they said they were going to win. But they didn't know, really, what they were talking about. They were too young.

Many a time that season Lewie wouldn't give any counsel in certain races. He said horses were mischievous sometimes; they would all gang up and everybody try not to win. And sometimes there would be two or three or even four horses in a race, each of whom would be confident he was going to win. And sometimes there would be a race with an outstanding horse in it, and the horse would say he didn't rightly know whether he felt like running or not today; and that was dangerous because, halfway round, far back in the pack, he might suddenly decide he felt like running after all and step out and win it from the other horse that had said he would win if the other guy felt lazy about it.

He said horses knew their own chances just as well as human runners; figured them out, figured out the other horse's jockey, knew each other's track likings. He said some of them were chatty and some dour, just like people. He said all of them were frank; they would say whatever they had to say, candidly, right in front of the others. They kept nothing back; they almost never pulled surprises.

He told me all this much later, when school was out for the summer and we used to go to Santa Anita every day we could spare. I am ashamed to confess it, but that year I had a bank balance that was awesome. The only reason I didn't retire was that no matter how monotonously and inexorably he picked a winner I always felt the next time he would fail. He never did. Not, that is, until he was out of high school.

His secret was very simple. He talked to the horses. They answered him.

I have noticed that if you don't tell a kid that he can't do some-

451

thing, something that is manifestly absurd to adult logic, the kid will simply go ahead and do it and think nothing of it. There is a strong bond between animals and young human animals. They seem to understand each other. They seem to inhabit the same animal world. They seem to anticipate each other and to reach across the chasm of logic that separates the animal from man; they seem able to communicate silently with each other. Some kids are closer to animals than others. Lewie the Horse just communicated with them outright. And they communicated back.

I have seen him do it so many, many times. I wish he'd never lost whatever it was. I wish I'd never profaned the thing by betting on it and capitalizing in pieces of paper and disks of metal on something like that. I'm a little ashamed.

I remember the day he told Jock Whitney that a horse he once owned would win the next race. We were down at the paddock, Lewie, Gloria Swanson, Whitney, and myself. Jock snorted. The odds on the horse were twenty-two to one. Jock preferred another. Lewie said Jock's pick was lame. Jock squinted, looked again, looked very carefully, then turned to Lewie.

"That horse is sounder than you, my boy," he patronized.

The horses went on the track. The race ended. The twenty-two-to-one shot won. I didn't bet on him. Who was I to take Lewie's word against that of the renowned Jock Whitney? The horse Lewie said was lame folded in the third furlong and came in limping.

Finally the word got out, and from then on I had trouble keeping Lewie from being borrowed. Everybody wanted to take him to the track. He didn't care. He'd go with anyone. He loved to watch the horses exercise, to be near them and talk to them. Many a morning he would get up at 3 A.M. and hitchhike twenty-five miles just to sit on the rail with a stop watch in his hand. He wanted to be a jockey. His bones were too big. Then he wanted to be a trainer. I let him have his head. I let him plan and dream his heart out. I got him books. I introduced him to owners. If it were possible for him to be a horse he would have tried for it; and I would not have balked him.

My favorite director is Sam Wood. He is a gentleman and he has tremendous knowledge of his craft and his mind is a pleasure. When Sam asked me if he could borrow Lewie and asked me to go along, I assented. Sophie Tucker went along. And Sam's lovely daughter. All the way they kept tucking Lewie in with robes, anxiously. The day's performance opened with a horse named Cerro. Sam went down to the paddock with Lewie and me. The women stayed in the clubhouse. Sam watched Lewie talk to the horses. Then Lewie came back and said Number Seven. That was Cerro. Thirty to one.

"Number Seven," said Lewie.

Sam thanked him gravely. He didn't change expression. He walked up to the mutual window and laid a hundred on his nose. Cerro won. In our box there was absolute silence. Everybody was watching Lewie. Lewie was watching the horses pulling slowly to a halt before cantering back to the judges' stand. Finally he lowered his glasses.

"Did ya see that jock on Number Two? They ought to set down a guy like that. Lookit him!"

Sam went down and collected his three-thousand-odd dollars. The next was something called Red Ensign.

"Number Four," said Lewie.

We bet on Number Four. Number Four won. Odds on. And then there was a blurred succession of races, winner after winner, and Sam's face was white and so was mine, for we were both plunging. Sophie Tucker, as usual with her, was betting on every horse in every race but playing Lewie's choice heavier than the rest. And even betting on every horse, she was so far ahead that she kept worrying about a holdup on the way home.

The fifth race came up. Lewie liked Number One.

Number One headed the pack by two and a half lengths. We went down to the pay-off windows. We collected our money. And Lewie was through for the day. He wouldn't pick the sixth race. Said any horse could win it. Said all of them thought they could do it.

We begged and pleaded with him.

"I can't tell you!" he cried. "They don't know themselves."

We bet anyhow. We lost. It was the same for the seventh. Only this time somebody came along with one of those hot studio-crowd tips; and we plunged. But plunged! We lost.

I hate to think of that eighth race. To this day I hate to think about it. We were frantic. There were three horses that could win, and Lewie said all three of them could win it and he wouldn't pick any of them. He was astonished at us. There were nine horses in that race, and I bet on six of them. Sophie bet on the whole nine of them —twice over. Sam bet on four red-hot tips. At the last minute he went down and bet on a hunch of his own.

We went home in a barrel.

There was all that frantic, lovely, growing money gone and we had had our hands on it, and if we'd only quit! Lewie was calm and entirely satisfied. He'd had a day at the races. He'd talked to some swell horses, he had steeped himself in the smell, sound, sight, and touch of horses, and nothing else mattered. And it really didn't. It took me six years to realize it.

But that, at any rate, is how Lewie, now twenty and fast becoming a writer, came to be called Lewie the Horse. When he left the San Diego school the horses cried to see him go, his own horse in particular, for I saw him do it when Lewie stood in the stable and told him he was going away.

When he was sixteen he suddenly stopped talking to horses and they stopped talking back to him. He got to be a little indignant about it.

"I don't know what you're talking about," he'd sometimes say. But I think he was a little miserable. I saw him try to recapture whatever it was, now and then, but it always failed and at last he gave it up. I think he outgrew it. Perhaps the city robbed him of the bond; perhaps if he'd stayed close to horses all his life he'd have kept it. He got to fiddling with form charts and reading voraciously about horses, to replace the knowledge he used to have instinctively. He can still outhandicap any newspaper predictor in the business. He can still reach into a clear sky and pick them and stun even himself; last year he picked Bayview, and I didn't have pockets enough to put the money in. He can still ride anything that doesn't fly. He can still move among angry, kicking horses and quiet them with a pat, a cluck, an easy eye. He loves them. He reaches for them.

But it's gone.

He doesn't talk to them.

Not any more.

And they don't answer back.

The cow-doctor [1]

We commend to the attention of Dan Marble [2] a report in the Boston Daily Advertiser the case of M. Maynard vs. Litchfield, to recover damages for the loss of a valuable cow. The testimony of one witness (Dr. Stoddard) was as follows:

"I live in Scituate, and am sixty years of age. I am a cow doctor, have followed the business these forty years. I doctor sheep, hogs, and horned critters. I set broken bones, jints, etc. I never read no books on critters. I took the business kind of nat'ral. I doctor in Scituate, Hanover, Hanson, and all about. Mr. Maynard and Mr. Litchfield came to me about this cow. I told them to give her a pint and a half of castor ile, and if they hadn't got that, to give her a pint of lamp ile, or a pound of hog's lard. I went down to see her the day before she died. I gave her a dose of thorough-stalk tea, strong. I went to see her agin on Saturday, and dosed her agin. I thought if I could start up

---

[1] From Porter's *Spirit of the Times*, April 22, 1848.
[2] An itinerant actor and impersonator of the period (the 1840's).

her ideas a little, and kinder jog nater, she might git along. She revived up a little and I left her. I went down agin Sunday morning, got there about half past ten, and found her as dead as a herrin. I was mightily struck up. We skinned her, and snaked her out upon the snow. I then cut her open and examined her. She had what I called the overflow of the gall. I found a bushel basket full of fox grass hay and nothin' else, in her intrils. I found a peck more in the mainfold, all matted down and dried on. My neighbors use this kind of hay. It will do for young critters that browse, but I never see any livin' critter touch it growin'. Even grasshoppers will run from it for life. I took some spirits down with me Sunday morning. The cow having no further use for any, I took a dose myself.

Harold Peavey's fast cow[1]

When Harold Peavey graduated from the State Agricultural College and won a prize in oratory on "The Plow is Mightier than the Pen," we all thought he was a pretty smart boy, but when he leased the Eppingwell place on shares we changed our mind. The last family that took it worked five years and then they owed Old Lady Eppingwell five hundred and the bank another odd thousand. Parks, the man's name was, told me all he got out of it was a lame back and three more kids to raise.

So, when I saw smoke coming out of the chimney after two years when there wasn't any, I went over to call on my nearest neighbor. He was just carrying in a load of apple wood as I came in the front gate and, seeing me, he put it down.

"Hullo, Bud," I says, "how's tricks?"

"Oke," he says, grinning. He was a nice-looking kid, standing over six feet, with a good set of teeth and hair that needed pruning. "Are you Pete Crumm?"

"Same," I says, "I used to know your folks at Medford. Your dad did me on a lumber deal, but I guess he's got you well educated."

"I don't know," he says thoughtfully, "I know all the spray formulas and the life history of the Woolly Aphis but I guess I've got plenty to learn."

"You have," I says, looking over the twenty-seven acres of Eppingwell's Folly that was called an apple ranch. "Plenty. Your trees will stand a little pruning."

---

[1] By George Cronyn. Copyright, 1935, by Story Magazine, Inc.

"Yes," he says. "They're pretty brushy. I've been working a couple of days and I've got twelve trees pruned."

"Not bad," I says. "You've only got two months' work ahead of you pruning at that rate, and it's the middle of March now. And there's another three weeks repairing the irrigation flumes that are all shot to hell. And maybe a week or two clearing the meadow patch—"

"You mean I've got work ahead of me?"

"Not more'n fifteen hours a day. Have you got a good plow team?"

"None better. I've made a deal with Morrison to work his team and plow one day a week in return for helping him three days."

"I see. That leaves you four days for your own work, counting Sundays."

"Sundays I got a job driving the Sunday School bus."

"Well then," I says, "everything's jake. You can just sit down and take it easy the rest of the time. When are you getting a wife to do the house chores and cooking?"

"Not till I've saved about three hundred dollars," he says.

"I see," I says. "You'd as leave stay a bachelor."

"No, I wouldn't. I'd like to start a family." He looked out over the place in a sort of dreamy way. "And I'd like to have a cow." He picked up his chunks of apple wood and said, "It's a good view from the house here, with old Mount Sherman and Pine Butte and—"

"I see you've painted your hen house," I says.

"Yes," he says. "It matches up with the scenery. Morrison says he's got a good cow, a heifer. Black Jersey. I never heard of a black Jersey before. There can't be many of 'em."

"I've heard of *that* black Jersey," I says. "Her name is Mabel, but I don't know if I'd call her a cow."

"Why not?" he asks in surprise.

"Well," I says, "I don't know. It just never struck me that way. When are you getting her?"

"Tomorrow."

"I'll drive you over in my gas waggon," I says. "It's a mile and a half to Morrison's—quite a piece to lead Mabel."

So the next day about seven in the morning, after about a dozen flapjacks, I tuned up the old bus and drove over to pick up Harold. There was a lot of smoke coming out of the kitchen door and when I stepped inside at first I couldn't see nothing but I could hear Harold coughing and choking around the wood stove.

"Morning," I says.

"How's tricks?"

"It's the prunes," he sort of gasped. "I left 'em to cook while I started running a ditch through the meadow. I guess there wasn't enough water."

"Maybe there was too much prunes," I suggested. "Can you salvage any?"

"Sure," he says. "The top layer is only burnt on one side. Would you care for any?"

"No," I says. "Prunes is a fruit that just spoils in me. I swell all up."

"Well," he says, scraping off half a dozen from the top, "they're full of vitamins."

"I know," I says. "That's why we always buy them in the package. The vitamins don't get into the packages."

After he ate as much as he could stand of the prunes and drunk what he said was coffee, we climbed in the bus and drove over to Morrison's. On the way over I asked him how much Morrison was asking for the heifer.

"Only $35.50," he said, "and she's just coming fresh."

"What's the fifty cents for?"

"That's for the rope, and a dollar for the halter, so she really only comes to $34."

"Cheap enough," I says, "if she milks."

"She'll milk all right," he says hopefully. "Morrison guarantees that."

"Morrison guaranteed me a Poland China sow once," I says. "She wasn't no good raising pigs but she made fair to middling bacon. Old man Morrison's girl Sadie has got considerable of a shape."

"I met her at the Grange dance," the kid sort of stammered, "and I noticed she had blue eyes."

"Blue as a new pair of jumpers," I says. "And them lips of hers are just made for pecking at. She acts sort of stand-offish but if a fellow would just grab her—"

"Look at the sun," he says, "on Mount Sherman. The way it hits that glacier is something pretty!"

Old man Morrison was standing in the front yard with his two boys and the extra hand. The older boy, Perley, was coiling a rope and the young one, Sid, was mending an old halter with a piece of bailing wire. Old man Morrison looked as mean as ever but when he saw us drive in he brightened up like a winter sunset.

"Hullo, Mr. Peavey," he says. "Hallo, Pete. You're up bright and early."

"The early buzzard catches the snake," I says. "How's all the lawsuits?"

"Them lawyers," he says, "keep ahounding me. In the end they take all. But what's a poor man to do?"

457

"Keep out of court," I says. "Where's the heifer?"

"Down in the pasture," he says. "We're all fixed to bring her in."

"I mean Sadie," I says.

"Oh she!" he grunts. "She stays abed 'til 'most noontime. Says the morning air is bad for her complexion. If I thought tanning her hide would do any good—"

"Here's ten dollars down," says Harold stiffly, "and I'll pay the rest at the beginning of next month."

"You wouldn't need a receipt, I take it, Mr. Peavey?"

He was starting to say no when I says, "You bet. Business is business. You just write out the receipt while we go down and fetch the heifer."

"The boys'll do that for you," he says, scowling at me. "They know her better."

We went on in the kitchen where Mrs. Morrison was cooking up a mess of apples. The kitchen was full of the week's wash, the table was heaped with dirty dishes, and a couple of kids was crawling on the floor playing with the butcher knife and a meat chopper.

"You men must be hungry," she says. "Set down and have some apple sauce."

"I'm not hungry," I says, looking around the kitchen, "but maybe Harold here is. He's batching."

"Poor man! He must be starved," she says, and began to ladle apple sauce into a soup bowl that you could see just had oatmeal in it. Mrs. Morrison is good hearted even if she has got a figure like a female walrus.

Harold made a noise in his throat, meaning "No thank you," but hunger got the best of him and he began wolfing down the sauce.

"Sadie has been speaking of you, Mr. Peavey," says Mrs. Morrison, throwing a bunch of diapers into the washtub. "She heard all about your taking the prize for that speech on 'The Club is Mightier than the Pen,' and she thinks you dance real graceful. She'll be sorry to miss you. Maybe if I give her a call she might come down."

"Oh," says Harold, gurgling into the apple sauce, "Don't—please don't disturb her!"

"It's all right," she says, "Sadie was going to town today anyhow." And rolling over to the upstairs door, she calls out, "Sa-die!"

After a few minutes, while I was trying to keep one of the kids from untying my shoelace, a voice like a sick cat calls down, "What do you want, Ma? Can't you ever let me be when I'm trying to get a little rest?"

"There's a young man here to see you," says the Missus, "and he ain't got long to stay."

"Who is it? What does he want to see me for so early in the

morning? Can't he come back in the afternoon? Who is it, anyway?"

"It's Mr. Peavey and he's taking his cow home."

"Oh!" said the voice, sweet as honey. "Tell him to stop a while and I'll be right down!"

I looked at Harold. He had his spoon full of apple sauce half way to his mouth and he'd forgotten about the next bit. His expression was like a calf when it hears the milk pail rattle—sort of eager and vacant.

"Gorry!" I thinks to myself. "The boy is caught! Hope Sadie don't fill out like her ma!"

Just then old man Morrison stuck his head in the outside door.

"The heifer's come up. You'd better take her right along. She's kind of restive."

Harold looked like he'd as lief stay there till moonrise but I took him by the elbow and he got up, pushing back the wobbly kitchen chair. I stooped down to tie the shoelace one of the brats had been playing with and when I looked up again Sadie was standing at the foot of the stairs. I will say she looked pretty, if a man could stand her ways. Her hair was tousled but she'd thrown it up in a coil like a bundle of corn silk, and she had a pink kimono with yellow dots that set off her figure. There aren't many girls that look good just out of bed, but Sadie could get away with it, rubbing her eyes and half smiling at Harold.

"I'm so glad you came over to see me, Harold," she says, holding out her hand. "It was nice of you!"

"Well," said Harold, turning red, "I don't usually come around when people are in bed, but I had to get my cow—"

"Oh," she says coolly, "the cow, of course! I hope you like her! Some day when your mind isn't taken up with your cow you might call around, if I'm home. Anyway, Ma'll be here."

That's the way with the female, always trying to knock the pins out from under a man.

Harold gulped and I says, "He'll be back, missie, don't you worry. He don't give all his time to cows, he's—"

Right then we heard a commotion in the yard and old man Morrison hollering, "Hold her, dod blast it! Keep her out'n them lilies!"

"Well, goodbye, Mr. Peavey," says Mrs. Morrison, wiping her sudsy hands on a dish cloth. "I suppose we can call you Harry?"

"Sure, you could!" says Harold. "I'll be around—"

Old man Morrison stuck his head in the door. He looked sort of red-purple and his eyes was bugged out. "Better take the heifer right along home," he says. "She's feeling skittish this mornin'."

Harold looked calfish again at Sadie, we shook hands all around, and stepped out into the yard. The heifer was there waiting for us, and at first I couldn't make out exactly what they was doing with her. They had slung a hitch in the rope around her horns. One of the Morrison boys had a hold of one end and the other boy had a hold of the other end, and the extra hand was holding onto her halter rope. But what struck me as curious was the cow herself. The Morrisons had one of these rope swings hung from a big oak tree, that the three middle-size Morrison youngsters played in, and the cow was in the swing. I don't mean setting. She had got her front legs and forepart through it so that the rope was under her belly, and she would take a run, dragging the two Morrisons and the extra hand, until the rope brought her up sharp, then she'd back up, kicking like a steer.

Harold looked at her like he was sort of puzzled and says, "She's pretty active for a cow, ain't she?"

"If it was the deer season," I says, "she'd pass for a young buck."

The fact is, Mabel did look more like a deer than anything. She was small, shiny black, and built lean and slender. Pretty, yes. But I couldn't see her as a milker.

"She's all right," old man Morrison mutters. "She'll give milk that's more'n half cream."

"I'd say she'd give butter, the way she's churning," I says.

Mabel put her head down and stood quiet. Perley Morrison yells, "Pa! Slip the swing out from under! She's all tuckered out!"

Before the old man could get to her, though, she made a lunge and brought the swing down out of the tree. Off she went, headed for the road, with the three boys hanging on for dear life. Luckily, the rope swing hooked onto the gate post as she went through and that held her.

"Well," I says to old man Morrison, "she seems to be stopped at the thirty-yard line. Guess we might as well amble along with her. Would you think maybe she'd go better in front or behind the bus?"

"Back up your car and we'll tie her on behind," he says, sort of gruff. "I'll put a half hitch around her muzzle."

I backed up the Ford. Harold climbed in, and they tied her up to the rear springs, with only about three feet of lead rope. Then they got the swing rope out from under her and untied the other one from her horns. All the while she stood quiet as a lamb, like she was meditating.

"Take it easy," says the extra hand. "You don't want to strain her."

"No," I says, putting the bus into low, "I don't want to—"

Right then she made a dive for the car and tried to climb into the rumble seat where I had two sacks of lime, a peck of oats, and a job lot of tools I had lately bought in town. She had got her front hoofs onto the rumble seat and it looked bad for the car, which is an old sport model and none too strong.

"Keep her out," I says to Harold. "We don't want her riding with us."

There was a cant hook in the rumble seat and Harold managed to yank it out. He shoved the end of it against her chest and she got off the car and tried to climb over the right fender. When she found she couldn't make it she headed off the other way, and the car nearly went into the ditch. I put the machine into second and for the next two minutes she did 'most everything an animal can do without twisting itself into knots. She reared, she bucked, side-stepped, swung from side to side, and played the devil with both fenders. Finally she fell down on her knees and I dragged her a dozen feet before I could stop.

"What this heifer seems to want is exercise," I says to Harold, who was beginning to look grim.

"I'll give it to her!" he says beneath his teeth, starting to get out.

"What the hell are you doing, Harold?"

"Going to lead her!"

"Don't be a fool! We'll borrow a horse off Jake Lentz down the road a piece and you can herd her back home. It'll be less wear and tear."

"I was fullback on the Ag. eleven and captain of the track team," he says with a stubborn look, "and I'm going to lead my cow home."

"Oke!" I says. "It's your cow."

While he was walking around the car I untied her halter rope, and thinking he would need some extra line to pay out in case of trouble, I tied onto it a length of stout hemp rope, about thirty feet, that was tucked away in the rumble seat. Mabel never made a move. She was still on her knees, like she was praying.

"I'll stay behind you, Harold," I says as I passed over the rope to him, "and if she starts any monkey business, I'll be right there to help out."

Harold went over and gave her a kick and she scrambled to her feet sort of dazed. He begun to pull her and she followed along like all the spirit had left her.

"See?" he calls out. "All she needs is the right handling."

He hadn't no more than got the words out of his mouth when that cow got into motion, and she had only one speed, which was high. She spun Harold around and the line started running through his hand like a hawser on a big boat but he had sense enough to wrap the end of it twice around his fist. Or maybe it wasn't such good sense either, for when the line was all paid out he started traveling. I guess he must have been a pretty good runner at college for he sure made tracks, sometimes not hitting the ground for a yard or so. When I caught up with them, my speedometer showed they was going exactly fifteen miles an hour. The road here ran straight for half a mile before turning off to our places and for the first quarter Mabel didn't slacken a mite. Then she eased up a bit, to about twelve.

"Whoopee!" I yells. "Stick to her, kid! She's a good pace-maker!"

Harold must have begun to lose some of his wind because I noticed he was maneuvering. The orchards came down close to the road at this point, so that some of the trees hung over it. Harold was trying to pick up enough speed on the heifer so's he could swing off and take a turn around a tree with the line and bring her hard to. But every time he'd make for a tree and get part way around, the cow would be so much ahead that he'd be jerked back around and have to try for another tree further down. I saw he wasn't going to make it that way and for fear he'd go on past the turn I stepped on the gas and shot around them, and at the turn I swung the bus sideways, blocking the road. For a minute I thought Mabel was going to jump right over the car, but I yelled bloody Moses and she swerved off down the home stretch. At Harold's gate I pulled the same trick, and so headed her into his barnyard. In another five minutes the two of us had hauled her into the barn and had her tied tight to a post. Then Harold sat down on the manure pile, looking all in.

"Well, boy," I says, "she's beginning to know her master."

After breathing hard for a few minutes he managed to gasp out, "And believe me, she's going to!"

When he had rested a while we came back on up to my place to get some liniment for Mabel's knees that had been badly skinned and Minnie, my old woman, thinking he looked hungry, passed him out a platter of doughnuts and bowl of apple sauce. He ate them with relish and drank three cups of strong coffee while he explained a new spray formula for Woolly Aphis. About half-past ten we came back down, as I had volunteered to hold Mabel while he bandaged the knees. I wasn't sure but that we would have to hobble her if she was anything like she had been. He was talking about planting nasturtiums in the front yard when we got to the barn.

"Nasturtiums in a center bed and patches of Golden Glow and maybe phlox—"

"It looks to me as if your barn door got kicked off its hinges, Harold," I says.

The barn was pretty old, a good ten years older than the house, and the barn door was lying flat and one plank had been knocked out of it. We looked inside but there was no Mabel. No cow and no post, either. The post she had been tied to was not a part of the frame; it was just a brace and probably not even toe-nailed. Anyway, it was gone. We looked down the waggon road that led to the meadow and we could see a furrow where she had dragged the post.

"She's a mighty strong and vigorous heifer you got, Harold," I says, "but she won't get far with that post. It's as good as a man could do to lift it, let alone a cow. Maybe it's just as well she took the post, she'll learn what it is to go pulling a man's barn apart. About the time she hits a stump or a ditch with that post, she's going to want to come back and be a nice cow."

Harold snorted. "I'll teach her to be a nice cow!" he growled.

"Is that your 'phone ringing?" I asked. Harold listened.

"Three rings—that's mine! Maybe somebody has caught her. Jake Lentz's place comes down to mine on the other side of the meadow. Maybe Jake has caught her and wants me to come and get her."

"I expect anybody that got her *would* want you to come and fetch her," I suggested.

"I'll go find out," he says.

He was gone quite a spell so I had time to smoke a pipeful, setting on the manure pile. I was thinking about the nature of cows in general, and how if they get off on the wrong hoof they are likely to run wild, like this one, same as some women folks, when he come running down, looking sort of wild-eyed and troubled.

"What's up?" I asks.

"Well! I don't know—damned funny! I can't make head nor tail of it. I guess I'm going nuts or else I didn't hear right."

"Has Jake got the cow?"

"No, but he saw her passing through his orchard. She took down a whole row of young Winter Bananas."

"That's no loss, Harold. The Winter Banana is a mighty poor apple. It won't keep and it's losing out in the open market. Now, I had a patch of Winter Bananas that I yanked out—"

"He saw her and ran out of his house and started after her, yelling. She stopped and he thought he had her. He says she couldn't budge that post, walking. But then she made a run and got going with it again at a dead gallop, smashing a row of Delicious—"

"That's too bad! The Delicious is a first rate fruit. Now, I took down a load—"

"And then she disappeared into the Larson place next to his."

"Well, now that's good! She'll never get across the Larson place. Too much barb-wire fences. They'll stop her! Did you call Larson?"

"Yes, I called Larson, and he said he'd go right out and take a look to see what she'd damaged, and—" Again that queer look came over him and he sort of choked out, "after a few minutes Larson rang me back and said—and said . . . that she was up in one of his trees!"

"Aw now, Harold! Larson was just kidding you. Larson is a great kidder."

"He didn't sound like he was kidding. He sounded mad. He said, 'You come quick and take your goddamn cow out of my tree before she spoil him!' "

"So he was mad, eh? He shouldn't get mad about a thing like that! It couldn't be a very big tree if she was up in it."

" 'But that's it!' Larson said. 'That cow she's up in my biggest, best walnut tree. Up clear in the top!' "

I got up off the manure pile. "Look here, Harold," I says, "I don't know which of you is lying or is nuts, but we might as well go and find out. I can swallow anything but about a cow in a walnut tree. Why, I know those walnut trees of Larson and nary one is less than thirty feet tall, and it ain't easy to climb a walnut tree, even for a man, without a ladder. And I *know* that cow didn't go up no ladder—not with that post tied to her! Come on, let's go!"

The trail of Mabel was easy enough to follow. It went down into the meadow and then across the meadow to where she'd taken a panel out of the snake fence on the other side. Then we came into Lentz's orchard and we could see where she'd laid down a row of young Winter Bananas, just as if she'd planned to do it—which, no doubt, she had.

"They're not hurt bad," I says, "just scraped on one side, and they'll all have to be staked again."

We also saw where she'd barked the row of Delicious. She had run straight down the row figuring, I guess, that she couldn't turn a corner with that post. Right at the end of the row Lentz's orchard stopped, and all at once I had a hunch about that walnut tree. The orchards in our valley are all laid out on "benches," and some of them mark the boundary lines. Now Jake's place was on a bench lying about thirty feet on the average above Larson's place. It dropped off so sudden that there was just a narrow fringe of alder thicket between the upper orchard and the lower one. Larson was an economical Swede and he had planted right up to the line. Apples wouldn't do any good so close to a high bank, so he had put in a row of walnuts and they generally brought in a paying crop.

When we pushed through the thicket we saw Mabel. She was astraddle of a crotch in the walnut tree and for once her head was hanging low, for the halter rope was still attached to the post; it was let out as far as it would go, and the end of the post just barely touched the ground. If the rope had been six inches shorter, Mabel would have broke her neck.

Larson was standing under the tree and when he saw us he began to yell, "Take her out! Do you think I want a cow in my best walnut tree? Do you want to make a fool of me, letting a cow in my tree?"

"Shut up!" I yells back. "You'll make her nervous!"

Jake Lentz had come up and no sooner saw what a fix Mabel was in than he said, "Why, that's nothing! I got a hog out of my sixty-foot well once! Don't cut her halter rope till I get back or she'll start to flounder."

He ambled off and after a while came back with his tractor and a lot of heavy ropes and straps. I climbed into the tree and rigged her out in a sort of harness, slung a strand over a higher limb to hold her from hitting against the bank, then Harold cut the halter rope and Lentz drew her out with his tractor. It took a couple of hours and didn't bother nobody much except Larson, who kept dancing around and cursing underneath the tree.

When Harold unhitched her finally and began to lead her home, she followed along as meek and quietly subdued as any cow.

"How about them trees, and the hire of my tractor, and my own time?" Jake asked.

"Don't worry," says Harold. "I'll come over and work it all out."

"Looks to me, Harold," I says, "as if you was doing more work for that cow than she is for you."

"Never mind," he says, stubborn again, "I'll work it out of her!"

He began working it out of her the next morning and kept it up every day for the next three weeks. I was so busy with bud spraying I didn't have a chance to get over for about a week, but I would see him go past with her around 6 A.M. and come back nearly an hour later. The first three mornings she led him, but after he got into training form he led her. And I'm saying they *traveled!* There was a stretch of road the opposite way from Morrison's, about two mile and a quarter. He told me afterwards he'd let her hit her stride the whole way down, then give her five minutes to catch her wind, turn her around and head her back. He didn't get much milk—about a quart a day—but he got plenty of exercise. You'd think Mabel would tire of it. If she did, she didn't give any sign, and he would have to hobble her hind legs when he turned her out in the meadow.

At that, she learned to manage her hind quarters so she could get around, with a motion something like a hobby horse. The funny thing was, so far as milking went, she was docile enough. Just so soon as Harold would set down on the old wobbly milking stool, she'd turn and look at him, contented and satisfied, and if she had been a cat she would have purred.

It came Sunday so I ambled over to see how Harold was making out. He was stirring up something in a big bowl that he said was going to be corn fritters, but I told him my stomach was delicate and we fell to talking.

"How's the heifer, Harold?" I says.

"I don't give her any rest in the morning. First thing, I go down and give her a kick—"

"I mean Sadie. How are you and Sadie hitting it off?"

"Oh, Sadie's too hightoned for me. I called her up three times and she said she had a date each time. It's that lawyer, Murfree, from Portland. He's handling a couple of her dad's lawsuits and he's got a Cadillac. I was coming back from Lentz's Wednesday when they passed me, going lickety-split. Sadie didn't even wave. Well, if she gets him I guess she'll be coming into a little piece of jack. It's jake with me. I guess when I've put in three or four years on this place, I'll pick me a girl who doesn't set so much store by mere wealth."

"If Sadie's set her cap for Murfree, she's not going to win no prize studhorse. He's slicker'n a whistle and slipperier than a greased pig. Wait till he puts in his bill to the old man. Maybe she won't fancy him so well."

"It makes no difference to me who she fancies," he says. I could see he didn't want to talk about Sadie so I changed the subject to water coring and dry rot. After he had stowed away his mess of corn fritters, or whatever they was, he said, "I want you to come down and see a little contrivance I've rigged up for Mabel. I found something in the barn that's going to improve her disposition a lot."

"A goad?"

"No, I don't believe in using harsh methods in dealing with a cow. They're like human beings, you have to analyze 'em psychologically, then treat their complexes."

"I've always used Glover's Horse Tonic," I says. "It works for cows the same as horses."

"I don't mean that sort of remedy, Pete. It's for what is wrong in their heads. Now take Mabel. She's got a complex on running. Maybe she was repressed when she was a calf and couldn't run. Now she just *has* to run. Well to treat that, you have to let her run as much as she wants, but you have to direct her running, 'channel' it, as they say."

"I don't know," I says, "about channeling a cow to run. I'd rather channel her to milk."

"That will come later," he says.

We got to the barn and he showed me what he had fixed up for Mabel. It was a racing sulky, all painted bright and new, in green, with red trimming on the wheels.

"By gorry!" I says. "You ain't going to hitch the heifer onto that rig, are you?"

"Sure as shooting," he says. "And I've greased the wheels and oiled up the harness. I had to adjust the harness. The belly band had to be lengthened, and of course there's no bit. You can't drive a cow like you can a horse—no use trying! And she doesn't need a check rein. She runs with her head up." It was plain that he was mighty proud of his work.

"I'm not throwing a wet blanket on your project, Harold," I says, "but how do you aim to stop her or turn her?"

"I won't have to. If I'm right about this, she'll stop herself and turn around. She does it every morning now. I've conditioned her to do it and she'll keep on."

"I hope you're right, Harold," I says, "but you had better be ready to jump—in case she don't stay in condition."

"I'll tell you, Pete, I intend to try her out tomorrow. I'm pretty sure she'll work into it all right, but I'd like to have you down at the end of the stretch, and if she starts to go through the fence where the roads turns, you could stop her with a pitchfork."

"I don't know about stopping her, but I'll be mighty glad to be there and tell you when to jump."

So the next morning I told Minnie I had to have an early breakfast on account of going up to the head-gate to see about the irrigation, and at quarter to six I was driving down to the turn. I hadn't been there five minutes and was just taking the first puff on the corncob when I saw them coming over the rise about a mile away. I will say this for Mabel, she had lots of style and no end of speed as a racer. She had as pretty a pace as any gelding that ever come down a track and she never broke her gait in the whole two miles. When they got nearer it was fine sight, with the rising sun making the new-painted wheels all a glitter of whizzing spokes and Harold holding onto the reins, which was more for decoration than use as they was fastened onto the halter.

I had jumped from the car and had my pitchfork ready. For a minute I thought I'd have to go into action and was just getting ready to holler to Harold to jump when she pulled up so sudden that Harold went right out of his little seat and landed plumb on her back. He fell off as Mabel came to a dead halt. Then, without his saying a word, she turned around. Off she went again, quick as lightning, and Harold, being taken by surprise, stood there with his mouth open.

"Oh well," he says, "it's no use my trying to catch her. She'll run right to the barn."

"Harold," I says, "you sure have got confidence in that cow!"

"It isn't confidence in her," he says. "I just know my psychology."

"Harold," I says, "I hope Larson isn't getting home from one of his all-night jags. If that cow passes him the way she's going, he's going right into D.T.'s!"

You might think that Harold Peavey's fast cow would get noised about the neighborhood but there were several things in the way of it. For instance, the hour of day, which was either milking or breakfast time. Then, it was the season when everybody was in a rush to get the spring work done and the first spray on the trees. Mainly it was because Harold and I were the only ones on our road except a shack that hadn't been occupied in ten years, and then only partly, the owner having been a half-wit. I didn't see much of Harold myself except Sundays while Minnie was taking herself to the United Congregational Church and that would give me a little time to rest. I found out in May that he'd gone so far in his cow-training that he was able to cut down the morning workouts without Mabel getting restless, and he was getting two quarts of rich milk a day. As for his orchard, I've seen worse. Considering the time he had to work out for his neighbors, training Mabel, and thinking about Sadie, he didn't do so bad for the first year. At any rate, he rubbed off a lot he'd learned down at the Ag.

Sadie I saw a couple of times when her old man and me was negotiating over a boar-pig. Once I says to her, "Sadie, that young Peavey sure is a hustler! He's getting his place into jim-dandy shape. Wouldn't surprise me none if he went wife-hunting one of these days."

"Well!" she said, tossing her mop of corn-silk hair. "Now that's news! I thought he was a born bachelor. I hope he gets one that likes to cook and scrub dirty clothes and tend chickens and garden, for I don't!"

"Oh, I don't know," I says. "Some girls like it better when there's a husky young buck on the place than riding with an old codger that's half mummy!"

"Are you telling *me*?" she says saucily. "Thanks for your kind advice, Mr. Crumm! I prefer roses!"

"Humph!" I says. "To me they look prettier on the vine than wired up in a florist's shop!"

Old man Morrison, while he was arguing over the boar-pig, said that Murfree had gone back to Portland but was coming down again in June when one of his cases came to trial.

By the time June come along Harold told me he had cut the driving down to once a week. He said Mabel didn't like it but he had irrigation on his hands and was in the middle of cultivating the orchard and an acre of carrots. Besides he was deep in cookery, studying cookbooks, and trying his hand at Birds'-Nest Pudding, Aunty Phelps' Pie crust, and such. I told Minnie he was looking peaked and she invited him to Sunday dinners.

One Sunday, the last week in June, Harold was at our place for dinner. While Minnie was putting the finishing touches to chicken

468

with dumplings, he was poring over the Sunday edition of the *Tilla-mook Gazette.*

"Say!" he said suddenly, sort of excited. "I see there's going to be big doings at Tillamook on Fourth of July."

"Always is. Parade and fireworks and speeches."

"And racing!"

"Yep! They open up the county fair grounds for some racing. But it ain't much. Just local talent. Still, there's some pretty fast horses in the county and sometimes you see quite a few fast heats. I remember last year—"

"Look here, Pete," he says, shoving the paper at me. "Read that and tell me what it says."

I took the paper and read, " 'Final Event. Free-for-all One Mile Race for Drivers. All classes of racers may be entered and any style gig. This classic event, for one heat only, takes a purse of $100. Entries accepted up to the last minute.' That," I says, "is the windup of the whole shebang. And what a sight it is! Plenty of fun, too. Usually a couple of wrecks and a few wheels lost. Now I remember the year the President stopped over—"

"Does it say anywhere in that announcement that the racers have got to be *horses?*"

I looked at Harold with my eyes bugged out. "Young fellow," I says, "just what have you got on your mind?"

We kept the whole thing a dead secret. The rest was simple. I hooked the sulky on behind the Ford and drove over on July 3. We made a deal with Jake Lentz to take Mabel over in his truck the same day, telling him she had to be treated at the veterinary for milk fever. He was going over for a load of fertilizer anyway, so he said he'd do it for $5, but we would have to get her back some other way.

It was a broiling hot day and Tillamook was jammed. There was a parade of Boy Scouts, firemen, and Knights of Pythias in uniforms that made them look sort of proud and desperate. There were plenty of speeches, ending up with a long one by Lawyer Murfree. He kept wiping his bald head with a silk handerchief and talking about the Constitution till my throat went plumb dry and I had to find the nearest bar. We stayed there an hour or two drinking beers, then we ambled over to the fair grounds where I'd parked the sulky in a shed off in a patch of fir near the track. Harold had brought Mabel over there and while they were running off the first heats he curry-combed her until she shone all over like a black silk purse.

"The only thing that worries me, Pete," he says, "is whether she'll stick to a circular road. She's used to a straightaway, but if I can get

469

her next to the fence I know she'll follow it because there's a fence runs along our stretch back home, and she's conditioned to a fence. How long is the track?"

"It's an even mile. How'll you stop her when she passes the judges' stand?"

"Oh, that won't matter. If she runs beyond, it makes no difference. They can't disqualify her for going over the finish line a piece. Anyway, if she runs too far, I can make a jump from the seat and bull-dog her. I guess I could steer her by the horns if I had to."

"Well, Harold," I says, "I'll be rooting for you and her." I looked at my watch. It was a quarter to four and the free-for-all was scheduled at four sharp. "Guess we'd better hitch up," I says.

We hitched up. Harold took hold of the lead rope, and we pulled over toward the starting line. The grandstands were packed from top to bottom and about a thousand cars were parked around the track. The crowd was milling around so and raising such a hullabaloo over each entry, what with the various kinds of vehicles in the race, that they didn't hardly notice our entry till we pulled up before the judges' box. Then they busted loose plenty. Harold walked over, holding out a five dollar bill, and says, "I'm entering my racer, Mabel."

One of the judges turned red as a beet, like he was mad, and the other two began laughing fit to kill.

"You can't enter a cow," says the red-faced one.

"Oh yes I can!" says Harold, cool as a cucumber. He had the announcement with him and handed it over to the judge. "Read that," he says, "and see if it says anything about disqualifying racing cows."

"I say, you can't enter that animal!" bellows Red-face. "This is no cattleshow!"

Just then Judge Olney, whom I knew personal, pushed his way through and says, "What's the trouble?"

"This man," the other judge bawls, "is trying to enter a cow in the last race!"

"Well," says Olney politely, "why not?" He winked at the other two judges.

"It's a free-for-all, isn't it?"

"That's right, judge," says one of the others. "I guess a good-looking cow like that one has as good a right to run as some of them nags out on the track that look like they was ready for the bone yard!"

The upshot was that the judges voted, two to one, to allow Mabel to run. Harold filled out a card and led her over to the starting line. If you had looked at her then, you would have said she was just getting ready to be milked, she was that docile. The rest of the entries were snorting and neighing and prancing, and the drivers was all yelling "Whoa!" and "Git up, there!" but Harold climbed into his seat and said nothing, and Mabel stood with her front hoofs just touching the line, as if she had her mind on green fodder.

One of the judges took a megaphone and hollered, "Now, men, there won't be no false starts. When the gun goes, you just lick in to it, and the first one home wins."

Then the starter fired his gun and they started off. Mabel was three places away from the inside fence and for a minute I didn't think she'd start at all. She took a few short steps, then she sort of ambled for about ten yards, and finally she settled down to her pace. By that time the rest of the field was a good twenty-five yards ahead of her and there was nobody between her and the fence. She turned right in and stuck to it from then on. At the first turn the other drivers was still a good bit ahead of Harold, but the crowd was yelling like mad, throwing up their hats and ice-cream cones, and leaning on each other laughing. On the far side of the track she began to pick up on them. At the other turn she had passed all but three of the horses, one of them being a big gray mare, a trotter, and in the profession class. I heard that she belonged to Murfree. Her name was Peaches-and-Cream, and they said Murfree was trying her out before sending her south to the big tracks. Harold told me afterward that at the turn Peaches-and-Cream either caught a whiff of Mabel or heard the sound she made, which was a sort of fierce "moo!" At any rate, Peaches-and-Cream suddenly broke. She reared and jumped sideways, and Mabel passed her in a cloud of dust while the crowd went mad.

They came down the home stretch, Mabel running neck and neck with a sorrel gelding. That made me feel pretty good for in the first two minutes of the race I had placed two five-dollar bets on Mabel at ten to one.

She pulled away from the gelding and came over the line with three yards to spare. I guess you never heard such a rumpus!

When the yelling died down a little, the man with the megaphone yelled, "Mabel wins first place! Grand Mogul, second! Peaches-and-Cream, third!"

But Mabel was still going. If anything, she picked up a little speed on the second lap. I'm telling you, that was a cow! Nobody on the track or in the grandstand thought she'd keep up more than half way around, but she did. The finish line was like it is after a race. There was still gigs and sulkies standing around and little crowds milling around them, all talking and arguing when somebody hollered, "Look out! Here comes that cow!"

She drove through them like a whirlwind, stopped dead just beyond the judges' stand, turned around, and started back. By that time there was wild horses all over the place. Drivers was tangled up every way, and the loafers on the track broke and ran for cover like a flock of quail. When she come around the reverse way, some misguided fool, thinking the cow had gone loco, ran out with a horse blanket and tried to stop her by waving the blanket.

She hit the blanket square and it settled down over her and Harold but she kept right on going. I guess with the blanket over her head she must have lost her direction for she made a beeline straight off the track, taking out a section of guard rail, and headed for the cars that were parked all over the grounds. I heard a crash and started running.

When I got up where it happened there was a crowd standing around looking at Harold. He was sitting on top of a limousine, wrapped in a blanket; one of the shafts of the sulky had gone through the top and the other had busted off. Mabel wasn't nowhere.

He stuck his head up out of the blanket, looking sort of dazed, and asked, "Did we win?"

"Hands down!" I yelled, reaching up to help him down.

On the way back home, Harold was feeling pretty blue about losing Mabel. We had traced her as far as the edge of town but we couldn't get any word of her after that.

"Well, Harold," I says, to cheer him up, "she ain't a total loss! After all, you paid $34 for her and she brought in a hundred-buck prize, that leaves a good profit even deducting the damage to Jake Lentz's orchard."

"Yeah?" he says gloomily. "Didn't you hear that circus fellow offer me five hundred on the spot for her?"

About five o'clock in the afternoon of the fourth day after the race, Harold come running over to my place. I could see right off he was all steamed up about something.

"She's come home!" he panted. "Walked right into the barn and stood in her stall, waiting to be milked! She looks pretty worn down and she didn't give more than half a pint of milk, but hell! she's no milker, anyway; she's a racer! I'll fix up the old sulky, break her in again, and sell her for five hundred!"

Well, Harold went to work on her and I'll say he worked hard. He let her rest up two days, then he hitched her up, and took her out for a spin. But she wouldn't spin, no sir, not even a slow trot! She wouldn't do any more than an ordinary cow! He fooled around with her a while and I came out to help, but it wasn't any good; she'd turn around and look at us, all meek and gentle, like she was asking what in the world we were up to, and then she'd start, the way cows do, at a walk so slow you could pick daisies and keep up with her! Just seemed like the old racing spirit was gone. After a week of trying, Harold gave up.

472

"I'm beaten," he said, "and plumb disgusted! She don't milk and she don't run; I guess I'll have to beef her!"

Luckily, while he was making up his mind and too busy to take her down to the butcher, she began to show signs of being in the family way. In another few weeks it was plain enough she was going to calve. Well, we talked it over and decided that on the way back from Tillamook she must have dawdled.

"I guess," said Harold, "her racing days are over."

The piebald bull calf, when it came, was as pretty as a picture and built like a fawn. At first Harold thought of training it to be a racer like its mother, and maybe breeding a strain of fast cows but I argued that after that race they'd never let another bovine enter a track with horses, so he gave the calf to Sadie, which was a good thing because Harold for all of his studying hadn't really learned to cook.

He's got other cows now but they keep Mabel for sentiment.

Doubtless that noble American tradition the lying match best flourishes in the close neighborhood of a cracker-barrel or a campfire, but these adjuncts are not absolutely necessary. Owen Wister describes a Homeric one whose background is a railway track, and Frank R. Stockton provides a setting and a victorious narrator of even more original type; but Stockton was nothing if not original. Incidentally, the two stories are very instructive in their documentation of two kinds of American humor. It is an Eastern woman in Wister's narrative who says indignantly of the Virginian: "He's merely making that stuff up out of his head," whereas her husband, Eastern but male, says with more discernment: "This beats the geysers or anything we're likely to find in the Yellowstone." The widow Ducket would have understood this.

In Wister's story there is the tension of strong latent hostility between the narrators; in Stockton's, merely the desire to give as good as you get. But both are little classics.

Trampas and the Virginian[1]

It has happened to you, has it not, to wake in the morning and wonder for a while where on earth you are? Thus I came half to life in the caboose, hearing voices, but not the actual words at first.

But presently, "Hathaway!" said some one more clearly. "Portland 1291!"

This made no special stir in my intelligence, and I drowsed off again to the pleasant rhythm of the wheels. The little shock of stopping next brought me to, somewhat, with the voices still round me; and when we were again in motion, I heard: "Rosebud! Portland 1279!" These figures jarred me awake, and I said, "It was 1291 before," and sat up in my blankets.

The greeting they vouchsafed and the sight of them clustering expressionless in the caboose brought last evening's uncomfortable memory back to me. Our next stop revealed how things were going to-day.

[1] From Owen Wister: *The Virginian* (New York: The Macmillan Co.; 1902), pp. 174–200. By permission of The Macmillan Company, publishers.

474

"Forsythe," one of them read on the station. "Portland 1266."
They were counting the lessening distance westward. This was the undercurrent of war. It broke on me as I procured fresh water at Forsythe and made some toilet in their stolid presence. We were drawing nearer the Rawhide station—the point, I mean, where you left the railway for the new mines. Now Rawhide station lay this side of Billings. The broad path of desertion would open ready for their feet when the narrow path to duty and Sunk Creek was still some fifty miles more to wait. Here was Trampas's great strength; he need make no move meanwhile, but lie low for the immediate temptation to front and waylay them and win his battle over the deputy foreman. But the Virginian seemed to find nothing save enjoyment in this sunny September morning, and ate his breakfast at Forsythe serenely.

That meal done and that station gone, our caboose took up again its easy trundle by the banks of the Yellowstone. The mutineers sat for a while digesting in idleness.

"What's your scar?" inquired one at length, inspecting casually the neck of his neighbor.

"Foolishness," the other answered.

"Yourn?"

"Mine."

"Well, I don't know but I prefer to have myself to thank for a thing," said the first.

"I was displaying myself," continued the second. "One day last summer it was. We come on a big snake by Torrey Creek corral. The boys got betting pretty lively that I dassent make my word good as to dealing with him, so I loped my cayuse full tilt by Mr. Snake, and swung down and catched him up by the tail from the ground, and cracked him same as a whip, and snapped his head off. You've saw it done?" he said to the audience.

The audience nodded wearily.

"But the loose head flew agin me, and the fangs caught. I was pretty sick for a while."

"It don't pay to be clumsy," said the first man. "If you'd snapped the snake away from yu' instead of toward yu', its head would have whirled off into the brush, same as they do with me."

"How like a knife-cut your scar looks!" said I.

"Don't it?" said the snake-snapper. "There's many that gets fooled by it."

"An antelope knows a snake is his enemy," said another to me. "Ever seen a buck circling round and round a rattler?"

"I have always wanted to see that," said I, heartily. For this I knew to be a respectable piece of truth.

"It's worth seeing," the man went on. "After the buck gets close in, he gives an almighty jump up in the air, and down comes his four hoofs in a bunch right on top of Mr. Snake. Cuts him all to hash. Now you tell me how the buck knows that."

Of course I could not tell him. And again we sat in silence for a while—friendlier silence, I thought.

"A skunk'll kill yu' worse than a snake bite," said another presently. "No, I don't mean that way," he added. For I had smiled. "There is a brown skunk down in Arkansaw. Kind of a prairie-dog brown. Littler than our variety, he is. And he is mad the whole year round, same as a dog gets. Only the dog has a spell and dies; but this here Arkansaw skunk is mad right along, and it don't seem to interfere with his business in other respects. Well, suppose you're camping out, and suppose it's a hot night, or you're in a hurry, and you've made camp late, or anyway you haven't got inside any tent, but you have just bedded down in the open. Skunk comes travelling along and walks on your blanket. You're warm. He likes that, same as a cat does. And he tramps with pleasure and comfort, same as a cat. And you move. You get bit, that's all. And you die of hydrophobia. Ask anybody."

"Most extraordinary!" said I. "But did you ever see a person die from this?"

"No, sir. Never happened to. My cousin at Bald Knob did."

"Died?"

"No, sir. Saw a man."

"But how do you know they're not sick skunks?"

"No, sir! They're well skunks. Well as anything. You'll not meet skunks in any state of the Union more robust than them in Arkansaw. And thick."

"That's awful true," sighed another. "I have buried hundreds of dollars worth of clothes in Arkansaw."

"Why didn't yu' travel in a sponge bag?" inquired Scipio. And this brought a slight silence.

"Speakin' of bites," spoke up a new man, "how's that?" He held up his thumb.

"My!" breathed Scipio. "Must have been a lion."

The man wore a wounded look. "I was huntin' owl eggs for a botanist from Boston," he explained to me.

"Chiropodist, weren't he?" said Scipio. "Or maybe a sonnabulator?"

"No, honest," protested the man with the thumb; so that I was sorry for him, and begged him to go on.

"I'll listen to you," I assured him. And I wondered why this politeness of mine should throw one or two of them into stifled mirth. Scipio, on the other hand, gave me a disgusted look and sat back

476

sullenly for a moment, and then took himself out on the platform, where the Virginian was lounging.

"The young feller wore knee-pants and ever so thick spectacles with a half-moon cut in 'em," resumed the narrator, "and he carried a tin box strung to a strap I took for his lunch till it flew open on him and a horn toad hustled out. Then I was sure he was a botanist—or whatever yu' say they're called. Well, he would have owl eggs—them little prairie-owl that some claim can turn their head clean around and keep a-watchin' yu', only that's nonsense. We was ridin' through that prairie-dog town, used to be on the flat just after yu' crossed the south fork of Powder River on the Buffalo trail, and I said I'd dig an owl nest out for him if he was willin' to camp till I'd dug it. I wanted to know about them owls some myself—if they did live with the dogs and snakes, yu' know," he broke off, appealing to me.

"Oh, yes," I told him eagerly.

"So while the botanist went glarin' around the town with his glasses to see if he could spot a prairie-dog and an owl usin' the same hole, I was diggin' in a hole I'd seen an owl run down. And that's what I got." He held up his thumb again.

"The snake!" I exclaimed.

"Yes, sir. Mr. Rattler was keepin' house that day. Took me right there. I hauled him out of the hole hangin' to me. Eight rattles."

"Eight!" said I. "A big one."

"Yes, sir. Thought I was dead. But the woman—"

"The woman?" said I.

"Yes, woman. Didn't I tell yu' the botanist had his wife along? Well, he did. And she acted better than the man, for he was losin' his head, and shoutin' he had no whiskey, and he didn't guess his knife was sharp enough to amputate my thumb, and none of us chewed, and the doctor was twenty miles away, and if he had only remembered to bring his ammonia—well, he was screechin' out most everything he knew in the world, and without arranging it any, neither. But she just clawed his pocket and burrowed and kep' yelling, 'Give him the stone, Augustus!' And she whipped out one of them Injun medicine-stones, —first one I ever seen—and she clapped it on to my thumb, and it started in right away."

"What did it do?" said I.

"Sucked. Like blotting-paper does. Soft and funny it was, and gray. They get 'em from elks' stomachs, yu' know. And when it had sucked the poison out of the wound, off it falls of my thumb by itself! And I thanked the woman for saving my life that capable and keeping her head that cool. I never knowed how excited she had been till afterward. She was awful shocked."

477

"I suppose she started to talk when the danger was over," said I, with deep silence around me.

"No; she didn't say nothing to me. But when her next child was born, it had eight rattles."

Din now rose wild in the caboose. They rocked together. The enthusiast beat his knee tumultuously. And I joined them. Who could help it? It had been so well conducted from the imperceptible beginning. Fact and falsehood blended with such perfect art. And this last, an effect so new made with such world-old material! I cared nothing that I was the victim, and I joined them; but ceased, feeling suddenly somehow estranged or chilled. It was in their laughter. The loudness was too loud. And I caught the eyes of Trampas fixed upon the Virginian with exultant malevolence. Scipio's disgusted glance was upon me from the door.

Dazed by these signs, I went out on the platform to get away from the noise. There the Virginian said to me: "Cheer up! You'll not be so easy for 'em that-a-way next season."

He said no more; and with his legs dangled over the railing, appeared to resume his newspaper.

"What's the matter?" said I to Scipio.

"Oh, I don't mind if he don't," Scipio answered. "Couldn't yu' see? I tried to head 'em off from yu' all I knew, but yu' just ran in among 'em yourself. Couldn't yu' see? Kep' hinderin' and spoilin' me with askin' those urgent questions of yourn—why, I had to let yu' go your way! Why, that wasn't the ordinary play with the ordinary tenderfoot they treated yu' to! You ain't a common tenderfoot this trip. You're the foreman's friend. They've hit him through you. That's the way they count it. It's made them encouraged. Can't yu' see?"

Scipio stated it plainly. And as we ran by the next station, "Howard!" they harshly yelled. "Portland 1256!"

We had been passing gangs of workmen on the track. And at that last yell the Virginian rose. "I reckon I'll join the meeting again," he said. "This filling and repairing looks like the washout might have been true."

"Washout?" said Scipio.

"Big Horn bridge, they say—four days ago."

"Then I wish it came this side Rawhide station."

"Do yu'?" drawled the Virginian. And smiling at Scipio, he lounged in through the open door.

"He beats me," said Scipio, shaking his head. "His trail is turrble hard to anticipate."

We listened.

"Work bein' done on the road, I see," the Virginian was saying, very friendly and conversational.

478

"We see it too," said the voice of Trampas.

"Seem to be easin' their grades some."

"Roads do."

"Cheaper to build 'em the way they want 'em at the start, a man would think," suggested the Virginian, most friendly. "There go some more I-talians."

"They're Chinese," said Trampas.

"That's so," acknowledged the Virginian, with a laugh.

"What's he monkeyin' at now?" muttered Scipio.

"Without cheap foreigners they couldn't afford all this hyeh new gradin'," the Southerner continued.

"Grading! Can't you tell when a flood's been eating the banks?"

"Why, yes," said the Virginian, sweet as honey. "But 'ain't yu' heard of the improvements west of Big Timber, all the way to Missoula this season? I'm talkin' about them."

"Oh! Talking about them. Yes, I've heard."

"Good money-savin' scheme, ain't it?" said the Virginian. "Lettin' a freight run down one hill an' up the next as far as she'll go without steam, an' shavin' the hill down to that point." Now this was an honest engineering fact. "Bettern settin' dudes squintin' through telescopes an' cipherin' over one per cent re-ductions," the Southerner commented.

"It's common sense," assented Trampas. "Have you heard the new scheme about the water-tanks?"

"I ain't right certain," said the Southerner.

"I must watch this," said Scipio, "or I shall bust." He went in, and so did I.

They were all sitting over this discussion of the Northern Pacific's recent policy as to betterments, as though they were the board of directors. Pins could have dropped. Only nobody would have cared to hear a pin.

"They used to put all their tanks at the bottom of their grades," said Trampas.

"Why, yu' get the water easier at the bottom."

"You can pump it to the top, though," said Trampas, growing superior. "And it's cheaper."

"That gets me," said the Virginian, interested.

"Trains after watering can start down hill now and get the benefit of the gravity. It'll cut down operating expenses a heap."

"That's cert'nly common sense," exclaimed the Virginian, absorbed. "But ain't it kind o' tardy?"

"Live and learn. So they gained speed, too. High speed on half the coal this season, until the accident."

"Accident!" said the Virginian, instantly.

479

"Yellowstone Limited. Man fired at engine-driver. Train was flying past that quick the bullet broke every window and killed a passenger on the back platform. You've been running too much with aristocrats," finished Trampas, and turned on his heel.

"Haw, haw!" began the enthusiast, but his neighbor gripped him to silence. This was a triumph too serious for noise. Not a mutineer moved; and I felt cold.

"Trampas," said the Virginian, "I thought yu'd be afeard to try it on me."

Trampas whirled round. His hand was at his belt. "Afraid!" he sneered.

"Shorty!" said Scipio, sternly, and leaping upon that youth, took his half-drawn pistol from him.

"I'm obliged to yu'," said the Virginian to Shorty.

Trampas's hand left his belt. He threw a slight, easy look at his men, and keeping his back to the Virginian, walked out on the platform and sat on the chair where the Virginian had sat so much.

"Don't you comprehend," said the Virginian to Shorty, amiably, "that this hyeh question has been discussed peaceable by civilized citizens? Now you sit down and be good, and Mr. Le Moyne will return your gun when we're across that broken bridge, if they have got it fixed for heavy trains yet."

"This train will be lighter when it gets to that bridge," spoke Trampas, out on his chair.

"Why, that's true, too!" said the Virginian. "Maybe none of us are crossin' that Big Horn bridge now, except me. Funny if yu' should end by persuadin' me to quit and go to Rawhide myself! But I reckon I'll not. I reckon I'll worry along to Sunk Creek, somehow."

"Don't forget I'm cookin' for yu'," said Scipio, gruffly.

"I'm obliged to yu'," said the Southerner.

"You were speaking of a job for me," said Shorty.

"I'm right obliged. But yu' see—I ain't exackly foreman, the way this comes out, and my promises might not bind Judge Henry to pay salaries."

A push came through the train from forward. We were slowing for the Rawhide station, and all began to be busy and to talk. "Going up to the mines today?" "Oh, let's grub first." "Guess it's too late, anyway." And so forth; while they rolled and roped their bedding, and put on their coats with a good deal of elbow motion, and otherwise showed off. It was wasted. The Virginian did not know what was going on in the caboose. He was leaning and looking out ahead, and Scipio's puzzled eye never left him. And as we halted for the water-tank, the Southerner exclaimed, "They 'ain't got away yet!" as if it were good news to him.

He meant the delayed trains. Four stalled expresses were in front of us, besides several freights. And two hours more at least before the bridge would be ready.

Travellers stood and sat about forlorn, near the cars, out in the sage-brush, anywhere. People in hats and spurs watched them, and Indian chiefs offered painted bows and arrows and shiny horns.

"I reckon them passengers would prefer a laig o' mutton," said the Virginian to a man loafing near the caboose.

"Bet your life!" said the man. "First lot has been stuck here four days."

"Plumb starved, ain't they?" inquired the Virginian.

"Bet your life! They've eat up their dining-cars and they've eat up this town."

"Well," said the Virginian, looking at the town, "I expaict the dining-cyars contained more nourishment."

"Say, you're about right there!" said the man. He walked beside the caboose as we puffed slowly forward from the water-tank to our siding. "Fine business here if we'd only been ready," he continued. "And the Crow agent has let his Indians come over from the reservation. There has been a little beef brought in, and game, and fish. And big money in it, bet your life! Them Eastern passengers has just been robbed. I wisht I had somethin' to sell!"

"Anything starting for Rawhide this afternoon?" said Trampas, out of the caboose door.

"Not until morning," said the man. "You going to the mines?" he resumed to the Virginian.

"Why," answered the Southerner, slowly and casually, and address-ing himself strictly to the man, while Trampas, on his side, paid ob-vious inattention, "this hyeh delay, yu' see, may unsettle our plans some. But it'll be one of two ways,—we're all goin' to Rawhide, or we're all goin' to Billings. We're all one party, yu' see."

Trampas laughed audibly inside the door as he rejoined his men. "Let him keep up appearances," I heard him tell them. "It don't hurt us what he says to strangers."

"But I'm goin' to eat hearty either way," continued the Virginian. "And I ain' goin' to be robbed. I've been kind o' promising myself a treat if we stopped hyeh."

"Town's eat clean out," said the man.

"So yu' tell me. But all you folks has forgot one source of revenue that yu' have right close by, mighty handy. If you have got a gunny sack, I'll show you how to make some money."

"Bet your life!" said the man.

"Mr. Le Moyne," said the Virginian, "the outfit's cookin' stuff is aboard, and if you'll get the fire ready, we'll try how frawgs' laigs go fried." He walked off at once, the man following like a dog. Inside the caboose rose a gust of laughter.

"Frogs!" muttered Scipio. And then turning a blank face to me, "Frogs?"

"Colonel Cyrus Jones had them on his bill of fare," I said. " *'Frogs' Legs a la Delmonico.'* "

"Shoo! I didn't get up that thing. They had it when I came. Never looked at it. Frogs?" He went down the steps very slowly, with a long frown. Reaching the ground, he shook his head. "That man's trail is surely hard to anticipate," he said. "But I must hurry up that fire. For his appearance has given me encouragement," Scipio concluded, and became brisk. Shorty helped him, and I brought wood. Trampas and the other people strolled off to the station, a compact band.

Our little fire was built beside the caboose, so the cooking things might be easily reached and put back. You would scarcely think such operations held any interest, even for the hungry, when there seemed to be nothing to cook. A few sticks blazing tamely in the dust, a frying-pan, half a tin bucket of lard, some water, and barren plates and knives and forks, and three silent men attending to them—that was all. But the travellers came to see. These waifs drew near us, and stood, a sad, lorn, shifting fringe of audience; four to begin with; and then two wandered away; and presently one of these came back, finding it worse elsewhere. "Supper, boys?" said he. "Breakfast," said Scipio crossly. And no more of them addressed us. I heard them joylessly mention Wall Street to each other, and Saratoga; I even heard the name Bryn Mawr, which is near Philadelphia. But these fragments of home dropped in the wilderness here in Montana beside a freight caboose were of no interest to me now.

"Looks like frogs down there, too," said Scipio. "See them marshy sloos full of weeds?" We took a little turn and had a sight of the Virginian quite active among the ponds. "Hush! I'm getting some thoughts," continued Scipio. "He wasn't sorry enough. Don't interrupt me."

"I'm not," said I.

"No. But I'd 'most caught a-hold." And Scipio muttered to himself again, "He wasn't sorry enough." Presently he swore loud and brilliantly. "Tell yu'!" he cried. "What did he say to Trampas after that play they exchanged over railroad improvements and Trampas put the josh on him? Didn't he say, 'Trampas, I thought you'd be afraid to do it?' Well, sir, Trampas had better have been afraid. And that's what it meant. There's where he was bringin' it to. Trampas made an awful bad play then. You wait. Glory, but he's a knowin' man! Course he wasn't sorry. I guess he had the hardest kind of work to look as sorry as he did. You wait."

"Wait? What for? Go on, man! What for?"

"I don't know! I don't know! Whatever hand he's been holdin' up, this is the show-down. He's played for a show-down here before the caboose gets off the bridge. Come back to the fire, or Shorty'll be leavin' it go out. Grow happy some, Shorty!" he cried on arriving, and his hand cracked on Shorty's shoulder. "Supper's in sight, Shorty. Food for reflection."

"None for the stomach?" asked the passenger who had spoken once before.

"We're figuring on that, too," said Scipio. His crossness had melted entirely away.

"Why, they're cowboys!" exclaimed another passenger; and he moved nearer.

From the station Trampas now came back, his herd following him less compactly. They had found famine, and no hope of supplies until the next train from the East. This was no fault of Trampas's; but they were following him less compactly. They carried one piece of cheese, the size of a fist, the weight of a brick, the hue of a corpse. And the passengers, seeing it, exclaimed, "There is Old Faithful again!" and took off their hats.

"You gentlemen met that cheese before, then?" said Scipio, delighted.

"It's been offered me three times a day for four days," said the passenger. "Did he want a dollar or a dollar and a half?"

"Two dollars!" blurted out the enthusiast. And all of us save Trampas fell into fits of imbecile laughter.

"Here comes our grub, anyway," said Scipio, looking off toward the marshes. And his hilarity sobered away in a moment.

"Well, the train will be in soon," stated Trampas. "I guess we'll get a decent supper without frogs."

All interest now settled upon the Virginian. He was coming with his man and his gunny sack, and the gunny sack hung from his shoulder heavily, as a full sack should. He took no notice of the gathering, but sat down and partly emptied the sack. "There," said he, very businesslike, to his assistant, "that's all we'll want. I think you'll find a ready market for the balance."

"Well, my gracious!" said the enthusiast. "What fool eats a frog?"

"Oh, I'm fool enough for a tadpole!" cried the passenger. And they began to take out their pocket-books.

"You can cook yours right hyeh, gentlemen," said the Virginian, with his slow Southern courtesy. "The dining-cyars don't look like they were fired up."

"How much will you sell a couple for?" inquired the enthusiast.

The Virginian looked at him with friendly surprise. "Why, help yourself! We're all together yet awhile. Help yourselves," he repeated, to Trampas and his followers. These hung back a moment, then, with a slinking motion, set the cheese upon the earth and came forward nearer the fire to receive some supper.

"It won't scarcely be Delmonico style," said the Virginian to the passengers, "nor yet Saynt Augustine." He meant the great Augustin, the traditional *chef* of Philadelphia, whose history I had sketched for him at Colonel Cyrus Jones's eating palace.

Scipio now officiated. His frying-pan was busy, and prosperous odors rose from it.

"Run for a bucket of fresh water, Shorty," the Virginian continued, beginning his meal. "Colonel, yu' cook pretty near good. If yu' had sold 'em as advertised, yu'd have cert'nly made a name."

Several were now eating with satisfaction, but not Scipio. It was all he could do to cook straight. The whole man seemed to glisten. His eye was shut to a slit once more, while the innocent passengers thankfully swallowed.

"Now, you see, you have made some money," began the Virginian to the native who had helped him get the frogs.

"Bet your life!" exclaimed the man. "Divvy, won't you?" And he held out half his gains.

"Keep 'em," returned the Southerner. "I reckon we're square. But I expaict they'll not equal Delmonico's, seh?" he said to a passenger.

"Don't trust the judgment of a man as hungry as I am!" exclaimed the traveller, with a laugh. And he turned to his fellow-travellers. "Did you ever enjoy supper at Delmonico's more than this?"

"Never!" they sighed.

"Why, look here," said the traveller, "what fools the people of this town are! Here we've been all these starving days, and you come and get ahead of them!"

"That's right easy explained," said the Virginian. "I've been where there was big money in frawgs, and they 'ain't been. They're all cattle hyeh. Talk cattle, think cattle, and they're bankrupt in consequence. Fallen through. Ain't that so?" he inquired of the native.

"That's about the way," said the man.

"It's mighty hard to do what your neighbors ain't doin'," pursued the Virginian. "Montana is all cattle, an' these folks must be cattle, an' never notice the country right hyeh is too small for a range, an' swampy, anyway, an' just waitin' to be a frawg ranch."

At this, all wore a face of careful reserve.

"I'm not claimin' to be smarter than you folks hyeh," said the Virginian, deprecatingly, to his assistant. "But travellin' learns a man many customs. You wouldn't do the business they done at Tulare, California, north side o' the lake. They cert'nly utilized them hopeless swamps splendid. Of course they put up big capital and went into it scientific, gettin' advice from the government Fish Commission, an' such like knowledge. Yu' see, they had big markets for their frawgs,—San Francisco, Los Angeles, and clear to New York afteh the Southern Pacific was through. But up hyeh yu' could sell to passengers every day like yu' done this one day. They would get to know yu' along the line. Competing swamps are scarce. The dining-cyars would take your frawgs, and yu' would have the Yellowstone Park for four months in the year. Them hotels are anxious to please, an' they would buy off yu' what their Eastern patrons esteem as fine eatin'. And you folks would be sellin' something instead o' nothin'."

"That's a practical idea," said a traveller. "And little cost."

"And little cost," said the Virginian.

"Would Eastern people eat frogs?" inquired the man.

"Look at us!" said the traveller.

"Delmonico doesn't give yu' such a treat!" said the Virginian.

"Not exactly!" the traveller exclaimed.

"How much would be paid for frogs?" said Trampas to him. And I saw Scipio bend closer to his cooking.

"Oh, I don't know," said the traveller. "We've paid pretty well, you see."

"You're late for Tulare, Trampas," said the Virginian.

"I was not thinking of Tulare," Trampas retorted. Scipio's nose was in the frying-pan.

"Mos' comical spot you ever struck!" said the Virginian, looking round upon the whole company. He allowed himself a broad smile of retrospect. "To hear 'em talk frawgs at Tulare! Same as other folks talks hawsses or steers or whatever they're raisin' to sell. Yu'd fall into it yourselves if yu' started the business. Anything a man's bread and butter depends on, he's going to be in earnest about. Don't care if it is a frawg."

"That's so," said the native. "And it paid good?"

"The only money in the country was right there," answered the Virginian. "It was a dead country, and only frawgs was movin'. But that business was a-fannin' to beat four of a kind. It made yu' feel strange at first, as I said. For all the men had been cattle-men at one time or another. Till yu' got accustomed, it would give 'most anybody a shock to hear 'em speak about herdin' the bulls in a pasture by themselves." The Virginian allowed himself another smile, but became serious again. "That was their policy," he explained. "Except at certain times o' year they kept the bulls separate. The Fish Commission told 'em they'd better, and it cert'nly worked mighty well. It or something did—for, gentlemen, hush! but there was millions. You'd have said all the frawgs in the world had taken charge at Tulare. And the money rolled in! Gentlemen, hush! 'twas a gold mine for the owners. Forty per cent they netted some years. And they paid generous wages. For they could sell to all them French restaurants in San Francisco, yu' see. And there was the Cliff House. And the Palace Hotel made it a specialty. And the officers took frawgs at the Presidio, an' Angel Island, an' Alcatraz, an' Benicia. Los Angeles was beginnin' its boom. The corner-lot sharps wanted something by way of varnish. An' so they dazzled Eastern investors with advertisin' Tulare frawgs clear to N'Yol'ans an' New York. 'Twas only in Sacramento frawgs was dull. I expaict the California legislature was too or'n'ry for them fine-raised luxuries. They tell of one of them senators that he raked a million out of Los Angeles real estate, and started in for a bang-up meal with champagne. Wanted to scatter his new gold thick and quick. But he got astray among all the fancy dishes, an' just yelled right out before the ladies, 'Damn it! bring me forty dollars' worth of ham and aiggs.' He was a funny senator, now."

The Virginian paused, and finished eating a leg. And then with diabolic art he made a feint at wandering to new fields of anecdote. "Talkin' of senators," he resumed, "Senator Wise—"

"How much did you say wages were at Tulare?" inquired one of the Trampas faction.

"How much? Why, I never knew what the foreman got. The regular hands got a hundred. Senator Wise—"

"A hundred a *month?*"

"Why, it was wet an' muddy work, yu' see. A man risked rheumatism some. He risked it a good deal. Well, I was going to tell about Senator Wise. When Senator Wise was speaking of his visit to Alaska—"

"Forty per cent, was it?" said Trampas.

"Oh, I must call my wife!" said the traveller behind me. "This is what I came West for." And he hurried away.

"Not forty per cent the bad years," replied the Virginian. "The frawgs had enemies, same as cattle. I remember when a pelican got in the spring pasture, and the herd broke through the fence—"

"Fence?" said a passenger.

"Ditch, seh, and wire net. Every pasture was a square swamp with a ditch around, and a wire net. Yu've heard the mournful, mixed-up sound a big bunch of cattle will make? Well, seh, as yu' druv from the railroad to the Tulare frawg ranch yu' could hear 'em a mile. Springtime they'd sing like girls in the organ loft, and by August they were about ready to hire out for bass. And all was fit to be soloists, if I'm a judge. But in a bad year it might only be twenty per cent. The pelican rushed 'em from the pasture right into the San Joaquin River, which was close by the property. The big balance of the herd

486

stampeded, and though of course they came out on the banks again, the news had went round, and folks below at Hemlin eat most of 'em just to spite the company. Yu' see, a frawg in a river is more helpless than any maverick loose on the range. And they never struck any plan to brand their stock and prove ownership."

"Well, twenty per cent is good enough for me," said Trampas, "if Rawhide don't suit me."

"A hundred a month!" said the enthusiast. And busy calculations began to arise among them.

"It went to fifty per cent," pursued the Virginian, "when New York and Philadelphia got to biddin' agaynst each other. Both cities had signs all over 'em claiming to furnish the Tulare frawg. And both had 'em all right. And same as cattle trains, yu'd see frawg trains tearing across Arizona—big glass tanks with wires over 'em—through to New York, an' the frawgs starin' out."

"Why, George," whispered a woman's voice behind me, "he's merely deceiving them! He's merely making that stuff up out of his head."

"Yes, my dear, that's merely what he's doing."

"Well, I don't see why you imagined I should care for this. I think I'll go back."

"Better see it out, Daisy. This beats the geysers or anything we're likely to find in the Yellowstone."

"Then I wish we had gone to Bar Harbor as usual," said the lady, and she returned to her Pullman.

But her husband stayed. Indeed the male crowd now was a goodly sight to see, how the men edged close, drawn by a common tie. Their different kinds of feet told the strength of the bond—yellow sleeping-car slippers planted miscellaneous and motionless near a pair of Mexican spurs. All eyes watched the Virginian and gave him their entire sympathy. Though they could not know his motive for it, what he was doing had fallen as light upon them—all except the excited calculators. These were loudly making their fortunes at both Rawhide and Tulare, drugged by their satanically aroused hopes of gold, heedless of the slippers and the spurs. Had a man given any sign to warn them, I think he would have been lynched. Even the Indian chiefs had come to see in their show war bonnets and blankets. They naturally understood nothing of it, yet magnetically knew that the Virginian was the great man. And they watched him with approval. He sat by the fire with the frying-pan, looking his daily self—engaging and saturnine. And now as Trampas declared tickets to California would be dear and Rawhide had better come first, the Southerner let loose his heaven-born imagination.

"There's a better reason for Rawhide than tickets, Trampas," said he. "I said it was too late for Tulare."

"I heard you," said Trampas. "Opinions may differ. You and I don't think alike on several points."

"Gawd, Trampas!" said the Virginian, "d' yu' reckon I'd be rotting hyeh on forty dollars if Tulare was like it used to be? Tulare is broke."

"What broke it? Your leaving?"

"Revenge broke it, and disease," said the Virginian, striking the frying-pan on his knee, for the frogs were all gone. At those lurid words their untamed child minds took fire, and they drew round him again to hear a tale of blood. The crowd seemed to lean nearer.

But for a short moment it threatened to be spoiled. A passenger came along, demanding in an important voice, "Where are these frogs?" He was a prominent after-dinner speaker, they whispered me, and out for a holiday in his private car. Reaching us and walking to the Virginian, he said cheerily, "How much do you want for your frogs, my friend?"

"You got a friend hyeh?" said the Virginian. "That's good, for yu' need care taken of yu'." And the prominent after-dinner speaker did not further discommode us.

"That's worth my trip," whispered a New York passenger to me.

"Yes, it was a case of revenge," resumed the Virginian, "and disease. There was a man named Saynt Augustine got run out of Domingo, which is a Dago island. He come to Philadelphia, an' he was dead broke. But Saynt Augustine was a live man, an' he saw Philadelphia was full o' Quakers that dressed plain and eat humdrum. So he started cookin' Domingo way for 'em, an' they caught right ahold. Terrapin, he gave 'em, and croakeets, an' he'd use forty chickens to make a broth he called consommay. An' he got rich, and Philadelphia got well known, an' Delmonico in New York he got jealous. He was the cook that had the say-so in New York."

"Was Delmonico one of them I-talians?" inquired a fascinated mutineer.

"I don't know. But he acted like one. Lorenzo was his front name. He aimed to cut—"

"Domingo's throat?" breathed the enthusiast.

"Aimed to cut away the trade from Saynt Augustine an' put Philadelphia back where he thought she belonged. Frawgs was the fashionable rage then. These foreign cooks set the fashion in eatin', same as foreign dressmakers do women's clothes. Both cities was catchin' and swallowin' all the frawgs Tulare could throw at 'em. So he—"

"Lorenzo?" said the enthusiast.

"Yes, Lorenzo Delmonico. He bid a dollar a tank higher. An' Saynt Augustine raised him fifty cents. An' Lorenzo raised him a dollar. An' Saynt Augustine shoved her up three. Lorenzo he didn't expect

Philadelphia would go that high, and he got hot in the collar, an' flew round his kitchen in New York, an' claimed he'd twist Saynt Augustine's Domingo tail for him, and crack his ossified system. Lorenzo raised his language to a high temperature, they say. An' then quite sudden off he starts for Tulare. He buys tickets over the Santa Fe, and he goes a-fannin' and a-foggin'. But, gentlemen, hush! The very same day Saynt Augustine he tears out of Philadelphia. He travelled by the way o' Washington, an' out he comes a-fannin' and a-foggin' over the Southern Pacific. Of course Tulare didn't know nothin' of this. All it knowed was how the frawg market was on soarin' wings, and it was feelin' like a flight o' rawckets. If only there'd been some preparation,—a telegram or something,—the disaster would never have occurred. But Lorenzo and Saynt Augustine was that absorbed watchin' each other—for, yu' see, the Santa Fe and the Southern Pacific come together at Mojave, an' the two cooks travelled a matter of two hundred an' ten miles in the same cyar—they never thought about a telegram. An' when they arruv, breathless, an' started in to screechin' what they'd give for the monopoly, why, them unsuspectin' Tulare boys got amused at them. I never heard just all they done, but they had Lorenzo singin' and dancin', while Saynt Augustine played the fiddle for him. And one of Lorenzo's heels did get a trifle grazed. Well, them two cooks quit that ranch without disclosin' their identity, and as soon as they got to a safe distance they swore eternal friendship, in their excitable foreign way. And they went home over the Union Pacific, sharing the same stateroom. Their revenge killed frawgs. The disease—"

"How killed frogs?" demanded Trampas.

"Just killed 'em. Delmonico and Saynt Augustine wiped frawgs off the slate of fashion. Not a banker in Fifth Avenue'll touch one now if another banker's around watchin' him. And if ever yu' see a man that hides his feet an' won't take off his socks in company, he has worked in them Tulare swamps an' got the disease. Catch him wadin', and yu'll find he's web-footed. Frawgs are dead, Trampas, and so are you."

"Rise up, liars, and salute your king!" yelled Scipio. "Oh, I'm in love with you!" And he threw his arms around the Virginian.

"Let me shake hands with you," said the traveller, who had failed to interest his wife in these things. "I wish I was going to have more of your company."

The widow's cruise[1]

The widow Ducket lived in a small village about ten miles from the New Jersey sea coast. In this village she was born, here she had married and buried her husband, and here she expected somebody to bury her, but she was in no hurry for that, for she had scarcely reached middle age. She was a tall woman with no apparent fat in her composition, and full of activity, both muscular and mental.

She rose at six in the morning, cooked breakfast, set the table, washed the dishes when the meal was over, milked, churned, swept, washed, ironed, worked in her little garden, attended to the flowers in the front yard, and in the afternoon knitted and quilted and sewed, and after tea she either went to see her neighbors or had them come to see her. When it was really dark she lighted the lamp in her parlor and read for an hour, and if it happened to be one of Miss Mary Wilkins' books[2] that she read she expressed doubts as to the realism of the characters therein described.

These doubts she expressed to Dorcas Networthy, who was a small, plump woman, with a solemn face, who had lived with the widow for many years and who had become her devoted disciple. Whatever the widow did that also did Dorcas; not so well, for her heart told her she could never expect to do that, but with a yearning anxiety to do everything as well as she could. She rose at five minutes past six, and in a subsidiary way she helped to get the breakfast, to eat it, to wash up the dishes, to work in the garden, to quilt, to sew, to visit and receive, and no one could have tried harder than she did to keep awake when the widow read aloud in the evening.

All these things happened every day in the summer time, but in the winter the widow and Dorcas cleared the snow from their little front path instead of attending to the flowers, and in the evening they lighted a fire as well as a lamp in the parlor.

Sometimes, however, something different happened, but this was not often, only a few times in the year. One of the different things occurred when Mrs. Ducket and Dorcas were sitting on their little front porch one summer afternoon, one on the little bench on one side of the door, and the other on the little bench on the other side of the door, each waiting, until she should hear the clock strike five, to pre-

---

[1] Reprinted from *A Story-Teller's Pack* by Frank R. Stockton; copyright 1897 by Charles Scribner's Sons, 1925 by Marie Louise Stockton and Frances A. Stockton; used by permission of the publisher, Charles Scribner's Sons. Pp. 83–109.

[2] Mary E. (Wilkins) Freeman (1862–1930) wrote of New England life, and excelled in depicting just such characters as the widow Ducket.

pare tea. But it was not yet a quarter to five when a one-horse wagon containing four men came slowly down the street. Dorcas first saw the wagon, and she instantly stopped knitting.

"Mercy on me!" she exclaimed. "Whoever those people are they are strangers here and they don't know where to stop, for they first go to one side of the street and then to the other."

The widow looked around sharply. "Humph!" said she. "Those men are sailor-men. You might see that in the twinkling of an eye. Sailor-men always drive that way because that is the way they sail ships. They first tack in one direction and then in another."

"Mr. Ducket didn't like the sea?" remarked Dorcas, for about the three-hundredth time.

"No, he didn't," answered the widow, for about the two hundred and fiftieth time, for there had been occasions when she thought Dorcas put this question inopportunely. "He hated it, and he was drowned in it through trusting a sailor-man, which I never did nor shall. Do you really believe those men are coming here?"

"Upon my word I do!" said Dorcas, and her opinion was correct.

The wagon drew up in front of Mrs. Ducket's little white home, and the two women sat rigidly, their hands in their laps, staring at the man who drove.

This was an elderly personage with whitish hair, and under his chin a thin whitish beard, which waved in the gentle breeze and gave Dorcas the idea that his head was filled with hair which was leaking out from below.

"Is this the widow Ducket's?" inquired this elderly man, in a strong penetrating voice.

"That's my name," said the widow, and laying her knitting on the bench beside her she went to the gate. Dorcas also laid her knitting on the bench beside her and went to the gate.

"I was told," said the elderly man, "at a house we touched at about a quarter of a mile back, that the widow Ducket's was the only house in this village where there was any chance of me and my mates getting a meal. We are four sailors and we are making from the bay over to Cuppertown, and that's eight miles ahead yet and we are all pretty sharp set for something to eat."

"This is the place," said the widow, "and I do give meals if there is enough in the house and everything comes handy."

"Does everything come handy to-day?" said he.

"It does," said she, "and you can hitch your horse and come in, but I haven't got anything for him."

"Oh, that's all right," said the man, "we brought along stores for him, so we'll just make fast and then come in."

The two women hurried into the house in a state of bustling

491

preparation, for the furnishing of this meal meant one dollar in cash.

The four mariners, all elderly men, descended from the wagon, each one scrambling with alacrity over a different wheel.

A box of broken ship-biscuit was brought out and put on the ground in front of the horse, who immediately set himself to eating with great satisfaction.

Tea was a little late that day, because there were six persons to provide for instead of two, but it was a good meal, and after the four seamen had washed their hands and faces at the pump in the back yard and had wiped them on two towels furnished by Dorcas, they all came in and sat down. Mrs. Ducket seated herself at the head of the table with the dignity proper to the mistress of the house, and Dorcas seated herself at the other end with the dignity proper to the disciple of the mistress. No service was necessary, for everything that was to be eaten or drunk was on the table.

When each of the elderly mariners had had as much bread and butter, quickly-baked soda biscuit, dried beef, cold ham, cold tongue and preserved fruit of every variety known, as his storage capacity would permit, the mariner in command, Captain Bird, pushed back his chair, whereupon the other mariners pushed back their chairs.

"Madam," said Captain Bird, "we have all made a good meal, which didn't need to be no better nor more of it, and we're satisfied, but that horse out there has not had time to rest himself enough to go the eight miles that lies ahead of us, so if it's all the same to you and this good lady, we'd like to sit on that front porch awhile and smoke our pipes. I was a-looking at that porch when I came in, and I bethought to myself what a rare good place it was to smoke a pipe in."

"There's pipes been smoked there," said the widow rising, "and it can be done again. Inside the house I don't allow tobacco, but on the porch neither of us minds."

So the four Captains betook themselves to the porch, two of them seating themselves on the little bench on one side of the door, and two of them on the little bench on the other side of the door, and lighted their pipes.

"Shall we clear off the table and wash up the dishes," said Dorcas, "or wait until they are gone?"

"We will wait until they are gone," said the widow, "for now that they are here we might as well have a bit of a chat with them. When a sailor-man lights his pipe he is generally willing to talk, but when he is eatin' you can't get a word out of him."

Without thinking it necessary to ask permission, for the house belonged to her, the widow Ducket brought a chair and put it in the hall close to the open front door, and Dorcas brought another chair and seated herself by the side of the widow.

"Do all you sailor-men belong down there at the bay?" asked Mrs. Ducket, and thus the conversation began, and in a few minutes it had reached a point at which Captain Bird thought it proper to say that a great many strange things happen to sea-men sailing on the sea, which lands-people never dream of.

"Such as anything in particular?" asked the widow, at which remark Dorcas clasped her hands in expectancy.

"There's a good many strange things happened to me and my mates at sea. Would you and that other lady like to hear any of them?" asked Captain Bird.

"We would like to hear them if they are true," said the widow.

"There's nothing happened to me and my mates that isn't true," said Captain Bird, "and here is something that once happened to me: I was on a whaling v'yage when a big sperm whale, just as mad as a fiery bull, came at us, head on, and struck the ship at the stern with such tremendous force that his head crashed right through her timbers and he went nearly half his length into her hull. The hold was mostly filled with empty barrels, for we was just beginning our v'yage, and when he had made kindling wood of them, there was room enough for him. We all expected that it wouldn't take five minutes for the vessel to fill and go to the bottom, and we made ready to take to the boats, but it turned out we didn't need to take to no boats, for as fast as the water rushed into the hold of the ship that whale drank it and squirted it up through the two blow holes in the top of his head, and as there was an open hatchway just over his head the water all went into the sea again, and that whale kept working day and night pumping the water out until we beached the vessel on the island of Trinidad—the whale helping us wonderful on our way over by the powerful working of his tail, which, being outside in the water, acted like a propeller. I don't believe anything stranger than that ever happened to a whaling ship."

"No," said the widow, "I don't believe anything ever did."

Captain Bird now looked at Captain Sanderson, and the latter took his pipe out of his mouth and said that in all his sailing around the world he had never known anything queerer than what happened to a big steamship he chanced to be on, which ran into an island in a fog. Everybody on board thought the ship was wrecked, but it had twin screws and was going at such a tremendous speed that it turned the island entirely upside down and sailed over it, and he had heard tell that even now people sailing over the spot could look down into the water and see the roots of the trees and the cellars of the houses.

Captain Sanderson now put his pipe back into his mouth and Captain Burress took out his pipe.

"I was once in a obelisk ship," said he, "that used to trade regular

between Egypt and New York carrying obelisks. We had a big
obelisk on board. The way they ship obelisks is to make a hole in the
stern of the ship and run the obelisk in, p'inted end foremost, and
this obelisk filled up nearly the whole of that ship from stern to bow.
We was about ten days out and sailing afore a northeast gale with the
engines at full speed when suddenly we spied breakers ahead, and our
Captain saw we was about to run on a bank. Now if we hadn't had
an obelisk on board we might have sailed over that bank, but the
Captain knew that with an obelisk on board we drew too much water
for that, and that we'd be wrecked in about fifty-five seconds if something wasn't done quick. So he had to do something quick, and this
is what he did. He ordered all steam on and drove slam-bang on that
bank. Just as he expected we stopped so suddint that that big obelisk
bounced for'ard, its p'inted end foremost, and went clean through the
bow and shot out into the sea. The minute it did that the vessel was
so lightened that it rose in the water and we easily steamed over the
bank. There was one man knocked overboard by the shock when we
struck, but as soon as we missed him we went right back after him and
we got him all right. You see when that obelisk went overboard its
butt end, which was heaviest, went down first, and when it touched
the bottom it just stood there, and it was such a big obelisk there was
about five and a half feet of it stuck out of the water. The man who
was knocked overboard he just swum for that obelisk and he climbed
up the hiryglyphics. It was a mighty fine obelisk and the Egyptians
had cut their hiryglyphics good and deep so that the man could get
hand and foot hold. And when we got to him and took him off he
was sitting high and dry on the p'inted end of that obelisk. It was a
great pity about the obelisk, for it was a good obelisk, but as I never
heard the company tried to raise it I expect it is standing there yet."

Captain Burress now put his pipe back into his mouth and looked
at Captain Jenkinson, who removed his pipe and said:

"The queerest thing that ever happened to me was about a shark.
We was off the Banks and the time of year was July, and the ice was
coming down and we got in among a lot of it. Not far away, off our
weather bow, there was a little iceberg which had such a queerness
about it that the Captain and three men went in a boat to look at it.
The ice was mighty clear ice and you could see almost through it,
and right inside of it, not more than three feet above the waterline,
and about two feet, or maybe twenty inches, inside the ice, was a
whopping big shark, about fourteen feet long,—a regular man-eater—
frozen in there hard and fast. 'Bless my soul,' said the Captain, 'this
is a wonderful curiosity and I'm going to git him out.' Just then one of
the men said he saw that shark wink, but the Captain wouldn't believe him, for he said that shark was frozen stiff and hard and couldn't

wink. You see the Captain had his own idees about things, and he knew that whales was warm-blooded and would freeze if they was shut up in ice, but he forgot that sharks was not whales and that they're cold-blooded just like toads. And there is toads that has been shut up in rocks for thousands of years, and they stayed alive, no matter how cold the place was, because they was cold-blooded, and when the rocks was split out hopped the frog. But as I said before, the Captain forgot sharks was cold-blooded and he determined to git that one out.

"Now you both know, being housekeepers, that if you take a needle and drive it into a hunk of ice you can split it. Now the Captain had a sail-needle with him and so he drove it into the iceberg right along-side of the shark and split it. Now the minute he did it he knew that the man was right when he said he saw the shark wink, for it flopped out of that iceberg quicker nor a flash of lightning."

"What a happy fish he must have been!" ejaculated Dorcas, forget-ful of precedent, so great was her emotion.

"Yes," said Captain Jenkinson, "it was a happy fish enough, but it wasn't a happy Captain. You see that shark hadn't had anything to eat, perhaps for a thousand years, until the Captain came along with his sail-needle."

"Surely you sailor-men do see strange things," now said the widow, "and the strangest thing about them is that they are true."

"Yes, indeed," said Dorcas, "that is the most wonderful thing."

"You wouldn't suppose," said the widow Ducket, glancing from one bench of mariners to the other, "that I have a sea-story to tell, but I have, and if you like I will tell it to you."

Captain Bird looked up a little surprised. "We would like to hear it, indeed we would, madam," said he.

"Aye, aye!" said Captain Burress, and the other two mariners nodded.

"It was a good while ago," she said, "when I was living on the shore near the head of the bay, that my husband was away and I was left alone in the house. One mornin' my sister-in-law, who lived on the other side of the bay, sent me word by a boy on a horse that she hadn't any oil in the house to fill the lamp that she always put in the window to light her husband home, who was a fisherman, and if I would send her some by the boy she would pay me back as soon as they bought oil. The boy said he would stop on his way home and take the oil to her, but he never did stop, or perhaps he never went back, and about five o'clock I began to get dreadfully worried, for I knew if that lamp wasn't in my sister-in-law's window by dark she might be a widow before midnight. So I said to myself, 'I've got to get that oil to her, no matter what happens or how it's done.' Of course I couldn't tell what might happen, but there was only one way it could be done, and that was for me to get into the boat that was tied to the post down by the water and take it to her, for it was too far for me to walk around by the head of the bay. Now the trouble was I didn't know no more about a boat and the managin' of it than any one of you sailor-men knows about clear-starchin'. But there wasn't no use of thinkin' what I knew and what I didn't know, for I had to take it to her and there was no way of doin' it except in that boat. So I filled a gallon can, for I thought I might as well take enough while I was about it, and I went down to the water and I unhitched that boat and I put the oil-can into her and then I got in, and off I started, and when I was about a quarter of a mile from the shore—"

"Madam," interrupted Captain Bird, "did you row or—or was there a sail to the boat?"

The widow looked at the questioner for a moment. "No," said she, "I didn't row. I forgot to bring the oars from the house, but it didn't matter for I didn't know how to use them, and if there had been a sail I couldn't have put it up, for I didn't know how to use it either. I used the rudder to make the boat go. The rudder was the only thing that I knew anything about. I'd held a rudder when I was a little girl and I knew how to work it. So I just took hold of the handle of the rudder and turned it round and round, and that made the boat go ahead, you know, and—"

"Madam!" exclaimed Captain Bird, and the other elderly mariners took their pipes from their mouths.

"Yes, that is the way I did it," continued the widow briskly; "big steamships are made to go by a propeller turning round and round at their back ends, and I made the rudder work in the same way, and I got along very well, too, until suddenly, when I was about a quarter of a mile from the shore, a most terrible and awful storm arose. There must have been a typhoon or a cyclone out at sea, for the waves came up the bay bigger than houses, and when they got to the head of the bay they turned around and tried to get out to sea again; so in this way they continually met, and made the most awful and roarin' pilin' up of waves that ever was known.

"My little boat was pitched about as if it had been a feather in a breeze, and when the front part of it was cleavin' itself down into the water the hind part was stickin' up until the rudder whizzed around like a patent churn with no milk in it. The thunder began to roar and the lightnin' flashed, and three sea-gulls, so nearly frightened to death that they began to turn up the whites of their eyes, flew down and sat on one of the seats of the boat, forgettin' in that awful moment that man was their nat'ral enemy. I had a couple of biscuits in my pocket, because I had thought I might want a bite in crossing, and I crumbled up one of these and fed the poor creatures. Then I began to wonder what I was goin' to do, for things were gettin' awfuller and awfuller every minute, and the little boat was a-heavin' and a-pitchin' and a-rollin' and h'istin' itself up, first on one end and then on the other, to such an extent that if I hadn't kept tight hold of the rudder handle I'd slipped off the seat I was sittin' on.

"All of a sudden I remembered that oil in the can, but just as I was puttin' my fingers on the cork my conscience smote me. 'Am I goin' to use this oil,' I said to myself, 'and let my sister-in-law's husband be wrecked for want of it?' And then I thought that he wouldn't want it all that night and perhaps they would buy oil the next day, and so I poured out about a tumblerful of it on the water, and I can just tell you sailor-men that you never saw anything act as prompt as that did. In three seconds, or perhaps five, the water all around me, for the distance of a small front yard, was just as flat as a table and as smooth as glass, and so invitin' in appearance that the three gulls jumped out of the boat and began to swim about on it, primin' their feathers and lookin' at themselves in the transparent depths, though I must say that one of them made an awful face as he dipped his bill into the water and tasted kerosene.

"Now I had time to sit quiet in the midst of the placid space I had made for myself and rest from workin' of the rudder. Truly it was a wonderful and marvelous thing to look at. The waves was roarin' and leapin' up all around me higher than the roof of this house, and sometimes their tops would reach over so that they nearly met and shut out all view of the stormy sky, which seemed as if it was bein' torn to pieces by blazin' lightnin', while the thunder pealed so tremendous that it almost drowned the roar of the waves. Not only above and all around me was everything terrific and fearful, but even under me it was the same, for there was a big crack in the bottom of the boat as wide as my hand, and through this I could see down into the water beneath, and there was—"

"Madam!" ejaculated Captain Bird, the hand which had been holding his pipe a few inches from his mouth now dropping to his knee, and at this motion the hands which held the pipes of the other three mariners dropped to their knees.

"Of course it sounds strange," continued the widow, "but I know that people can see down into clear water, and the water under me was clear, and the crack was wide enough for me to see through, and down under me was sharks and sword-fishes and other horrible water creatures, which I had never seen before, all driven into the bay, I haven't a doubt, by the violence of the storm out at sea. The thought of my bein' upset and fallin' in among those monsters made my very blood run cold, and involuntary-like I began to turn the handle of the rudder, and in a moment I shot into a wall of ragin' sea water that was towerin' around me. For a second I was nearly blinded and stunned, but I had the cork out of that oil-can in no time, and very soon, you'd scarcely believe it if I told you how soon, I had another placid millpond surroundin' of me. I sat there a-pantin' and fannin' with my straw hat, for you'd better believe I was flustered, and then I began to think how long it would take me to make a line of mill-ponds clean across the head of the bay and how much oil it would need and whether I had enough. So I sat and calculated that if a tumblerful of oil would make a smooth place about seven yards across, which I should say was the width of the one I was in, which I calculated by a measure of my eye as to how many breadths of carpet it would take to cover it, and if the bay was two miles across, betwixt our house and my sister-in-law's, and although I couldn't get the thing down to exact figures, I saw pretty soon that I wouldn't have oil enough to make a level cuttin' through all those mountainous billows, and besides, even if I had enough to take me across, what would be the good of going if there wasn't any oil left to fill my sister-in-law's lamp?

"While I was thinkin' and calculatin' a perfectly dreadful thing happened, which made me think if I didn't get out of this pretty soon I'd find myself in a mighty risky predicament. The oil-can, which I had forgotten to put the cork in, toppled over, and before I could grab it every drop of oil ran into the hind part of the boat, where it was soaked up by a lot of dry dust that was there. No wonder my heart sank when I saw this. Glancin' wildly around me, as people will do when they are scared, I saw the smooth place I was in gettin' smaller and smaller, for the kerosene was evaporatin', as it will do even off woolen clothes if you give it time enough. The first pond I had come out of seemed to be covered up, and the great, towerin', throbbin' precipice of sea water was a-closin' around me.

"Castin' down my eyes in despair I happened to look through the crack in the bottom of the boat, and oh! what a blessed relief it was, for down there everything was smooth and still, and I could see the sand on the bottom as level and hard, no doubt, as it was on the beach. Suddenly the thought struck me that the bottom would give me the only chance I had of gettin' out of the frightful fix I was in. If I could fill that oil-can with air and then puttin' it under my arm and takin' a long breath, if I could drop down on that smooth bottom, I might run along toward shore, as far as I could, and then, when I felt my breath was givin' out, I could take a pull at the oil-can and take another run, and perhaps the can would hold air enough for me till I got near enough to shore to wade to dry land. To be sure the sharks and other monsters were down there, but then they must have been awfully frightened and perhaps they might not remember that man was their nat'ral enemy. Anyway, I thought it would be better to try the smooth water passage down there than stay and be swallowed up by the ragin' waves on top.

"So I blew the can full of air and corked it, and then I tore up some of the boards from the bottom of the boat so as to make a hole big enough for me to get through—and you sailor-men needn't wriggle so when I say that, for you all know a divin' bell hasn't any bottom at all and the water never comes in—and so when I got the hole big enough I took the oil-can under my arm and was just about to slip down through it when I saw an awful turtle a-walkin' through the sand at the bottom. Now, I might trust sharks and sword-fishes and sea-serpents to be frightened and forget about their nat'ral enemies, but I never could trust a gray turtle as big as a cart, with a black neck a yard long, with yellow bags to its jaws, to forget anything or to remember anything. I'd as lieve get into a bath-tub with a live crab as to go down there. It wasn't of no use even so much as thinkin' of it, so I gave up that plan and didn't once look through that hole again."

"And what did you do, madam?" asked Captain Bird, who was regarding her with a face of stone.

"I used electricity," she said. "Now don't start as if you had a shock of it. That's what I used. When I was younger than I was then and sometimes visited friends in the city, we often amused ourselves by rubbing our feet on the carpet until we got ourselves so full of electricity that we could put up our fingers and light the gas. So I said to myself that if I could get full of electricity for the purpose of lightin' the gas I could get full of it for other purposes, and so, without losin' a moment, I set to work. I stood up on one of the seats, which was dry, and I rubbed the bottoms of my shoes backward and forward on it with such violence and swiftness that they pretty soon got warm and I began fillin' with electricity, and when I was fully charged with it from my toes to the top of my head I just sprang into the water and swam ashore. Of course I couldn't sink, bein' full of electricity."

Captain Bird heaved a long sigh and rose to his feet, whereupon the other mariners rose to their feet. "Madam," said Captain Bird, "what's to pay for the supper and—the rest of the entertainment?"

"The supper is twenty-five cents apiece," said the widow Ducket, "and everything else is free, gratis."

Whereupon each mariner put his hand into his trousers pocket, pulled out a silver quarter, and handed it to the widow. Then with four solemn "Good-evenin's" they went out to the front gate.

"Cast off, Captain Jenkinson," said Captain Bird, "and you, Captain Burress, clew him up for'ard. You can stay in the bow, Captain Sanderson, and take the sheet lines. I'll go aft."

All bêing ready, each of the elderly mariners clambered over a wheel, and having seated themselves, they prepared to lay their course for Cuppertown.

But just as they were about to start Captain Jenkinson asked that they lay-to a bit, and clambering down over his wheel, he re-entered the front gate and went up to the door of the house, where the widow and Dorcas were still standing.

"Madam," said he, "I just came back to ask what became of your brother-in-law through his wife's not bein' able to put no light in the window?"

"The storm drove him ashore on our side of the bay," said she, "and the next mornin' he came up to our house and I told him all that had happened to me; and when he took our boat and went home and told that story to his wife she just packed up and went out West, and got divorced from him; and it served him right, too."

"Thank you, ma'am," said Captain Jenkinson, and going out of the gate he clambered up over the wheel and the wagon cleared for Cuppertown.

When the elderly mariners were gone the widow Ducket, still standing in the door, turned to Dorcas:

"Think of it!" she said, "to tell me all that, in my own house! And after I had opened my one jar of brandied peaches that I'd been keepin' for special company!"

"In your own house!" ejaculated Dorcas. "And not one of them brandied peaches left!"

The widow jingled the four quarters in her hand before she slipped them into her pocket.

"Anyway, Dorcas," she remarked, "I think we can now say we are square with all the world, and so let's go in and wash the dishes."

"Yes," said Dorcas, "we're square."

The two tall tales that follow are alike in their denouements and in little else, except that both wind their way skillfully from plausible detail to frantic impossibility. The older story is the neater, but Thurber, on this occasion, is not trying to be neat. He is pleasing himself (somewhat as Mark Twain used to) with the depiction of a narrator afflicted with what psychologists refer to as total recall.

An incidental point of merit in the Thurber tale is its gradual and cumulative dating—for instance, "Hank was built like a Pope-Hartford and he couldn't run no faster'n President Taft." Under scrutiny, this chronological detail stands up rather well, a welcome circumstance at a moment when lesser humorists seek to amuse us with a wholly imaginary "gay nineties," whose supposed distinguishing features they select at random from any period between 1860 and 1920.

You could look it up [1]

It all begun when we dropped down to C'lumbus, Ohio, from Pittsburgh to play a exhibition game on our way out to St. Louis. It was gettin' on into September, and though we'd been leadin' the league by six, seven games most of the season, we was now in first place by a margin you could 'a' got it into the eye of a thimble, bein' only a half a game ahead of St. Louis. Our slump had given the boys the leapin' jumps, and they was like a bunch a old ladies at a lawn fete with a thunderstorm comin' up, runnin' around snarlin' at each other, eatin' bad and sleepin' worse, and battin' for a team average of maybe .186. Half the time nobody'd speak to nobody else, without it was to bawl 'em out.

Squawks Magrew was managin' the boys at the time, and he was darn near crazy. They called him "Squawks" 'cause when things was goin' bad he lost his voice, or perty near lost it, and squealed at you like a little girl you stepped on her doll or somethin'. He yelled at

[1] From James Thurber: *My World and Welcome to It* (New York: Harcourt, Brace and Co.; 1942; Copyright 1942 by James Thurber). "You Could Look It Up" is copyright by Curtis Publishing Co., 1941. It appeared in the *Saturday Evening Post*, April 5, 1941, pp. 9–11.

everybody and wouldn't listen to nobody, without maybe it was me. I'd been trainin' the boys for ten year, and he'd take more lip from me than from anybody else. He knowed I was smarter'n him, anyways, like you're goin' to hear.

This was thirty, thirty-one year ago; you could look it up, 'cause it was the same year C'lumbus decided to call itself the Arch City, on account of a lot of iron arches with electric-light bulbs into 'em which stretched across High Street. Thomas Albert Edison sent 'em a telegram, and they was speeches and maybe even President Taft opened the celebration by pushin' a button. It was a great week for the Buckeye capital, which was why they got us out there for this ex-hibition game.

Well, we just lose a double-header to Pittsburgh, 11 to 5 and 7 to 3, so we snarled all the way to C'lumbus, where we put up at the Chittaden Hotel, still snarlin'. Everybody was techy, and when Billy Klinger took a sock at Whitey Cott at breakfast, Whitey throwed marmalade all over his face.

"Blind each other, whatta I care?" says Magrew. "You can't see nothin' anyways."

C'lumbus won the exhibition game, 3 to 2, whilst Magrew set in the dugout, mutterin' and cursin' like a fourteen-year-old Scotty. He bad-mouthed everybody on the ball club and he bad-mouthed every-body offa the ball club, includin' the Wright brothers, who, he claimed, had yet to build an airship big enough for any of our boys to hit it with a ball bat.

"I wisht I was dead," he says to me. "I wisht I was in heaven with the angels."

I told him to pull hisself together, 'cause he was drivin' the boys crazy, the way he was goin' on, sulkin' and bad-mouthin' and whinin'. I was older'n he was and smarter'n he was, and he knowed it. I was ten times smarter'n he was about this Pearl du Monville, first time I ever laid eyes on the little guy, which was one of the saddest days of my life.

Now, most people name of Pearl is girls, but this Pearl du Monville was a man if you could call a fella a man who was only thirty-four, thirty-five inches high. Pearl du Monville was a midget. He was part French and part Hungarian, and maybe even part Bulgarian or somethin'. I can see him now, a sneer on his little pushed-in pan, swingin' a bamboo cane and smokin' a big cigar. He had a gray suit with a big black check into it, and he had a gray felt hat with one of them rainbow-colored hatbands onto it, like the young fellas wore in them days. He talked like he was talkin' into a tin can, but he didn't have no foreign accent. He mighta been fifteen or he mighta been a hundred, you couldn't tell. Pearl du Monville.

After the game with C'lumbus, Magrew headed straight for the
Chittaden bar,—the train for St. Louis wasn't goin' for three, four
hours—and there he set, drinkin' rye and talkin' to this bartender.

"How I pity me, brother," Magrew was tellin' this bartender. "How
I pity me." That was alwuz his favorite tune. So he was settin' there,
tellin' this bartender how heartbreakin' it was to be manager of a
bunch a blindfolded circus clowns, when up pops this Pearl du Monville outa nowheres.

It give Magrew the leapin' jumps. He thought at first maybe the
D.T.'s had come back on him; he claimed he'd had 'em once, and
little guys had popped up all around him, wearin' red, white and blue
hats.

"Go on, now!" Magrew yells. "Get away from me!"

But the midget clumb up on a chair acrost the table from Magrew
and says, "I seen that game today, Junior, and you ain't got no ball
club. What you got there, Junior," he says, "is a side show."

"Whatta ya mean, 'Junior'?" says Magrew, touchin' the little guy
to satisfy hisself he was real.

"Don't pay him no attention, mister," says the bartender; "Pearl
calls everybody 'Junior', 'cause it alwuz turns out he's a year older'n
anybody else."

"Yeh?" says Magrew. "How old is he?"

"How old are you, Junior?" says the midget.

"Who, me? I'm fifty-three," says Magrew.

"Well, I'm fifty-four," says the midget.

Magrew grins and asts him what he'll have, and that was the beginnin' of their beautiful friendship, if you don't care what you say.

Pearl du Monville stood up on his chair and waved his cane around
and pretended he was ballyhooin' for a circus. "Right this way,
folks!" he yells. "Come on in and see the greatest collection of freaks in
the world! See the armless pitchers, see the eyeless batters, see the
infielders with five thumbs!" and so on and on like that, feedin'
Magrew gall and handin' him a laugh at the same time, you might
say.

You could hear him and Pearl du Monville hootin' and hollerin'
and singin' way up to the fourth floor of the Chittaden, where the
boys was packin' up. When it come time to go to the station, you can
imagine how disgusted we was when we crowded into the doorway of
that bar and seen them two singin' and goin' on.

"Well, well, well," says Magrew, lookin' up and spottin' us. "Look
who's here. . . . Clowns, this is Pearl du Monville, a monseer of the
old, old school. . . . Don't shake hands with 'em, Pearl, 'cause their
fingers is made of chalk and would bust right off in your paws," he
says, and he starts guffawin' and Pearl starts titterin' and we stand

503

there givin' 'em the iron eye, it bein' the lowest ebb a ball-club manager'd got hisself down to since the national pastime was started.

Then the midget begun givin' us the ballyhoo. "Come on in!" he says, wavin' his cane. "See the legless base runners, see the outfielders with the butter fingers, see the southpaw with the arm of a little chee-ild!"

Then him and Magrew begun to hoop and holler and nudge each other till you'd of thought this little guy was the funniest guy than even Charlie Chaplin. The fellas filed outa the bar without a word and went on up to the Union Depot, leavin' me to handle Magrew and his new-found crony.

Well, I got 'em outa there finely. I had to take the little guy along, 'cause Magrew had a holt onto him like a vise and I couldn't pry him loose.

"He's comin' along as masket," says Magrew, holdin' the midget in the crouch of his arm like a football. And come along he did, hollerin' and protestin' and beatin' at Magrew with his little fists.

"Cut it out, will ya, Junior?" the little guy kept whinin'. "Come on, leave a man loose, will ya, Junior?"

But Junior kept a holt on him and begun yellin', "See the guys with the glass arm, see the guys with the cast-iron brains, see the fielders with the feet on their wrists!"

So it goes, right through the whole Union Depot, with people starin' and catcallin', and he don't put the midget down till he gets him through the gates.

"How'm I goin' to go along without no toothbrush?" the midget asts. "What'm I goin' to do without no other suit?" he says.

"Doc here," says Magrew, meaning me— "Doc here will look after you like you was his own son, won't you, doc?"

I give him the iron eye, and he finally got on the train and prob'ly went to sleep with his clothes on.

This left me alone with the midget. "Lookit," I says to him, "Why don't you go on home now? Come mornin', Magrew'll forget all about you. He'll prob'ly think you was somethin' he seen in a nightmare maybe. And he ain't goin' to laugh so easy in the mornin', neither," I says. "So why don't you go on home?"

"Nix," he says to me. "Skidoo," he says, "twenty-three for you," and he tosses his cane up into the vestibule of the coach and clam'ers on up after it like a cat. So that's the way Pearl du Monville come to go to St. Louis with the ball club.

I seen 'em first at breakfast the next day, settin' opposite each other; the midget playin' Turkey in the Straw on a harmonium and Magrew starin' at his eggs and bacon like they was a uncooked bird with its feathers still on.

504

"Remember where you found this?" I says, jerkin' my thumb at the midget. "Or maybe you think they come with breakfast on these trains," I says, bein' a good hand at turnin' a sharp remark in them days.

The midget puts down the harmonium and turns on me. "Sneeze," he says; "your brains is dusty." Then he snaps a couple drops of water at me from a tumbler. "Drown," he says, tryin' to make his voice deep.

Now, both them cracks is Civil War cracks, but you'd have thought they was brand new and the funniest than any crack Magrew'd ever heard in his whole life. He started hoopin' and hollerin', and the midget started hoopin' and hollerin', so I walked on away and set down with Bugs Courtney and Hank Metters, payin' no attention to this weak-minded Damon and Phidias acrost the aisle.

Well, sir, the first game with St. Louis was rained out, and there we was facin' a double-header next day. Like maybe I told you, we lose the last three double-headers we play, makin' maybe twenty-five errors in the six games which is all right for the intimates of a school for the blind, but is disgraceful for the world's champions. It was too wet to go to the zoo, and Magrew wouldn't let us go to the movies, 'cause they flickered so bad in them days. So we just set around, stewin' and frettin'.

One of the newspaper boys come over to take a pitture of Billy Klinger and Whitey Cott shakin' hands—this reporter'd heard about the fight—and whilst they was standin' there, toe to toe, shakin' hands, Billy give a back lunge and a jerk, and throwed Whitey over his shoulder into a corner of the room, like a sack a salt. Whitey come back at him with a chair, and Bethlehem broke loose in that there room. The camera was tromped to pieces like a berry basket. When we finely got 'em pulled apart, I heard a laugh, and there was Magrew and the midget standin' in the door and givin' us the iron eye.

"Wrasslers," says Magrew, cold-like, "that's what I got for a ball club, Mr. du Monville, wrasslers,—and not very good wrasslers at that, you ast me."

"A man can't be good at everythin'," says Pearl, "but he oughta be good at somethin'."

This sets Magrew guffawin' again, and away they go, the midget taggin' along by his side like a hound dog, and handin' him a fast line of so-called comic cracks.

When we went out to face that battlin' St. Louis club in a double-header the next afternoon, the boys was jumpy as tin toys with keys in their back. We lose the first game, 7 to 2, and are trailin', 4 to o, when the second game ain't but ten minutes old. Magrew set there like a stone statue, speakin' to nobody. Then, in their half a the fourth, somebody singled to center and knocked in two more runs for St. Louis.

That made Magrew squawk. "I wisht one thing," he says. "I wisht I was manager of a old ladies' sewin' circus 'stead of a ball club."

"You are, Junior, you are," says a familyer and disagreeable voice.

It was that Pearl du Monville again, poppin' up outa nowheres, swingin' his bamboo cane and smokin' a cigar that's three sizes too big for his face. By this time we'd finely got the other side out, and Hank Metters slithered a bat acrost the ground, and the midget had to jump to keep both his ankles from bein' broke.

I thought Magrew'd bust a blood vessel. "You hurt Pearl and I'll break your neck!" he yelled.

Hank muttered somethin' and went on up to the plate and struck out.

We managed to get a couple runs acrost in our half a the sixth, but they come back with three more in their half a the seventh, and this was too much for Magrew.

"Come on, Pearl," he says. "We're gettin' outa here."

"Where you think you're goin'?" I ast him.

"To the lawyer's again," he says cryptly.

"I didn't know you'd been to the lawyer's once, yet," I says.

"Which that goes to show how much you don't know," he says.

With that, they was gone, and I didn't see 'em the rest of the day, nor know what they was up to, which was a God's blessin'. We lose the nightcap, 9 to 3, and that puts us into second place plenty, and as low in our minds as a ball club can get.

The next day was a horrible day, like anybody that lived through it can tell you. Practice was just over and the St. Louis club was takin' the field, when I hears this strange sound from the stands. It sounds like the nervous whickerin' a horse gives when he smells somethin' funny on the wind. It was the fans ketchin' sight of Pearl du Monville like you have prob'ly guessed. The midget had popped up onto the field all dressed up in a minacher club uniform, sox, cap, little letters sewed onto his chest, and all. He was swingin' a kid's bat and the only thing kept him from lookin' like a real ballplayer seen through the wrong end of a microscope was this cigar he was smokin'.

Bugs Courtney reached over and jerked it outa his mouth and throwed it away. "You're wearin' that suit on the playin' field," he says to him, severe as a judge; "you go insultin' it and I'll take you out to the zoo and feed you to the bears."

Pearl just blowed some smoke at him which he still has in his mouth.

Whilst Whitey was foulin' off four or five prior to strikin' out, I went on over to Magrew. "If I was as comic as you," I says, "I'd laugh myself to death," I says. "Is that any way to treat the uniform, makin' a mockery out of it?"

"It might surprise you to know I ain't makin' no mockery outa the uniform," says Magrew. "Pearl du Monville here has been made a bone-of-fida member of this so-called ball club. I fixed it up with the front office by long-distance phone."

"Yeh?" I says; "I can just hear Mr. Dillworth or Bart Jenkins agreein' to hire a midget for the ball club. I can just hear 'em." Mr. Dillworth was the owner of the club and Bart Jenkins was the secretary, and they never stood for no monkey business. "May I be so bold as to inquire," I says, "just what you told 'em?"

"I told 'em," he says, "I wanted to sign up a guy they ain't no pitcher in the league can strike him out."

"Uh-huh," I says, "and did you tell 'em what size of a man he is?"

"Never mind about that," he says, "I got papers on me, made out legal and proper, constitutin' one Pearl du Monville a bone-of-fida member of this former ball club. Maybe that'll shame them big babies into gettin' in there and swingin', knowin' I can replace any one of 'em with a midget, if I have a mind to. A St. Louis lawyer I seen twice tells me it's all legal and proper."

"A St. Louis lawyer would," I says, "seein' nothin' could make him happier than havin' you makin' a mockery outa this one-time baseball outfit," I says.

Well, sir, it'll all be there in the papers of thirty, thirty-one year ago, and you could look it up. The game went along without no scorin' for seven innings, and since they ain't nothin' much to watch but guys poppin' up or strikin' out, the fans pay most of their attention to the goin' on of Pearl du Monville. He's out there in front a the dugout, turnin' handsprings, balancin' his bat on his chin, walkin' a imaginary line, and so on. The fans clapped and laughed at him, and he ate it up.

So it went up to the last a the eighth, nothin' to nothin', not more'n seven, eight hits all told, and no errors on neither side. Then up come a fella name of Porter or Billings, or some such name, and he lammed one up against the tobacco sign for three bases. The next guy up slapped the first ball out into left for a base hit, and in come the fella from third for the only run of the ball game so far. The crowd yelled, the look a death come onto Magrew's face again, and even the midget quit his tomfoolin'. Their next man fouled out back a third, and we come up for our last bats like a bunch a schoolgirls steppin' into a pool of cold water. I was lower in my mind than I'd been since the day in Nineteen-four when Chesbro throwed the wild pitch in the ninth inning with a man on third and lost the pennant for the Highlanders. I knowed somethin' just as bad was goin' to happen, which shows I'm a clairvoyun, or was then.

When Gordy Mills hit out to second, I just closed my eyes. I open 'em again to see Dutch Miller standin' on second, dustin' off his pants, him havin' got his first hit in maybe twenty time to the plate. Next up was Harry Loesing, battin' for our pitcher, and he got a base on balls, walkin' on a fourth one you could a combed your hair with.

Then up come Whitey Cott, our lead-off man. He crotchs down in what was prob'ly the most fearsome stanch in organized ball, but all he can do is to pop out to short. That brung up Billy Klinger, with two down and a man on first and second. Billy took a cut at one you could a knocked a plug hat offa this here Carnera with it, but then he gets sense enough to wait 'em out, and finely he walks, too, fillin' the bases.

Yes, sir, there you are; the tyin' run on third and the winnin' run on second, first a the ninth, two men down, and Hank Metters comin' to the bat. Hank was built like a Pope-Hartford and he couldn't run no faster'n President Taft, but he had five home runs to his credit for the season, and that wasn't bad in them days. Hank was still hittin' better'n anybody else on the ball club, and it was mighty heartenin' to see him stridin' up towards the plate. But he never got there.

"Wait a minute!" yells Magrew, jumpin' to his feet. "I'm sendin' in a pinch hitter!" he yells.

You could a heard a bomb drop. When a ball-club manager says he's sendin' in a pinch hitter for the best batter on the club, you know and I know and everybody knows he's lost his holt.

"They're goin' to be sendin' the funny wagon for you, if you don't watch out," I says, grabbin' a holt of his arm.

But he pulled away and run out towards the plate, yellin', "Du Monville battin' for Metters!"

All the fellas begun squawlin' at once, except Hank, and he just stood there starin' at Magrew like he'd gone crazy and was claimin' to be Ty Cobb's grandma or somethin'. Their pitcher stood out there with his hands on his hips and a disagreeable look on his face, and the plate umpire told Magrew to go on and get a batter up. Magrew told him again Du Monville was battin' for Metters, and the St. Louis manager finely got the idea. It brung him outa his dugout, howlin' and bawlin' like he'd lost a female dog and her seven pups.

Magrew pushed the midget towards the plate and he says to him, he says, "Just stand up there and hold that bat on your shoulder. They ain't a man in the world can throw three strikes in there 'fore he throws four balls," he says.

"I get it, Junior!" says the midget. "He'll walk me and force in the tyin' run!" And he starts on up to the plate as cocky as if he was Willie Keeler.

I don't need to tell you Bethlehem broke loose on that there ball field. The fans got onto their hind legs, yellin' and whistlin', and everybody on the field began wavin' their arms and hollerin' and shovin'. The plate umpire stalked over to Magrew like a traffic cop, waggin' his jaw and pointin' his finger, and the St. Louis manager kept yellin' like his house was on fire. When Pearl got up to the plate and stood there, the pitcher slammed his glove down onto the ground and started stompin' on it, and there ain't nobody can blame him. He's just walked two normal-sized human bein's, and now here's a guy up to the plate they ain't more'n twenty inches between his knees and his shoulders.

The plate umpire called in the field umpire, and they talked a while, like a couple doctors seein' the bucolic plague or somethin' for the first time. Then the plate umpire come over to Magrew with his arms folded acrost his chest, and he told him to go on and get a batter up, or he'd forfeit the game to St. Louis. He pulled out his watch, but somebody batted it outa his hand in the scufflin', and I thought there'd be a free-for-all, with everybody yellin' and shovin' except Pearl du Monville, who stood up at the plate with his little bat on his shoulder, not movin' a muscle.

Then Magrew played his ace. I seen him pull some papers outa his pocket and show 'em to the plate umpire. The umpire begun lookin' at 'em like they was bills for somethin' he not only never bought it, he never even heard of it. The other umpire studied 'em like they was a death warren, and all this time the St. Louis manager and the fans and the players is yellin' and hollerin'.

Well, sir, they fought about him bein' a midget, and they fought about him usin' a kid's bat, and they fought about where'd he been all season. They was eight or nine rule books brung out and everybody was thumbin' through 'em, tryin' to find out what it says about midgets, but it don't say nothin' about midgets, 'cause this was somethin' never'd come up in the history of the game before, and nobody'd ever dreamed about it, even when they has nightmares. Maybe you can't send no midgets in to bat nowadays, 'cause the old game's changed a lot, mostly for the worst, but you could then, it turned out.

The plate umpire finely decided the contrack papers was all legal and proper, like Magrew said, so he waved the St. Louis players back to their places and he pointed his finger at their manager and told him to quit hollerin' and get on back in the dugout. The

509

manager says the game is percedin' under protest, and the umpire bawls, "Play ball!" over'n above the yellin' and booin', him havin' a voice like a hog-caller.

The St. Louis pitcher picked up his glove and beat at it with his fist six or eight times, and then got set on the mound and studied the situation. The fans realized he was really goin' to pitch to the midget, and they went crazy, hoopin' and hollerin' louder'n ever, and throwin' pop bottles and hats and cushions down onto the field. It took five, ten minutes to get the fans quieted down again, whilst our fellas that was on base set down on the bags and waited. And Pearl du Monville kept standin' up there with the bat on his shoulder, like he'd been told to.

So the pitcher starts studyin' the setup again, and you got to admit it was the strangest setup in a ball game since the players cut off their beards and begun wearin' gloves. I wisht I could call the pitcher's name—it wasn't old Barney Pelty nor Nig Jack Powell nor Harry Howell. He was a big right-hander, but I can't call his name. You could look it up. Even in a crotchin' position, the ketcher towers over the midget like the Washington Monument.

The plate umpire tries standin' on his tiptoes, then he tries crotchin' down, and he finally gets hisself into a stanch nobody'd ever seen on a ball field before, kinda squattin' down on his hanches.

Well, the pitcher is sore as a old buggy horse in fly time. He slams in the first pitch, hard and wild, and maybe two foot higher'n the midget's head.

"Ball one!" hollers the umpire over'n' above the racket, 'cause everybody is yellin' worsten ever.

The ketcher goes on out toward the mound and talks to the pitcher and hands him the ball. This time the big right-hander tries a under-shoot, and it comes in a little closer, maybe no higher'n a foot, foot and a half above Pearl's head. It would 'a' been a strike with a human bein' in there, but the umpire's got to call it, and he does.

"Ball two!" he bellers.

The ketcher walks out to the mound again, and the whole infield comes over and gives advice to the pitcher about what they'd do in a case like this, with two balls and no strikes on a batter that oughta be in a bottle of alcohol, 'stead of up there at the plate in a big-league game between the teams that is fightin' for first place.

For the third pitch, the pitcher stands there flat-footed and tosses up the ball like he's playin' ketch with a little girl.

Pearl stands there motionless as a hitchin' post, and the ball comes in big and slow and high—high for Pearl, that is, it bein' about on a level with his eyes, or a little higher'n a grown man's knees.

There ain't nothin' else for the umpire to do, so he calls, "Ball three!"

Everybody is onto their feet, hoopin' and hollerin', as the pitcher sets to throw ball four. The St. Louis manager is makin' signs and faces like he was a contorturer, and the infield is givin' the pitcher some more advice about what to do this time. Our boys who was on base stick right onto the bag, runnin' no risk of bein' nipped for the last out.

Well, the pitcher decides to give him a toss again, seein' he come closer with that than with a fast ball. They ain't nobody ever seen a slower ball throwed. It come in big as a balloon, and slower'n any ball ever throwed before in the major leagues. It come right in over the plate in front of Pearl's chest, lookin' prob'ly big as a full moon to Pearl. They ain't never been a minute like the minute that followed since the United States was founded by the Pilgrim grandfathers.

Pearl du Monville took a cut at that ball, and he hit it! Magrew give a groan like a poleaxed steer as the ball rolls out in front a the plate into fair territory.

"Fair ball!" yells the umpire, and the midget starts runnin' for first, still carryin' that little bat, and makin' maybe ninety foot an hour. Bethlehem breaks loose on that ball field and in them stands. They ain't never been nothin' like it since creation was begun.

The ball's rollin' slow, on down towards third, goin' maybe eight, ten foot. The infield comes in fast and our boys break from their bases like hares in a brushfire. Everybody is standin' up, yellin' and hollerin', and Magrew is tearin' his hair outa his head, and the midget is scamperin' for first with all the speed of one of them little dash-hounds carryin' a satchel in his mouth.

The ketcher gets to the ball first, but he boots it out past the pitcher's box, the pitcher fallin' on his face tryin' to stop it, the shortstop sprawlin' after it full length and zaggin' it on over towards the second baseman, whilst Muller is scorin' with the tyin' run and Loesing is roundin' third with the winnin' run. Ty Cobb could 'a' made a three-bagger outa that bunt, with everybody fallin' over their-self tryin' to pick the ball up. But Pearl is still maybe fifteen, twenty feet from the bag, toddlin' like a baby and yeepin' like a trapped rabbit, when the second baseman finely gets a holt of that ball and slams it over to first. The first baseman ketches it and stomps on the bag, the base umpire waves Pearl out, and there goes your old ball game, the craziest ball game ever played in the history of the organized world.

Their players start runnin' in, and then I see Magrew. He starts after Pearl, runnin' faster'n any man ever run before. Pearl sees him comin' and runs behind the base umpire's legs and gets a holt onto 'em. Magrew comes up, pantin' and roarin', and him and the midget plays ring-around-a-rosy with the umpire, who keeps shovin' at Magrew with one hand and tryin' to slap the midget loose from his legs with the other.

Finely Magrew catches the midget, who is still yeepin' like a stuck sheep. He gets holt of that little guy by both his ankles and starts whirlin' him round and round his head like Magrew was a hammer thrower and Pearl was the hammer. Nobody can stop him without gettin' their head knocked off so everybody just stands there and yells. Then Magrew lets the midget fly. He flies on out towards second, high and fast, like a human home run, headed for the soap sign in center field.

Their shortstop tries to get to him, but he can't make it, and I knowed the little fella was goin' to bust to pieces like a dollar watch on a asphalt street when he hit the ground. But it so happens their center fielder is just crossin' second, and he starts runnin' back, tryin' to get under the midget, who had took to spiralin' like a football 'stead of turnin' head over foot, which give him more speed and more distance.

I know you never seen a midget ketched, and you prob'ly never even seen one throwed. To ketch a midget that's been throwed by a heavy-muscled man and is flyin' through the air, you got to run under him and with him and pull your hands and arms back and down when you ketch him, to break the compact of his body, or you'll bust him in two like a match-stick. I see Bill Lange and Willie Keeler and Tris Speaker make some wonderful ketches in my day, but I never seen nothin' like that center fielder. He goes back and back and still further back and he pulls that midget down outa the air like he was liftin' a sleepin' baby from a cradle. They wasn't a bruise onto him, only his face was the color of cat's meat and he ain't got no air in his chest. In his excitement, the base umpire, who was runnin' back with the center fielder when he ketched Pearl, yells, "Out!" and that give hysterics to the Bethlehem which was ragin' like Niagry on that ball field.

Everybody was hoopin' and hollerin' and yellin' and runnin', with the fans swarmin' onto the field, and the cops tryin' to keep order, and some guys laughin' and some of the women fans cryin', and six or eight of us holdin' onto Magrew to keep him from gettin' at that midget and finishin' him off. Some of the fans picks up the St. Louis pitcher and the center fielder, and starts carryin' them around on their shoulders, and they was the craziest goin's-on knowed to the history of organized ball on this side of the 'Lantic Ocean.

I seen Pearl du Monville strugglin' in the arms of a lady fan with a ample bosom, who was laughin' and cryin' at the same time, and him beatin' at her with his little fists and bawlin' and yellin'. He clawed his way loose finely and disappeared in the forest of legs which made that ball field look like it was Coney Island on a hot summer's day.

That was the last I ever seen of Pearl du Monville. I never seen hide nor hair of him from that day to this, and neither did nobody else. He just vanished into the thin of the air, as the fella says. He was ketched for the final out of the ball game and that was the end of him, just like it was the end of the ball game, you might say, and also the end of our losin' streak, like I'm goin' to tell you.

That night we piled onto a train for Chicago, but we wasn't snarlin' and snappin' any more. No, sir, the ice was finely broke and a new spirit come into that ball club. The old zip come back with the disappearance of Pearl du Monville out back a second base. We got to laughin' and talkin' and kiddin' together, and 'fore long Magrew was laughin' with us. He got a human look onto his pan again, and he quit whinin' and complainin' and wishtin' he was in heaven with the angels.

Well, sir, we wiped up that Chicago series, winnin' all four games, and makin' seventeen hits in one of 'em. Funny thing was, St. Louis was so shook up by that last game with us, they never did hit their stride again. Their center fielder took to misjudgin' everything that come his way, and the rest a the fellas followed suit, the way a club'll do when one guy blows up.

'Fore we left Chicago, I and some of the fellas went out and bought a pair of them little baby shoes, which we had 'em golded over and give 'em to Magrew for a souvenir, and he took it all in good spirit. Whitey Cott and Billy Klinger made up and was fast friends again, and we hit our home lot like a ton of dynamite and they was nothin' could stop us from then on.

I don't recollect things as clear as I did thirty, forty year ago. I can't read fine print no more, and the only person I got to check with on the golden days of the national pastime, as the fella says, is my friend, old Milt Kline, over in Springfield, and his mind ain't as strong as it once was.

He gets Rube Waddell mixed up with Rube Marquand, for one thing, and anybody does that oughta be put away where he won't bother nobody. So I can't tell you the exact margin we win the pennant by. Maybe it was two and a half games, or maybe it was three and a half. But it'll all be there in the newspapers and record books of thirty, thirty-one year ago, and, like I was sayin', you could look it up.

Where Joe Meriweather went to [1]

I do believe that's Bill Meriweather," said the old lady hostess of the sign of "The Buck" tavern, as attracted by the noise of a horse's hoofs, she raised her eyes from her occupation of stringing dried slips of pumpkin, and descried, this side of the first bend in the road, a traveller riding a jaded horse towards the mansion.

"I do believe that's Bill Meriweather. It's about time for him to be round agin a buyin' shoats. But whar's Joe? Phillisy Ann," continued Mrs. Harris, raising her voice, "catch a couple of young chickens, and get supper ready soon as ye can, you dratted lazy wench you, for here comes Bill Meriweather. But whar's Joe? How do you do, Mr. Meriweather," concluded the old lady, as the stranger arrived in front of the porch.

"Lively," replied that individual, as he proceeded to dismount and tie his horse. "How do you come on yourself, old 'omen?"

"Pretty well, Bill; how's craps down in your parts?"

"Bad, uncommon bad," replied Bill, "there's a new varmint come around in our country, that's got a mortal likin' fur the tobacker crap. They looks a good deal like a fox, but are as big as a three year old nigger, and kin climb a tree like a squearl, and they steals a dozen or so 'hands' every night, and next mornin' if you notice, you'll see all the tops of the pine-oaks around the plantation kivered with them a dryin', and the infernal chawtobacks—that's what we call 'em, —a settin' in a crotch, a chawin' what is *cured*, and squirtin' ambeer all over the country. Got any on 'em up here yet?"

"The goodness, Lord ha' mercy, no, Bill! But whar's Joe?" Up to this time Mr. Meriweather had been as pleasant and jovial a looking Green River man, as you might find in a week's ride along the southern border of Kentucky, and had finished his lecture on the natural history of the chawtoback and the unsaddling his horse at the same time; but no sooner had the old lady asked the question, "Whar's Joe?" than he instantaneously dropped on the bench alongside the questioner, gave her an imploring look of pity and despair, let his head fall into his open palms, and bending down both until they nearly touched his knees, he uttered such a sigh as might a Louisville and New Orleans eight boiler steam-packet in the last stage of collapsed flues.

---

[1] By C. A. P., from *Ring-Tailed Roarers: Tall Tales of the American Frontier, 1830–1860,* edited, with an Introduction, by V. L. O. Chittick (Caldwell, Idaho: Caxton Printers; 1941), pp. 41–5.

"Goodness, gracious, Bill! what's the matter?" cried the old lady, letting her stringing apparatus fall. "Hev you got the cramps? Phillisy Ann, bring that bottle here outen the cupboard, quick, and some pepper pods!"

"Ah-h! no!" sighed the sufferer, not changing his position, but mournfully shaking his head, "I ain't got no cramps." However, Phillisy Ann, arriving in "no time" with the articles of household furniture called for, that gentleman, utterly disregarding the pepper pods, proceeded to pour out into a tumbler, preparatory to drinking, a sufficient quantity of amber coloured fluid to utterly exterminate any cramps that might, by any possibility, be secretly lingering in his system, or fortify himself against any known number that might attack him in the distant future; and having finished, immediately assumed his former position, and went into most surprisingly exact imitations of a wheezy locomotive on a foggy morning.

"Merciful powers! what can the matter be?" exclaimed the widow, now thoroughly excited, as Mr. Meriweather appeared to be getting no better, but was rocking himself up and down, "like a man who is sawing marble," groaning and muttering inarticulate sounds, as if in the last extremity of bodily anguish. But Mr. Meriweather was for some time unable to make any reply that could be understood, until at length, at the conclusion of a very fierce paroxysm, the widow thought she could catch the two words, "Poor Joe!"

"Is there anything the matter with Joe?" asked the old lady. If it were possible for any *one* man to feel and suffer, as far as appearances went, all the agony and misery that a half dozen of the most miserable and unfortunate of the human family ever have felt and suffered, and yet live, Mr. Meriweather certainly was that individual, for he immediately went off into such a state of sighs, groans, and lamentations, mingled with exclamations of "Poor Joe!" "Poor Brother Joe!" that the widow, aroused to the highest state of sympathy and pity, could do nothing but wipe her eyes with her apron, and repeat the question.

"Whar is Joe, Mr. Meriweather, is he sick?"

"Oh-h-no!" groaned his mourning brother.

"Is he dead then? poor Joe!" faintly inquired the old lady.

"I don't know that," was the broken reply.

"The Lord ha' mercy on our sinful sowls! then *whar* is he?" cried the widow, breaking out afresh. "Is he run away to Orleans—or gone to Californey? Yes, that's it! and the poor boy will be eaten' up by them 'diggers' that they say goes rootin' round that outlandish country, like a set of mean stinkin' ground-hogs. Poor Joe! he was a fine little fellow, an' it was only the other day last year, when you was on your rounds, that he eat all my little bo—"

"No, he ain't gone to Californey as I know," interrupted his brother.

515

"Then, for mercy's sake! do tell a body what's become on him!" rather tartly inquired the old lady.

"Why, you see, Mrs. Harris," replied Mr. Meriweather, still keeping the same position, and interrupting the narrative with several bursts of grief, (which we'll leave out). "You see, Mrs. Harris, Joe and I went up airly in the spring to get a boat load of rock from Boone county, to put up the foundation of the new houses we're buildin', fur there ain't no rock down in them rich sily bottoms in our parts. Well, we got along pretty considerable, fur we had five kegs of blast along, and what with the hire of some niggers, we managed to get our boat loaded, an' started fur home in about three weeks. You never did see anything rain like it did the fust day we was floatin' down, but we worked like a cornfilled nigger ov a Crismus week, and pretty near sundown we'd made a matter ov nigh twenty mile afore we were ashore and tied up. Well, as we didn't have any shelter on the flat, we raised a rousin' big fire on the bank, close to whar she was tied up, and cooked some grub; and I'd eaten a matter of two pounds ov side, and half of a possum, and was sittin' on a log, smokin' a Kaintuck regaly, and a talkin' to Brother Joe, who was a standin' chock up agin the fire, with his back to it. You recollex, Mrs. Harris, Brother Joe allers was a dressy sort of a chap—fond of brass buttons on his coat and the flaim'est kind of red neckershers; and this time he had buckskin breeches, with straps under his boots. Well, when I was a talkin' to him ov the prospect fur the next day, all ov a sudden I thought the little feller was a growin' uncommon tall; till I diskivered that the buckskin breeches, that wur as wet as a young rooster in a spring rain, wur beginning to smoke and draw up kinder, and wur a liftin' Brother Joe off the ground.

" 'Brother Joe,' sez I, 'you're a goin' up.'

" 'Brother Bill,' sez he, 'I ain't a doin' anything else.'

And he scrunched down mighty hard; but it warn't ov no use, fur afore long he wur a matter of some fifteen feet up in the air.

"Merciful powers," interrupted the widow.

" 'Brother Joe,' sez I.

" 'I'm here,' sez he.

" 'Catch hold ov the top ov that black-jack,' sez I.

" 'Talk!' sez Brother Joe, and he sorter leaned over and grabbed the saplin', like as maybe you've seed a squ'el haul in an elm switch ov a June mornin'. But it warn't ov no use, fur, old 'omen, ef you'll believe me, it gradually begun to give way at the roots, and afore he'd got five foot higher, it jist slipped out er the ground, as easy as you'd pull up a spring reddish.

" 'Brother Joe!' sez I agin.

" 'I'm a list'ning,' sez he.

516

" 'Cut your straps!' sez I, for I seed it was his last chance.

" 'Talk!' sez Brother Joe, tho' he looked sort—reproachful like at me fur broachin' such a subject; but arter apparently considerin' awhile he outs with his jack-knife, an' leanin' over sideways, made a rip at the sole of his left foot. There was a considerable deal ov craklin' fur a second or two, then a crash sorter like as if a waggon-load of wood had bruck down, and the fust thing I know'd, the t'other leg shot up like, and started him; and the last thing I seed ov Brother Joe, he was *a whirlin' round like a four-spoked wheel with the rim off, away overclost toward sundown!*"

BOOK VI

AMERICA'S MEN

AMERICA'S MEN: *Explorers and pioneers,*

benefactors, demigods, supermen,

myth-makers, and jokers

EVERYTHING about North America was from its earliest settlement up to at least the mid nineteenth century, favorable to the manufacture of mythology. There was, first, of course, the country's bigness; on a local level, the height of its mountains, breadth of its rivers, denseness of its forests. There were dangers both natural and supernatural; the Puritans and the Jesuit fathers knew that the Devil was at hand in this new country, full of mischief; Crockett and Boone knew bears and wildcats, Carson and Frémont were two among hundreds who fought Indians, and fought for their lives. Other tamers of the wilderness worked in less spectacular ways, but they too became a focus for legend; John Chapman (Johnny Appleseed), for instance, and Roy Bean.

American Negro folklore is a subject by itself, but it is like our pioneer tales in its exaltation of physical strength, and of shrewdness as well. In John Henry, Big John the Conqueror, and other huge mythmen, the Negro felt his race triumphant, strong, happy. And Mike Fink (the legendary, not the real one) and Liverpool Jarge and Pecos Bill and Paul Bunyan; they are but the American imagination playing about with the notion of omnipotence; it is more fun than the child's game of "If I had a million dollars."

Hardly soberer than the Bunyan-makers are the great raconteurs like Shepherd Tom Hazard. They know the flavor of their own corners of America, and know just how much they can exaggerate it without overshooting the mark, which is wonder, delight, and laughter. They let themselves go advisedly.

And finally, the jokers. Here America lets itself go completely, to the mystification of all foreigners, but the inexpressible appreciation of all fellow Americans.

Early missionaries had their own special way of looking at the wonders of America. The Indians told them much that was marvelous enough, but the missionaries knew that the Indians were, as Père Allouez puts it, "poor blind creatures." Whatever they said was, to quote Allouez again, "what passes here for truth." But the missionaries, more than a little bemused, wrote much of it down; fortunately for us, they could not entirely resist the wonderful.

In like manner, an explorer of scientific bent, like William Bartram, seems to hold up both hands in amazement at the creatures of the American wilderness, as he cries: "What expressions can sufficiently declare the scene?" He contrives to find adequate ones, however.

Père Allouez meets idols and absurdities [1]

Of the False Gods and some Superstitious Customs of the Savages of that Country.

I have seen," says Father Allouez, "an idol set up in the middle of a village; and to it, among other presents, ten dogs were offered in sacrifice, in order to prevail on this false god to send elsewhere the disease that was depopulating the village. Everyone went daily to make his offerings to this idol, according to his needs.

"Besides these public sacrifices, they have some that are private and domestic; for often in their cabins they throw tobacco into the fire, with a kind of outward offering which they make to their false gods.

"During storms and tempests, they sacrifice a dog, throwing it into the lake. 'That is to appease thee,' they say to the latter, 'keep quiet.' At perilous places in the rivers, they propitiate the eddies and rapids by offering them presents; and so persuaded are they that they honor their pretended divinities by this external worship, that those among them who are converted and baptized observe the same ceremonies toward the true God, until they are disabused.

---

[1] From "Father Allouez's Journey to Lake Superior, 1665–1667," in *Early Narratives of the Northwest, 1634–1699*, edited by Louise Phelps Kellogg (New York: Barnes & Noble, Inc., publishers), pp. 112–14; 125–7 *passim*.

"As, moreover, these people are of a gross nature, they recognize no purely spiritual divinity, believing that the sun is a man, and the moon his wife; that snow and ice are also a man, who goes away in the spring and comes back in the winter; that the evil spirit is in adders, dragons, and other monsters; that the crow, the kite, and some other birds are genii, and speak just as we do; and that there are even people among them who understand the language of birds, as some understand a little that of the French.

"They believe, moreover, that the souls of the departed govern the fishes in the lake; and thus, from the earliest times, they have held the immortality, and even the metempsychosis of the souls of dead fishes, believing that they pass into other fishes' bodies. Therefore they never throw their bones into the fire, for fear that they may offend these souls, so that they will cease to come into their nets.

"They hold in very special veneration a certain fabulous animal which they have never seen except in dreams, and which they call Missibizi, acknowledging it to be a great genius, and offering it sacrifices in order to obtain good sturgeon-fishing.

"They say also that the little nuggets of copper which they find at the bottom of the water in the lake, or in the rivers emptying into it, are the riches of the gods who dwell in the depths of the earth.

"I have learned," says the Father who has brought to light all these follies, "that the Iliniouek, the Outagami, and other savages toward the south, hold that there is a great and excellent genius, master of all the rest, who made Heaven and Earth; and who dwells, they say, in the East, toward the country of the French.

"The fountain-head of their religion is libertinism; and all these various sacrifices end ordinarily in debauches, indecent dances, and shameful acts of concubinage. All the devotion of the men is directed toward securing many wives, and changing them whenever they choose; that of the women, toward leaving their husbands; and that of the girls, toward a life of profligacy.

"They endure a great deal on account of these ridiculous deities; for they fast in their honor, for the purpose of learning the issue of some affair. I have," says the Father, "seen with compassion men who had some scheme of war or hunting pass a whole week, taking scarcely anything. They show such fixity of purpose that they will not desist until they have seen in a dream what they desire—either a herd of moose, or a band of Iroquois put to flight, or something similar—no very difficult thing for an empty brain, utterly exhausted with hunger, and thinking all day long of nothing else.

"Let us say something about the art of medicine in vogue in this country. Their science consists in ascertaining the cause of the ailment, and applying the remedies.

"They deem the most common cause of illness to come from failure to give a feast after some successful fishing or hunting excursion; for then the Sun, who takes pleasure in feasts, is angry with the one who has been delinquent in his duty, and makes him ill.

"Besides this general cause of sickness, there are special ones, in the shape of certain little spirits, malevolent in their nature, who thrust themselves of their own accord, or sent by some enemy, into the parts of the body that are most diseased. Thus, when any one has an aching head, or arm, or stomach, they say that a manitou has entered this part of the body, and will not cease its torments until it has been drawn or driven out.

"The most common remedy, accordingly, is to summon the juggler, who comes attended by some old men, with whom he holds a sort of consultation on the patient's ailment. After this, he falls upon the diseased part, applies his mouth to it, and, by sucking, pretends to extract something from it, as a little stone, or a bit of string, or something else, which he has concealed in his mouth beforehand, and which he displays, saying: 'There is the manitou; now thou art cured, and it only remains to give a feast.'

"The Devil, bent on tormenting those poor blind creatures even in this world, has suggested to them another remedy, in which they place great confidence. It consists in grasping the patient under the arms, and making him walk barefoot over the live embers in the cabin; or, if he is so ill that he cannot walk, he is carried by four or five persons, and made to pass slowly over all the fires, a treatment which often results in this, that the greater suffering thereby produced cures, or induces unconsciousness of, the lesser pain which they strive to cure.

"After all, the commonest remedy, as it is the most profitable for the physician, is the holding of a feast to the Sun, which is done in the belief that this luminary, which takes pleasure in liberal actions, being appeased by a magnificent repast, will regard the patient with favor, and restore him to health."

Of the Mission to the Pouteouatamiouec.

"I must not omit here a rather strange circumstance: on the day after (this aged man's death) his relatives, contrary to all usage, of this country, burned his body and reduced it entirely to ashes. The cause of this is found in a legend which passes here for truth.

"It is held beyond dispute that this old man's father was a hare, an animal which runs over the snow in winter, and that thus the snow, the hare, and the old man are of the same village, that is, are relatives. It is further said that the hare told his wife that he disapproved of their children's remaining in the depths of the earth, as that did not befit their condition, they being relatives of the snow, whose country is above, toward the sky; and, if it ever occurred that they were put into the ground after their death, he would pray the snow, his relative, in order to punish the people for this offense, to fall in such quantities and so long that there should be no spring. And, to confirm this story, it is added that three years ago the brother of our good old man died, in the beginning of the winter; and, after he had been buried in the usual manner, snow fell to such an extent, and the winter was so long, that people despaired of seeing the spring in its season. Meanwhile, all were dying of hunger, and no remedy could be found for this general suffering. The elders assembled, and held many councils, but all in vain; the snow still continued. Then some one of the company said he remembered the threats which we have related. Straightway they went and disinterred the dead man, and burned him; when immediately the snow ceased, and spring followed. Who would think that people could give credence to such absurd stories? And yet they regard them as true beyond dispute.

. . . .

"We can also relate, among the marvels that God has wrought in this Church, what happened in regard to another family of this nation. A young man, in whose canoe I had a place on my journey to this country, was seized, toward the close of the winter, with the contagious disease which was prevalent. I tried to show him as much kindness as he had shown me ill usage on the journey. As he was a man of considerable importance, no kind of jugglery was spared for his cure; and it was carried so far that at length they came to tell me that they had extracted from his body two dog's teeth. 'That is not what causes his illness,' said I to them, 'but rather the tainted blood which he has in his body,' for I judged that he had the pleurisy. Meanwhile, I began to instruct him in good earnest; and on the next day, finding him well prepared, I gave him holy baptism with the name of Ignace, hoping that great saint would confound the evil spirit and the jugglers. Indeed, I bled him; and, showing the blood to the juggler, who was present, 'There,' said I to him, 'is what is killing this sick man. Thou shouldst, with all thy affected arts, have drawn from him every drop of this corrupt blood, and not some alleged dog's teeth.' But he, perceiving the relief which this bleeding had afforded the sick man, determined to have the glory of his cure; and, to that end, made him take a kind of medicine, which produced such an ill effect that the patient remained for three whole hours as one dead. This result was proclaimed throughout the village, and the juggler, much surprised by the turn of affairs, confessed that he had killed the poor man, and begged me not to forsake him. He was not, in truth, forsaken by his patron, Saint Ignatius, who restored him to life, in order to confound the superstitions of these infidels."

Bartram's subtle greedy alligator[1]

The verges and islets of the lagoon were elegantly embellished with flowering plants and shrubs; the laughing coots with wings half spread were tripping over the little coves, and hiding themselves in the tufts of grass; young broods of the painted summer teal, skimming the still surface of the waters, and following the watchful parent unconscious of danger, were frequently surprised by the voracious trout; and he, in turn, as often by the subtle greedy alligator. Behold him rushing forth from the flags and reeds. His enormous body swells. His plaited tail brandished high, floats upon the lake. The waters like a cataract descend from his opening jaws. Clouds of smoke issue from his dilated nostrils. The earth trembles with his thunder. When immediately from the opposite coast of the lagoon, emerges from the deep his rival champion. They suddenly dart upon each other. The boiling surface of the lake marks their rapid course, and a terrible conflict commences. They now sink to the bottom folded together in horrid wreaths. The water becomes thick and discoloured. Again they rise, their jaws clap together, re-echoing through the deep surrounding forests. Again they sink, when the contest ends at the muddy bottom of the lake, and the vanquished makes a hazardous escape, hiding himself in the muddy turbulent waters and sedge on a distant shore. The proud victor exulting returns to the place of action. The shores and forests resound his dreadful roar, together with the triumphing shouts of the plaited tribes around, witnesses of the horrid combat.

My apprehensions were highly alarmed after being a spectator of so dreadful a battle. It was obvious that every delay would but tend to increase my dangers and difficulties, as the sun was near setting, and the alligators gathered around my harbour from all quarters. From these considerations I concluded to be expeditious in my trip to the lagoon, in order to take some fish. Not thinking it prudent to take my fusee with me, lest I might lose it overboard in case of a battle, which I had every reason to dread before my return, I therefore furnished myself with a club for my defence, went on board, and penetrating the first line of those which surrounded my harbour, they

[1] From *The Travels of William Bartram* (Philadelphia, 1791; reprinted, New York: Macy-Masius; 1928), pp. 115–19.

gave way; but being pursued by several very large ones, I kept strictly on the watch, and paddled with all my might towards the entrance of the lagoon, hoping to be sheltered there from the multitude of my assailants; but ere I had half-way reached the place, I was attacked on all sides, several endeavouring to overset the canoe. My situation now became precarious to the last degree: two very large ones attacked me closely, at the same instant, rushing up with their heads and part of their bodies above the water, roaring terribly and belching floods of water over me. They struck their jaws together so close to my ears, as almost to stun me, and I expected every moment to be dragged out of the boat and instantly devoured. But I applied my weapons so effectually about me, though at random, that I was so successful as to beat them off a little; when, finding that they designed to renew the battle, I made for the shore, as the only means left me for my preservation; for, by keeping close to it, I should have my enemies on one side of me only, whereas I was before surrounded by them; and there was a probability, if pushed to the last extremity, of saving myself, by jumping out of the canoe on shore, as it is easy to outwalk them on land, although comparatively as swift as lightning in the water. I found this last expedient alone could fully answer my expectations, for as soon as I gained the shore, they drew off and kept aloof. This was a happy relief, as my confidence was, in some degree, recovered by it. On recollecting myself, I discovered that I had almost reached the entrance of the lagoon, and determined to venture in, if possible, to take a few fish, and then return to my harbour, while day-light continued; for I could now, with caution and resolution, make my way with safety along shore; and indeed there was no other way to regain my camp, without leaving my boat and making my retreat through the marshes and reeds, which, if I could even effect, would have been in a manner throwing myself away, for then there would have been no hopes of ever recovering my bark, and returning in safety to any settlements of men. I accordingly proceeded, and made good my entrance into the lagoon, though not without opposition from the alligators, who formed a line across the entrance, but did not pursue me into it, nor was I molested by any there, though there were some very large ones in a cove at the upper end. I soon caught more trout than I had present occasion for, and the air was too hot and sultry to admit of their being kept for many hours, even though salted or barbecued. I now prepared for my return to camp, which I succeeded in with but little trouble, by keeping close to the shore; yet I was opposed upon re-entering the river out of the lagoon, and pursued near to my landing (though not closely attacked), particularly by an old daring one, about twelve feet in length, who kept close after me; and when I stepped on shore and turned about, in order to draw up my canoe, he rushed up near my feet, and lay there for some time, looking me in the face, his head and shoulders out of water. I resolved he should pay for his temerity, and having a heavy load in my fusee, I ran to my camp, and returning with my piece, found him with his foot on the gunwale of my boat, in search of fish. On my coming up he withdrew sullenly and slowly into the water, but soon returned and placed himself in his former position, looking at me, and seeming neither fearful nor any way disturbed. I soon dispatched him by lodging the contents of my gun in his head, and then proceeded to cleanse and prepare my fish for supper; and accordingly took them out of the boat, laid them down on the sand close to the water, and began to scale them; when, raising my head, I saw before me, through the clear water, the head and shoulders of a very large alligator, moving slowly towards me. I instantly stepped back, when, with a sweep of his tail, he brushed off several of my fish. It was certainly most providential that I looked up at that instant, as the monster would probably, in less than a minute, have seized and dragged me into the river. This incredible boldness of the animal disturbed me greatly, supposing there could now be no reasonable safety for me during the night, but by keeping continually on the watch: I therefore, as soon as I had prepared the fish, proceeded to secure myself and effects in the best manner I could. In the first place, I hauled my bark upon the shore, almost clear out of the water, to prevent their oversetting or sinking her; after this, every moveable was taken out and carried to my camp, which was but a few yards off; then ranging some dry wood in such order as was the most convenient, I cleared the ground round about it, that there might be no impediment in my way, in case of an attack in the night, either from the water or the land; for I discovered by this time, that this small isthmus, from its remote situation and fruitfulness, was resorted to by bears and wolves. Having prepared myself in the best manner I could, I charged my gun, and proceeded to reconnoitre my camp and the adjacent grounds; when I discovered that the peninsula and grove, at the distance of about two hundred yards from my encampment, on the land side, were invested by a cypress swamp, covered with water, which below was joined to the shore of the little lake, and above to the marshes surrounding the lagoon; so that I was confined to an islet exceedingly circumscribed, and I found there was no other retreat for me, in case of an attack, but by either ascending one of the large oaks, or pushing off with my boat.

It was by this time dusk, and the alligators had nearly ceased their roar, when I was again alarmed by a tumultuous noise that seemed to be in my harbour, and therefore engaged my immediate attention. Returning to my camp, I found it undisturbed, and then continued on to the extreme point of the promontory, where I saw a scene, new and surprising, which at first threw my senses into such a tumult, that it was some time before I could comprehend what was the matter; however, I soon accounted for the prodigious assemblage of crocodiles at this place, which exceeded every thing of the kind I had ever heard of.

How shall I express myself so as to convey an adequate idea of it to the reader, and at the same time avoid raising suspicions of my veracity? Should I say, that the river (in this place) from shore to shore, and perhaps half a mile above and below me, appeared to be one solid bank of fish, of various kinds, pushing through this narrow pass of St. Juan's into the little lake, on their return down the river, and that the alligators were in such incredible numbers, and so close together from shore to shore, that it would have been easy to have walked across on their heads, had the animals been harmless? What expressions can sufficiently declare the shocking scene that for some minutes continued, whilst this mighty army of fish were forcing the pass? During this attempt, thousands, I may say hundreds of thousands, of them were caught and swallowed by the devouring alligators. I have seen an alligator take up out of the water several great fish at a time, and just squeeze them betwixt his jaws, while the tails of the great trout flapped about his eyes and lips, ere he had swallowed them. The horrid noise of their closing jaws, their plunging amidst the broken banks of fish, and rising with their prey some feet above the water, the floods of water and blood rushing out of their mouths, and the clouds of vapor issuing from their wide nostrils, were truly frightful.

George Washington's comment on being shot at by an Indian was that the Indian "fortunately missed." Few American pioneers were quite as laconic as the father of his country. They were just as hardy, and just as "fortunate," but they boasted. David Crockett is the type, although his own style (so far as we can definitely distinguish between him and his imitators or "ghost-writers") is merely naïvely proud and not at all pompous. The Crockett almanacs, which pleased the not so gentle reader of the forties, make David a peg on which they can hang the wildest extravagances of speech and action. Mike Fink, too, though he was also a real person, becomes a type of the American wilderness at its toughest, loudest, and, one should in fairness add, its bravest. At their most rowdy and Gargantuan, these heroes are not wholly false; their inventors (so to speak) did not leave the real Crockett and Fink entirely behind when they soared into fantasy— nor the American frontier either. There is an important grain of truth in the boldest of these imaginings. Then too, the bears were real, and the Indians.

It is well that we should remember this. Otherwise Wister's grisly picture of the Apaches might seem merely a literary exercise in the macabre. On the contrary, it belongs to the America of not so long ago. If few men today can remember such an America, there are many whose fathers knew it well, and it is the special merit of such a narrative as Wister's not merely that it seems vivid, but that it sprang out of interviews and discussions with men whose lives had hung in the balance, men who bridged the gap of time between two stages of our national life.

Through the forest from Murdering Town

G eorge Washington is not reckoned, usually, among the pioneers of the American wilderness, but some of the experiences of his young manhood equaled anything later undergone by Boone, Crockett, and their like. It is only Washington's dignified reserve that makes his narratives of personal experience less colorful than theirs; sometimes, however, his comments can be supplemented by others. Thus, in his journal for December 27, 1753, he says that a "French Indian" fired

530

"at Mr. Gist or me, not fifteen steps off, but fortunately missed." Fortunately we have the diary of Mr. Gist, the guide, who is not quite so concise. He and Washington were traveling alone in the wilderness, near what was later to be Pittsburgh. (Washington was returning from an unsuccessful mission to the French in behalf of the British government.) They were on foot. Says Mr. Gist: [1]

We rose early in the morning, and set out about two o'clock, and got to the Murdering Town on the southeast fork of Beaver Creek. Here we met with an Indian, whom I thought I had seen at Joncaire's, at Venango, when on our journey up to the French fort. This fellow called me by my Indian name, and pretended to be glad to see me. He asked us several questions, as, how we came to travel on foot, when we left Venango, where we parted with our horses, and when they would be there. Major Washington insisted on travelling by the nearest way to the Forks of the Allegany. We asked the Indian if he could go with us, and show us the nearest way. The Indian seemed very glad, and ready to go with us; upon which we set out, and the Indian took the Major's pack. We travelled very brisk for eight or ten miles, when the Major's feet grew very sore, and he very weary, and the Indian steered too much northeastwardly. The Major desired to encamp; upon which the Indian grew churlish, and pressed us to keep on, telling us there were Ottawa Indians in those woods, and they would scalp us, if we lay out; but go to his cabin, and we should be safe.

I thought very ill of the fellow, but did not care to let the Major know I mistrusted him. But he soon mistrusted him as much as I did. The Indian said he could hear a gun from his cabin, and steered us more northwardly. We grew uneasy, and then he said two whoops might be heard from his cabin. We went two miles further. Then the Major said he would stay at the next water; but before we came to water, we came to a clear meadow. It was very light, and snow was on the ground. The Indian made a stop, and turned about. The Major saw him point his gun towards us, and he fired. Said the Major, "Are you shot?" "No," said I; upon which the Indian ran forward to a big standing white oak, and began loading his gun, but we were soon with him. I would have killed him, but the Major would not suffer me. We let him charge his gun. We found he put in a ball; then we took care of him. Either the Major or I always stood by the guns. We made him make a fire for us by a little run, as if we intended to sleep there. I said to the Major, "As you will not have him killed, we must get him away, and then we must travel all night"; upon which I said to the Indian, "I suppose you were lost, and fired your gun." He said he knew the way to his cabin, and it was but a little way. "Well," said I, "do you go home, and, as we are tired, we will follow your track in the morning, and here is a cake of bread for you, and you must give us meat in the morning." He was glad to get away. I followed him, and listened, until he was fairly out of the way; and then we went about half a mile, when we made a fire, set our compass, fixed our course, and travelled all night.

But they were (literally) not out of the woods yet. The next night they reached the Allegheny; they had hoped to cross on the ice, but

---

[1] As quoted in Jared Sparks: *The Life of George Washington* (Boston, 1843), pp. 28–31.

the river was open, and they had to sleep on the snow. The next forty-eight hours brought them within sight of civilization, but its adventures almost brought a touch of emotion into Washington's own journal. He wrote

> There was no way of getting over but on a raft; which we set about with but one poor hatchet, and finished just after sunsetting. This was a whole day's work. We next got it launched, and went on board of it; then set off. But before we were half way over, we were jammed in the ice in such a manner that we expected every moment our raft would sink, and ourselves perish. I put out my setting pole to try to stop the raft, that the ice might pass by; when the rapidity of the stream threw it with so much violence against the pole, that it jerked me out into ten feet water. But I fortunately saved myself by catching hold of one of the raft logs. Notwithstanding all our efforts we could not get the raft to either shore, but were obliged, as we were near an island, to quit our raft, and make to it.

Next day the river had frozen enough to bear them, and they reached a trading post in safety, though Gist's hands and feet were frozen.

Audubon meets Daniel Boone[1]

D aniel Boon, or, as he was usually called in the western country, Colonel Boon, happened to spend a night with me under the same roof, more than twenty years ago. We had returned from a shooting excursion, in the course of which his extraordinary skill in the management of the rifle had been fully displayed. On retiring to the room appropriated to that remarkable individual and myself for the night, I felt anxious to know more of his exploits and adventures than I did, and accordingly took the liberty of proposing numerous questions to him. The stature and general appearance of this wanderer of the western forests approached the gigantic. His chest was broad and prominent; his muscular powers displayed themselves in every limb; his countenance gave indication of his great courage, enterprise and perseverance; and when he spoke, the very motion of his lips brought the impression that whatever he uttered could not be otherwise than strictly true. I undressed, whilst he merely took off his hunting shirt, and arranged a few folds of blankets on the floor, choosing rather to lie there, as he observed, than on the softest bed. When we had both disposed of ourselves, each after his own fashion, he related to me the following account of his powers of memory, which

---

[1] From John James Audubon: *Ornithological Biography* (Philadelphia: Judah Dobson; 1831), Vol. I, pp. 503–6. *Boone* seems to be the correct spelling.

I lay before you, kind reader, hoping that the simplicity of his style may prove interesting to you.

· "I was once," said he, "on a hunting expedition on the banks of the Green River, when the lower parts of this State (Kentucky) were still in the hands of nature, and none but the sons of the soil were looked upon as its lawful proprietors. We Virginians had for some time been waging a war of intrusion upon them, and I, amongst the rest, rambled through the woods in pursuit of their race, as I now would follow the tracks of any ravenous animal. The Indians outwitted me one dark night, and I was as unexpectedly as suddenly made a prisoner by them. The trick had been managed with great skill; for no sooner had I extinguished the fire of my camp, and laid me down to rest, in full security, as I thought, than I felt myself seized by an indistinguishable number of hands, and immediately pinioned, as if about to be led to the scaffold for execution. To have attempted to be refractory, would have proved useless and dangerous to my life; and I suffered myself to be removed from my camp to theirs a few miles distant, without uttering even a word of complaint. You are aware, I dare say, that to act in this manner was the best policy, as you understand that by so doing, I proved to the Indians at once, that I was born and bred as fearless of death as any of themselves.

"When we reached the camp, great rejoicings were exhibited. Two squaws and a few papooses appeared particularly delighted at the sight of me, and I was assured, by very unequivocal gestures and words, that, on the morrow, the mortal enemy of the Red-skins would cease to live. I never opened my lips, but was busy contriving some scheme which might enable me to give the rascals the slip before dawn. The women immediately fell a searching about my hunting-shirt for whatever they might think valuable, and, fortunately for me, soon found my flask filled with *monongahela* (that is, reader, strong whisky). A terrific grin was exhibited on their murderous countenances, while my heart throbbed with joy at the anticipation of their intoxication. The crew immediately began to beat their bellies and sing, as they passed the bottle from mouth to mouth. How often did I wish the flask ten times its size, and filled with aqua-fortis! I observed that the squaws drank more freely than the warriors, and again my spirits were about to be depressed, when the report of a gun was heard at a distance. The Indians all jumped on their feet. The singing and drinking were both brought to a stand, and I saw, with inexpressible joy, the men walk off to some distance and talk to the squaws. I knew that they were consulting about me, and I foresaw that in a few moments the warriors would go to discover the cause of the gun having been fired so near their camp. I expected that the squaws would be left to guard me. Well, sir, it was just so. They returned; the men took up their guns, and walked away. The squaws sat down again, and in less than five minutes had my bottle up to their dirty mouths, gurgling down their throats the remains of the whisky.

"With what pleasure did I see them becoming more and more drunk, until the liquor took such hold of them that it was quite impossible for these women to be of any service. They tumbled down, rolled about, and began to snore; when I, having no other chance of freeing myself from the cords that fastened me, rolled over and over toward the fire, and, after a short time, burned them asunder. I rose on my feet, stretched my stiffened sinews, snatched up my rifle, and, for once in my life, spared that of Indians. I now recollected how desirous I once or twice felt to lay open the skulls of the wretches with my tomahawk; but when I again thought upon killing beings unprepared and unable to defend themselves, it looked like murder without need, and I gave up the idea.

"But, sir, I felt determined to mark the spot, and walking to a thrifty ash sapling, I cut out of it three large chips, and ran off. I soon reached the river, soon crossed it, and threw myself deep into the cane-brakes, imitating the track of an Indian with my feet, so that no chance might be left for those from whom I had escaped to overtake me.

"It is now nearly twenty years since this happened, and more than five since I left the White's settlements, which I might probably never have visited again, had I not been called on as a witness in a law-suit that was pending in Kentucky, and I really believe never would have been settled had I not come forward, and established the beginning of a certain boundary line. This is the story, Sir.

"Mr. —— moved from Old Virginia into Kentucky, and having a large tract granted him, in the new State, laid claim to a certain parcel of land adjoining Green River, and as chance would have it, took for one of his corners the very Ash tree on which I had made my mark, and finished his survey of some thousands of acres, beginning, as it expressed in the deed, 'at an Ash marked by three distinct notches of the tomahawk of a white man.'

"The tree had grown much, and the bark had covered the marks; but somehow or other, Mr. —— heard from some one all that I have already said to you, and thinking that I might remember the spot alluded to in the deed, but which was no longer discoverable, wrote for me to come and try at least to find the place or the tree. His letter mentioned that all my expenses should be paid, and not caring much about once more going back to Kentucky, I started and met Mr. ——. After some conversation, the affair with the Indians came to my recollection. I considered for a while, and began to think that after all I could find the very spot, as well as the tree, if it was yet standing.

"Mr. —— and I mounted our horses, and off we went to the Green River Bottoms. After some difficulties, for you must be aware, Sir, that great changes have taken place in those woods, I found at last the spot where I had crossed the river, and waiting for the moon to rise, made for the course in which I thought the Ash tree grew. On approaching the place, I felt as if the Indians were still there, and as if I was still a prisoner among them. Mr. —— and I camped near what I conceived the spot, and waited until the return of day.

"At the rising of the sun, I was on foot, and after a good deal of musing, thought that an Ash tree then in sight must be the very one on which I had made my mark. I felt as if there could be no doubt of it, and mentioned my thought to Mr. ——. 'Well, Colonel Boon,' said he, 'if you think so, I hope it may prove true, but we must have some witnesses; do you stay here about, and I will go and bring some of the settlers whom I know.' I agreed. Mr. —— trotted off, and I, to pass the time, rambled about to see if a deer was still living in the land. But, ah! Sir, what a wonderful difference thirty years makes in the country! Why, at the time that I was caught by the Indians, you would not have walked out in any direction for more than a mile without shooting a buck or a bear. There were then thousands of Buffaloes on the hills in Kentucky; the land looked as if it never would become poor; and to hunt in those days was a pleasure indeed. But when I was left to myself on the banks of Green River, I dare say for the last time in my life, a few *signs* only of a deer were to be seen, and, as to a deer itself, I saw none.

"Mr. —— returned, accompanied by three gentlemen. They looked upon me as if I had been Washington himself, and walked to the Ash tree, which I now called my own, as if in quest of a long lost treasure. I took an axe from one of them, and cut a few chips off the bark. Still no signs were to be seen. So I cut again until I thought it was time to be cautious, and I scraped and worked away with my butcher knife, until I *did* come to where my tomahawk had left an impression in the wood. We now went regularly to work, and scraped at the tree with care, until three hacks as plain as any three notches ever were, could be seen. Mr. —— and the other gentlemen were astonished, and, I must allow, I was as much surprised as pleased myself. I made affidavit of this remarkable occurrence in presence of these gentlemen. Mr. —— gained his cause. I left Green River for ever, and came to where we now are; and, Sir, I wish you a good night."

I trust, kind reader, that when I again make my appearance with another volume of Ornithological Biography, I shall not have to search in vain for the impression which I have made, but shall have the satisfaction of finding its traces still unobliterated. I now withdraw, and, in the words of the noted wanderer of the western wilds, "wish you a good night."

David Crockett's double bull's-eye[1]

Well, I shouldered my Betsey, and she is just about as beautiful a piece as ever came out of Philadelphia, and I went out to the shooting ground, followed by all the leading men in Little Rock, and that was a clear majority of the town, for it is remarkable that there are always more leading men in small villages than there are followers.

I was in prime order. My eye was as keen as a lizard, and my nerves were as steady and unshaken as the political course of Henry Clay; so at it we went, the distance one hundred yards. The principal marksmen, and such as had never been beat, led the way, and there was some pretty fair shooting, I tell you. At length it came to my turn. I squared myself, raised my beautiful Betsey to my shoulder, took deliberate aim, and smack I sent the bullet right into the centre of the bull's eye. "There's no mistake in Betsey," said I, in a sort of careless way, as they were all looking at the target, sort of amazed, and not at all over pleased.

"That's a chance shot, Colonel," said one who had the reputation of being the best marksman in those parts.

"Not as much chance as there was," said I, "when Dick Johnson took his darkie for better for worse. I can do it five times out of six any day in the week." This I said in as confident a tone as "the Government"[2] did when he protested that he forgave Colonel Benton[3] for shooting him, and he was now the best friend he had in the world. I knew it was not altogether as correct as it might be, but when a man sets about going the big figure, halfway measures won't answer nohow; and "the greatest and the best"[4] had set me the example that swaggering will answer a good purpose at times.

They now proposed that we should have a second trial; but knowing that I had nothing to gain, and everything to lose, I was for back-

---

[1] From *Colonel Crockett's Exploits and Adventures in Texas* (Philadelphia: T. K. and P. G. Collins; 1837), pp. 51–4.

[2] I.e. Andrew Jackson.

[3] Colonel Thomas Hart Benton. The facts are as stated.

[4] Jackson again. Crockett had been a Jacksonian before he went to Congress, but in Washington he became friendly with the Whig faction, and boasted that he was no satellite of the President.

ing out and fighting shy; but there was no let-off, for the cock of the village, though whipped, determined not to stay whipped; so to it
● again we went. They were now put upon their mettle, and they fired much better than the first time; and it was what might be called pretty sharp shooting. When it came to my turn, I squared myself, and turning to the prime shot, I gave him a knowing nod, by way of showing my confidence; and says I, "Look out for the bull's eye, stranger." I blazed away, and I wish I may be shot if I didn't miss the target. They examined it all over and could find neither hair nor hide of my bullet, and pronounced it a dead miss; when says I, "Stand aside and let me look, and I warrant you I get on the right trail of the critter."

They stood aside and I examined the bull's eye pretty particular, and at length cried out, "Here it is; there is no snakes if it ha'n't followed the very track of the other."

They said it was utterly impossible, but I insisted on their searching the hole, and I agreed to be stuck up as a mark myself if they did not find two bullets there. They searched for my satisfaction, and sure enough it all come out just as I had told them; for I had picked up a bullet that had been fired and stuck it deep into the hole without anyone perceiving it. They were all perfectly satisfied, that fame had not made too great a flourish of trumpets when speaking of me as a marksman; and they all said they had had enough of shooting for that day, and they moved that we adjourn to the tavern and liquor.

We had scarcely taken drinks round before the landlord announced that dinner was ready, and I was escorted into the dining room by the committee, to the tune of "See the conquering hero comes."

David Crockett meets a bear[1]

I n the morning I left my son at the camp, and we started on towards the harricane;[2] and when we had went about a mile, we started a very large bear, but we got along mighty slow on account of the cracks in the earth occasioned by the earthquakes. We, however, made out to keep in hearing of the dogs for about three miles, and then we come to the harricane. Here we had to quit our horses, as old Nick himself couldn't have got through it without sneaking it along in the

---

[1] From *The Adventures of Davy Crockett*, told mostly by himself (New York and London: Charles Scribner's Sons; 1934; copyright Scribner's, 1934; a reprint of *The Autobiography of David Crockett*, 1834), pp. 123-8.
[2] A stretch of hurricane-felled timber.

form that he put on to make a fool of our old grandmother Eve. By this time several of my dogs had got tired and come back; but we went ahead on foot for some little time in the harricane, when we met a bear coming straight to us, and not more than twenty or thirty yards off. I started my tired dogs after him, and McDaniel pursued them, and I went on to where my other dogs were. I had seen the track of the bear they were after, and I knowed he was a screamer. I followed on to about the middle of the harricane, but my dogs pursued him so close, that they made him climb an old stump about twenty feet high. I got in shooting distance of him and fired, but I was all over in such a flutter from fatigue and running, that I couldn't hold steady; but, however, I broke his shoulder, and he fell. I run up and loaded my gun as quick as possible, and shot him again and killed him. When I went to take out my knife to butcher him, I found I had lost it in coming through the harricane. The vines and briers was so thick that I would sometimes have to get down and crawl like a varment to get through at all; and a vine had, as I supposed, caught in the handle and pulled it out. While I was standing and studying what to do, my friend came to me. He had followed my trail through the harricane, and had found my knife, which was mighty good news to me; as a hunter hates the worst in the world to lose a good dog, or any part of his hunting tools. I now left McDaniel to butcher the bear, and I went after our horses, and brought them as near as the nature of case would allow. I then took our bags, and went back to where he was; and when we had skin'd the bear, we fleeced off the fat and carried it to our horses at several loads. We then packed it up on our horses, and had a heavy pack of it on each one. We now started and went on till about sunset, when I concluded we must be near our camp; so I hollered and my son answered me, and we moved on in the direction to the camp. We had gone but a little way when I heard my dogs make a warm start again; and I jumped down from my horse and gave him up to my friend, and told him I would follow them. He went on to the camp, and I went ahead after my dogs with all my might for a considerable distance, till at last night came on. The woods were very rough and hilly, and all covered over with cane.

I now was compel'd to move on more slowly; and was frequently falling over logs, and into the cracks made by the earthquakes, so that I was very much afraid I would break my gun. However I went on about three miles, when I came to a good big creek, which I waded. It was very cold, and the creek was about knee deep; but I felt no great inconvenience from it just then, as I was all over wet with sweat from running, and I felt hot enough. After I got over the creek and out of the cane, which was very thick on all our creeks, I listened for my dogs. I found they had either treed or brought the bear to a stop, as they continued barking in the same place. I pushed on as near in the direction to the noise as I could, till I found the hill was too steep for me to climb, and so I backed and went down the creek some distance till I came to a hollow, and then took up that, till I come to a place where I could climb up the hill. It was mighty dark, and was difficult to see my way or any thing else. When I got up the hill, I found I had passed the dogs; and so I turned and went to them. I found, when I got there, they had treed the bear in a large forked poplar, and it was setting in the fork.

I could see the lump, but not plain enough to shoot with any certainty, as there was no moonlight; and so I set in to hunting for some dry brush to make me a light; but I could find none, though I could find that the ground was torn mightily to pieces by the cracks.

At last I thought I could shoot by guess, and kill him; so I pointed as near the lump as I could, and fired away. But the bear didn't come; he only clomb up higher, and got out on a limb, which helped me to see him better. I now loaded up again and fired, but this time he didn't move at all. I commenced loading for a third fire, but the first thing I knowed, the bear was down among my dogs, and they were fighting all around me. I had my big butcher in my belt, and I had a pair of dressed buckskin breeches on. So I took out my knife, and stood, determined, if he should get hold of me, to defend myself in the best way I could. I stood there for some time, and could now and then see a white dog I had, but the rest of them, and the bear, which were dark coloured, I couldn't see at all, it was so miserable dark. They still fought around me, and sometimes within three feet of me; but at last, the bear got down into one of the cracks, that the earthquake had made in the ground, about four feet deep, and I could tell the biting end of him by the hollering of my dogs. So I took my gun and pushed the muzzle of it about, till I thought I had it against the main part of his body, and fired; but it happened to be only the fleshy part of his foreleg. With this, he jumped out of the crack, and he and the dogs had another hard fight around me, as before. At last, however, they forced him back into the crack again, as he was when I had shot.

I had laid down my gun in the dark, and I now began to hunt for it; and, while hunting, I got hold of a pole, and I concluded I would punch him awhile with that. I did so, and when I would punch him, the dogs would jump in on him, when he would bite them badly, and they would jump out again. I concluded, as he would take punching so patiently, it might be that he would lie still enough for me to get down in the crack, and feel slowly along till I could find the right place to give him a dig with my butcher. So I got down, and my dogs got in before him and kept his head toward them, till I got along easily up to him; and placing my hand on his rump, felt for his shoulder, just behind which I intended to stick him. I made a lounge with my long knife, and fortunately stuck him right through the heart; at which he just sank down, and I crawled out in a hurry. In a little time my dogs all come out too, and seemed satisfied, which was the way they always had of telling me that they had finished him.

I suffered very much that night with cold, as my leather breeches, and everything else I had on, was wet and frozen. But I managed to get my bear out of this crack after several hard trials, and so I butchered him, and laid down to try to sleep. But my fire was very bad, and I couldn't find anything that would burn well to make it any better; and I concluded I should freeze, if I didn't warm myself in some way by exercise. So I got up, and hollered a while, and then I would just jump up and down with all my might, and throw myself into all sorts of motions. But all this wouldn't do; for my blood was now getting cold, and the chills coming all over me. I was so tired, too, that I could hardly walk; but I thought I would do the best I could to save my life, and then, if I died, nobody would be to blame. So I went to a tree about two feet through, and not a limb on it for thirty feet, and I would climb up it to the limbs, and then lock my arms together around it, and slide down to the bottom again. This would make the insides of my legs and arms feel mighty warm and good. I continued this till daylight in the morning, and how often I clomb up my tree and slid down I don't know, but I reckon at least a hundred times.

Mike Hooter's bear story[1]

(Mike Hooter, a backwoodsman, is telling how a rival hunter, Ike Hamberlin, was discomfited by a bear, which Ike's dogs refused to attack.)

While Ike was er lammin' the dogs, I hearn the allfiredest crackin' in the cane, an' I looked up, and thar was one of the eternalist whollopin' bars cummin crack, crack, through the cane an' kerslesh over the creek, and stopped right plumb slap up whar Ike's gun was. Torectly he tuck hold er the old shooter, an' I thought I see him tinkerin' 'bout the lock, an kinder whistlin', and blowin' into it. I was 'stonished, I tell you, but I wanted to see Ike outdone so bad that I lay low and kep' dark, an' in about a minit Ike got done lickin' the

---

[1] From Thomas C. Haliburton: *Traits of American Humor* (London, 1852), Vol. III.

dogs, an' went to git his gun. Jeeminy, criminy! if you'd only been whar I was! I do think Ike was the maddest man that ever stuck an axe into a tree, for his har stuck rite strait up, and his eyes glared like two dogwood blossoms. But the bar didn't seem to care shucks for him, for he jist sot the old rifle back agin the saplin', and walked off on his hind legs jist like any human. Then, you see, I gin to git sorter jelus, and sez I to myself, "Mister Bar," says I, "the place whar you's er standin' ain't prezactly healthy, an' if you don't wabble off from thar purty soon, Mizis Bar will be a widder, by gum!" With that, Ike grabbed up ole Mizis Rifle, and tuk most pertickler aim at him, and by hokey, she snapped! Now, says I, "Mister Bar, go it, or he'll make bacon of you!" But the varmint didn't wink, but stood still as a post, with the thumb of his right paw on the end of his smeller, and wigglin' his t'other finger. . . . Torectly I see Ike take down the ole shooter and kinder kersamine the lock, an' when he done that, he laid her on his shoulder, and shook his fist at the bar, and walked toward home, an' the bar he shuk his fist, an' went into the cane brake.

Mike Fink meets David Crockett[1]

I expect, stranger," said Davy, "You think old Davy Crockett war never beat at the long rifle; but he war, though. I expect that there's no man so strong but what he will find some one stronger.

"If you haven't heerd tell of one Mike Fink, I'll tell you something about him, for he war a helliferocious fellow, and made an almighty fine shot. Mike was a boatman on the Mississip', but he had a little cabin on the head of the Cumberland, and a horrid handsome wife, that loved him the wickedest that ever you see.

"Mike only worked enough to find his wife in rags, and himself in powder and lead and whiskey, and the rest of the time he spent in knocking over b'ar and turkeys, and bouncing deer, and sometimes drawing a lead on an Injun. So one night I fell in with him in the woods, where him and his wife shook down a blanket for me in his wigwam.

"In the morning says Mike to me, 'I've got the handsomest wife, and the fastest horse, and the sharpest shooting iron in all Kentuck, and if any man dare doubt it, I'll be in his hair quicker than hell could scorch a feather.'

"This put my dander up, and sez I, 'I've nothing to say agin your wife, Mike, for it can't be denied she's a shocking handsome woman, and Mrs. Crockett's in Tennessee, and I've got no horses. Mike, I don't

---

[1] *Crockett Almanac* for 1840, Vol. II.

exactly like to tell you you lie about what you say about your rifle, but I'm damned if you speak the truth, and I'll prove it. Do you see that are cat sitting on the top rail of your potato patch, about a hundred fifty yards off? If she hears agin, I'll be shot if it shan't be without ears!"

"So I blazed away, and I'll bet you a horse, the ball cut off both the old tom cat's ears close to his head, and shaved the hair clean off the skull, as slick as if'd done it with a razor, and the critter never stirred, nor knew he'd lost his ears till he tried to scratch 'em.

" 'Talk about your rifle after that, Mike!' sez I.

" 'Do you see that are sow off furder than the end of the world,' sez Mike, 'with a litter of pigs around her?' And he lets fly.

"The old sow gave a grunt, but never stirred in her tracks, and Mike falls to loading and firing for dear life, till he hadn't left one of them are pigs enough tail to make a toothpick on.

" 'Now,' sez he, 'Colonel Crockett, I'll be pretticularly obleedged to you if you'll put them are pigs' tails on again,' sez he.

" 'That's onpossible, Mike,' sez I, 'but you've left one of 'em about an inch to steer by, and if that had a-been my work, I wouldn't have done it so wasteful. I'll mend your shot.' And I lets fly, and cuts off the apology he's left the poor cretur for decency. I wish I may drink the whole Mississip', without a drop of the rale stuff in it, if you wouldn't have thort the tail had been drove in with a hammer.

"That made Mike kinder sorter wrothy, and he sends a ball after his wife as she was going to the spring after a gourd full of water, and knocked half her comb out of her head, without stirring a hair, and calls out to her to stop for me to take a blizzard at what was left on it. The angeliferous critter stood still as a scarecrow in a cornfield, for she'd got used to Mike's tricks by long practice.

" 'No, no, Mike,' sez I. 'Davy Crockett's hand would be sure to shake, if his iron war pointed within a hundred mile of a shemale, and I give up beat, Mike.' "

Mike Fink in a tight place[1]

Mike Fink, a notorious Buckeye-hunter, was contemporary with the celebrated Davy Crockett, and his equal in all things relating to human prowess. It was even said that the animals knew the crack of his rifle, and would take to their secret hiding-places, on the

---

[1] From the *Spirit of the Times*, March 22, 1851 (credited there to the *Miltonian*, of Milton, Pa., and signed "Scroggins").

first intimation that Mike was about. Yet strange, though true, he was but little known beyond his immediate "settlement."

When *we* knew him he was an old man—the blasts of seventy winters had silvered o'er his head, and taken the elasticity from his limbs; yet in the whole of his life was Mike never worsted, except upon one occasion. To use his own language, he never "gin in," used up, to anything that travelled on two legs or four, but once.

"That *once* we want," said Bill Slasher, as some dozen of us sat in the bar-room of the only tavern in the "settlement."

"Gin it to us now, Mike; you've promised long enough, and you're old now, and needn't care," continued Bill.

"Right, right, Bill," said Mike; "but we'll open with a *licker* all around fust, it'll kind o' save my feelin's I reckon."

"Thar, that's good. Better than t'other barrel, if anything."

"Well, boys," commenced Mike, "you may talk o' your scrimmages, tight places and sich like, and subtract 'em altogether in one all-mighty big 'un, and they hain't no more to be compared to the one I war in, than a dead kitten to an old she-bar. I've fout all kinds of varmints, from a Ingun down to a rattlesnake, and never was willin' to quit fust, but this once, and t'was with a bull!

"You see, boys, it was an awful hot day in August, and I war near runnin' off into pure *ile,* when I war thinkin' that a *dip* in the creek mout save me. Well, thar was a mighty nice place in old Deacon Smith's medder for that partic'lar bizziness. So I went down among the bushes to unharness. I jest hauled the old red shirt over my head, and war thinkin' how scrumptious a feller of my size would feel a wallerin' round in that ar water, and was jest 'bout goin' in when I seed the old Deacon's bull makin a b-line to whar I stood.

"I know'd the old cuss, for he'd skar'd more people than all the parsons in the 'settlement,' and cum mighty near killin' a few. Think's I, Mike, you're in rather a tight place. Get your fixin's on, for he'll be drivin' them big horns o' his in yer bowels afore that time. Well, you'll hev to try the old varmint naked, I reck'n.

"The bull war one side o' the creek, and I on t'other, and the way he made the 'sile' fly for a while, as if he war diggin' my grave, war distressin'!

" 'Come on, ye bellerin' old heathen,' said I, 'and don't be a standin' there; for, as the old Deacon says o' the devil, yer not comely to look on.'

"This kind o' reached his understandin', and made him more wishious; for he hoofed a little like, and made a drive. And as I don't like to stand in anybody's way, I gin him plenty sea-room. So he kind o' passed by me, and cum out on t'other side; and as the captain o' the mud-swamp rangers would say: ' 'bout face for another charge.'

"Though I war ready for him this time, he come mighty nigh runnin' foul o' me. So I made up my mind the next time he went out he wouldn't be alone. So when he passed, I grappled his tail, and he pulled me out on the 'sile,' and as soon as we were both atop o' the bank, old Brindle stopped, and was about comin' round again, when I begin pull'n t'other way.

"Well, I reckon this kind o' *riled* him, for he fust stood stock still, and look'd at me for a spell, and then commenced pawin' and bellerin', and the way he made his hind gearing play in the air, war beautiful!

"But it warn't no use, he couldn't *tech* me, so he kind o' stopped to get wind for suthin' develish, as I *judged* by the way he stared. By this time I had made up my mind to stick to his tail as long as it stuck to his back-bone! I didn't like to holler for help, nuther, it war agin my principles; and then the Deacon had preached at his house, and it warn't far off nuther.

"I know'd if he *hern* the noise, the hull congregation would come down; and as I warn't a married man, and had a kind o' hankerin' arter a gal that war thar, I didn't feel as if I would like to be seed in that ar predicament.

" 'So,' ses I, 'you old sarpent, do yer cussedst!'

"And so he did; for he drug me over every briar and stump in the field until I was sweatin' and bleedin' like a fat *bar* with a pack o' hounds at his heels. And my name ain't Mike Fink, if the old critter's tail and I didn't blow out sometimes at a dead level with the varmint's back!

"So you may kalkilate we made good time. Bimeby he slackened a little, and then I had him for a spell, for I jest dropped behind a stump, and that snubbed the critter.

" 'Now,' ses I, 'you'll pull up this 'ere white oak, break your *tail*, or jist hold in a bit till I blow.'

"Well, while I war settin' thar, an idea struck me that I had better be a gettin' out o' this in some way. But *how*, adzackly was the *pint!* If I let go and run, he'd be a foul o' me sure.

"So lookin' at the matter in all its bearins, I cum to the conclusion that I'd better let somebody *know* whar I was. So I gin a *yell* louder than a locomotive whistle, and it warn't long before I see the Deacon's two dogs a comin' down like as if they war seein' which could get thar fust.

"I knowed who they war arter—and they'd jine the bull agin me, I war sartin, for they war awful wenimous, and had a spite agin me.

" 'So,' ses I, 'old Brindle, as ridin' is as cheap as walkin' on this rout, if you've no objections, I'll jest take a deck passage on that ar back o' your'n.'

544

"So I wasn't long gettin' astride of him, and then if you'd been thar, you'd 'ave sworn thar warn't nothin' human in that ar *mix;* the sile flew so orrfully as the critter and I rolled round the field— one dog on one side and one on t'other, tryin' to clinch my feet!

"I pray'd and cuss'd, and cuss'd and pray'd, until I couldn't tell which I did last—and neither warn't of any use, they war so orrfully mix'd up.

"Well, I reckon I rid about an hour this way, when old Brindle thought it war time to stop and take in a supply of wind and cool off a little! So when we got round to a tree that stood thar, he nat'rally halted!

" 'Now,' ses I, 'old boy, you'll lose *one* passenger sartin!'

"So I just clum upon a branch, kalkilating to roost thar till I starved, afore I'd be rid round that ar way any more.

"I war makin' tracks for the top of the tree, when I heard suthin' a makin' an orful buzzin' over head, I kinder looked up, and if thar warn't—well thar's no use swearin' now, but it war the biggest *hornet's nest* ever built!

"You'll gin in now, I reckon, Mike, case thar's no help for you! But an idea struck me, then, that I'd stand a heap better chance a ridin' the old bull than where I war. Ses I, 'Old feller, if you'll hold on, I'll ride to the next *station* any how, let that be whar it will!'

"So I jest drapped aboard him agin, and looked aloft to see what I'd gained in changing quarters, and, gentlemen, I'm a liar if thar warn't nigh half a bushel of the stingin' varmints ready to pitch into me when the word 'go' was gin!

"Well, I reckon they got it, for 'all hands' started for our *company!* Some on 'em hit the dogs—about a *quart* struck me, and the rest charged old Brindle.

"This time, the dogs led off fust, 'dead' beat, for the old Deacon's, and as soon as old Brindle and I could get under way, we *followed.* And as I war only a deck passenger, and had nothin' to do with stearin' the craft, I swore if I had we shouldn't have run that channel, any how!

"But, as I said before, the dogs took the lead—Brindle and I next, and the hornets dre'kly arter. The dogs yellin', Brindle bellerin', and the hornets buzzin' and stingin'! I didn't say nothin' for it warn't no use.

"Well, we'd got bout two hundred yards from the house, and the Deacon hearn us and cum out. I seed him hold up his hands and turn *white!* I reckon he war prayin' then, for he didn't expect to be called for so soon, and it warn't long, neither, afore the hull congregation, men, women, and children, cum out, and then all hands went to yellin'!

"None of 'em had the fust notion that Brindle and I belonged to this world. I jest turned my head, and passed the *hull* congregation! I seed the run would be up soon, for Brindle couldn't turn an inch from a fence that stood dead ahead.

"Well, we reached that fence, and I went *ashore*, over the old critter's head, landin' on t'other side, and lay thar stunned. It warn't long afore some of 'em as war not so scared, come round to see what I war, for all hands kalkilated that the bull and I belonged *together!* But when Brindle walked off by himself, they seed how it war, and one of 'em said:

" 'Mike Fink has got the *worst of the scrimmage once in his life!'*

"Gentlemen, from that day I drapped the *courtin'* bizziness, and never spoke to a gal since! And when my hunt is up on this yearth, thar won't be any more FINKS and it's all owin' to Deacon Smith's Brindle Bull."

NOTE ON THE TWO FOLLOWING STORIES.

The extract entitled "Indians!" is actually a letter written by Kit Carson in 1847. It is reprinted here from an anonymous book published in New York in 1885 by Hurst & Co., and entitled *The Daring Adventures of Kit Carson and Frémont among Buffaloes, Grizzlies, and Indians.* As a whole, the book is a conspicuous example of what I have termed [1] "dressing the story up." The anonymous author compares Carson and Frémont to Castor and Pollux, and follows Carson's letter with the remark that "ere he started [for California] Frémont determined to give the Flamaths a severe chastisement for their cowardly attack." When Carson decided to burn an Indian camp, the writer says he "determined to wipe it out with flame."

The Apache episode is taken from Owen Wister's short story "Specimen Jones." Although it is fiction, it is, like the other stories in Wister's volume *Red Men and White,* based on two years of research in the West, during which Wister collected all the details he could of Indian fights, especially from "participants and witnesses." [2]

Indians! [3]

M r. Gillespie had brought the Colonel letters from home, the first he had had since leaving the States the year before, and he was up and kept a fire burning until midnight. The rest of us were tired out, and all went to sleep. This was the only night, in all our

---

[1] Pp. 53 ff. of this book.

[2] Owen Wister: *Roosevelt, the Story of a Friendship* (New York: The Macmillan Co.; 1930), p. 74.

[3] From *The Daring Adventures of Kit Carson and Frémont* (New York: Hurst & Co.; 1885), pp. 57–8. This whole passage is from a letter that Kit Carson wrote to the *Washington Union* in 1847. "The Colonel" was Frémont.

travels, except the one night on the island in the Salt Lake, that we failed to keep guard; and as the men were so tired and we expected no attack now that we had sixteen in the party, the Colonel did not like to ask it of them, but sat up late himself. Owens and I were sleeping together, and we were waked at the same time by the licks of the axe that killed our men. At first I didn't know it was that; but I called to Basil, who was on that side—"What's the matter there? What's that fuss about?" he never answered, for he was dead then, poor fellow, and he never knew what killed him—his head had been cut in his sleep; the other groaned a little as he died. The Delawares (we had four with us) were sleeping at the fire, and they sprang up as the Flamaths charged them. One of them caught up a gun, which was unloaded; but, although he could do no execution, he kept them at bay, fighting like a soldier, and didn't give up till he was shot full of arrows—three entering his heart; he died bravely. As soon as I had called out, I saw it was Indians in the camp and I and Owens together cried out "Indians!" There were no orders given; things went on too fast, and the Colonel had men with him that didn't need to be told their duty. The Colonel and I, Maxwell, Owens, Godey and Stepp, jumped together, we six, and ran to the assistance of our Delawares. I don't know who fired and who didn't, but I think it was Stepp's shot that killed the Flamath chief, for it was at the crack of Stepp's gun that he fell. He had an English half-axe slung to his wrist by a cord, and there were forty arrows left in his quiver—the most beautiful and warlike arrows I ever saw. He must have been the bravest man among them, from the way he was armed and judging by his cap. When the Flamaths saw him fall they ran, but we lay, every man with his rifle cocked, until daybreak expecting another attack. In the morning we found by the tracks that from fifteen to twenty of the Flamaths had attacked us. They had killed three of our men and wounded one of the Delawares, who scalped the chief, whom we left where he fell. Our dead men we carried on mules; but, after going about ten miles, we found it impossible to get them any further through the thick timber, and finding a secret place, we buried them under logs and chunks, having no way to dig a grave. It was only a few days before this fight that some of these same Indians had come into our camp, and, though we had only meat for two days and felt sure that we should have to eat mules for ten or fifteen days to come, the Colonel shared among them, and gave them several useful little articles, although to get at them we were obliged to take the pack from the mule. This was a terrible lesson to all hands, and thenceforth a guard was always carefully posted.

Routing the Apaches[1]

Presently Jones remarked to Mr. Adams that he wondered what Ephraim was doing and went out. The old gentleman was left alone in the room, and he swiftly noticed that the belt and pistol of Specimen Jones were left alone with him. The accoutrement lay by the chair its owner had been lounging in. It is an easy thing to remove cartridges from the chambers of a revolver, and replace the weapon in its holster so that everything looks quite natural. The old gentleman was entertained with the notion that somewhere in Tucson Specimen Jones might have a surprise, and he did not take a minute to prepare this, drop the belt as it lay before, and saunter innocently out of the saloon. Ephraim and Jones were criticising the tenderfoot's property as he packed his burro.

"Do y'u make it a rule to travel with ice-cream?" Jones was inquiring.

"They're for water," Cumnor said. "They told me at Tucson I'd need to carry water for three days on some trails."

It was too good-sized milk-cans that he had, and they bounced about on the little burro's pack, giving him as much amazement as a jackass can feel. Jones and Ephraim were hilarious.

"Don't go without your spurs, Mr. Cumnor," said the voice of old Mr. Adams, as he approached the group. His tone was particularly civil.

The tenderfoot had, indeed, forgotten his spurs, and he ran back to get them. The cream-colored lady still had the chain[2] hanging upon her, and Cumnor's problem was suddenly solved. He put the chain in his pocket, and laid the price of one round of drinks for last night's company on the shelf below the chromo. He returned with his spurs on, and went to his saddle that lay beside that of Specimen Jones under the shed. After a moment he came with his saddle to where the men stood talking by his pony, slung it on, and tightened the cinches; but the chain was now in the saddle-bag of Specimen Jones, mixed up with some tobacco, stale bread, a box of matches, and a hunk of fat bacon. The men at Twenty Mile said good-day to the tenderfoot, with monosyllables and indifference, and watched him depart into the heated desert. Wishing for a last look at Jones, he turned once, and saw the three standing, and the chocolate brick of the cabin, and the windmill white and idle in the sun.

[1] From Owen Wister: *Red Men and White*—Copyright, 1895, by Harper and Brothers. Copyright, 1923, by Owen Wister. Pp. 54–63.

[2] (Which Jones had pawned for a round of drinks.)

"He'll be gutted by night," remarked Mr. Adams.

"I ain't buryin' him, then," said Ephraim.

"Nor I," said Specimen Jones. "Well, it's time I was getting to Tucson."

He went to the saloon, strapped on his pistol, saddled, and rode away. Ephraim and Mr. Adams returned to the cabin; and here is the final conclusion they came to after three hours of discussion as to who took the chain and who had it just then:

Ephraim. Jones, he hadn't no cash.

Mr. Adams. The kid, he hadn't no sense.

Ephraim. The kid, he lent the cash to Jones.

Mr. Adams. Jones, he goes off with his chain.

Both. What damn fools everybody is, anyway!

And they went to dinner. But Mr. Adams did not mention his relations with Jones's pistol. Let it be said, in extenuation of that performance, that Mr. Adams supposed Jones was going to Tucson, where he said he was going, and where a job and a salary were awaiting him. In Tucson an unloaded pistol in the holster of so handy a man on the drop as was Specimen would keep people civil, because they would not know, any more than the owner, that it was unloaded; and the mere possession of it would be sufficient in nine chances out of ten— though it was undoubtedly for the tenth that Mr. Adams had a sneaking hope. But Specimen Jones was not going to Tucson. A contention in his mind as to whether he would do what was good for himself, or what was good for another, had kept him sullen ever since he got up. Now it was settled, and Jones in serene humor again. Of course he had started on the Tucson road, for the benefit of Ephraim and Mr. Adams.

The tenderfoot rode along. The Arizona sun beat down upon the deadly silence, and the world was no longer of crystal, but a mesa, dull and gray and hot. The pony's hoofs grated in the gravel, and after a time the road dived down and up among lumpy hills of stone and cactus, always nearer the fierce glaring Sierra Santa Catalina. It dipped so abruptly in and out of the shallow sudden ravines that, on coming up from one of these into sight of the country again, the tenderfoot's heart jumped at the close apparition of another rider quickly bearing upon him from gullies where he had been moving unseen. But it was only Specimen Jones.

"Hello!" said he, joining Cumnor. "Hot, ain't it?"

"Where are you going?" inquired Cumnor.

"Up here a ways." And Jones jerked his finger generally towards the Sierra, where they were heading.

"Thought you had a job in Tucson."

"That's what I have."

Specimen Jones had no more to say, and they rode for a while, their ponies' hoofs always grating in the gravel, and the milk-cans lightly clanking on the burro's pack. The bunched blades of the yuccas bristled steel-stiff, and as far as you could see it was a gray waste of mounds and ridges sharp and blunt, up to the forbidding boundary walls of the Tortilita one way and the Santa Catalina the other. Cumnor wondered if Jones had found the chain. Jones was capable of not finding it for several weeks, or of finding it at once and saying nothing.

"You'll excuse my meddling with your business?" the boy hazarded. Jones looked inquiring.

"Something's wrong with your saddle pocket."

Specimen saw nothing apparently wrong with it, but perceiving Cumnor was grinning, unbuckled the pouch. He looked at the boy rapidly, and looked away again, and as he rode, still in silence, he put the chain back round his neck below the flannel shirt-collar.

"Say, kid," he remarked, after some time, "what does J stand for?"

"J? Oh, my name! Jock."

"Well, Jock, will y'u explain to me as a friend how y'u ever come to be such a fool as to leave yer home—wherever and whatever it was—in exchange for this here God-forsaken and iniquitous hole?"

"If you'll explain to me," said the boy, greatly heartened, "how you come to be riding in the company of a fool, instead of goin' to your job at Tucson."

The explanation was furnished before Specimen Jones had framed his reply. A burning freight-wagon and five dismembered human stumps lay in the road. This was what had happened to the Miguels and Serapios and the concertina. Jones and Cumnor, in their dodging and struggles to exclude all expressions of mutual esteem from their speech, had forgotten their journey, and a sudden bend among the rocks where the road had now brought them revealed the blood and fire staring them in the face. The plundered wagon was three parts empty; its splintered, blazing boards slid down as they burned into the fiery heap on the ground; packages of soda and groceries and medicines slid with them, bursting into chemical spots of green and crimson flame; a wheel crushed in and sank, spilling more packages that flickered and hissed; the garbage of combat and murder littered the earth, and in the air hung an odor that Cumnor knew, though he had never smelled it before. Morsels of dropped booty up among the rocks showed where the Indians had gone, and one horse remained, groaning, with an accidental arrow in his belly.

"We'll just kill him," said Jones; and his pistol snapped idly, and snapped again, as his eye caught a motion—a something—two hundred yards up among the bowlders on the hill. He whirled round. The

550

enemy was behind them also. There was no retreat. "Yourn's no good!" yelled Jones, fiercely, for Cumnor was getting out his little, foolish revolver. "Oh, what a trick to play on a man! Drop off yer horse, kid; drop, and do like me. Shootin's no good here, even if I was loaded. *They* shot, and look at them now. God bless those ice-cream freezers of yourn, kid! Did y'u ever see a crazy man? If you ain't, *make it up as y'u go along!*"

More objects moved up among the bowlders. Specimen Jones ripped off the burro's pack, and the milk-cans rolled on the ground. The burro began grazing quietly, with now and then a step towards new patches of grass. The horses stood where their riders had left them, their reins over their heads, hanging and dragging. From two hundred yards on the hill the ambushed Apaches showed, their dark, scattered figures appearing cautiously one by one, watching with suspicion. Specimen Jones seized up one milk-can, and Cumnor obediently did the same.

"You kin dance, kid, and I kin sing, and we'll go to it," said Jones. He rambled in a wavering loop, and diving eccentrically at Cumnor, clashed the milk-cans together. " 'Es schallt ein Ruf wie Donnerhall,' " he bawled, beginning the song of "Die Wacht am Rhein." "Why don't you dance?" he shouted sternly. The boy saw the terrible earnestness of his face, and, clashing his milk-cans in turn, he shuffled a sort of jig. The two went over the sand in loops, toe and heel; the donkey continued his quiet grazing, and the flames rose hot and yellow from the freight-wagon. And all the while the stately German hymn pealed among the rocks, and the Apaches crept down nearer the bowing, scraping men. The sun shone bright, and their bodies poured with sweat. Jones flung off his shirt; his damp, matted hair was half in ridges and half glued to his forehead, and the delicate gold chain swung and struck his broad, naked breast. The Apaches drew nearer again, their bows and arrows held uncertainly. They came down the hill, fifteen or twenty, taking a long time, and stopping every few yards. The milk-cans clashed, and Jones thought he felt the boy's strokes weakening. "Die Wacht am Rhein" was finished, and now it was " 'Ha-ve you seen my Flora pass this way?' " "Y'u mustn't play out, kid," said Jones, very gently. "Indeed y'u mustn't"; and he at once resumed his song. The silent Apaches had now reached the bottom of the hill. They stood some twenty yards away, and Cumnor had a good chance to see his first Indians. He saw them move, and the color and slim shape of their bodies, their thin arms, and their long black hair. It went through his mind that if he had no more clothes on than that, dancing would come easier. His boots were growing heavy to lift, and his overalls seemed to wrap his sinews in wet, strangling thongs. He wondered how long he had been keeping this up. The legs of the

Apaches were free, with light moccasins only half-way to the thigh, slenderly held up by strings from the waist. Cumnor envied their un-encumbered steps as he saw them again walk nearer to where he was dancing. It was long since he had eaten, and he noticed a singing dulness in his brain, and became frightened at his thoughts, which were running and melting into one fixed idea. The idea was to take off his boots, and offer to trade them for a pair of moccasins. It terri-fied him—this endless, molten rush of thoughts; he could see them coming in different shapes from different places in his head, but they all joined immediately, and always formed the same fixed idea. He ground his teeth to master this encroaching inebriation of his will and judgment. He clashed his can more loudly to wake him to reality, which he still could recognize and appreciate. For a time he found it a good plan to listen to what Specimen Jones was singing, and tell himself the name of the song, if he knew it. At present it was "Yankee Doodle," to which Jones was fitting words of his own. These ran: "Now I'm going to try a bluff, And mind you do what I do"; and then again, over and over. Cumnor waited for the word "bluff"; for it was hard and heavy, and fell into his thoughts, and stopped them for a moment. The dance was so long now he had forgotten about that. A numbness had been spreading through his legs, and he was glad to feel a sharp pain in the sole of his foot. It was a piece of gravel that had somehow worked its way in, and was rubbing through the skin into the flesh. "That's good," he said aloud. The pebble was eating the numbness away, and Cumnor drove it hard against the raw spot, and relished the tonic of its burning friction. The Apaches had drawn into a circle. Standing at some interval apart, they entirely surrounded the arena. Shrewd, half convinced, and yet with awe, they watched the dancers, who clashed their cans slowly now in rhythm to Jones's hoarse, parched singing. He was quite master of himself, and led the jig round the still blazing wreck of the wagon, and circled in figures of eight between the corpses of the Mexicans, clashing the milk-cans above each one. Then, knowing his strength was coming to an end, he approached an Indian whose splendid fillet and trappings denoted him of consequence; and Jones was near shouting with relief when the Indian shrank backward. Suddenly he saw Cumnor let his can drop, and without stopping to see why, he caught it up, and, slowly rattling both, approached each Indian in turn with tortuous steps. The circle that had never uttered a sound till now receded, chanting almost in a whisper some exorcising song which the man with the fillet had be-gun. They gathered round him, retreating always, and the strain, with its rapid muttered words, rose and fell softly among them. Jones had supposed the boy was overcome by faintness, and looked to see where he lay. But it was not faintness. Cumnor, with his boots off, came by, and walked after the Indians in a trance. They saw him, and quickened their pace, often turning to be sure he was not overtaking them. He called to them unintelligibly, stumbling up the sharp hill, and pointing to the boots. Finally he sat down. They continued ascending the mountain, herding close round the man with the feathers, until the rocks and the filmy tangles screened them from sight; and like a wind that hums uncertainly in grass, their chanting died away.

The sun was half behind the western range when Jones next moved. He called, and, getting no answer, he crawled painfully to where the boy lay on the hill. Cumnor was sleeping heavily; his head was hot, and he moaned. So Jones crawled down, and fetched blankets and the canteen of water. He spread the blankets over the boy, wet a handkerchief and laid it on his forehead; then he lay down himself.

The earth was again magically smitten to crystal. Again the sharp cactus and the sand turned beautiful, and violet floated among the mountains, and rose-colored orange in the sky above them.

"Jock," said Specimen at length.

The boy opened his eyes.

"Your foot is awful, Jock. Can y'u eat?"

"Not with my foot."

"Ah, God bless y'u, Jock! Y'u ain't terrible sick. But *can* y'u eat?"

Cumnor shook his head.

"Eatin's what y'u need, though. Well, here." Specimen poured a judicious mixture of whiskey and water down the boy's throat, and wrapped the awful foot in his own flannel shirt. "They'll fix y'u over to Grant. It's maybe twelve miles through the cañon. It ain't a town any more than Carlos is, but the soldiers'll be good to us. As soon as night comes you and me must somehow git out of this."

Somehow they did, Jones walking and leading his horse and the imperturbable little burro, and also holding Cumnor in the saddle. And when Cumnor was getting well in the military hospital at Grant, he listened to Jones recounting to all that chose to hear how useful a weapon an ice-cream freezer can be, and how if you'll only chase Apaches in your stocking feet they are sure to run away.

Johnny Appleseed's story is an expanding one. Johnny has been canonized by local patriots, occasional orators, and minor poets; his strong appeal ever growing, he has been extolled in schoolrooms, represented in pageants (and sculpture), and impersonated on the radio. He has, in short, become a beloved part of the legend of pioneer America, and it seems most unlikely that any discovery (or rediscovery) of cold prosaic facts about the real man will reduce the hero's stature or the popular belief in his exploits. Americans, especially if from Ohio, hold that his name was Jonathan Chapman, and that he journeyed, in rags, through the wilderness as a horticultural missionary, planting apple seeds wherever he went, making friends with the Indians and with wild animals, talking with angels, and bringing their messages to mankind. All through the Middle West flourished the orchards that he planted.

That is the fable [1] (a word that many romantics would resent); some of the few known facts are given below, plus some frankly inventive but entirely typical legend.

Roy Bean's legend, unlike Johnny's, is a contracting one, for Roy is (for one thing) not a very lovable character. He played a useful role in a wild country, and he distinguished himself by some fantastic "legal" decisions, but the authentic stories about him, though often told, are few in number, and much repetition has dulled the edge of some of them; not, it is hoped, of those quoted below.

Johnny Appleseed

The fundamental facts about "Johnny Appleseed" have been told concisely by Harlan Hatcher,[2] who remarks: "This legend has been taking form right before our eyes, in touching disregard of the facts." [3] Says Mr. Hatcher:

---

[1] The Appleseed legends seem to have started in 1871, with an article by W. D. Haley, in *Harper's Magazine*, entitled "Johnny Appleseed, a Pioneer Hero." This is a well-written and attractive narrative, but it contains a good many errors of fact, besides a good deal of admitted hearsay. It has been taken as solid history, especially by the poets.

[2] From Harlan Hatcher: *The Buckeye Country* (New York: H. C. Kinsey & Co.; 1940), p. 167. Copyright, 1940, by Harlan Hatcher, Courtesy G. P. Putnam's Sons.

[3] Ibid., p. 166.

Johnny Appleseed, the philanthropic eccentric, has been created out of John Chapman, the Yankee nurseryman, by the unconscious longing of the folk mind for color and kindliness. Chapman was apparently a shrewd and courageous business man. He was born at Leominster, Massachusetts, September 26, 1774, son of Nathaniel Chapman, soldier, and captain of wheelwrights, who moved to Ohio in 1805 and died at Salem in Washington County, February 18, 1807. John came to Ohio in 1801. He saw how rapidly the country was filling up. He knew the limited diet of the wilderness, and believed there should be a good market for fruit trees as soon as the fields were cleared and the corn planted. He was right. He raised young apple trees from seeds gathered at Pennsylvania cider presses, had nurseries at Pittsburgh, Steubenville, and along the Muskingum and elsewhere, ready for the incoming farmers, and sold his trees to successive waves of immigrants for six and a half cents apiece, or in exchange for tools and other goods. He himself was an engaging and kindly fellow who made friends with the settlers and was always welcomed by them. His good nature showed in his sparkling dark eyes, and his entertaining conversation. His enterprises prospered, and when he died, unmarried, at Fort Wayne, Indiana, March 18, 1845, he left a tidy little fortune. His death was news to the Fort Wayne *Sentinel*: "Died in the neighborhood of this city, on Tuesday last, Mr. John Chapman, better known as Johnny Appleseed. . . . He followed the occupation of Nurseryman." Monuments to him stand at Fort Wayne, and at Mansfield and Ashland.

It is not, evidently, in the life of the real John Chapman that we shall discover the hero that America has come to love; to find that friend of man we must leave veracious chronicle behind. A satisfying account is that which follows; it is provided by that excellent story-teller Walter Blair,[1] and the reader should be advised that Mr. Blair confesses: "I've made improvements of my own."[2] Even when it comes to statements usually accepted as facts, he has, as he puts it, "truthened them up" a bit.

Just what happened isn't clear. Some say that a woman somehow found she couldn't keep her promise to marry Johnny, and that affected him. Some say Johnny got malaria, and it did things to him he didn't get over. Some claim that he got kicked in the head by a horse he was trying to doctor. Still others incline to the idea that it wasn't any one of these things, but all three working together. And if all three of these things did happen to him within the space of a short time, you can understand that there'd be likely to be some noticeable results.

Whatever the cause was, Johnny hit on the idea of getting into this business—or "mission," as he called it—of spreading apple trees all over the Middle West.

---

[1] Reprinted by permission of Coward-McCann, Inc., from *Tall Tale America: A Legendary History of Our Humorous Heroes* by Walter Blair; copyright, 1944, by Walter Blair; pp. 98–102.

[2] Ibid., p. 257.

His idea was that there ought to be more apple trees in the pioneer parts of Pennsylvania and Ohio and Indiana, and he was the fellow to see that there were. So each fall, in cider making time, he'd get around to the sweet-smelling cider presses in Pennsylvania. There he'd collect the pomace, the mashed up stuff that was left after the juice had been squoze out of the apples. Then he'd wash the seeds out, and let them dry in the sun. There were only a few things he liked better than rubbing his finger tips over the slick seeds.

The next spring, he'd bag these seeds, some in old coffee sacks, some in little deerskin pouches. Then he'd start tromping westward, carrying seed packets of one kind and another along with him. He'd hand out the little pouches to the movers West, one to each family. The big bundles he'd tote along to use himself, stopping here and there to plant the seeds all along rivers, in meadows, wherever people would let him or there weren't any people. Even after the seedlings got a good start in some of the orchards, Johnny Appleseed (as he was called by now) would drop around every so often to tend them.

What Johnny would do, in short, was to go traipsing all over the country, sleeping out in the open, eating whatever was handy, stumbling through the trackless forest or tramping through mud and snow, to get these apple orchards started. As the years passed, he covered plenty of ground, too—made it as far south as Tennessee and as far west as the Rocky Mountains.

Some people claimed it was pretty silly.

Maybe you'll ask what people thought was foolish about it. The answer they'd give would be that he wouldn't take any money for going to all this trouble—not a red cent. And it's well known, these people point out, that the only reason that makes sense for doing things is to make money.

"Money?" Johnny Appleseed would say, "*that* for money!" And he'd snap his horny fingers. "I've got a mission, that's what I've got. What do you do with money? Just spend it for clothes or houses or food, I understand, and a saint doesn't care a snippet for any of these. Fact is, he sneers at them, every time he gets a chance. Only thing I want is to get these apples, and herbs that're good for folks, scattered all over the Middle West."

So he'd give those pioneer families appleseeds—free. And if they'd let him have a little ground for his tree nurseries, he'd plant whole orchards for them, and tend the seedlings too—free. In the course of a few years, he had nurseries all along the shores of Lake Erie, along Elk Creek, Walnut Creek, French Creek, along the Grand River, the Muskingum, the Tuscarawas, the Mohican, and hundreds of other lakes, rivers, and creeks. And instead of selling the seedlings from

556

these nurseries (as he easily could have done), he'd heel them in and wrap them in wet straw and give them to the movers—free.

People that held Johnny was on the queer side said that if these facts didn't prove their point, they had other facts about the way he'd go wandering around in the Indian country, even when the redskins were on a rampage, without a gun or even a knife on him.

"Indians?" the little cuss would say. "*That* for Indians!" And he'd snap his bony fingers. "What'll Indians do to you if you go along peaceful-like and don't hurt them? Nothing—that's what they'll do. A saint gets onto some facts that other people don't, and one of them is that Indians are our brothers."

Well, there is some reason for saying that this was a cracked idea— one that, on the face of it, was plumb crazy. But there's one little detail that keeps it from being a clincher—the fact that, somehow, the Indians *didn't* hurt him—just the way he'd said they wouldn't. Whether the redmen were scared off by his strange looks, or whether they thought he was a heap big medicine man, or what it was, is hard to say. Anyhow, he got along with Indians better than a good many white people got along with white people.

When anybody brought up the matter of animals, Appleseed was likely to go through that finger-snapping business again. "Leave animals alone," he'd say, "and they'll do the same by you. They're brothers and sisters to you, sort of, only they don't borrow clothes and other truck and they don't misunderstand you the way human brothers and sisters do."

And he'd do the strangest things about varmints you ever heard tell of. One night some of those Ohio mosquitoes came along—some of those pests that are so big that, to set them apart from the common little ones, some people call them gallinippers. Well, Johnny had a fire out there in the woods, and considerable smoke was coming out with the flames. He noticed that these gallinippers kept getting into the smoke and choking to death, or maybe flying into the flames and getting cremated.

At a time like that, most people would just say, "Yaah, serves the brutes right," and chuck more wood on the fire.

But Johnny said, "Poor things! Guess I'll have to put out that fire." Then he sloshed water over the blaze, and lay there shivering in the dark—and being et by gallinippers, the rest of the night.

Then there was the time that Johnny was going from Mansfield to Mount Vernon one cold winter's day, slushing through the snow in those bark sandals of his. Night came, no cabin was near, and he looked around for some big hollow log to sleep in. He found a dandy, built a fire near by, cooked his mush, slupped the stuff up, and started to crawl into the hollow log.

When he'd got in about to his hips, though, he heard a groaning grunt. Peeking in, helped by the light of the fire, he saw a big bear lying in there with his paws crossed on his chest, enjoying his winter snooze.

Johnny backed out, inch by inch, slow as a snail, being quiet so as not to interrupt the bear's sleep. "Beg your pardon, Brother Bear," he whispered. "I didn't mean to bother your sleep. Saints love bears too much to disturb them any."

Then he yawned, stretched, and curled up in the snow.

People that claimed Johnny was touched said that if all these facts didn't show it, they could mention at least three more. One was that he never ate meat, because of this liking he had for varmints. A second was that he kept planting dog fennel, as well as appleseeds, all over the country. "Dog fennel," he said, "keeps away malaria and typhoid and heaven knows what all." (He was wrong, of course: all that it does is smell bad and choke up vegetable gardens.) A third was that, though he never exactly came out and said it, he kept hinting all the time that he was a saint.

But some people kept arguing against anybody that tried to run down Johnny Appleseed in any way. "He was a hero and a saint," they'd say. "He had something he believed in, enough to suffer for— and he went to a lot of trouble to bring it about. Talk about overcoming hardships! Why he'd go traipsing around without any shoes, in his bare feet, dressed up in a gunny sack, in the coldest weather. He didn't even have a decent hat: either he'd wear that pan he cooked mush in or he'd wear that cardboard affair he'd made that looked like a conductor's cap. And why? Simply because he was sweet and good and he wanted to get orchards scattered all over the countryside to look pretty and grow apples for folks."

Well, you can see there are arguments for both sides.

Roy Bean[1]

R oy Bean was a real person and did administer a sort of rough justice in West Texas in the 1880's and 1890's. His nickname, of which he was outrageously proud, "Law West of the Pecos," was taken from a Texan saying that is in the best tradition of frontier exaggeration: "West of the Pecos there is no law, and west of El Paso

---

[1] These facts about Roy Bean have been sifted from very numerous accounts. Particularly useful were *Coyote Wisdom* (Texas Folk-lore Society, 1938), *On the Old West Coast*, by Major Horace Bell (William Morrow & Co., 1930), and (the only book on the subject) *Roy Bean*, by C. L. Sonnichsen (Macmillan, 1943.)

there is no God." In 1882, when Bean was in his early fifties, he had settled as squatter, justice of the peace, and saloonkeeper on the right of way of the Southern Pacific Railway near the Pecos River. He had seen and fallen in love (of a sort) with a picture of the famous Lily Langtry, and in honor of her had named his saloon "The Jersey Lilly." (The spelling was Roy's own.) Later he contrived to have the little settlement officially named Langtry.

It was here, when one of the Chinese railroad laborers had been killed, that Roy sat in judgment on the murderer and turned him loose, saying that he could find no law making it a crime to kill a Chinaman. It was here, too, that he granted a dubious divorce to a couple whom he had married, and explained that he was "correcting a mistake." Here, in 1882, when ten men had fallen from the nearly finished railroad bridge across the Pecos, seven being killed and the others fatally injured, Roy was called as coroner to look at the bodies. Over each he pronounced the words: "This man came to his death by them big timbers falling on him," but a bystander ventured to point out that three of the men were still living. Roy retorted (and the numerous versions of the tale agree rather precisely as to his words): "Say, you gander-eyed galoot, who is running this here inquest? Don't you see them three fellers is bound to die? Do you think I'm damn fool enough to ride thirty miles on a sore-backed mule again to hold another inquest? Officially and legally them fellers is dead, and so I pronounce them dead, every mother's son of 'em, and you will render it as your verdict that they came to their deaths by them big timbers a-fallin' on 'em."

Roy Bean—Coroner[1]

The story that everybody knows about Roy Bean the coroner comes from another bridge accident which happened a little earlier than this.

It was a Sunday afternoon in February, 1892. A number of bridge carpenters from the Pecos project had come up to pass the day at the Jersey Lily, among them a quiet fellow named Pat O'Brien who didn't care much for the carousing and hell raising that was going on. Towards evening he decided to take a walk. There were no shady lanes or pasture paths in those parts so he started off down the rail-

---

[1] From C. L. Sonnichsen: *Roy Bean, Law West of the Pecos* (New York: The Macmillan Company; 1943), pp. 126–8. By permission of The Macmillan Company, publishers.

road tracks, a smile on his face and a six-shooter in his hip pocket. Why he wanted the weapon is not clear. Maybe he was from the East. Easterners were more careful about this article of dress than native Texans.

When he got to the Myers Canyon bridge, three miles east of Langtry, a heavy wind was blowing as usual down the draw, and one gust was strong enough to take him off his feet and land him at the bottom where the sharp rocks ended his career. Section workers and track walkers were always very careful when they crossed this bridge, but the stranger never suspected his danger until it was too late.

That evening he was found and Roy was notified. He and Jim King (now of Del Rio) went out in a buckboard, brought the body back, and laid it out on the table in the saloon. Nobody knew who the man was beyond his name, so they searched him for identification and in so doing found the six-shooter and forty dollars.

"Now," said Coroner Bean, "I've got to bury this poor devil and it's hard digging in these rocks. I hereby fine this defendant forty dollars for carrying concealed weapons."

Turning to Jim King he added, "Don't you think that's the way to handle it, Jimmy?" Jimmy thought so, and Roy had no idea that he had made an historic decision, but one man told another and pretty soon Texas was chuckling again at Roy Bean's way of conducting his business. The San Antonio *Express* got hold of the story of Roy's verdict in March and passed it on to the world.

"Gentlemen," said Roy to the jury and onlookers, "there is nothing to find out how that man came to his death. He fell from the bridge and that's all there is about it. But there is one thing that is not so plain, and that is what was he doing with that gun? Of course he is dead and can't explain, but that ain't the fault of the law; it's his own misfortune. Justice is justice, and law is law, and as he can't offer no satisfactory explanation of the matter I shall be obliged to fine him forty dollars for carrying on or about his person that pistol. Because a man chooses to put on a pair of wings is no reason why the great state of Texas should not have what is coming to her all the same."

A few hours after the inquest the body was buried. It was not buried very deep in the stony soil, and the coffin was a plain wooden box, but some of that forty dollars was needed to do what was done.

At least one other time, Roy fined a dead body. It was about a year later when two Mexicans got into a squabble at Painted Cave. One was shot in the mouth and killed. Roy found a pistol on him and ten dollars, which he kept. Maybe he was just seeing if the same system would work twice.

The American Negro has found compensations for his hard lot in his religion, his songs, and his stories, especially the stories of mighty black men whose strength and cleverness put them on the level with, or even above, the master race. This is why they love Daddy Mention and Big John the Conqueror (or High John de Conquer) and Uncle Monday.

Daddy Mention[1]

D addy Mention didn't have nothin' in particular against the Polk County jails, exceptin' the dirty little jug outside of Lakeland. He told 'em when they locked him up in there he didn't think he'd be able to stay with 'em so very long. They had him locked up for vagrancy. He tried to tell 'em he'd be glad to go to work if only he could find a job, but you know a colored man can't say much in Polk County.

"They gave him ninety days straight up—no time off for good behavior. After he had stayed in the Lakeland Jail awhile they sent him out to the County Farm and put him on the stump-grubbing gang. It was afternoon when he got there and started to work, and he made the day all right. But when supper-time came and he seen what he had to eat I could hear him grumble under his breath.

"The next mornin' we et grits with bacon grease for breakfast, and Daddy Mention grumbled some more. At sun-up we went out to the woods and started to work. Before it was ten o'clock Cap'm Higgenbothem had done cussed out Daddy Mention four times; Daddy didn't work fast anuff to suit him. When we took time out for lunch I heered Daddy growl, 'They ain't treatin' me right.'

"After lunch we lined up to go back to the woods and Cap'm Higgenbothem walked over to Daddy. 'Boy,' he hollered. 'You gonna work this afternoon or would you rather go to the sweat box?'

"Daddy Mention didn't say nothin' at first, then kinda slow he said, 'Whatever you want me to do, Cap'm.'

---

[1] Reprinted by permission of the publishers, Duell, Sloan & Pearce, Inc., from Stetson Kennedy: *Palmetto Country*, pp. 133–6. Copyright 1942 by Stetson Kennedy.

"Cap'm Higgenbotham didn't know what to make of that, so he slapped Daddy into the box in a hurry. He didn't go back to look at him that day, neither. He didn't go back till the next day. 'Hey, boy,' he called. 'You feel like workin' today?'

" 'Whatever you want me to do, Cap'm,' answered Daddy Mention.

"I didn't see Cap'm Higgenbotham then, but they tell me he got so hot you could fry eggs on him. He spit in the box and walked off and didn't come back all that day. Every mornin' after that he would come to the box and ask Daddy Mention the same thing, and every mornin' Daddy answered him the same way.

"Finally Cap'm Higgenbotham got to thinkin' that maybe Daddy Mention wasn't tryin' to be smart-aleck or sassy, but was just plain dumb. So he let Daddy out of the box and put him on the tree-choppin' gang that was workin' just ahead of us.

"Daddy Mention was glad to get out of the box, cause he had done set his mind on goin' to Tampa. He told some of his gang about it when the Cap'm wasn't listenin'. But Daddy knew bettern to try to run away; you can't get away with that in Polk County. They'd sooner shoot you than go to all the trouble of tryin' to ketch you. Even if you got away the hounds would ketch up with you before you could even get to Mulberry.

"Daddy Mention knew he had to have a better plan. He got busy and thought one up. None of us knew much about it cause he didn't talk about it. But we began to notice he was doin' more work than anybody else in his gang; he would chop a tree down all by hisself, and it didn't take but one more man to help him tote it to the pile. Then one day when he was sure the Cap'm was watchin' him, he picked up a tree all by hisself and carried it all the way to the pile before he put it down.

"The Cap'm couldn't hardly b'lieve his own eyes. He didn't see how any man could lift one of them big pines all by hisself, much less carry one around. So he made Daddy Mention do it again, just to be sure. Then he called the other guards to see Daddy do it again.

"It wasn't long before the Cap'm and some of the other guards was pickin' up a little easy money bettin' folks that Daddy Mention could pick up any tree they could cut. And the Cap'm didn't fuss so very much when Daddy won a coupla bumpers (nickels) at it hisself.

"It got to be a regular sight to see Daddy Mention walkin' around the jailyard carryin' a big tree in his arms. Everybody was used to seein' it by then. That was just what Daddy Mention wanted. One afternoon when we come in from the woods Daddy Mention brought a tree-butt with him. The Cap'm thought one of the other guards musta asked him to bring it in to do tricks with, so he didn't say nothin' about it.

"Daddy Mention took his tree-butt in the dinin'-hall with him and stood it up by the wall, then went on to the table with the rest of us and et his supper. He didn't seem to be in no hurry or nothin', but I noticed he didn't have much to say to nobody.

"After supper he waited till nearly everybody got finished, then he got up and went back to his log. Most of the Cap'ms and guards was around the yard, and they watched while Daddy picked up that big log. Daddy clowned around in front of the guards for a while, then he started walkin' tords the gate with the log still on his shoulder. None of the guards didn't bother him, cause they never thought a man would try to escape with a log on his shoulder.

"You know you have to pass the guards' quarters before you get to the gate in the Lakeland Blue Jay. But Daddy Mention didn't even turn around when he passed, and nobody didn't say nothin' to him. The guards at the gate musta thought one of the Cap'ms had sent Daddy to take the log somewheres, or was makin' a bet or sumpum. Right on out the gate Daddy Mention went, and onto the road that goes to Tampa. Off he walked down that road with the log on his shoulder, and he kept right on walkin' till he was plumb out of sight . . .

"I never saw Daddy Mention again until a long time after, in Tampa. I never had been able to figger out how he got to Tampa after he left the Lakeland Blue Jay, so I asked him.

" 'Why, I didn't have no trouble a-tall,' Daddy Mention said. 'I jus' kept that log on my shoulder, and everybody I passed thought it musta fallen offa truck and I was carryin' it back. They knew nobody would have the nerve to steal a good pine log like that and walk along the highway with it. Soon's I got to Plant City I took the log to a woodyard and sold it. Then I had me enough money to ride to Tampa.—Ain't nobody ever gonna ketch me in Polk County nomore.' "

Big John the Conqueror[1]

Every night Big John used to go up to the Big House and stand in the chimney corner and listen to what Old Massa talked about. That way he learned a lot about what was goin' to happen. If he heard Old Massa say he was gonna kill hogs the next day, Big John would slip back to the quarters and tell the other niggers, 'Tomorrow we kills hogs.'

---

[1] Reprinted by permission of the publishers, Duell, Sloan & Pearce, Inc., from Stetson Kennedy: *Palmetto Country*, pp. 127–31. Copyright 1942 by Stetson Kennedy.

" 'How you know that?' they asked him.

" 'I can tell fortunes, that's how,' said Big John. 'Ain't nothin' hid from me.'

"And the next mornin' when Old Massa come out and told all the niggers to get ready for a big hog killin', they decided Big John was a fortune teller for true. From then on they believed anything he told them.

"One day when Big John was hangin' around the back door of the Big House, he seen his Mistress throw the water out of her wash basin, and in it he saw her diamond ring. But before he could pick it up, a turkey gobbler gobbled it down.

"Soon the whole house was raisin' a ruckus lookin' for the lost ring, so Big John went to Old Massa and told him he knew where it was. Old Massa promised him if he could find the ring he would make him a present of a fine fat shoat. So Big John told him to kill the gobbler and he would find the ring. At first Old Massa didn't want to kill his prize gobbler, and he told Big John that if he was foolin' him he would kill him sure. But when he killed the gobbler, there was the ring. From then on Old Massa thought Big John was a fortune teller too.

"One day Old Massa was braggin' to some white folks that he had a nigger who could tell fortunes. One man disputed his word, so Old Massa said, 'I'll bet you forty acres of good bottomland my nigger can tell fortunes!'

" 'If you so sure, what you spuddin' for?' asked the man. 'Why don't you make a real bet? I'll bet you my whole plantation.'

" 'Since you really wants to make a bettin' thing outa my statement,' said Old Massa, 'let's made it worth my time. We'll bet our whole plantations and every horse and mule and hog and nigger on the place.'

"So they agreed on it, and decided to prove the thing out a week from that day. Old Massa took Big John aside and told him about the bet, and said, 'I bet everything I got in this world on you, and if you make me lose I'll kill you!'

"The provin' day came and Old Massa was up bright and early. He was up so early he had to saddle his own horse and then go wake up Big John. Big John climbed on a mule, and off they rode to the provin' ground. When they got there it looked like everybody and their brother was on hand to see the sight. The other bettin' man had the privilege of fixin' the proof, so Big John was led away a little piece. Then they brought him back and showed him a great big old black iron washpot turned upside down, and they asked him what was under it.

"Everybody knew but Big John. Old Massa told him he better

think good if he wanted to live. Everybody kept quiet waitin' to hear what Big John would say. He looked hard at the pot and walked around it three or four times, but he didn't have the least idea what was under it. He began to sweat and scratch his head and Old Massa looked at him and began to sweat too. At last Big John decided he might just as well give up and get the killin' over with.

" 'You got the old coon,' he said.

"When he said that Old Massa throwed his hat up in the air and let out a whoop, and everybody else was yellin' with surprise, cause that's what was under the pot,—a big old coon. So Old Massa went off to Philadelphia to celebrate, but before he left he give Big John his freedom and a hundred dollars and left him in charge of the plantation.

"Old Massa and Old Miss had no sooner got on the train than Big John sent word to the niggers on all the plantations, 'Massa is gone to Philamayork and won't be back for three weeks. He done left me in charge of everything. Come on over to the Big House for a big time.' While the invite was bein' carried round, he told some of the hands to go into Massa's lot and kill hogs till you could walk on 'em.

"That night Big John really spread a scrumptious table. Everybody that could get hold of white folks' clothes had 'em on. Big John, he opened up the whole house and took Old Massa's big rockin' chair and put it on top of Massa's bed. Then he climbed up and sat down in it to call the figures for the dance. He was sittin' in his high seat with a box of Massa's cigars under his arm and two in his mouth when he seen a couple of poor-lookin' white folks come in.

" 'Take them poor folks out of here and carry them back to the kitchen where they belongs,' Big John said. 'Don't allow 'em back up front again.'

" 'Nothin' but quality up here.'

"He didn't know that they was Old Massa and Miss, who had slipped back to see how he would behave while they was gone. They washed the dirt off their faces and came back up front where Big John was still sittin'.

" 'John,' said Old Massa, 'after I trusted you with my place you done smoked up my fine cigars and killed all my hogs and let all these niggers in my house to act like they was crazy. Now I'm goin' take you out to the persimmon tree and hang you. You is entitled to a good hangin', and that's what you gon get.'

"While Old Massa was gone to fetch a rope, Big John called his friend Ike to one side and said, 'Ike, Old Massa is gonna take me out and hang me to the persimmon tree. Now I want you to hurry out to that tree and climb up in it. Take a box of matches with you, and every time you hear me ask God for a sign, you strike a match.'

"After a while here come Old Massa with a rope, and he led Big John out to the tree. He tied a noose in the rope and put it around Big John's neck and then threw the other end of the rope over a limb.

" 'I got just one favor to ask of you, Old Massa,' said Big John.— 'Let me pray before I die.'

" 'All right,' said Old Massa, 'but hurry up and get it over with, cause I never been so anxious to hang a nigger in my life.'

"So Big John kneeled down under the tree and prayed, 'O Lord, if you mean for Massa not to hang me, give me a sign.'

"When he said that, Ike struck a match and Old Massa seen it and began to shake. Big John kept on prayin', 'O Lord, if you mean to strike Massa dead if he hangs me, give me a sign.' Ike struck another match and Old Massa said, 'Never mind, John, you done prayed enough—the hangin' 's off!' But Big John prayed right on, 'O Lord, if you means to put Old Massa and all his family to death unless he turns us niggers loose, give me a sign.' This time Ike struck a whole handful of matches, and Old Massa lit out from there as fast as he could run.

"And that's how the slaves was freed."

Uncle Monday[1]

In his native Africa, Uncle Monday was a big-time medicine man— a leader in the powerful crocodile cult of men who claimed brotherhood with the savage saurians. Captured and brought to America as a slave, Uncle Monday soon escaped and made his way from South Carolina and Georgia down into the Indian Territory of Florida. There he made medicine among the Seminoles and their Negro allies, the Maroons.

"When the white men drove the tribes deeper and deeper into the peninsula, Uncle Monday rallied the warriors on the shores of Lake Maitland. Again they were defeated by superior arms and numbers, and Uncle Monday was forced to retreat with his men to the dense woods around Blue Sink Lake. He told them the gods had revealed to him that further resistance would be useless. But Uncle Monday swore that he would never submit to slavery or death at the hands of the whites. He said he would change himself into an alligator, and join his brother saurians in the Blue Sink until the wars were over. Then he would come forth from the lake and walk the land in peace.

---

[1] Reprinted by permission of the publishers, Duell, Sloan & Pearce, Inc., from Stetson Kennedy: *Palmetto Country*, pp. 131-3. Copyright 1942 by Stetson Kennedy.

"So the tribe held a ceremony on the banks of the Blue Sink. As the men beat savage rhythms on their drums, Uncle Monday danced. As he danced his face grew long and terrible, his arms and legs grew shorter, his skin grew thick and scaly, and his voice changed to thunder. From the Blue Sink came an answering roar of deep-throated bellows, and a thousand 'gators swept up from the lake in a double column. Uncle Monday was the biggest 'gator of them all, and he marched majestically between their ranks and slid into the Blue Sink. With a mighty roar all the other 'gators plunged after him.

"That's how Uncle Monday changed himself into an alligator. He still lives in the Blue Sink, but every now and then he changes himself back into a man and walks through the land casting all sorts of good and bad spells on folks.

"Not long ago old Judy Bronson of Maitland was braggin' around that Uncle Monday wasn't no better hoodoo doctor than what she was. She said she could not only undo any spell he cast, but she could throw it right back at him. When Uncle Monday heard about her braggin', all he said was, 'The foolishness of tongues is higher than mountains.'

"One day Judy asked her grandson to rig up a pole and dig her a can of worms; she was goin' fishin' down at the Blue Sink, even if the mosquitoes and red-bugs did eat her old carcass up. Folks tried to get her not to go, because Blue Sink is bottomless a few feet from shore; but Judy said she just *had* to go, and that's all there was to it. She got there at sundown, and had no sooner got her hook baited and in the water than she felt the dark slippin' up and grabbin' hold of her like a varmint.

"Judy wanted to get up and run off through the brush, but her legs were paralyzed. Then she heard a big wind come rushin' across the brush, and the next thing she knew she had fallen into the Blue Sink. Of all things on earth, Judy was most afraid of the dark and the water, and now they both had her in their claws. She was afraid to move for fear she might slip off into the deep. Finally she found strength enough to scream. At the sound of her voice a bright beam of light fell across the Blue Sink like a flaming sword, pointing straight at her.

"Then Judy saw Uncle Monday. He was clad in flowing robes and marched across the water toward her. Behind him swam an army of 'gators.

"'I brought you here,' said Uncle Monday, 'and here you will stay till you own up that you can't do no such magic as me.' The light faded, and Uncle Monday and the 'gators sank beneath the water. But one big 'gator remained, and sidled up so close to Judy she couldn't help touching him when she breathed.

"Judy hated like everything to give in to Uncle Monday, but she was too scared to let pride stand in her way. First she admitted it inside, then she said it out loud. When she did, the 'gator swam off into the darkness, and she heard her grandson calling to her. Soon she was lifted out of the Blue Sink and carried home. Folks still try to tell Judy that she only suffered a stroke and fell into the lake, but she knows better. She threw away all her voodoo stuff, and says she has Uncle Monday to thank for being able to walk again.

"Uncle Monday still walks through the countryside as a man, but he always changes to a 'gator again and returns to the Blue Sink. When he does all the other 'gators in the lake keep up an all-night bellowing, and folks in the village hear them and say with a sigh of relief, 'Uncle Monday has gone back.'"

Liverpool Jarge has not lived in the land of myth quite as long as has Paul Bunyan, nor has his legend migrated like Paul's. Hence he has fewer followers; those few, however, are devoted. One sample of his narrative, as repeated by the equally apocryphal but plausible Halliday Witherspoon, will show why there are those who love him. As Mr. Scott remarks, "It is all in the best tradition of tall-tale-telling."

Pecos Bill may have existed as an American legend before Edward O'Reilly wrote him up.[1] Mr. O'Reilly says he did, and it would be rude to contradict; to all present intents, however, we may fairly think of Mr. O'Reilly as his creator. Other men have nevertheless tried their hands at developing Bill, and I have chosen a yarn spun about him by William C. White.

Paul Bunyan has been called (not quite accurately) the only American myth. No doubt he is the best-known one today. About his origin there is a good deal of mystery. Did he exist at all before, say, 1900? Many have said so, but the evidence they produce is not wholly satisfactory. Since about 1915 Paul has been taken for granted as a creation of American lumbermen, and, whatever his origin, they know about him now. My first selection is taken from Mr. J. H. Plenn, who admits that his imagination is his primary source for Bunyan material. James Stevens has probably done more for Paul than has any other writer; therefore we should regard his stories of Thunder Bay and the He-man Country authentic. On the other hand, it must be said frankly that the Bunyan stories recounted by Mr. Blair and by Mr. Laughead sound a good deal like fiction.

In perspective: Halliday Witherspoon[2]

Only recently I learned of the death sometime earlier this year of Halliday Witherspoon, who was off and on for a good many years a newspaperman in Boston. I wonder if anyone around here

[1] In the *Century Magazine*, Vol. CVI, pp. 827ff. (October 1923).

[2] By Winfield T. Scott, from the *Providence Journal*, September 9, 1941. Mr. Scott is literary editor of the *Providence Journal*, and is a poet. *To Marry Strangers* (New York: Thomas Y. Crowell; 1945) is his latest book.

ever heard of him. . . . I never met the man, but I'd heard of him for as long as I can remember because he was a cousin of mine. That is, he was really a cousin of my grandfather, to whose generation he more or less belonged; but anyway, he was the only newspaperman— the only writer—any branch of the family had produced within memory.

To my then completely infantile mind, there was a faint suggestion of the romantic about this distant relative who dwelt in Boston and sometimes in even remoter and more glamorous climes; and I gathered that to the grownups, Halliday Witherspoon carried some such aura, albeit tinged with a suspicion that he was by no means the most respectable member of the tribe. This is understandable. Let any family produce a whole line of hardware men, or plumbers, doctors, ministers of the gospel, or even perhaps newspapermen, and the worth of the line will be such common fact as to pass unacknowledged within the family itself. But let one member of the family strike a different path: he may have an aura, yet it will be—in Yankee New England at any rate—tinged, a little impure merely with his difference. Though as to that, I admit Halliday Witherspoon appeared unconnected with any church activity and his series of rough yarns about that sea-going, bar-loving scum, Liverpool Jarge, were mighty easy in their use of colorful detail. He didn't seem to have to stretch for it much.

His name was really Will Nutter. He favored the old-fashioned flair of a nom de plume. And more than this little I shouldn't know about him had he not, in 1933, issued a book of ten of his Liverpool Jarge columns; and at that time a Boston freelancer, Lewis E. Stoyle, did a handsome lot of writing up of Jarge's creator.

Well, it seems the romance wasn't all fiction. Though there are gaps in Stoyle's account of Witherspoon's life from its beginning at Grove-land, Mass. on, it was discoverable that he spent some of his childhood around the docks at Portsmouth, New Hampshire, and that in his teens he was freightcar-riding all over the country, often with full-fledged hoboes. Still later, after some cub-reporting and three years at Williams College, he spent a few years prospecting and promoting copper and silver mines in Mexico. In 1913 he returned to Mexico, having become an editorial and feature writer in Boston through the encouragement of Philip Hale; and as a reporter of Villa's rebellion, Witherspoon nearly lost his life. In a wave of revenge against America, Witherspoon was among those Americans jailed and sentenced to be shot. He escaped, and, when the World War broke out, twice went abroad as a correspondent.

He ghost-wrote two books on the war, but his best work was in the flavorsome yarns of Liverpool Jarge. According to Jarge's shipmate, John Savage Shaghellion, a boozer who allegedly spun the stuff for the reporter, Jarge died violently at the end of every yarn. The stories began with an alleged letter from Shaghellion which itself began: "And why shouldn't a man use his wooden leg to brain an enemy? Wouldn't it be his natural weapon? Not a word. Of course it would. I mind a shipmate of mine, a savage from New London, down on the ship's articles as cook, but a handy man and willing, with only one arm, having had the other burned away in the bight of an out-running line with a big bull sperm at the other end. He had a wooden stump with three steel hooks at the end, kept always shiny and neat, and very thefty he was with 'em either in the galley or aloft. I saw him once ungut a Lascar in Liverpool Lou's place in Sidney as tidy as you like. Could he have done such with the hand the devil gave him? He could not.—But I wanted to tell you about Liverpool Jarge, no connection with Lou. Jarge was a one-eyed man, the other having been knocked out with a belaying-pin. . . ." And so he goes on: Jarge who "had things tattooed onto him that would have got him life, if he'd tried to send himself through the post."

It is all—to be serious about it—in the best tradition of tall-tale-telling American humor. Whether the little book can still be got anywhere I don't know, but it should become at least a minor classic; and it makes me think that the family's only newspaperman until very recent years is still the better of the two we've allowed ourselves.

Liverpool Jarge: must of et somethin' [1]

Mr. John Savage Shaghellion was, in one respect, totally unlike other men of his class. Most of these old fellows, retired seamen and the like, are a good deal like rabbits. They run around in circles. They have their regular beats. You know where to find them.

Not so with John. He had, indeed, his favorite haunts along the water front, and he was often to be found at the Bell in Hand; but on the whole he was an indiscriminating rambler. You were quite as likely to find him in Kerry Village as on Court Street; or he might bob up in Chinatown or the North End or Dover Street way. Any place where men gathered to eat and drink with warmth in the Winter and a big electric fan going in the Summer, any place where hard-earned cash was easily spent was a snug haven for John Shaghellion. Nor was he a finical chooser. I have even seen him erupt

---

[1] From Halliday Witherspoon (Will Nutter): *Liverpool Jarge* (Boston: Square Rigger Co.; 1933; copyright Square Rigger Co., Boston, 1933), Yarn 6. (The book is not paginated.)

with unostentatious haste and with remnants of free lunch clinging in his whiskerage from superior places of the gilded sort like Frank Locke's or the Congress.

There was no reason, then, why I should be surprised at finding John late one afternoon in Mike Leveroni's on North Street. Nor was I. I had ordered a whiskey and anisone when the old gentleman spied me. Deserting, without any hesitation whatever, the preoccupation of watching a game of pin pool he rolled across the room, hove to at my elbow, and announced with a bland, childlike faith:

"I'll take the same. Them sweet smellin' drinks always makes me think of warm countries with palm trees wavin' and folks in white clothes and,—pretty gals heavin' roses at you out the winders." John leered coquettishly.

Well, I paid for the drink,—and another one. And then I conceived the brilliant idea of testing Mr. Shaghellion's capacity. Not for alcoholic stimulants; but for food and drink together. I had thought of it before but the financial hazard seemed too great. Today, however, I was flush; and the wherewithal for the test was at hand. There was a tidy little eating place at the rear where the ravolis were good and the rabbit, hunter-style, was beyond compare. Wherefore I suggested food. John accepted gracefully and we made our way aft to the tables. No need to go into the details. The check came to three dollars and something, my end being the something.

When he had finished, Mr. Shaghellion lolled back in his chair and wheezed:

"I feel kinder stuffed up. It's very queer what a little bite of grub does to a man like me. I feel some like Liverpool Jarge did that time in New Orleans."

"How was that?" I queried, being minded if possible to have some small return for my dollars three.

"Jarge died," said Shaghellion sadly. "I can hear his last words now like he'd just said 'em."   \

I handed over a cigar and held a match. The sated old glutton puffed contentedly and droned off into more or less connected narrative. Like this:

"A couple of weeks ago a good-for-nothin' nevvy of mine brang home a book that he had off a second-hand shop with a piece in it about the last words of great men and I read the thing though my eyes ain't what they was. It comes out that none of 'em says what you'd think. You got a right to expect a soldier to say somethin' about war and a sailor to say somethin' about ships. But they don't. The same way you'd say a sailor ought to die at sea and Davy Jones's locker is the only grave for him if he's a real sailor, but some of 'em dies ashore and it can't be helped.

572

"And that brings up what happened to me and Liverpool Jarge once in New Orleans. I mind it like yesterday. We took a tow up the river in the bark Belgian Prince four months out of Sidney, and when we docked New Orleans looked like the promised land, what with our being near starved livin' on salt horse and weevily biscuit and lime juice. The skipper says we lay there ten days, and me and Jarge goes ashore the first day.

"Jarge says he's going to eat and then he don't know what he will do. Unluckily, he had got all filled up with tattooin' in Sidney and hadn't any place empty on him, barrin' his face. He'd thought some of havin' that done, but Jarge fancied himself and he'd promised a gal he knew not to have his face tattooed. That didn't keep him from gettin' a design drawed out by an artist for a shillin' showin' decorations like a Fiji islander, and Jarge said he might get it done if things got dull in New Orleans. They didn't.

"First thing ashore him and me went into a little eatin' house and Jarge had a bit of beef, maybe a couple of pounds, with onions and cauliflower and four cups of coffee and half an apple tart, and Jarge loosened up his belt and paid a dollar and a half without grumblin', which showed there was somethin' the matter with him from the start. Directly after that walkin' up Canal Street Jarge was talkin' about findin' a tattooer to have his face done, when we run foul of a smart young cove what said he was the water-front reporter for some paper. He asked would we like to drink and we said we would, so he steered us into a very swagger place full of mirrors and brass work and ordered three that he said was made of egg and sody and gin.

"You couldn't notice the gin, but Jarge said it was very tasty and the reporter lad bought three or four more. Jarge started in then and pitched a scandalous yarn about gettin' cast away in the Solomons and bein' loved by a native princess, and how he lived on human flesh for a year all in hope of the reporter buyin' a round of real liquor that would have a bite to it.

" 'You ain't ever et,' says Jarge, 'until you've tasted human flesh.'

"And all the time him and me was eyein' a long table over to one side that was set out with the most amazin' mess of grub anybody ever did see. After a bit Jarge whispered to the reporter and asked what it cost to eat off the table and he says it's free. Jarge gulped down the drink he was holdin' and turned to on the grub.

"There was little brown sausages, and a mess of potatoes and onion with grease over it, and some kind of white meat and green stuff with yeller slush and about six kinds of sausage cut up in slices and sardines and mustard. Jarge tried 'em all once and some several times and after a bit one of the men in the white jackets come over

573

with a little wooden mallet in his hand and comes toward Jarge with a mean look in his eye. The reporter whispers to him and gives him somethin' and he grins and goes back and Jarge has some more of the pickled tripe.

"Well, the grub Jarge has had seems to rather brace him up, and he tells the reporter he'd like some other kind of grog. So he orders what he says is a cocktail, and when Jarge smells of it he begins to cry a little because he says it reminds him of the spring medicine his mother used to give him. But he got it down and went back and found a platter of pigs' feet he'd overlooked and had about six and threw the bones under the table.

"We went to about three more places and had drinks called punch and more grub, and finally hove to in what was called the old Absinthe House, and the man sets out three glasses of soap and water. Jarge drinks his and a wild look comes in his eye, and he swings on the reporter without any talk; but the lad is very thefty on his feet and runs out, and Jarge after, and me, but we didn't catch him, us bein' bad runners and a good deal of cargo aboard anyhow.

"After that we brought up in a kind of a market that looked like Whitechapel with coster carts and we finds one that was loaded with boiled crabs, ten for five cents. Jarge said he preferred periwinkles, but he bought ten crabs in a sack, and I did, too. Up the street we found another cart with twelve crabs for five cents, and Jarge said they were a bargain, and had a sack, and I did, too. Then we finds a man that give fourteen for five cents, and Jarge said that was a big bargain, and had twenty-eight, and made me, too. Shortly we begin to spill crabs, and we sat down in a narrer doorway, and I got out a mouth organ I'd bought somewhere and begins to play 'Rule Britannia,' and Jarge shells crabs and eats 'em. After he'd had about thirty he falls back with a groan and lays there with his eyes shut and near covered with shells and legs with the meat sucked out.

"I was just startin' the 'British Grenadiers' when up comes a nigger woman and says it's her door and what do we mean by clutterin' it all up. Jarge opened his eyes a second and kicks her very savage on both shins and she screams and a crowd comes and a bobby and a black maria, and me and Jarge brings up in a police station, with him unconscious.

"They tries to make out we're drunk, but I showed how it couldn't be only havin' sweet drinks, and said Jarge was sick. And they said he was, and had a doctor in. The saw-bones took Jarge's pulse and listened to his heart and shook his head. There he lay on a cot with a blanket over and still huggin' his last sack of crabs. I bent down and says 'Jarge.' And he opened his eyes and picked at the blanket. 'Jarge,' says I, 'what's the matter?'

574

"He says in a kind of rough whisper: 'I must of et somethin',' and he gave a gasp and died. And that was the end of him, and them was his last words, and he's buried in New Orleans."

Mr. Shaghellion finished his tale, chuckled slily and shot a sleepily inquiring glance in my direction. I made no comment,—offered no criticism. He sighed gustily, let his chin down on his chest and closed his eyes. And presently a mellow rumble like the sound of distant thunder filled all the air and I knew that my aged troubador was sleeping it off. I reached the sidewalk on tiptoes.

Pecos Bill and the willful coyote[1]

No one of the many stories tells precisely what happened to him at the end of his career. They don't tell because no one knows except Panhandle Pete who was there and he wouldn't talk until just recently.

Here, for the first time, is Pete's story.

There were a lot of things Pecos Bill used to like, Pete says, and liquor and women and the smell of sagebrush and the way the prairie looked in spring and shooting and riding and singing and the taste of beef broiled over a little outdoor fire were just a few of the things he liked. But I guess what he liked best was hunting coyotes. Ever since he'd been a small boy, he'd chased coyotes, trapped coyotes, shot coyotes, thrown rocks at coyotes, and run them ragged on foot until they dropped, with their tongues hanging out. "They're smart animules," Bill always said; "It's a test of a man's intelligence to out-think 'em."

As Bill got older and his wind wasn't so good any more, he had to give up chasing coyotes, that is, until Baby came along.

I was with him the night he ran into Baby and I'll never forget it. We were riding along forty miles south of El Paso on as nice a night as I ever saw. The stars were out and it was bright. There was even a piece of moon. That was what made it so funny. We were riding along and Bill was singing cheerfully,

> "Beat the drums lowly and play your fifes slowly,
> Play the dead march as you drag me along.
> Take me to the graveyard and lay a sod o'er me.
> For I'm a poor cowboy and I know I done wrong."

---

[1] By William C. White. Copyright 1943 by Whit Burnett. Originally in *Story*, July-August 1942, pp. 48–59; reprinted in Whit Burnett (editor): *Two Bottles of Relish* (New York: Dial Press; 1943), pp. 98–115. Copyright, 1942, by Story Magazine, Inc.

Pecos Bill always sang that song when he was feeling extra happy.
All of a sudden he says, "That's funny!"

"What's funny?"

"There, on that ridge, that thunderstorm coming up."

I looked and saw a black cloud coming up all right but the stars and
the moon were still shining.

"Never saw a thunderstorm on a starbright night," Bill said. "I'd
call that almost a first-class miracle."

Something flashed on the ridge and Bill said, "It's lightning all
right." We rode on faster. Bill stopped sudden. "That's funny!"

"What's funny?"

"Did you hear any thunder after that lightning?"

"Nope." I said that because I didn't hear any thunder and we were
close enough to the storm to hear it if there was any thunder. "Nope, I
didn't hear any."

"Look! Lightning again and no thunder!" Bill shook his head.
"I believe in miracles but only one at a time. A thunderstorm so close
with lightning and no thunder, that's almost a first-class miracle."

We rode closer and suddenly we heard a sound. I guess you'd call it
laughter but it was child's laughter and a woman's laughter and a
waterfall's laughter, mixed with a horse's neigh and the noise of a tin
can full of pebbles, and the roar of a lot of cowboys howling at a joke.
It sounded like "Hayheehaw! Haiharhoo! Hearhoiheh!" and ended
with "Huh, huh, huh!" delicate, like a sceptical baby.

"A laughing thunderstorm," Bill said, angry, "would be a third
miracle. Hell, that's a coyote and the lightning is his eyes flashing!"

The black cloud raised a head and we could see right enough it was
a coyote and the biggest one I ever saw and no one ever saw a bigger
one. It was easy to tell it was a female because she walked dainty. She
was so big she'd have to lie on her side and bend her neck out of shape
to nibble at sagebrush. She must have heard us for the next thing she
came at us, just like a thunderstorm that got up on its heels and began
chasing you. She went by in such a rush, the air around was chilly for
the next half hour. Bill didn't have a chance to draw his gun and
fire. All he said was "Oh, Baby!"

That's how Baby got her name.

"Baby!" Bill repeated.

Somewhere, off in the distance, in the next county or maybe over in
New Mexico we heard the "Hayheehaw" and so on and then the final
"Huh, huh, huh!"

Bill was awful thoughtful for a while. "I'm going to hunt that baby
and get her if it's the last thing I do. Baby! There's a coyote's a
coyote!"

576

Me and Bill hunted Baby all that year and all the next and the year after that and the year after that, too. Maybe there were even more years but those are all I remember. It was a long time.

Hunting Baby wasn't hard. She was always obliging and willing to hang around and be hunted. We chased her over most of Texas. When we couldn't find her on dark nights she'd let out that laugh of hers, particularly the "Huh, huh, huh" part, and off we'd go. Other times her eyes would flash in the distance and there we'd go again. Sometimes that fooled us—more than fifty times we saw flashes like that and went off hell for leather and found that what we were chasing on the horizon was really a thunderstorm or a twister. Of course, when it thundered, then we knew it wasn't Baby. Half the time Baby'd have been lying low, watching us make fools of ourselves. As we turned back soaking wet we'd hear her "Huh, huh, huh" off in the other direction. Other times we could get on her trail by waiting till she went to a water hole. She had a thirst like a desert and could drink a hole dry with the noise of a rusty pump. Some nights when we thought we'd lost her, her tracks would help us. They were always deep round holes and you couldn't miss 'em. It's getting off my story, but it was those tracks that helped develop West Texas—they were so deep they caught a lot of rain water and held it through dry spells and the grass grew thick around 'em. A lot of cattlemen today still use those tracks for water holes.

It wasn't hunting Baby that was tough, it was bagging her. In five years Pecos Bill must have had a thousand shots at her, from all distances from a hundred feet to a mile, and he shot at her with lead and iron and silver and a couple of times with a shotgun full of scrap iron. Nothing took any effect. Sometimes the stuff we fired hit Baby's sides and bounced back at us. Once we had to hide under a *mesquite* thicket for an hour, while it rained railroad scrap all around us. As a six-inch piece of steel rail hit Bill on the neck he said, "We just won't try that one again. It's like being hunted by a coyote and shot at."

Other times when Baby was feeling frisky she didn't bother to bounce bullets back at us. She just timed the shot so that as it came to her she leaped up into the air, and the bullets went right under her. Then she'd land with a smack you could hear a long way off and sometimes the earth would crack under her. Half the *arroyos,* those little canyons, in West Texas is from where Baby landed after those jumps. She'd have probably started up a couple of earthquakes in any country not so tough as West Texas.

"That Baby!" Bill would say, after missing her once again. He sounded awful proud. "She's just willful! Plumb willful!"

577

I guess it got to be a game with Baby because no matter what we tried to do, her laugh never changed or got angry or snarly. Some nights when Bill didn't feel like going out after her, Baby'd hang around and there was a kind of disappointment in her laugh, like a kid you promised ice-cream for supper he didn't get.

I know it got to be a game with Bill and I never saw him so happy. Of course, from time to time we'd take a job to get money enough to try out some new scheme Bill had thought up for getting Baby. That was all he did think about, night after night. He figured out all kinds of baits and snares and devices but none of 'em worked. He figured out every kind of trap. After Baby picked up one of 'em and heaved it in the air with her hind foot and it landed on Bill and me and kept us pinned down for five days, we gave up traps. Even that didn't make Bill sore. He laughed and shook his head. "That Baby! She's smart." That was the way he was talking about her. Sometimes when he saw Baby running in the moonlight he'd say, "Look at the way that moonlight shines her gray fur! I bet you never saw anything prettier." And when she'd run fast, Bill'd say, "I bet that's the fastest animule there is!" The way he'd talk, you might have thought Bill was raising a child to show off at the State Fair.

One idea Bill had almost did get Baby. The idea was to chase her into the middle of Randall County, which we did, and then to run barbed wire right around the boundaries of the county, which we did. We used all the barbed wire in West Texas doing it and we strung it right. When we got done, stringing it over trees and poles and houses, I never saw such a mess of barbed wire. There wasn't a hole in it big enough for a rattlesnake to crawl through and we ran it so high that not even Baby could jump over it. There we had Baby penned up right and all we had to do now was to wait until she got too weak to move. That wouldn't take too long because we'd been having a drought and the water holes were dry as sun-bleached bones. And Baby was always thirsty.

We must have waited outside that barbed wire a couple of weeks and all the time Bill kept saying, "We got her this time all right, we got her! She won't be willful no more!" And Bill would jump around excited like a colt in a loco patch. "When man matches his intelligence with animules," Bill would say, "man must win. That's natchural!" Every night we heard Baby crying inside there behind the wire like she was trying to find a way out and getting madder and madder. The more she cried the more Bill grinned and yelled, "We got her this time!"

Then one night when we were watching, there was a new sound behind the wire, a soft "Plop, plop, plop!"

"What's that mean?" Bill asked, nervous. "Sounds like she was throwing mudpies." Then he guessed it. "Baby's digging, that's what it is. She's trying to dig her way out, and she's throwing up dirt!" He looked half proud as he said, "I knew she'd figure out something to do." He looked half mad as he said, "That won't get her nowhere. We'll surround the fence and when her head shows we'll wallop her."

So Bill called out all the people from Potter, Armstrong, Swisher, and Deaf Smith counties, the ones around Randall. They were glad to stand watch because they're always glad to take a crack at anyone or anything coming from Randall county.

Three days and three nights we waited and the "Plop, plop, plop" continued but it got fainter and fainter as Baby dug deeper. "This time we got her sure," Bill said. He patrolled the fence day and night with a paddle made from a wagon tongue.

About midnight we heard a new kind of noise. It began as a hiss and turned into a roar and the earth shook and half the people around the fence ran like hell. The roar got louder and right then I felt rain in my face. It felt like rain, it was wet, but when I got some on my hand it had a funny smell.

In the midst of the loud roaring we heard a funny noise. It was "Hayhee haw," and the rest of it and then "Huh, huh, huh!" It sounded awful frightened, but it wasn't coming from back of the fence, it was coming from somewhere behind us.

"That's Baby!" Bill started to jump. "And she's out, she's gotten out!" I never saw a man so mad but he wasn't so mad he couldn't say, "She's that smart, that Baby."

It was beginning to rain even harder. "How'd she get out?"

"Blew out," Bill said. "That's not rain, it's oil. It's got the same smell as the stuff I used to rub on my stiff joints. She dug to hit a pocket and a gusher blew her out."

Way off in the distance, running like a breeze towards Mexico, we heard Baby. "That scared her," Bill said, rueful. "She ought to know I didn't mean to have it happen like that. She's scared. She won't come back."

His laugh was awful faint. "She must be over the Rio Grande by now."

Bill nodded, "I didn't think she'd take it like that." He sounded all choked up and he went to his horse and rode off like mad toward Amarillo.

It took me four days to find him. When I caught up with him he was in Amarillo at the Unweaned Calf bar. He wasn't alone, either. Somewhere he'd picked up a girl whose name was Kankakee Katie. I ain't much for women myself—I never learned how to tell a good one from a bad one and I've never been sure there's any real difference. Katie was a big blonde and from the way she was lapping up

pulque, a pretty fair forager. She was comforting Bill and that was
what mattered. I heard he'd been crying for three days when he got to
town. Now he sat gloomy like and all he'd say was "Baby!"

"Who's this Baby you're muling over?" Katie asked him.

He just shook his head.

"I never heard a man make as much fuss over me," Katie said, like
it annoyed her.

Bill just says "Baby," dreamy like.

"It's awful bad manners," Katie said, "to keep grieving over one
lady when you're in the company of another."

"Baby was no lady," Bill said.

"What was she, a hell cat?"

Bill shook his head. "A coyote!"

"That's no way to talk about her," Katie said, like she had to defend
her sex. "What was she, blonde or brunette?"

"Gray," Bill said, "gray like early morning. Baby!"

Katie lapped up some more *pulque.* "I think you're loco but I tell
you I could go for a man who'd say 'Katie' the way you say 'Baby.' "

Bill reached for the bottle and began to cry at the same time and
when he cries it's like the first freshets coming down an *arroyo* in
spring.

"Katie," I said, "he's really upset about a coyote." I told her about
Baby and how Bill was afraid she was gone for good.

"He's grieving like that about a four-footed long-haired howling
animal?" I didn't know whether Katie was going to laugh or upset the
table. She didn't do either. She began to cry. "I never thought I'd
meet such a tenderhearted person in all my life. Bill reminds me of my
mother—she was tenderhearted like that, too." And she cried as hard
as Bill.

Bill blinked and smiled at me. "Pete, here's what I need—sympathy
and a chance to forget Baby." As he pounded his fist on the table,
the walls of the Unweaned Calf shook and the barkeep looked scared.
"Katie, if you'll have me, I'm yours. How's for marrying me and
lighting out and we'll get a little ranch and raise cattle?"

Katie didn't know whether she was being kidded or not. Then she
hit the table with her fist and the walls shook even harder and down
to the floor dropped a little guy who was standing at the bar but not
holding on tight. "Pardner," Katie said. "I heard about marriage and
I always wanted to try it. It's a deal!" She stopped crying and dried
her eyes on her shirtwaist sleeve. "We'll get a ranch house and we'll
paper the walls with the pages of a mail-order catalogue and make
everything snug." Then she looked worried. "Nope, it's only a dream."

Bill's face got black. "When I make a promise it's a promise."

Katie shook her head. "What about Baby? I know men better than anything in the world except maybe women. Sooner or later you'll get the old hankering to go after Baby and then not even a good woman's love or a forty-foot fence could hold you."

"I told you I was through with Baby," Bill roared and he made such a noise the little guy at the bar hit the floor again.

"A man's a man and a woman's a fool for forgetting it," Katie said, almost ready to cry again. "I just can't risk having my heart broken over a coyote." She finished off the bottle of *pulque*. "Nope, we'll stay friends, Bill, and I'll be a sister to you."

"I'll be consternated!" Bill yelled. "I believe you're jealous of Baby."

"A lady has a right to her feelings, such as she feels," Katie said, wiping her eyes on her shirtwaist sleeve. "I'll tell you what to do, Bill. I ain't going to have no coyote come between us. You bring me Baby's hide and I'll marry you."

Bill just sat back in his chair.

"Besides, it'd be convenient to have," Katie said. "If Baby's as big as you say, we could use the hide for a parlor rug and have some lap over in the dining room and what's left we could stuff chinks with."

"I can't do that," Bill said promptly. "I've been trying for years with no luck."

"You don't sound like you even wanted to get it," Katie said with a pout.

"Sure, I want to get it, but how?"

"You talk like you're glad a coyote's smarter than Pecos Bill."

"That's enough." Bill banged the table and half the bottles on the bar fell down. "It's a bargain, I'll get it."

"Right now?"

"Right now!"

"Then I'll go off and hunt up a wedding dress and some shoes," Katie said. "You bring the hide back here and we'll have the hottest wedding there ever was in Amarillo." She headed for the door, like a barn being carried off in a spring flood.

Bill didn't say anything for quite a while. He picked up the *pulque* bottle and found it was empty. He asked, "Got any ideas, Pete?"

"About Katie?" I shook my head.

"About getting Baby. I can't let the little woman down."

He stood up and started to the bar. "Let's have a drink and start thinking."

When Bill asked the barkeep for *pulque* the barkeep shook his head. "You finished the last bottle. I haven't got a drop."

"Then gimme whiskey."

"On top of *pulque*?" The barkeep looked astonished and the little man beside the bar fell to the floor and lay there.

"What's wrong with that?" Bill asked, getting hot.

"You mix my drinks like that, they'll take the hide off you." But the barkeep poured out whiskey. "However, it's your hide."

Bill swung around like he was boiling mad. "What did you say?"

"I said if you mix my drinks they'll take the hide off you—!"

"Yeep!" Bill brought a fist down on the bar and cracked the top plank. "We got it!" He slugged down the whiskey. "We got it!"

I thought he was crazy. "Got what?"

He pounded me on the back and I bounced toward the front door. "Hurry out, Pete, and get two big water tanks."

Well, I came back to the bar with the tanks and when I got there Bill had every bottle off the shelves and he was opening them so fast the popping of corks sounded like gunfire. From somewhere he had got fifty gallons of *pulque* and that went into the tanks first. Then he poured in all the whiskey in the place.

He was awful enthusiastic. "We'll mix up a drink for Baby that'll take her hide off sure. There's been a drought in this Dust Bowl and we'll pick up a good dry water hole, fill it up with this mixture, and see what Baby does."

In the tanks went twenty gallons of rum, three cases of Bourbon, seven bottles of gin, and a bottle of soda water. The barkeep came up from the cellar with another armful of bottles. One of them had a funny shape.

"What's that?" Bill asked.

"Something called 'Cream dess Violets.' A salesman gave it to me."

"Put it in!"

"Here's Liquor dess Peaches."

"Put it in!"

In went cherry brandy, a bottle of bitters, and a gallon of Dago red. Bill didn't look satisfied. "Got anything else in bottles?"

The barkeep who was baldheaded handed over a flask of hair tonic.

Bill stuck his finger in the soup and licked it. "Tastes pretty nearly right. What else you got?"

The barkeep offered a bottle of catsup and that went in.

Again Bill sampled the results. "Almost right! Got anything else in a bottle?"

"Some perfume called Eau d'Amour I was saving for my wife."

"Put it in!"

Bill stuck his finger in once more. "That's perfect! It ought to take the hide off a cactus!"

Three teams of horses and ten men and the biggest dray in the county drew the tanks out to the water hole that Bill had decided to use. He had to hope the odor would attract Baby, wherever she was. The mixture from one tank went into the hole with a splash and the odor it gave off knocked seven men to the ground. I felt a little dizzy myself but Bill was too excited to notice anything. Twenty-one lizards who lived around that hole ran to it, took one small drink, and twenty of them lay on their backs with their toes turned up. The twenty-first just vanished in a small explosion.

After the men revived, they started to move the second tank to the hole but Bill stopped them. "Hold it! Baby may not come here before this stuff dries up and we'd better save the other tank for another night. We never could mix this drink again the same way."

With the hole half filled we drove off a piece and waited. We waited a long while and we tried to keep Bill quiet but he was pretty nervous. Most of the time he said, "I hope she comes." Sometimes he said, "This is a dirty trick to play on Baby!" Even from a mile away the water hole smelled like an old barroom on Sunday morning. Bill walked up and down saying, "I wonder where Baby is, I wonder what Katie's doing, I wonder if Baby is coming, I wonder if Katie is getting ready," until he sounded all mixed up, as if he was expecting Katie to turn up at the water hole while Baby got ready for a wedding.

Every so often there would be little explosions at the water hole and Bill said, "That must be jack rabbits coming in for a drink! Boy, if only Baby'd come."

Then we heard a funny noise off in the distance, the noise of a rush of a big wind. Bill knew what it was and yelled, "It's Baby! She's sniffing!" A minute later, over the horizon, came the black shadow that was Baby, running full speed. She came so fast that she had to stop herself at the water hole by braking with her front feet and threw up a sandstorm that blacked out El Paso three days later. We were too excited to pay any attention.

We saw the shadow stand by the hole and we watched Baby lower her head. We heard one more sniff, like a tornado taking a deep breath, and then there was an explosion and a roar that knocked us flat. Bill stood up first. "That got her!" He began jumping. "That got her!" And he started to the hole with all of us running like mad.

Bill beat us all there and when we caught up to him he said, "I'm consternated! Look at this!" There lay Baby's hide, thick, gray, tangled and matted, but there was nothing of Baby inside of it. Bill didn't know what to do or think. He just stood scratching his head. "I didn't think it would work as good as that." He shook his head. "Well, I got her at last!" His voice sounded funny. Then he said, "Load as much of the hide as you can on the wagon and drag the rest. We'll get back to town and see Katie."

We put a lot of the hide on the wagon and it was piled up like a hayrick. On the way back to town, Bill remembered the unused tank of the mixture. "I'm going to bottle and sell it," he said. "It'll be a wonderful thing for knocking off warts and freckles."

We pulled up in front of the Unweaned Calf and Bill yelled, "Hey, Katie!" He was feeling pretty good again. "Hey, Katie, come out and see what I got!"

A flock of barflies rushed out but no Katie, and Bill began to grumble. "Look at the trouble you go to, just for a woman and then she's off primping herself and too busy to come look." He decided to wait for her and invited everyone in for a drink. By this time fifty guys were going up and down the street boasting how they caught the coyote by putting whiskey on her tail.

The barkeep had renewed his stock from somewhere and Bill ordered drinks all around. After twenty minutes he began to yell, "Hey, Katie!"

The barkeep gave him a funny look. "You mean that blonde you were talking to yesterday?"

"Yeah, what about her?"

"Last night a cowhand comes in with a couple hundred dollars and said he was going up to San Antone. Katie said she always wanted to see San Antone so she goes with him. They left about midnight!"

Well, Bill stowed the hide and the tank of mixture away in a shed and he said, "Let's get out of this country, Pete." We went over to New Mexico for a time, punching cattle, but it wasn't the same Bill. He was thoughtful and silent and he never sang any more. He never talked about Baby, either. Then we drifted back to El Paso again and got a job at the One Legged M Ranch. Bill worked hard but his heart wasn't in his work. At night he used to leave our shack and go out and sit somewhere by himself and he got sore if I offered to go along. When he did talk he was pretty gloomy. "I'm getting old," he'd say, "I think we ought to go out to Californy for our last days. That's where rich Texans and poor Texans go before they die. They sit in the sun, I heard, and eat oranges."

Once he said, "I done wrong killing Baby. I shouldn'ta done it. I was so happy when she was around to chase, I didn't know how happy I was."

I couldn't get him interested in roping or riding or liquor or shooting. As for women, when the sister of the owner of the One Legged M came for a visit, Bill ran off and hid in the hills for a week.

He came back with a funny look on his face and he wouldn't talk. But that night he said, "Come along with me."

We walked a mile from the ranch buildings. Bill said mysteriously, "Hear anything?"

All I heard was a lot of crickets and maybe a lizard in the grass. I asked, "Where?"

"Over there, back of that hill."

I listened again and I heard a cow in heat and a horse neighing. "I don't hear nothing special."

Bill wasn't even listening to me. He was grinning like a kid. "I can hear her, coming nearer." He shook his head. "She sounds mighty lonesome tonight, mighty lonesome." He repeated, "So lonesome, that 'Huh, huh, huh!' "

I knew who he was talking about. I just chewed on a piece of grass and said nothing.

"You sure you don't hear nothing?" Bill asked.

"I got a cold," I tried to hide what I was thinking about Bill. "I don't hear nothing so good."

The next day I found Bill in the bunkhouse packing his kit. "I'm going back to Amarillo," he said and he wouldn't explain why. "I just got an idea, that's all."

He did explain on the way back. "Baby's still hanging around waiting for me, Pete, I know it." He glared at me. "You think I'm crazy."

I shook my head mighty quick. "Different people hear different things."

"The reason we can't see her is because she has no hide," Bill said, like he'd thought it out. "Did you ever see a coyote without a hide?"

"Nope, I never did."

"No one ever did and that proves it. If a coyote's going to be seen he just has to have a hide!"

We rode on quite a spell and I didn't have a word to say.

Then Bill said, "When we get to Amarillo, I'm going after Baby."

I almost fell off my horse and it wasn't the horse's fault. "How will you do that?"

Bill didn't say. We came into town and he went to the shed where he stored all the stuff after he got Baby's hide. It was still there but except to pat it once, he wasn't interested in it. He went right to the tank of mixture and pounded it.

It sounded as empty as a dry well.

"It's gone and I can't even mix it again," Bill said, and he sounded heartbroken; "I figured that maybe if I drank some of it, it'd put me in the same shape as Baby. Then I could have gone after her."

I just shook my head. I couldn't say a word.

Bill began to fuss around the tank. With the top off he lowered himself inside. Then I heard him yell, "Get a cup, Pete! There's just a little bit left here."

I got him a cup and he fished up one cupful and even for that he had to scrape bottom. When he came from the tank he was grinning from earlobe to earlobe. I was pretty worried but I figured he knew what he was doing.

"You going to drink this now?"

"No, sir," Bill said with a lot of pride. "I'm going to drink it fit and proper." And with that he began to sing

> "Oh, I'm wild and woolly
> And full of fleas,
> Ain't never been curried
> Below the knees!"

I tried to argue with him all the way to the Unweaned Calf but his mind was made up. He just kept singing. He told the barkeep, "This time I brought my own liquor."

The barkeep looked suspicious. "How about a chaser?"

"I hope I'll never need a chaser," Bill said, with a pleasant laugh. He looked around the room and saw about twenty people. "Come on folks, gather round and I'll show you something you can tell your grandchildren." He raised the cup but I was feeling too bad to watch close.

Before he tastes it he sings

> "Take me to the graveyard and lay a sod o'er me,
> For I'm a poor cowboy and I know I done wrong!"

When I heard that I knew he was extra happy again.

"Pete," he said to me. "You've been a good friend. When you find someone like Baby, don't treat her bad!"

Then he takes a good long swig from the cup.

There's a sort of flash and explosion, not loud but gentle like and when I look up, Bill's gone. Completely gone and not a sign of him! Then, and the men who were in the Unweaned Calf at that moment will swear to it, drunk or sober, we heard a gentle fluttering sound. Down from the ceiling like falling leaves came the clothes Bill had been wearing, his shirt, his pants, his boots, and the hand-carved belt he was so proud of. For a second they stood by themselves, just as if Bill was inside 'em, then they collapsed to the floor.

And that was the end of Pecos Bill, as far as anyone knew.

I hung around town for a couple of days but I was awful lonesome so I went back to my job at the One Legged M, feeling like a lost calf. I worked extra hard by day so I'd be good and tired at nights, but even then I couldn't sleep.

One night I got up and walked out to where Bill and me used to sit. I was there in the quiet and I just couldn't forget Bill. The only noise I heard was a couple of lizards in the grass.

Now, I ain't going to swear to this because I never heard it again, but as I was sitting there that night a wind came up sudden and it got real cold. The grass began to move or I thought it did. And right behind me I heard "Hayheehaw!" and so on and then "Huh, huh, huh!" Maybe it could have been the wind in the trees, but there wasn't any trees and anyway, where did that sudden wind come from? A minute later I swear I heard Bill's voice, as happy as a little child, laughing, "That Baby! she's just willful!" It sounded as if he was chasing along behind, doing what he liked to do most in all this world.

But I couldn't see a thing.

I would even think I had dreamed it except that the next morning Bert Simmons who owns the One Legged M called us outside and we followed him behind the barn. The ground there used to be as level and smooth as a piece of harness strap but this morning there was a brand new *arroyo,* fifty feet deep and running for a quarter mile, just like a big crack in the earth. It was the sort of crack we used to see when Bill and me shot and Baby jumped in the air to duck and then landed hard.

Well, I'm sure that wasn't the finish of the whole thing although I never again heard a sound like Baby or saw any traces. But I've been reading in the newspapers about those California earthquakes and I remember what Bill used to say about wanting to finish his days in California. No one knows what causes those earthquakes, I hear, but I got my own ideas ever since I heard that California was a sort of soft place, nowhere near as tough as West Texas and a whole lot more brittle.

Paul Bunyan and Kemp Morgan [1]

From the various bits, including my own extemporaneous contribution, I pieced together the story of Paul Bunyan and Kemp Morgan digging oil wells in Texas—the story, at least, as it was spun in the hotel-room bull session on Pete's day in Houston.

It seems that it all started when Paul's watch stopped running up in the north-woods lumber camp where Paul made his headquarters. Now Paul, as you may know, had fifty hard-grease and fifty soft-grease men at work all the time keeping the wheels running smoothly. But they had just come through a spell of dry rain and everything was caked up, including the watch-grease, so hard that not even the hundred greasemen working together could pry the wheels loose. The need was evident—some kind of lubricant that would not cake up. It was then that Kemp Morgan, who was up on a visit from the Lone Star State, told Paul about some stuff known as rock oil that he had found while digging artesian wells for ranchers.

---

[1] From *Saddle in the Sky,* by J. H. Plenn, copyright 1940. Used by special permission of the publishers, The Bobbs-Merrill Company. Pp. 216–20.

"Let's go," Paul said, "and if there's enough of it, maybe I can get my donkey-engines going, too. I haven't had any good fuel for them." So they went to Texas, and took the Blue Ox along.

They pitched their tent at a likely spot for the night and decided to start digging in the morning. But first they had to drive the pegs for the tent poles. Paul swung his ax around his head seven times, and then drove it into the ground. It went in so far that Paul had to hitch Babe to the handle to try to get it out again. Babe pulled and yanked, and yanked and pulled. The Blue Ox stopped to rest when most of the handle was already out and only the head of the ax was still imbedded in the ground.

While Babe rested, the axhead flew out of the ground as if it had been fired by a big cannon. It carried Babe four miles and a quarter up on top of a stream of black stuff shooting out of the ground. It was Paul's and Kemp's first gusher.

Then they begun digging what turned out to be the biggest oil field in the world. Some of their wells are still flowing, but the derricks in use today are midgets compared to the ones built by Paul and Kemp. Their derricks went up so high they had to waterproof the crownblocks to keep the clouds from warping them.

When the first gusher started, Paul tried to stop it by putting his hand over it. It stopped for a moment, but the next thing you know Paul was going up and up, spinning around. The gusher carried him about a mile up in the air, and he made such a big cloud up there that the folks in Texas didn't see the sun for three days.

That just gives you an idea of how big a fellow Paul was, and Kemp was almost as big, so that the working stiffs in the lumber camp used to call Kemp by the nickname of Big Shorty. Paul was so big that a pine tree looked like a stunted bush when he stood alongside of it.

Paul, held in the air by the gusher, threw out his watch chain, the one that had a half-ton anchor on the end of it as a charm. The anchor sank into the ground and steadied him. Then he pulled one of the barrels off his seven-barreled shotgun and rammed it down the gusher hole. He bent the barrel so the oil would flow out level, horizontal, instead of upward, vertical.

Kemp finished off the job, and set the style for the way oil workers have been completing wells ever since. The walking-beam was made from one of the logs that Paul used as a toothpick, and a bullwheel was shaped out of a button off his mackinaw. Then he clamped his elkskin cap over the end of the pipe till he could figure out how to make the stuff flow steadily. That is how capping a well came to be known as capping a well.

Since Paul had to work with both hands, he had to invent the left-handed monkey wrench. Because the ordinary pipes were too short for the Bunyan-Morgan wells, they invented the pipe-stretcher. Now all beginners in the oil fields, known as "boll-weevils," have to learn to use the left-handed monkey wrench and the pipe-stretcher before they can become full-fledged oil workers.

The deepest well they dug was Old Fifty-Seven. It went right on down to China. It was a gusher, too, but no oil came out of it. After the tools had blown up, a lot of white stuff started coming out. It was rice. Then there was a rush of wind and the rice stopped flowing. Soon there came a stream of hard, crisp fried noodles, and these were followed by a long gurgle, an escape of steam, and then a steady, pulsing flow of chow mein and chop suey. This came out over the noodles and stacked up into big mountains.

For months all the oil-field workers ate Chinese food. Five hundred of Paul's Chinese assistants were ordered to carry away all they wanted, after the men had begun squawking for a change of diet. Each Chinese went to a different part of the country and opened a restaurant. Some of them are still serving the original chop suey and chow mein that came from the Morgan-Bunyan well.

A lot of other things came out, too, like lichee nuts and candied ginger. Finally, a Chinese river started running out of the well, and on it was a whole fleet of Japanese gunboats. They floated over into a pool of oil and got stuck in it and their armor plate was all covered with crude. These were the granddaddies of Japanese beetles.

Before going any farther, Paul and Kemp decided to sample the field. This is done by bringing up a core to show the different layers through which the drill-bit is passing.

First they brought up a cylinder of corn pone.

"Now that's a peculiar stratum," Kemp said. "Very rare."

Then came up a slab of sow belly.

Then some stuff that was green in the first section, white in the middle, and red and pulpy at the bottom.

"Watermelon!" they both exclaimed at once.

And they knew the drill had slipped sideways and hit Georgia. They kept on drilling, pushing the drill southward, until it went down into the Gulf of Mexico, and that was the first salt-water well in history.

They moved the casing on across the Gulf till they hit dry land again. On the next sampling they got a lot of colored blankets and a stack of clay dishes, an Aztec calendar stone, a bottle of *tequila* and three tourists. They were sure it was Mexico.

"Aim to the left," Paul said.

Their first Mexican gusher came in at Tampico.

Out of it jumped the Contrary Englishman. He was one of a crew of British oil men who had been scouting down there. The Contrary

Englishman had a good head on him, but he had to be watched very carefully. When he was left alone, he always did things just the opposite of what folks expected. That's how he happened to be sucked up into the Kemp-Paul casing. He had been told to sink a pipe and instead he let the pipe sink him.

The last well they drilled in the Mexican field brought in the Great Rubber Flood. The flood started because the drill-bit bored into a forest of big rubber trees down in Tabasco. The rubber spread all over the field in a solid sheet, and for weeks everybody and everything was bouncing. Paul called for Sourdough Slim, the cook, to bring his big doughnut cutter, and Slim punched out a lot of tires. With what was left, Paul made some rubber boilers. These would stretch and stretch, no matter how high the temperature got, so there was never any danger of a boiler exploding. One of the men got the idea that he'd like to make some rubber dollars that would stretch enough to pay a fellow's expenses and leave a bit for smokes. But Paul told him no, because the government had a patent on dollar-making.

From the scraps, Paul manufactured some rubber type, about which any printer can tell you plenty. The rubber type solved a serious problem for make-up men, too, namely, what to do with the stuff left over for column nine of the front page. The Bunyan rubber type stretches or shrinks to fit the space where it is needed. It has proved to be a wonderful thing for the headline-writers.

Thunder Bay[1]

[A violent norther was blowing when Shot Gunderson, the iron man of the Saginaw, came across the ice to challenge Paul Bunyan.]

The iron man had his back to the wind. Paul Bunyan's battle plan called for an exactly opposite position, but he was forced to make the best of this one. At any rate, the shanty boys were safe. The logger still hoped to make the iron man face the wind. Just how to maneuver him into that position was the question.

To spar for time Paul engaged in a preliminary to actual battle. Shot Gunderson sneeringly participated. The iron man did not care. He had no fear or doubt about the outcome. He was invulnerable. He was likewise irresistible. Water was his only weakness, and he stood on seventeen feet of ice. So he scornfully followed the logger's lead.

---

[1] Reprinted from *The Saginaw Paul Bunyan* by James Stevens (New York: Alfred A. Knopf; 1932), pp. 141–6, by permission of Alfred A. Knopf, Inc. Copyright 1932 by Alfred A. Knopf, Inc.

"Go ahead and sashay," rasped the iron man. "But it ain't goin' to do yer a particle of good."

Paul Bunyan said nothing. Leaning hard into the wind, he grimly eyed Shot Gunderson, at the same time hefting a bay-shore boulder in his left hand.

Suddenly he tossed it in the wind and instantly pulverized the stone with a blow of his right fist. Clouds of grit blew down the necks of the wind-heaved shanty-boys on the shore. Grinning harshly, Shot Gunderson hauled fistfuls of black stuff from a mackinaw pocket and shoved them into his mouth. Then he struck sparks from his flint. A violent explosion rocked down the wind. The iron man of the Saginaw had fired a charge of blasting powder between his jaws without loosening a tooth. Paul Bunyan did not change expression.

His next move was to draw a sixteen-foot log from his hip-pocket and set it on his shoulder.

"Dast you to knock the log off my shoulder here," Paul Bunyan growled.

Shot Gunderson responded by gouging a furrow five feet deep in the ice with the toe of his boot.

"Dast you to cross that line there," he rasped.

"I'm going to make you look human," growled Paul Bunyan then. "For that you got to be peeled. So here and now I start in to peel off your iron hide."

"I'm making a patchwork cushion outer you there," rasped the iron man. "To make that I got to take you to pieces first. So I'm startin' in to make pieces of you now."

That ended the ceremonies, which were to serve as a model forever-more when men of the woods engaged in battle. They failed to swerve Paul Bunyan. The iron man had not budged from his position. He leaned back solidly into the norther, his anvil fists slowly but surely coming up for a fighting swing. The boss logger did not quail or re-treat, though fully convinced by now that Shot Gunderson was actually invulnerable and irresistible. The rumors had not told the half of it about the iron man. . . .

Now the norther began to prove that the biggest storms indeed have the longest lulls. After the lull before dawn the wind had steadily in-creased, first with its barrage of gusts, then with its first massed forces, and at last with a terrific flying wedge of wind aimed and hurled with solid violence at Thunder Bay. Now the weather unloosed its last and mightiest effort against the boss logger. The wind was backing up Shot Gunderson.

That was the iron man's main trouble when he tried to set himself for one straight finishing punch. . . .

Just an instant too late Shot Gunderson unloosed his irresistible

591

fist. Paul Bunyan was already lunging inside the blow. The iron man's arm shot harmlessly by Paul Bunyan's dodging head like a log plunging over a waterfall. Nobody was there.

It was the boss logger's great chance. The force of his missed blow and the drive of the wind hurled the iron man off balance. He whirled dizzily. Paul Bunyan felt his own feet fly off the ice, but he sturdily kept his grip on the iron man's corrugated throat. Shot Gunderson drove his spikes into the ice and hauled up, still on his feet. Paul Bunyan made his cleanest landing since the time he tumbled from the high jump of bucking Big Auger River. His vaulting feet curved down in a royal arc and struck true. Now Paul Bunyan had his back to the wind. Shot Gunderson, white-hot with frustrated wrath, leaned into the wind to seize his adversary in a death grapple.

The boss logger was at last set to carry out the battle plan his sagacity had formed. The iron man was hooking him close. At his rear the norther was battering with increasingly furious blasts. Paul Bunyan leaned back carefully into the wind. He dropped his left hand from Gunderson's neck, leaving his own jaw exposed.

Then he roared tauntingly into the iron man's funneled ear: "Scared to try another punch, hey? Scared to fight and bound to wrastle? Where's your killer's punch, iron man?"

The taunt was shrewd. Certainly it was Paul Bunyan alone who had done all the wrestling so far, and it was Shot Gunderson alone who had tried to fire a punch. The iron man raged. He heard nothing but the taunt, and he saw nothing but the exposed left jaw of the boss logger.

"Show yer who's skeered!" he rasped. "Show yer who's a wrastlin'! Right now I shatter that jaw of your'n inter shavin's!"

Even as he rasped out the boast, the iron man dropped his anvil of a fist down to his boot-top, to start an inside uppercut which would smash into the logger's unguarded jaw. At that, Paul took a yet heavier lean back into the norther. He tensed every muscle. The iron man's irresistible fist started up like a huge rock heaved by a powder blast. In the very same instant of an instant Paul Bunyan yanked the iron man toward him with his right hand and pivoted himself out to the right like sheet lightning. The battering norther hammered by him, driving with full force into Shot Gunderson.

The iron man's fist was shooting up like seventeen cannon-balls in one. The norther hit the irresistible fist when it was only inches from its mark and deflected its course. Shot Gunderson himself took the blow. The inside uppercut ended under his own chin with a shattering impact, lifted him explosively, hurled him backward in an enormous arc—and then the bay earned its loud name as the iron man of the Saginaw drove head first through its ice with a crash that resounded in echoes for five hours.

Huge foaming waves and ponderous floes broke upon the boots of horseshoe iron that turned their calks toward the sky. The boots quivered once and were still. That quick Shot Gunderson gave up the ghost.

Paul's popcorn[1]

Having got the water meandering around to make the soil moist, Paul figured he'd test the land out with popcorn. So he picked up a good healthy looking kernel, walked out to a likely looking place that had been irrigated lately, and dug a hole about a foot deep with his middle finger. He couldn't use his forefinger or thumb, naturally, because he was holding the corn between them.

Well, Paul had no more than started back to camp to get Ole to act as a witness, than there was a sort of sputtering up of brown dirt, and a cornstalk came skyhooting through. In no time at all, the corn was up to Paul's knee. And by the time he got back with Ole, the cornstalk had grown so much that the top was buried in a cloud.

"Ole!" says Paul. "Climb up to the top of that baby and chop the top off so she won't grow any more!"

Ole started shinning up the stalk at a great rate. But the thing kept shooting up, and in a minute or so Ole, too, was out of sight in that cloud. It was a handsome cloud with cottony bumps and scallopy edges, but Ole said afterwards that being inside of it wasn't different from being inside any old cloud. "Nothing but fog inside it," he said.

"When you chop the top off, throw her down," Paul yelled.

Ole's voice came booming down. "The top's above me," he said. "I can't get *to* the thing." Ole's big voice had something like the effect of thunder, and the cloud rained away from around him. But this new moisture made the stalk grow even faster.

"This won't do!" Paul yelled. "Come down, and we'll handle her some other way!"

"Can't come down, either," Ole yelled in a minute. "Every time I go down one yard, this thing shoots up three, and I'm losing ground. I'm getting hungry, too."

---

[1] Reprinted by permission of Coward-McCann, Inc., from *Tall Tale America: A Legendary History of Our Humorous Heroes* by Walter Blair; copyright, 1944, by Walter Blair; pp. 223–5.

Paul yelled for Babe, right then. And while he was waiting for Babe to come along, he used his shotgun to shoot up a few crullers which he hoped—for the time being, at any rate—would keep Ole from starving to death.

When Babe came along, Paul hurried with the beast over to Jim Hill's railroad, the Great Northern, which (by good luck) wasn't far away. Paul loaded Babe up with a pile of steel rails, then hurried back to the cornstalk with them.

"I'll see if I can't choke off the moisture in this cornstalk," Paul said. And with that he started tying those rails together and then knotting them around the cornstalk.

It worked, too.

Soon the ears of corn away up near the top stopped getting moisture and started to dry out. Then the hot sun hit them hard, and shortly the corn began to pop, making considerable noise, too.

After a while, this popped corn came drifting down like so many snowballs. Babe, who'd lived through so much fierce weather, didn't do any more than shiver a little. But a big herd of cattle grazing near by decided they were in a world-beating blizzard and promptly froze to death.

Meanwhile, growing in spite of those knotted steel rails the way it had, the cornstalk had been bitten into by the things, and had cut itself off of itself. Now it started to tumble, slow but sure. Ole rode it down to the ground, just like a logger standing on a log in white water, then at the right time he jumped off lightly and headed back for Paul, following along the cornstalk.

When Ole got there, the owner of the cattle herd, who'd hurried over, was talking up right sassy to Paul. "Look what you did to my cattle, just when they were fat for market!" he yelled. "You'll have to pay for them."

"Course I will," Paul said. And he settled for the cattle, right on the spot, for Paul was always fair and square, regardless of cost.

"Hello, Ole," says Paul. "Glad to see you back. Just bought me a herd of frozen cattle."

"Goodness gracious!" Ole said. "And with our camp so far from where the cattle are, if we ship them they're likely to spoil."

"That won't do," Paul said. "We'll have to figure a way to use the critters. Teddy Roosevelt wouldn't like it if we wasted all those natural resources. Let me think."

After thinking a while, Paul snapped his fingers. "I've got it!" he said. "If the popcorn froze them, the popcorn can keep them frozen."

With that, he strolled over to the railroad and called on the head man, Jim Hill. Jim rented him a raft of box cars. Then, with the help of Babe, Paul stuffed those box cars with animals *and* popcorn.

And that way, the meat kept fine until it had been delivered at Paul's camp.

So, without knowing it at the time, Paul had gone and invented refrigerator cars.

The he man country[1]

In Paul Bunyan's time the He Man country was far from its present tame and safe condition. It was then a high, smooth valley which lay between the Cascade Mountains and the Rockies. The highest peaks towered only a few hundred feet above it. Down the center of the valley Moron River flowed, and on each side of this amazing stream the sage trees grew, the wild horses roved, and the long-eared, stub-tailed high-behinds sat with lifted front feet and savagely sniffed the air for the scent of their hereditary enemy, the blond wolf. There, too, the tigermunks lifted their tails and screamed in the moonlight. The professors maintain that the tigermunks, the blond wolves and the high-behinds got their great size from eating prune pits which were thrown out from Paul Bunyan's cookhouse, and that they were all shot by the settlers who followed the great logger. This notion is ridiculous. The truth is that these animals were cowards at heart, and . . . But this should be told at the end of the story.

Paul Bunyan moved to this region after his disastrous experience in New Iowa, when his loggers all turned poets. He depended on the He Man country to make plain, honest men of them again. The super-masculine sage trees, he was sure, would inspire them to anything but poetry; and the logging off of these hard forests would be a historical achievement. But the great logger left nothing to chance. He remembered a species of animal which his boss farmer, John Shears, had originated, and he ordered a herd of them to be brought West. John Shears had proved to him that the virility of buffalo milk was incomparable. So Paul Bunyan planned to stuff his loggers with buffalo milk hot cakes as an antidote to any poison of poetry that might remain in them.

Thus the great logger's first move in the He Man country was to build a great buffalo corral and milking pen. When it was completed the buffalos were brought from the old home camp, and a gang of scissor-bills came along to herd and milk them. After their first breakfast of the new man food the loggers got some of their old swagger

---

[1] Reprinted from *Paul Bunyan* by James Stevens (New York: Alfred A. Knopf; 1925), pp. 207–24, by permission of Alfred A. Knopf, Inc. Copyright 1925 by Alfred A. Knopf, Inc.

back, and Paul Bunyan was a picture of cheerfulness as he cruised the sage trees and planned the work of his men.

Moron River offered a chance for the most eventful and picturesque drive of logging history. From its source above the Border to its mouth on the Oregon coast it was like a huge child of a river, for it flowed ridiculously in every mile of its course. Here it ran smoothly for a short distance, then it would flow jerkily, making spasmodic waves; again, its surface would form into vast eddies that whirled like merry-go-rounds, and from these the waters rushed in heaving rolls of foam; there were quicksands where the river played hide and seek, nearly disappearing in places, miles where it turned and ran back and then curved into its course again, making a perfect figure eight. Moron River flowed everywhere in zigzags and curlicues, cutting all manner of capers and didos. Any man but Paul Bunyan would have admitted the impossibility of making a drive on it. But he only smiled when he saw it and said: "If my rivermen will forget poetry they can drive it easily."

The timber in this high, wide valley reached from the Eastern slopes of the Cascade Hills to the Western slopes of the Rockies. These sage trees resembled the desert sagebrush of today. They were not large; few of them were over two hundred feet in height, and not one of them could give a butt log over nine feet in diameter. But they all had many massive limbs which were crowded with silver gray leaves, each leaf being the size of a No. 12 shoe. The brown bark of the sage trees was thick, loose and stringy; it would have to be peeled from the logs before they were snaked to the landings by the blue ox.

"Splendid work for the swampers and limbers," said Paul Bunyan as he cruised the timber. "What a noble logging land is the He Man country! Surely my loggers will be re-born here into even better men than they were before they fell into an illness of poetry and ideas!"

The first day of logging in the He Man country seemed to justify the great logger's best hopes. The men came out from breakfast with a swinging, swaggering tramp, loudly smacking their lips over the lingering flavors of buffalo milk hot cakes. This potent food made them vigorously he in every action. Each man chewed at least three cans of Copenhagen and a quarter-pound of fire cut during his first twelve hours in the woods. "P-tt-tooey! P-tt-tooey! P-tt-tooey!" sounded everywhere among shouted oaths and coarse bellowing. Every ax stroke buried the bit deeply in the tough sage wood, and brown dust spurted and gushed constantly from every singing saw. Crash! Crash! Crash! The thunder of falling trees sounded like a heavy cannonade. On all the loggers' backs gray sweat stains spread from under their suspenders, and their hair hung in dripping strings over their red, wet faces. They had got up steam for the first time since leaving the

Hickory Hill country, and they were rejoicing in it. Even after the eleventh hour had passed their eyes were bright, though red-rimmed from stinging sweat, though wrinkles of weariness had formed around them. The men were tired indeed; the fallers and swampers were now panting through open mouths, and they were chewing nervously on their tongues, as is the habit of men when they are wearied out; but they never missed a lick, and when Paul Bunyan called them home they could still walk springily.

When they were back in camp they did not even complain of the smeared, sticky feeling which always follows great sweats. No one spoke delicately of bathing; the loggers all washed and combed carelessly; and soon they made a trampling, growling host around the cookhouse door.

The rafters and beams of the great cookhouse shook at this supper, so savagely did the loggers tackle the platters of bear meat. Even the bones were crushed, ground, and devoured; and Hot Biscuit Slim and his helpers were delighted when all the dishes were left slick and clean.

That night no poems were recited in the bunkhouses, but the loggers roared out "The Jam on Garry's Rock" and other plain old songs. The loggers all crawled into their blankets at an early hour, and every one of them emitted gruff snores as soon as he went to sleep.

Paul Bunyan listened to them, and he praised the saints for the He Man country. Had it not been for this region there was no telling what continuous plagues of poetry would have afflicted his simple men. Now they were back to normalcy.

The loggers continued to improve as summer passed and the short autumn of the He Man country ran its course. The first snow of the cold season fell on a redeemed camp. That snow flew in on a thundering wind; its flakes quickly made masses of dry snow around the bunkhouse doors; and these were swept into huge drifts that were window-high in places when the breakfast gong rang. The loggers roared and cheered when they rushed out for their buffalo milk cakes. Paul Bunyan listened to their basso growls of hunger, their rumbling jovial cursing, their bellows of laughter, and he chuckled so heartily that the snow which had gathered on his beard was shaken over a crowd of loggers, burying them. They dug themselves out, whooping their appreciation of the humorous happening, and they jestfully shook their fists at their chuckling leader. Then, without stopping to dig the snow from their shirt collars, they galloped on for the steaming cookhouse.

The stamping and banging, the clatter and crash, the smoking, sucking and grinding of meal time had never sounded with more vigor and power than on this wild winter morning. Breakfast done, the loggers came forth wiping their mouths with flourishing swipes of

597

their fists, and with much snorting thumb-blowings of noses. When they were back in the bunkhouses, they laced up their boots, arguing loudly the while as to whether true savages, real tough bullies, would wear mackinaws when it was only forty below zero.

"Mackinaws?" yelled the majority. "Where's your red bully blood, you Hunyoks? Mackinaws! Hell, no, burlies; we won't even button the collars of our shirts!"

And then Ford Fordsen, camp tinker, bunkhouse handyman, and prophet, got an idea which swiftly ran through all the bunkhouses.

"Real rough, red-blooded, burly, bully, savage, dirt-stomping, ear-chewing, tobacco-loving, whisker-growing, hell-roaring He Men are not going to wear their boots and pants like we've been doing," said he. "Look you now: here's a ten-inch boot top, here are two inches of wool sock above it; and there's a pants' leg all tucked down nice and pretty inside of it. Mates, it looks too delicate. It is no way for a fire-eating logger to wear his duds. Here now; watch me and do as I do, and be a real band of honest-to-God bullies. This way—look!"

He jerked open his horn-handled old knife, and he slashed off the legs of his tin breeches, his mackinaw pants and his overalls, just below his knees. He bit off a jaw-full of fire cut and then stood up, his fists on his hips, an unshaven cheek bulging with pepper-flavored tobacco, shapeless hat down over one eye, collar unbuttoned, suspenders stretching over his expanded chest, and—high mark of all high marks, distinction of distinctions—his pants ending in ragged edges below his knees. An inch of red drawers' legs showed below them, there followed bands of green wool socks, then black boot tops. Stagged pants! The finishing touch! Poetry was crushed to earth, never to rise triumphantly again in Paul Bunyan's camp. The inventive and prophetic Ford Fordsen had about killed it.

The great leader was delighted beyond words when he saw the loggers in their new costumes. He smiled indulgently when he heard some of the more modest among them saying that the brush would not bother them greatly now, and that Ford Fordsen's invention was a mighty good useful one. This is the reason loggers of today give for stagging their pants. But Paul Bunyan knew that his men had all taken up with the invention because it suited their natures, which had come back to them. Most of them indeed, admitted it. The loggers of our time should also be frank and admit that stagged pants spring from the he-bulliness of their souls. As Paul Bunyan said, "Etiquette, dainty speech, sweet scents, poetry and delicate clothes belong properly in the drawing-room, the study and the sanctum. They are hothouse growths. Loggers should take pride in hard labor and rough living. Anything that helps their Hesomeness makes them better men. All glory to you, Ford Fordsen, for the invention of stagged pants."

He offered the bunkhouse genius his little finger. Ford Fordsen got his arms a fourth of the way around it, and the two inventors shook hands.

The months went on and the loggers' rugged virtues continued to gain strength from the virile buffalo milk hot cakes. They did noble work among the sage trees and felled so many of them that the Big Swede and the blue ox had to go in a gallop during their working hours to snake all the logs to the landings.

Now, this was the year which is mentioned in history as the Year of the Hard Winter. But the bitterest cold could not now chill the blood of Paul Bunyan's He Men. They had never been so jolly as they were this Christmas, and they jigged and chortled when Paul Bunyan gave each of them a knife devised especially for pants-stagging. The great leader had cut out thousands of these excellent presents from two of Babe's old ox shoes. This was the merriest holiday season the camp had ever known, and even the incredible cold of New Year's Day did not lessen the noisy bunkhouse gayety.

On the last night of the old year the mercury in the great thermometer which hung on the camp office had dropped to four hundred degrees below zero. Then the tube burst, and no one could tell the temperature, but it got appreciably colder. The next morning the boiling coffee froze on the stove, despite the desperate stoking of the kitchen firemen, and the loggers had to drink hot brown ice for their morning's breakfast. But they tramped cheerfully to work, nevertheless, cracking their mittened hands together and stamping the ground as they went along. They worked so hard to keep warm on this day that they talked and swore but little. This was fortunate. For on this incomparable New Year's Day every spoken word froze solidly in the air as soon as it was uttered. The next day the temperature rose, but the words remained frozen, and many a logger bumped his mouth by walking into the HELLOS and DAMNS which were solid in the air. But the hardy victims only laughed through their split lips at such accidents. These words all thawed out at once on a warmer day; and they melted in one long-drawn-out, mournful echoing shout so unhumanly humorous in sound that the loggers rolled with laughter to hear it.

Cold as the winter was, Paul Bunyan and his men were reluctant to see it go, for every day had brought some tickling incident. But at last the gray frost crystals began to glitter occasionally from rays of sunshine which filtered through the white winter mists. Then Paul Bunyan began to plan for the hazardous historical drive down Moron River. Spring was at hand, and the great logger remembered his old whimsical query:

"If Springtime comes can Drives be far behind?"

The loggers, too, sensed the approach of the driving season, and every night the bunkhouses rang with sounds of filing, as the rivermen sharpened calks, pike poles and peavies. They bellowed the old driving songs as never before, and the floors shook as they leaped and pranced to show the marvelous springiness of their legs. They got so comradely in their merriment and exuberance that the last poet among them ventured a poem which began:

> "It's all very well to be profane,
> When life is as dark as night;
> But the man worth a fuss is the man who can cuss
> When everything 'round him is bright."

He got no further, for in an instant one bully had him down, chewing savagely on his ear, while others raked his ribs with their calks. It was the last sigh of poetry in the camp. Paul Bunyan heard about it and had one of the happiest hours of his life as he rejoiced over the good news.

"But every silver cloud has its shadows," he said sensibly, when his exaltation had passed. "I still expect great troubles and difficulties." He was wise indeed in this thought, for he got a troublous problem at once.

Sure as the great logger had been that the powerful buffalo milk hot cakes could only do good for his loggers, sure as he was they could not give his men too much red blood or make them too hellishly He, Paul Bunyan had yet failed to reckon on the dire effects that the virile food might have on weaker men. He had given no thought to the scissor-bills who herded and milked the buffalos. Throughout the fall these men had shown nothing but their usual tameness and amiability; during the Hard Winter they had shivered silently by their camp fires; but now they began to show that the powerful food was having a terrific effect on them. Many of the buffalos had died during the cold spell, and the scissor-bills had made pants from the shaggy hides. Some of the high-behinds had frozen also, and the scissor-bills had taken their skins and made tall, flapping hats of them. Colds had afflicted them during the winter, and for convenience they had tied their handkerchiefs around their necks. They took a fancy to this fashion and let the handkerchiefs remain after their colds were gone. Their next outbreak of virility was to unravel one of Babe's halter ropes and arrange a long little rope with a noose-end from each thread of it. They practiced throwing nooses over the posts of the buffalo corral fence until they became quite expert in casting them. The scissor-bills then caught wild horses with their ropes and broke them for riding. They got to be a crazy, noisy gang after this, and Paul Bunyan began to notice them as they rode through the sage trees, yipping shrilly. And then one morning they came to the hero-leader and requested that they be called "scissor-bills" no longer, but "buffalo boys" instead. Paul Bunyan admired their shaggy pants, their neckerchiefs and their tall hats, and he thoughtlessly consented to their wishes. He did not feel that the scissor-bills had it in them to become real He Men, but he was not a man to discourage worthy ambitions.

But Paul Bunyan soon had reason to remember one of his old sayings, that the road from the palace of generosity leads through a forest of perils. His one kindly gesture towards the lowly scissor-bills made them a powerful faction in the He Man country, and a fierce rivalry between them and the loggers soon developed. For they insisted on being called "buffalo boys," and Paul Bunyan's best men saw an intolerable dignity in the title. The buffalo boys painted large B.B.'s on their hats, they painted the letters on the buffalos and on their horses also. At calving time they devised some irons in the shape of double B.'s, and they branded the buffalo calves with these. The buffalo boys grew even bolder; they began to ride among the bunkhouses in the evenings, yipping and yelling at the men who were earnestly preparing for the greatest drive of history.

Such impudence was not long tolerated, of course, and it got so that every morning found buffalo boys mourning for lost ears and doctoring the wounds made by sharp calks. But buffalo milk was running hot in their veins, and their new courage carried them to still greater extremes. One morning when the loggers came to work they found that every sage tree had B.B. burned into its bark. That day the drive was not talked about, for the loggers plotted vengeance as they toiled. This night they turned the buffalos out of the corral, and the buffalo boys were out until morning rounding up the herd. The following night they, in turn, galloped past the bunkhouses and roped every stovepipe that stuck above a roof. They dragged them into the timber and hid them, and the loggers had to dress by cold stoves the next morning. That evening, during milking time, the loggers slipped into the buffalo boys' tents and poured water into their blankets; the next morning the loggers found their boots all filled with ice, for the buffalo boys had played such an evil trick on them during the night. The astonishing audacity of these lowly creatures was not to be longer endured.

Mark Beaucoup and his followers would not listen to the pleas of the moderates that the punishment of the buffalo boys be left until the drive was finished. The bunkhouse cranks had grown savage in the He Man country, and they now threw aside all restraint. They yelled their rage until all the loggers got excited; and in a short time all the bunkhouses were empty, and the loggers were marching on the buffalo boys' camp. They closed in silently and attacked with lion-like ferocity. The buffalo boys, their timidity vanished now, stood up and gave vigorous battle. When Paul Bunyan stepped into camp and called, "Roll out, my bullies! Roll out for the big drive!" he got no answer. Then he looked toward the buffalo corral and saw a sea of dust surging over miles of the valley. All over the gray surface of this sea fists were flashing up as whitecaps jump and fall on wind-blown waters. Paul Bunyan leaped toward the scene of conflict.

But the great logger's endeavors to separate the fighters were vain. When he got among them he had to stand still for fear of trampling them; the buffalo boys and the loggers crowded against his feet as they clinched and punched, and some of them rolled under the arches of his boots. He ordered the factions to their camps, but they would not hear. Then Paul Bunyan bellowed. The battlers were all thrown down, but they bounced up fighting. Ears and fingers were now flying up everywhere in the dust, and the leader was alarmed by the thought that a more fearful condition was in sight than even poetry had threatened to bring about. The ferocious masculinity that his two gangs of men had got from the virile hot cakes would leave him with camps of earless and fingerless cripples. Disaster loomed over the logging industry once more.

His brain racing like a dynamo as it conceived desperate ideas, Paul Bunyan failed to notice at first that the dust sea had mysteriously vanished, though the struggle still raged. Not until he saw all the loggers and buffalo boys stop fighting and throw themselves on the ground, each man clutching at his own legs and howling with fear, did he realize that an unnatural happening was saving his men from exterminating each other. Every frantic fighter was howling, "My boots is runnin' over with blood! I'm a goner sure!"

Paul Bunyan heard them with amazement, and with amazement he gazed on the valleys and hills. A thin mist was rising from the ground. It vanished soon; then Paul Bunyan saw that rain was springing from the earth, falling up—if the term may be used—for many feet, and then dropping back again. The first shower had rained up the legs of the buffalo boys and the loggers, and they had mistaken it for blood. Now they were still rolling, moaning and bellowing. Paul Bunyan's amazement soon passed, for he was accustomed to unnatural seasons, climates and happenings. He was all delight that the unusual rain had stopped the battle, and he saw no harm in it yet; he did not know that this was a rain of such tremendous force that it had poured through the earth.

For this was the Spring That the Rain Came Up From China. . . .

Harder and harder the rain came up, and it was not long before the loggers and the buffalo boys opened their eyes and stopped their yelling. They were soaked all over now, and they knew that the sudden warm wetness of their legs had not been from blood. Paul Bunyan laughed through his beard, which was high and dry, when he saw his men begin to run for the camp to get out of the strange rain. The fight was forgotten, and the logging industry was saved.

The ground hissed as the rain came up with new violence. The drops became streams . . . the streams doubled . . . trebled . . . and in an hour there were ten streams where only one had come up before. The rain became a downpour—or an uppour, rather. It got the proportions of a cloudburst—or, perhaps it should be said, an earthburst. The hillocks and hummocks had forests of small fountains. In the low places pools were forming, and these boiled with muddy foam as myriads of miniature geysers spurted up from them.

Paul Bunyan, feeling great satisfaction over the happy ending the rain had given to the conflict between his two tribes, did not at first realize the danger to his recent logging operations from the unnatural rain. When he did think of the logs piled along the river he ran swiftly to look after them. He was too late. Moron River had already risen far over its banks, and all of the brown, peeled sage logs, the fruit of a season's labor, were now tossing on a muddy flood. The rain was coming up through the river in sheets; torrents were pouring into the stream from every small gully. The water was rising at the rate of a foot a minute. It would soon be in the camp grounds. Paul Bunyan made no attempt to retrieve his lost logs; he now rushed to save his camp.

The loggers had turned their bunkhouses upside down, because the rain had come up through the floors. They had then set their bunks on the rafters, and they were now snug and dry, for the rain could not pour up through the tight roofs. The loggers left their cozy quarters reluctantly when they heard Paul Bunyan call, "Roll out or roll up!" They could imagine nothing more disagreeable than its raining up their pants' legs, rough He Men though they were. But when they saw the river rising in rushing waves they did not need Paul Bunyan's orders to make them run for the cookhouse. Johnny Inkslinger was wiring the camp office and Babe's stable to the mammoth building, and the Big Swede was making his fastest moves since the Dakota days as he hitched up the blue ox. Paul Bunyan roared, "Yay, Babe!" just as the river waters thundered into camp. The blue ox plunged towards the Cascade Hills. He dragged the three greatest buildings of the camp and all the loggers to safety. But the bunkhouses were rolling over and over in the flood.

Paul Bunyan and his two aides saved two of the buffalo boys, two buffalos, two high-behinds, two tigermunks, two blond wolves, and two wild horses from the raging waters, but all other life perished.

For forty days and forty nights it rained up from China, and then the flood receded. Paul Bunyan and his men looked down from the

Cascades and saw that all of the old He Man country had been washed away. It was now a low valley. There was sage in it still, but this sage was only brush. Ridges and buttes of gray rock were all of the old land that remained. There was no longer any logging in the greater part of it. But here on the new slopes of the Cascades was a more cheering sight. For the old land over these slopes had covered a magnificent forest of white pine which was even finer than that around the old home camp. The loggers shouted when they saw it. And was it a tear, that gleam of moisture in Paul Bunyan's beard? If so, it was from his new happiness.

"It's an ill rain," he chuckled, "that brings no logger wood."

The two buffalo boys, like the loggers, still heroic from their virile winter's diet, had come through their ordeal in good shape and the buffalos had slept all the forty days and nights. But the other poor animals! The wild horses were wild no longer; they had become tame and would now eat sugar out of any man's hand. The buffalo boys nicknamed them bronchos. The high-behinds, the blond wolves, and the tigermunks were all cowards at heart, and they had been scared out of twenty years' growth. Not one of them was knee-high to a logger now. The Big Swede made his first and only joke about the tigermunks, who had been scared into the size of chips.

"Tigermunks!" he grinned. "Aye tank these har ban chipmunks!"

And chipmunks they have been called ever since. Paul Bunyan's history does not tell how the high-behinds came to be named jack rabbits, or how the blond wolves came to be named coyotes. No doubt they were also named humorously, for the loggers were gay when the rain no longer came up from China. Anyhow, the old names are no longer used in the He Man's country.

Paul at home [1]

L ucy, Paul Bunyan's cow, was not, so far as we can learn, related in any way to either Babe or Benny. Statements that she was their mother are without basis in fact. The two oxen had been in Paul's possession for a long time before Lucy arrived on the scene.

No reliable data can be found as to the pedigree of this remarkable dairy animal. There are no official records of her butter-fat production nor is it known where or how Paul got her.

Paul always said that Lucy was part Jersey and part wolf. Maybe so.

[1] From *Paul Bunyan*, text and illustrations by W. B. Laughead (Westwood, California: Red River Lumber Co.) pp. 24, 25.

Her actions and methods of living seemed to justify the allegation of wolf ancestry, for she had an insatiable appetite and a roving disposition. Lucy ate everything in sight and could never be fed at the same camp with Babe or Benny. In fact, they quit trying to feed her at all but let her forage her own living. The Winter of the Deep Snow, when even the tallest White Pines were buried, Brimstone Bill outfitted Lucy with a set of Babe's old snowshoes and a pair of green goggles and turned her out to graze on the snowdrifts. At first she had some trouble with the new foot gear but once she learned to run them and shift gears without wrecking herself, she answered the call of the limitless snowfields and ran away all over North America until Paul decorated her with a bell borrowed from a buried church.

In spite of short rations she gave enough milk to keep six men busy skimming the cream. If she had been kept in a barn and fed regularly she might have made a milking record. When she fed on the evergreen trees and her milk got so strong of White Pine and Balsam that the men used it for cough medicine and liniment, they quit serving the milk on the table and made butter out of it. By using this butter to grease the logging roads when the snow and ice thawed off, Paul was able to run his logging sleds all summer.

The family life of Paul Bunyan, from all accounts, has been very happy. A charming glimpse of Mrs. Bunyan is given by Mr. E. S. Shepard of Rhinelander, Wis., who tells of working in Paul's camp on Round River in '62, the Winter of the Black Snow. Paul put him wheeling prune pits away from the cook camp. After he had worked at this job for three months Paul had him haul them back again as Mrs. Bunyan, who was cooking at the camp, wanted to use them to make the hot fires necessary to cook her famous soft nosed pancakes.

Mrs. Bunyan at this time used to call the men to dinner by blowing into a woodpecker hole in an old hollow stub that stood near the door. In this stub there was a nest of owls that had one short wing and flew in circles. When Mr. Shepard made a sketch of Paul, Mrs. Bunyan, with wifely solicitude for his appearance, parted Paul's hair with a handaxe and combed it with an old cross-cut saw.

From other sources we have fragmentary glimpses of Jean, Paul's youngest son. When Jean was three weeks old he jumped from his cradle one night and seizing an axe, chopped the four posts out from under his father's bed. This incident greatly tickled Paul, who used to brag about it to anyone who would listen to him. "The boy is going to be a great logger some day," he would declare with fatherly pride.

The last we heard of Jean he was working for a lumber outfit in the South, lifting logging trains past one another on a single track railroad.

Thomas Robinson Hazard (1797–1886), a prosperous and public-spirited Rhode Island Quaker, was one of the greatest of American story-tellers, beyond question. His *Jonny-Cake Papers* went out of print more than half a century ago; a handsome edition was privately printed in 1915, but copies of this are not easily obtained today.

"Shepherd Tom," as his relatives and friends called him, after one of his numerous successful activities, regarded his anecdotes as mere trivial entertainment, but no one can read them without feeling the man's tremendous zest. Emancipated reminiscence was his forte, emancipated, that is, from any hampering bonds of fact. He leads his audience on mischievously, breaks up his best yarns with deliberately perverse parentheses, glides from strictest truth to wildest lie, and has a wonderful time. So does the reader.

An interesting criticism[1]

Even before the Boston brown bread had become utterly worthless by the introduction of Western corn meal, made often of damaged corn, and tasteless Western rye to match, I remember bringing home with me, after a visit to that city, a loaf of the famous material, that my children might compare its quality with our family bread. They were all delighted at the prospect of tasting the famous luxury they had heard so much of; but after the first mouthful, not one of them seemed disposed to take a second. After breakfast I took the loaf and placed it in the trough for an old Berkshire sow to eat, that I knew was very fond of our Rhineinjun[2] bread, a piece of which I used almost daily to treat her with. The old creature—which had not been fed that morning—dove her nose greedily into it; but at the first taste she dropped the morsel, and regarding me askance, with a suspicious and sinister expression in her eye, she hastened to a stagnant, muddy pool in the corner of the yard, and rinsed her mouth.

---

[1] From Thomas Robinson Hazard: *The Jonny-Cake Papers of "Shepherd Tom"* (Boston: Printed for the Subscribers; 1915), p. 28.
[2] Rye and Indian (meal).

Precocious[1]

O ld nurse Gardiner, after making the remark that children were now born with their eyes wide open, instead of closed like kittens, as formerly, told me of an instance wherein she went as a three weeks' nurse of a young devil who was born at nine o'clock of a Saturday evening, whom she observed at daylight the next morning, criticising the portrait of his mother that hung on the wall opposite, evidently making odious comparisons between it and the lady at his side, to whom the ten-hour-old gentleman had condescended to surrender the occupancy for a limited period of a small portion of his bed. When the precocious chap caught nurse Gardiner's eye, she said he clapped the fore-finger of his left hand on the side of his nose and with a knowing wink pointed first to the picture and then to his mother, with his right hand, and signified in pantomime, that he considered the former a very much flattered likeness.

Themillboy[2]

P hillis always put the parched corn in the gumwood mortar and set Themillboy to pounding it as he sat in the corner in an armed easy-chair. Whether sleeping or waking, when Themillboy once began pounding he never ceased until Phillis touched his right arm, when the mortar was emptied and again replenished with parched corn. Phillis touched Themillboy's left arm, when he would again begin to pound. On one occasion Phillis forgot her no-cake[3] and went to bed, leaving Themillboy pounding. In the morning she found him fast asleep and still at work.

---

[1] T. R. Hazard, op. cit., p. 54.
[2] Ibid., p. 60. Mr. Hazard insisted on this (phonetic) spelling of this particular phrase.
[3] A kind of corn bread. The recipe had been learned from the Narragansett Indians.

It's the seasonin' [1]

I cannot recall to mind the exact time when a young friend of my grandfather chanced to pass a night at our house. He was fond of shooting, and prided himself on his skill as a sportsman, and his discriminating taste in respect to the quality of game and the pleasures of the table. He arrived past the middle of the afternoon, and shortly after went out with his pointer and gun to reconnoitre. After an hour's absence he returned with two birds in his bag, the one a woodcock, the other a crow. My grandfather handed the birds to Abe and told him to prepare the woodcock for Phillis, that she might roast it for the young gentleman's breakfast, he intending to leave the next morning at an early hour. Abe, who as I have related before, was a begotten son of the Devil, took in, as he supposed, the situation at once, arguing in his own mind that as the young man would be up and gone in the morning before any of the "great room" folks were stirring, he might safely keep the woodcock for his own delectation, and have the less fragrant bird roasted for the stranger guest. In the meantime my grandfather had given orders to Phillis about getting his young friend's breakfast at an early hour, with a charge that she should do her best in the matter of roasting the woodcock. Accordingly Phillis was up at dawn of day, and taking the game bird, which she thought had a wonderful suspicious look, from the larder, she proceeded to stuff and anoint it for roasting, after her very best fashion, Abe in the meantime turning the spit as usual, although as Phillis several times remarked to him, he seemed to be in an uncommon grimacing humor. It would have done a philanthropist's heart good to have seen the youthful New York sportsman enjoy the game he had bagged, every mouthful of which he swallowed with a gusto, picking the bones and grinding the smaller ones with his teeth until there was scarcely a vestige of the bird left in the dish. When he took leave of Phillis and Abe, he handed each of them a quarter of a dollar and remarked that he had never tasted so exquisite a dish of any kind of game before in all his life.

---

[1] T. R. Hazard, op. cit., p. 69.

Evidence[1]

I disremember the name of a burly descendant of one of my grandfather's great-grandfather's negroes, who used to spend his Christmas holidays at our house. The fellow would open a window opposite the big snowbank and then lay himself flat on his face on the floor beneath it, and raise his head, arms, shoulders, feet, legs, thighs, and all, entirely off the floor, so that he would just bear on a small part of the middle of his belly, and then begin to work the muscles that lie contiguous to the navel until, through their force and action alone, he would fetch a sudden spring and throw himself full length through the open window without touching its sides or sill, and bury himself entirely out of sight in the snow-bank outside. I can't say that I ever saw this feat performed with my own eyes, but then I remember seeing the snow-bank and heard Mose tell all about seeing it done, whose word I then had, and still have, as implicit faith in as I have in that of Moses of the Pentateuch.

At one puff[2]

Some faint idea of Potter's power of blowing, and consequently of loud laughing, may be guessed at by the fact that one day whilst a little snipper-snapper who sat about ten feet back of him, in the General Assembly, then in session at Little Rest, was speaking, he made some saucy remarks touching the South County, when Potter, without leaving his seat, merely turned his head around, and at one puff blew the little fellow clean out of an open window, although the impertinent chap could not have weighed much less than seventy-five pounds avoirdupois. It was a two-story window, and the poor fellow might have cracked his skull were it not that in his fall he lighted directly on top of old Prince Robinson's gingerbread and apple stand.

---

[1] Ibid., pp. 84–5.
[2] Ibid., pp. 116–17.

Timothy Crumb's courtship[1]

S peaking of Deacon Brown brings to my mind Timothy Crumb's courtship of his daughter, Sally.

Tim had hired by the month to Squire Champlin, who lived on a farm a little north-west of where the Kingston depot is now situated. Tim had taken a shine to Sally, and after three or four sittings up with her, had engaged to wait on her to meeting the next Sunday. So Tim got up early in the morning, and after getting through his chores and breakfast, he thought before dressing up to wait on Sal, he would go to the river and wash off. Accordingly he went down and undressed, hanging his red shirt, which was a little sweaty, in a swamp blueberry bush to dry while he was in the water. It so happened that Deacon Brown's old bull Wrinkle was lying on a little knoll near by, unnoticed by Tim. The sight of Tim's red shirt was not at all pleasing to old Wrinkle, who now got up and began to paw the ground and bellow. This did not, however, move Tim, as he had heard Wrinkle making pretenses of the kind several times before. Bime'by, however, old Wrinkle made for the red shirt, and before Tim could interfere, the enraged beast tossed it into the air and then stamped it into the ground, and when Tim started to the rescue of his undergarment, the old sarpent, not apparently recognizing him with his clothes off, gave chase to the naked biped, following Tim on the run, bellowing and shaking his horns as he went, right into the river. Things began to look rather squally, and just as the old varmint seemed getting ready to make a dive with both horns set for action, Tim seized the branches of a swamp white oak that hung over the water, and swung himself on a big limb out of reach of old Wrinkle, who now placed himself just beneath where Tim sat, roaring at the top of his voice and making sundry other threatening demonstrations. Tim, however, felt safe where he was, so far as Wrinkle was concerned, although he had some misgivings whether or not Sal Brown might not, in consequence of his enforced neglect to keep his engagement, permit that other fellow, Jim Arlington, who, too, was after her, to wait on her to hear Elder Northup preach. All at once Tim heard a buzzing over his head, and looking up, saw, to his horror, not more than two yards above his head, a hornets' nest, nigh upon as big as a bushel basket, covered all over with the worst kind of black hornets, who, he could see, were getting ready to attack him. Tim took in the situation at once, and

---

[1] Ibid., pp. 119–22. Compare this with "Mike Fink in a Tight Place," pp. 542–6 above, which Shepherd Tom evidently just rewrote, greatly improving it.

saw plainly that there was but one chance for him, desperate as it was. So seizing, with both hands, the limb on which he sat, he lowered himself quickly down a-straddle of old Wrinkle's neck, seizing a horn in each hand at the same moment, the better to enable him to retain his uneasy position. Just as he alighted on the neck of old Wrinkle, about two quarts of hornets dropped on Tim's bare neck and shoulders, about half a pint of which slopped over and fell straight into old Wrinkle's left ear. This did not help matters at all, but made the bull madder than ever, who now started off on the run for the Deacon's house, plunging and roaring as he went. Sally Brown had dressed herself to go to meeting, and was waiting in the great-room for Tim, when, hearing old Wrinkle making such a catouse, she stepped to the front door to see what was the matter. Just as Sally with her arms akimbo had placed herself in the open door-way, Wrinkle and Tim had reached a high chestnut rail fence that was within two rods of where she stood. Sal recognized Wrinkle at first sight, but was somewhat doubtful of the identity of Tim, as she exclaimed: "For the Lord's sake, is that you, Tim, or the dev—" She meant to say devil, and would have done so had she been allowed time, but before Sal got the last syllable out, old Wrinkle made a desperate dive through the fence, making kindling splinters of the big chestnut rails, and ejecting Tim with such velocity from his neck and horns, that, after three complete somersaults in the heavens, the nether parts of his body struck Sally Brown about midships, a big toe just grazing each side of her diaphragm as they passed, more like a forked thunder-bolt or streak of lightning than anything with human legs, and knocked her clean through the kitchen door, where she fell flat with her face towards the ceiling. As for Tim, he gathered himself up without saying a word, and rushed out of the back door into the big swamp near by, and pursuing a circuitous route in the bushes, recovered his red shirt and other clothes, and then made a bee-line west. A week afterwards, Jim Knowles, who had been out West to reconnoitre, reported that on his return from the Genesee country, in crossing the Connecticut river below Hartford, he passed Tim paddling a white pine log with a piece of bark, in an opposite direction, which was the last ever heard of Timothy Crumb in Narragansett.

Local pride[1]

I disremember the exact day when he [old Cyrus French] related of a winter evening to the company that usually gathered at Joe Runnell's, a remarkable adventure he had whilst on a sleigh ride, wherein his horse ran away, and after breaking the harness all to tatters, left him and the sleigh buried in a snow-bank full ten feet deep. After extricating himself, he proceeded on foot some distance, looking, without success, for assistance, until he came to some men mowing grass in a field, who went with him and helped lift the sleigh out of the snow-drift and reinstate his horse. After Cyrus had finished his story, Capt. Bill Rodman, who happened to be present, remarked in a way he had, "Stranger, I never saw you before, and I don't know as I shall ever see you again, but this I will say, that I should like to know whether grass is grown fit for the scythe in Massachusetts when snow lies all around in banks ten feet deep, as you have stated?" "I stated no such thing," retorted Cyrus, "the snow-bank was in Massachusetts, as I said, but the men were mowing more than a mile this side of the Rhode Island line!"

Rather tough[2]

I will just here say that when I was a boy, I used to hear a good deal about a wolf that came to his death in what is to this day called the "Wolf Bog," on the north border of Peace Dale. The story ran after this wise: A big gray wolf gave chase to an old slabsided, long-bodied, sharp-nosed sow of what was then called the land-shark breed, which kind of swine the late William French, of Kingston, always contended made the best pork and hams of any breed of swine, which I, too, think is the fact. Just before the old sow reached the edge of the aforesaid bog, the wolf grabbed her with his teeth, by the end of her tail, which caused the terrified creature to increase her speed so marvelously that, as old Jim Newberry, who was cutting wood near by, said, neither the sow nor wolf could be separately discerned with the naked eye, they somewhat resembled a streak of lightning as

---

[1] Ibid., p. 141.
[2] Ibid., pp. 346–7.

they passed along, only rather quicker in motion; so quick, in fact, that the terror-stricken old sow in her heedless course plunged directly through a maple tree two feet in diameter that stood in her way, dragging the gray wolf after her more than half his length, when he was caught by the rebound of the maple just forward of his hips and so held secure until Jim Newberry (whom I used to know) came forward and dispatched him with his wood axe. This story may be rather tough for people of contracted minds to swallow, much less digest; but yet it would seem to rest on a foundation, else why has the boggy swale where the wolf came to his end always to this day been known as the *wolf bog?*

Natural high spirits give the American story-teller a special humorous drive; what about induced high spirits? One cannot easily judge the product of an imagination that has been stimulated by alcohol. How much does the patient (so to speak) remember afterward? He may be in doubt about this himself; all reminiscence of alcoholic states suffers from this paradox. Suffers? Sometimes it is an advantage, of sorts, as in Arthur Train's narrative of a night when, as an undergraduate, he got drunk on principle.

"The fastest funeral on record" cannot be waved aside as inspired by alcohol; even as fable, which one hopes it is, the yarn is nothing but outrageous exuberance—of the type that people of other cultures hold against Americans as a bitter reproach. But that is taking it too seriously.

As for Sauerkraut Downs, that is the sort of incident, also, which makes Europeans shake their heads dubiously and mutter: "Americans, Americans!"

These wild outbursts are predominantly masculine, but the American woman sometimes obeys the impulse to leave all sober fact in the lurch. If the woman in question is both a wit and a wag—well, read the feather-boa story!

Under the influence[1]

It was not until my senior year that I so far escaped from my Puritan inhibitions as to conclude that, simply as a matter of human experience, I ought to get thoroughly "soused" at least once before leaving college. I had won second money in the Boylston Prize-Speaking Contest and, being in funds, took advantage of my opportunity by going into Boston alone and purchasing a box at an opera given by the Castle Square Opera Company. Sitting by myself in state while the curtain was up, for the occasion was too serious for company, I descended between the acts to the bar, where I proceeded to work my way through "The Barkeeper's Handbook"—beginning with A, for

---

[1] From Arthur Train: *Puritan's Progress* (New York: Charles Scribner's Sons; 1931), pp. 355–8.

ale, B, for burgundy, C, for champagne, etc.—until by the end of the performance I had achieved a fairly large percentage of the alphabet. Yet for some strange reason nothing of what I imbibed had the slightest effect upon me, one poison probably acting as the antidote for another.

It was moonlight and, having nowhere in particular to go, I strolled down to the old Adam's House bar on lower Boylston Street, where for a time I continued my alphabetical career, to be presently interrupted by an ingratiating person who, introducing himself as "General D'Olier of Virginia," invited me to share a bottle of claret. During the consumption of the bottle, which was quickly followed by another, the general, who had instantly formed a pronounced attachment for me, confided not only most of his family history but the fact that he was considered the best shot south of Mason and Dixon's line. There was seemingly no reason why this should have aroused any spirit of emulation on my part, yet I remember very well that it did and that it led me in turn to speak boastfully of my own marksmanship.

Accordingly, the general and I, arm in arm, each carrying a partially emptied bottle, sallied forth shortly after midnight, seeking for a place to demonstrate the pre-eminence of our marksmanship. I was still feeling fit as a fiddle—a well-tuned fiddle—being now the better off for perhaps fifteen or sixteen assorted drinks largely constituted of alcohol. On Tremont Row we found an open-air shooting-gallery still obligingly open—rabbits whirling around the periphery of a circle, ducks swimming and suddenly disappearing, silver balls dancing upon jets of water. In spite of the fact that the general had shown a marked inclination to lean upon my shoulder when walking down Tremont Row, he now took off his coat and hat, selected a Flaubert rifle, and proceeded with a good deal of dexterity to knock the silver ball off the jet fourteen times in succession, missing only upon the fifteenth and last shot. It was now my turn.

Solemnly General D'Olier watched me bring the rifle to my shoulder. "Pop!" Down went the ball!

"Hang it!" I muttered. "I *must* be sober! What is the use of going to all this trouble!" And that I was nowhere near the state which I desired to attain was demonstrated by the fact that, without the slightest expectation of doing so, I shot the ball down, not fourteen, but fifteen, times. I did not know whether to be disappointed at being so incontrovertibly sober or pleased at having won over so redoubtable a general, but on turning around to receive his congratulations I found that he had disappeared.

The event, however, that was to make the night epochal in the Train family had yet to come. Minus my general and also my hat I managed to catch the "last car" for Cambridge, which then left Scollay Square at 2 A.M., where I recall regaling my fellow passengers by appropriate selections from the "Siege of Lucknow," my prize rendition.

"Mine? Yes, a mine! Countermine!"

I crouched, an imaginary sapper listening for the invisible pick, then dug furiously with a phantom spade. I was possessed by the thrill of battle. Bullets fell upon and around me, cannons roared, bugles sounded, the wounded were carried off—"Millions of musket bullets, and thousands of cannon balls—" Hark! What was that? The cheers of the relieving column? Havelock! Thank God! Thank God!

"Saved! We are saved!—Saved by the valor of Havelock! Saved by the blessing of Heaven!—And ever aloft on the palace roof the old banner of England blew!"

Sobbing, I was at last ejected by the conductor in Harvard Square, and still holding my own, worked my way across the deserted yard. A single lamp gleamed like a friendly beacon from one of the windows of Hollis Hall—my own, I concluded. My thoughtful roommate, having arrived home before me, must have placed it there. "A light in the window for me, Mother!"

I had some difficulty in crossing the yard owing to the tangle of wire fences which had unaccountably sprung up and which I had never before observed. As fast as I got my legs over one I found myself confronted by another! And the steps of Hollis were so obstructed that I was obliged to negotiate them upon my hands and knees. Crouching like my "sapper" I slowly ascended the stairs amid a furious hail of bullets and cannon balls, until I reached a door beneath which shone a light.

"Saved! We are saved! Saved by the valor of Havelock! Saved by the blessing of Heaven!"

Still on all fours I butted my head against the door and pushed it open with my nose. To my bewilderment a fat man, in shirt sleeves and eye shade, was sitting at his desk, before a huge pile of blue books. He looked up good-naturedly and nodded.

"Good evening," he remarked in an ordinary conversational tone. "How do you do?"

It was Professor Byron Satterlee Hurlbut, later dean of Harvard College. I recognized, although I did not know him.

"Good evening, professor," I said. "I am very, very tired."

Professor Hurlbut regarded me searchingly.

"I should say that you were very, very drunk!" he replied. "Come in and lie down on my sofa for a while."

Although I knew his diagnosis to be erroneous, I was not offended. The fat man seemed a good fellow, and I decided to accept his invitation.

616

"The sofa is over here—not there," explained the professor as he assisted me to adjust my legs. "Rather a rough night?"

"Millions of musket bullets and thousands of cannon balls!" I replied, and then passed out entirely.

I had a vague recollection of being later half carried across the yard to my own room and of being put to bed by the fat man, whom I insisted upon calling "Havelock" instead of Hurlbut. Subsequently we became intimate friends.

The fastest funeral on record [1]

I had just crossed the long bridge leading from Boston to Cambridgeport, and was plodding my dusty way on foot through that not very agreeable suburb on a sultry afternoon in July, with a very creditable thunder-cloud coming up in my rear, when a stout elderly gentleman, with a mulberry face, a brown coat, and pepper-and-salt smalls, reined up his nag, and after learning that I was bound for Old Cambridge, politely invited me to take a seat beside him in the little sort of tax-cart he was driving. Nothing loth, I consented, and we were soon *en route*. The mare he drove was a very peculiar animal. She had few good points to the eye, being heavy-bodied, hammer-headed, thin in the shoulders, bald-faced, and rejoicing in a little stump of a tail which was almost entirely innocent of hair. But there were "lots of muscle," as Major Longbow says, in her hind quarters.

"She ain't no Wenus, sir," said my new acquaintance, pointing with his whip to the object of my scrutiny,—"but handsome is that handsome does. Them's my sentiments. She's a rum 'un to look at, but a good 'un to go."

"Indeed?"

"Yes, *Sir!* That there mare, sir, has made good time—I may say, *very* good time before the hearse."

"Before the hearse?"

"Before the hearst! S'pose you never heard of *burying a man on time!* I'm a sexton, sir, and undertaker—Jack Crossbones, at your service—'Daddy Crossbones' they call me at Porter's."

"Ah! I understand. Your mare ran away with the hearse."

"Ran away! A child could hold her. Oh! yes, of course she ran away," added the old gentleman, looking full in my face with a very quizzical expression, and putting the fore finger of his right hand on the right side of his party-colored proboscis.

---

[1] From Francis A. Durivage and George P. Burnham: *Stray Subjects Arrested and Bound Over* (Philadelphia: Carey & Hart; 1848), pp. 29–33.

"My dear sir," said I, "you have excited my curiosity amazingly, and I should esteem it a particular favor if you would be a little less oracular and a little more explicit."

"I don't know as I'd ought to tell you," said my new acquaintance, very slowly and tantalizingly, "If you was one of these here writing chaps, you might poke it in the 'Spirit of the Times,' and then it would be all day with me. But I don't care if I do make a clean breast of it. Honour bright, you know!"

"Of course."

"Well, then, I live a piece up beyond Old Cambridge—you can see our steeple off on a hill to the right, when we get a little further. Well, one day I had a customer—(he was carried off by the typhus)—which had to be toted into town—cause why? he had a vault there. So I rubbed down the old mare and put her in the fills. Ah! Sir! that critter knows as much as a Injun, and more than a Nigger. She's as sober'as be d—d when she gets the shop—that's what I call the hearse —behind her. You would not think she was a three-minute nag, to look at her. Well, sir, as luck would have it, by a sort of providential inspiration, the day before, I'd took off the old wooden springs and set the body on elliptics. For I thought it a hard case that a gentle-man who'd been riding easy all his life, should go to his grave on wooden springs. Ah! I deal well by my customers. I thought of patent boxes to the wheels, but *I* couldn't afford it, and the parish are so mighty stingy.

"Well, I got him in, and led off the string—fourteen hacks, and a dearborn wagon at the tail of the funeral. We made a fine show. As luck would have it, just as we came abreast of Porter's, out slides that eternal torment, BILL SIKES, in his new trotting sulky, with the brown horse that he bought for a fast crab, and *is* mighty good for a rush, but hain't got nigh so much bottom as the mare. Bill's light weight, and his sulky's a mere feather. Well, sir, Bill came up along-side, and walked his horse a bit. He looked at the mare and then at me, and then he winked. Then he looked at his nag and put his tongue in his cheek, and winked. I looked straight ahead, and only said to myself, 'Cuss you, Bill Sikes.' By and by, he let his horse slide. He travelled about a hundred yards, and then held up till I came abreast, and then he winked and bantered me again. It was d—d aggravating. Says I to myself, says I,—'that's twice you've done it, my buzzum friend and sweet-scented shrub—but you doesn't do that 'ere again.' The third time he bantered me, I let him have it. It was only saying 'Scat, you brute!' and she was off—that mare. He had all the odds, you know, for I was toting a two hundred pounder, and he ought to have beat me like breaking sticks, now hadn't he? He had me at the first brush, for I told you the brown horse was a mighty fast one for a little ways. But soon I lapped him. I had no whip and he could use his string—but he had his hands full. Side by side away we went. Rattle-te-bang! crack! buz! thump! And I afraid of losing my customer on the road. But I was more afraid of losing the race. The reputation of the old mare was at a stake, and I swore she should have a fair chance. Went so fast that the posts and rails by the roadside looked like a log fence. The old church and the new one, and the colleges, spun past like Merry Andrews. The hackmen did not know what the —— was to pay, and afraid of not being in at the death, they put the string onto their teams, and came clattering on behind as if Satan had kicked 'em on eend. Some of the mourners was sporting characters, and they craned out of the carriage windows and waved their handkerchiefs. The President of Harvard College himself, inspired by the scene, took off his square tile as I passed his house, and waving it three times around his head, cried, 'Go it, Boots!' It is a fact. And I beat him, sir! I beat him in three miles, a hundred rods. He gin it up, sir, in despair.

"His horse was off his feed for a week, and when he took to corn again he wasn't worth a straw. It was acknowledged on all hands to be the fastest funeral on record, though I say it as shouldn't. I'm an undertaker, sir, and I never yet was overtaken."

On subsequent inquiry at Porter's, where the sporting sexton left me, I found that his story was strictly true in all the main particulars. A terrible rumpus was kicked up about the race, but Crossbones swore lustily that the mare had run away—that he had sawed away two inches of her lip in trying to hold her up, and that he could not have done otherwise, unless he had run her into a fence and spilled his 'customer' into the ditch. If anyone expects to die anywhere near the sexton's *diggings,* I can assure him that the jolly old boy is still alive and kicking, the very 'Ace of Hearts' and 'Jack of Spades,' and that now both patent boxes and elliptic springs render his professional conveyance the easiest running thing on the road.

Sauerkraut Downs[1]

DAILY RACING AT SAUERKRAUT DOWNS;
G I HARDBOOTS SET UP HORSE TRACK.
Course in Germany is Complete, Except for
Rails, Even to Mutuels—Soldiers Ride
Mounts Borrowed from Hungarians.
BY FREDERICK GRAHAM
By Wireless to The New York Times.

Sauerkraut Downs, Germany, May 16—Big Red, the 6 or 8-year-old gelding that carries the black and blue colors of I Company's Stable, won the initial running of the Sauerkraut Downs Futurity for 4, 5, 6, 7, 8 and 9-year-olds yesterday before 1,000 soldiers of Maj. Gen. James Gavin's Eighty-second (All-American) Airborne Division.

Big Red broke first from the barrier, showed a lot of early foot and at the halfway mark was well out in front of eleven other entries and won going away. Naturally, he set a record for this half-mile classic, and although everyone agrees that it was a fine record, the exact time seems to have been forgotten.

Situated in a sandy wasteland a few miles from Ludwigslust, where the Eighty-second headquarters are, this plant was set up by the 505th Regiment of the oldest air-borne division in the American Army. It is the brainchild of several men—perhaps many, many men —but chief among them seems to be Maj. Walter C. Delong of Battle Creek, Mich., Capt. Charles Patterson of Pawtucket, R. I., and Pvt. Edward J. Pareti of 225 Sullivan Street, New York. All three deny vigorously that they ever made book in civilian life.

Major Delong is the Matt Winn of the plant. He serves as handicapper, odds-maker, judge, steward and chief of the pari-mutuel set-up. Captain Patterson is the official starter, and Private Pareti has charge of the actual betting.

The track has only white tape for a rail and because its bed is three or four inches of sand, it is just a bit slow. The horses are those taken from a Hungarian outfit that surrendered to the Eighty-second Division several days ago. Naturally, the jockeys are GI's—paratroopers and gliderborne infantrymen.

The track has been operating six days now. The attendance is high and the betting heavy. The biggest day's handle so far is said to be $10,000.

---

[1] From the *New York Times*, May 17, 1945.

The odds are fixed by the betting and the "tote" board shows odds up to the time the betting booths close.

There are two windows at which one can bet any amount, win or place. There is no show window because that would take more figuring than anyone cares to tackle.

Tickets and programs are printed by the public relations outfit of Pvt. Joe Stanger. The jockeys are weighed in on scales taken from a local bakery. Incidental music is furnished now and then by members of the regiment and beer is served free.

The only irregularities noticeable are that a jockey is allowed to ride with a ticket in his boot, and there are no saliva tests for the horses—or the man.

As Private Pareti, Pfc. Duane Van Weert of 33–11 148th Street, Flushing, Queens, N. Y., and Pfc. Michael Bradford of 1 University Place, New York, put it, "It isn't exactly Belmont Park, but it'll do till we get back there."

The horses have such names as Harpo, Chico, Groucho, Big Red, Old Bones and Twenty Grand and some even have four shoes. Harpo, who won a race the other day, lacks one but it does not seem to bother him.

The longest odds paid so far were 50 to 1. In a race of twelve entries only one horse finished. Some bolted, others got balky and a few simply quit.

The leading jockey is Pvt. Johnny Strenth.

If the outfit does not move, everyone in it is looking forward to the running of Sauerkraut Derby and the Sauerkraut Preakness soon. They may even run both the same day—that is how indifferent the airborne troops are to the dead hand of tradition.

The feather boa[1]

Years ago, when large feather boas were in style, Beatrice Herford (sister of Oliver[2] and a diseuse in her own right) was invited to a house party on Long Island, where, to her disgust, she found herself assigned to share a room with a fluffy young deb. She decided to get rid of her roommate, and, to that end, withdrew early from the party that first evening. When the deb came upstairs, Bea was already in bed. She opened proceedings by asking her roommate whether she

---

[1] As told to me by Samuel Hopkins Adams.
[2] Oliver Herford (1863–1935), witty American writer of light verse.

knew anything of the theory of evolution. Very little; in fact, the deb knew very little about anything. Bea proceeded with a short but vivid account of man's descent from the apes, and concluded: "I am, myself, an unhappy victim of the law of evolution. I have a tail." And, throwing aside the bedclothes, she revealed in all its lifelike sinuosity, the long boa. Exit the deb, with shrieks, to return no more.

BOOK VII

HARDY PERENNIALS

[623]

HARDY PERENNIALS: *Favorite lies, wandering*

"pieces," hoaxes, local characters,

America's recurrent yarns

A GOOD many American stories travel about the land, changing their personages and backgrounds, but easily recognizable by their simple plots; stigmatized by the critical as "chestnuts," but loved, decorated, and repeated by the majority, climbing or descending the social scale, from corner store to barber-shop to country-club and back again, related by the less imaginative members of story-telling groups only to be topped by the more imaginative. Sometimes only the diction and the geography change; consider, for example, a recent migrant as it appears in Alabama and in Massachusetts. In essence it seems to savor of New England—but who can say? Miss Early told it in print before Mr. Lomax did, and her version is given first.

The oldest and most popular of America's migrant yarns is probably the plot that may be called, in its simplest form, "two with one shot." But it is seldom that simple as actually told. Two victims are hardly enough for a boastful hunter, nor is a single type of game sufficiently amazing. The haul grows, the story likewise. Two types are common, the barely credible tale, and that other which no sane person expects any sane person to credit. This yarn is to be found in any part of America where wild creatures or their hunters can be found.

A different type of humorous invention is one that the folklorists have overlooked, because they have not considered (and do not like to contemplate)[1] its rather special type of transmission. This is the "piece" intended for elocutionary presentation. "Speaking pieces" is a little out of style today, but through most of the nineteenth century it flourished both in schools and outside. The pieces themselves might

---

[1] Most folklorists think too exclusively in terms of oral transmission. Thus even so careful a scholar as Miss Louise Pound, in the *Southern Folklore Quarterly* for June 1945, in presenting a ballad taken down from oral rendition, though she correctly identifies it as a lyric from Lewis's novel *Ambrosio, or the Monk*, allows herself to say that the ballad "made the long and perhaps mostly oral journey" to Nebraska "when probably dead except for print in its home region." As a matter of fact, this piece ("Alonzo the Brave and the fair Imogine") is to be found in any number of elocutionists' handbooks of the late nineteenth century. It was far from "dead except for print in its home region."

be literature—Shakespeare was a favorite—but often they were something nondescript, sometimes anonymous, which plummeted into bathos, pulled out the tremolo stop, or (when humorous) sought to be twice as funny as nature. Two of these old war-horses are included here.

Hoaxes and practical jokes, in America as elsewhere, begin with banality; the withdrawn chair, the "glass-crash," and the hot-foot are typical. But our land has produced real artists in this field. Some of these are professionals, engaged in the advertising "game," as it is more or less aptly called, but others appear to derive their mysterious internal propulsion from sheer joy in a jape. Examples of each type will be found below.

Every American village has its "shiftless" character (or characters), but since Americans are normally energetic, these persons become, *ipso facto,* not only bad examples,[1] but butts for ridicule. Their defects are looked at through the microscope, then through the telescope. Their neighbors (who knows with what secret envy?) embroider their faults with appalling improvements. One Eastern example will be found below, and one Western, obviously akin.

Not only the elocutionists' manual, but also the school reader (or "reading-book" [2]) has spread certain types of tales about our land. (This fact, too, the folklorists have mostly overlooked in their too exclusive preoccupation with oral transmission; some of them, indeed, appear to believe that all "transmission" must be "oral.") Good storytellers, especially the more naïve and less bookish ones, have drawn their plots from their slight book-knowledge far oftener than scholars have noticed. Two migrant myths of bookish ancestry are given in the next section of this collection.

Of the last group of stories, each has sometimes been told as true, and the majority are always so told. They are distinctly the sort that need sponsors; they have them, of course, but these sponsors melt away upon pursuit. It is a suspicious fact that most of these tales are localized in every section of this wide land, and still more suspicious that the best of them all, though its *dramatis personæ* are Americans, is not even supposed to have happened in this hemisphere. The final story in this group might have been included in the section headed "Newspaperdom" (pp. 317ff., above), but its climax and its moral seem to justify its ultimate position.

---

[1] As a small boy, I asked a Yankee uncle: "What's chronic lassitude, Uncle Henry?" and received the immediate answer: "Infernal laziness."

[2] A New England farmer's wife who professed to be "a great reader" was asked what she read. She replied in some surprise: "Why, I read my Bible and I read my reading-book." This last turned out to be a battered *Sixth Reader,* a treasured relic of school days long past.

The Early-Lomax story needs no further comment.

The yarn of the hunter who brings down anything from a brace to a bushel of any sort of game—and both boots full of fish—may have been imported to America by the early settlers. And maybe not; they were fully capable of inventing it, and it sounds indigenous enough. There is not the slightest evidence for the assertion that it originated in the West.

Nantucket round-trip[1]

A ticket agent in Nantucket told me about the old Nantucketer who married an off-islander—a woman from Maine. The woman died and the widower presented himself at the ticket window, and asked for two round-trip tickets to Bangor.

The ticket agent said, "But you don't want two round-trips, Obed. You want one round-trip and one one-way"—because a dead person can travel on a passenger ticket, and ride in the baggage car, instead of the coach.

But the old man said No—he wanted two round-trips.

The ticket agent tried to explain, but the widower interrupted. He knew what he was doing, he said. He wanted a round-trip for himself and another for his wife, because she was coming back with him in a few days. And then *he* explained.

If he had the funeral in Nantucket, all her off-island folks would come, he said, and he'd have them on his hands for the summer. So he was going to take her to Maine and let them look at her. And then he would bring her back and bury her. And they would have no excuse for a visit.

---

[1] From Eleanor Early: *An Island Patchwork* (Boston: Houghton Mifflin Co.; 1941), p. 31. Used by permission of the publishers, Houghton Mifflin Company.

Livingston round-trip[1]

A railway conductor told her[2] about an experience which took place on his run. He came to an old Negro man on his rounds. The Negro handed him two round-trip tickets from Livingston to Birmingham.

"Where is the other passenger?" the conductor asked.

"Dat's for my wife; she's a layin' a corpse in her box up in de baggage car."

"But you don't need a round-trip ticket for her."

"Yassuh, I does. You see, my wife's she's got lots o' kinfolks up to Bummingham. I'se takin' her body up dere for dem to mourn over, an' den I's goin' to bring her back to Livingston to bury her. If I had'a let all dem Bummingham folks come down to Livingston to mourn over her, dey'd et me out'a house an' home."

Prosper Leffingwell[3]

It were useless to attempt to detail all the events which marked the career of this famous sportsman [Prosper Leffingwell of Killingly]. He was the terror of the *foxes* and *rabbits* for ten miles around. Many instances I might relate to illustrate the degree of skill to which he attained, but let one suffice. It is said that on one occasion, while returning home from hunting, he met *three foxes* advancing towards him "all in a row." As his gun was not loaded, he seized a stone, and directed it, as well as he was able, in a straight line towards their heads. Wonderful to tell, he brought them all *down!* He gazed a moment in astonishment. He found he had struck the first in the nose, the second in the hip, and the third in the forehead—all with the same stone! The first was not quite dead, the second was badly lamed, but the third showed no signs of life whatever. While chasing the second, the first recovered and scampered away. Had he sprung upon them the moment he saw them fall, he might have secured the three.

---

[1] From John A. Lomax: "Adventures of a Ballad Hunter," *Southwest Review,* Vol. XXIX (1943-4), p. 313.

[2] Mrs. Ruby Pickens Tartt, of Livingston, Alabama, who was Mr. Lomax's informant.

[3] From John Warner Barber: *Connecticut Historical Collections* (New Haven: Durrie & Peck and J. W. Barber; Improved edition [1838]), p. 432.

Ruff Sam[1]

M r. Printer: I'm right from the Backwoods of Mississippi, and as I told you onct 'bout my fite at Bony Vista, the folks have been pesterin' me to death to tell 'em sumthin' of the bar and panther hunts I've had, how many I kilt and wether I was kilt or no, 'twill I've gist determined to tell 'em of a rale swingin' hunt I had last October.

You see, I left these parts in Ceptember and went strate hum. I arriv thar, and arter shakin' hands with all the wimin folkses and kissin' all the gals, the boys raised a bar hunt, and nuthin' would do but I must go 'long. Thar was Bill Beenyard and Long Jim—but that is no use in givin' names, for you doesn't know 'em—depend on it, thar was a parcel on 'em. We all got reddy at Squire Startises, at the forks of the road, kalkulating we'd start out next mornin' by crack of day. Sure nuff next mornin' kum—I shuck myself and got out in the yard, kommenced blowin' for the dogs. The other boys they haint much usen to huntin', so they was a snorin' 'bout that time. I blow'd agin and here kum the dogs a howlin' and waggin' thar tales, an' a lookin' so eager—but I hadn't orter sed that Boss was a waggin' his tale, 'cause he got it bit off onct by a darned old she tiger cat, an' 'taint never growed out yit. The boys kum a stretchin' themselves, and axed me what all fired thunder that was. You see they hearn my horn and took it for thunder—I'm prodeegeous on a wind insterment an' I sorter skeered 'em—but I insured 'em it wouldn't rain nor nuthin', and everything bein' fixed off we put. They wanted me to go along with the krowd, but I wasn't goin' to do nuthin' of the kind, so I tole 'em they'd fine me at the big bend in the kreek, an' then struck for the kane brake.

Thar haint never been a place yit whar Ruff Sam kouldn't git throo. I whistled for Boss and gin him a few injunkshuns, such as, "Look him up, sir-r-r!" "Mine what you 'bout, you bob-taled raskel!" —sorter urgin' of him on—didn't mean to hurt his feelins, an' he noed it. You ort to ha' seen him—Lord, how he riggled himself—a camel-lin' on the groun'—a kockin' his ears up, a histenin' his tale, and a whinin' an' cuttin' setch numbersome kapers, that you'd ha' thot he had tred in a wass ness. He seed I wasn't arter no turkeys nor deer, for he never let on he noticed 'em.

We had pushed throo 'bout a mile of kane brake when I began to *feel* a varmint of sum sort nigh me, and Boss felt him too. 'Twas powerful dark—the sun wasn't more an up, an' it didn't stan' no

---

[1] From Porter's *Spirit of the Times*, March 4, 1848.

chance for the kane, 'twas so 'mazin' thick. "What is ail you, you skoundrel?" says I, a turnin' roun' to Boss. Thar he stood, his legs spraddled out, and his grizzly sides a swellin' in an' out like a pair of bellowses. "What on airth is the matter?" sez I agin, a gettin' mad—I patted him on the back an' a coaxin' him; 'twant no use—he wouldn't budge. That made me rale feerce, and, rip, rip, diff! I gin it to him in the ribs with my fist shet up. "Now what ails you?" sez I. Boss looked at me and said, jest as plane as a dog kin say, he was skeered. I knowd sumthin' most orful was kummin', or Boss would never ha' been skeered. I stopped and considered, an' I mout ha' taken a little sumthin' what I have 'long in a goard; but I won't say I did. I studdied on an' speclated, an' I mout ha' taken a nuther drop or so, but I won't swar to it. I looks at Boss, an' sez I, "Boss, is you goin' to foller me, or is you not?" He wanted to sodger out of the skrape, an' I seed it in him; his har was stanin' strate out all over him. Sez I—"If it's a whale you shall fite him, you kowardly Mexikin raskil!" You must ha' knowd I was savage, or I never would a called my dog a Mexikin! Suddenly I hearn sumthin' an' turnin' I seed one of the most stonishin' big she bars that ever wor'd fur standin' afore me, within ten foot. When she seed me a lookin' at her she grunted, as much as to say—"Who's afeered?" Sez I, "Say your prayers quick; I wants your hide!" and lets drive with my rifle. Jest as I fired she thro'd her head round, an' it took her in the shoulder. That riled her tremendious, and she kum at me afore I kould say who's who. I looked round and seed Boss a watchin' on close by, jest as the kritter klosed in with me. "Charge her in the rair!" I shouted out to Boss. Zip! I kum down with the butt eend of my rifle, smashin' it to pieces. She shuck her head an' grabbed for me; but, feelin' the enimy a worryin' her in the rair, she wheeled. That gin me time to git out my old bowie-knife, and I flanked her with it rale quick. She manoovered an' kum to the charge again in a bilin' swet, bitin' an' showin' fite in dead airnest. I was a fallin' back for a new position as my foot slipped an' kefetchup! I kum on my back! I thot the thing was out then, an' kommenced thinkin' 'bout kingdom kum. She got me in her arms rale sure nuff, an' if you say she didn't squeeze me, you dosn't know nuthin' tall 'bout it. I tried to breathe, but the wind in me was so skase I couldn't. She hugged me so tite that my fingers got as strate as stixs; my head begin to swell 'bout the size of a whisky barl, an' I sorter thot I might bust, or brake, or sumthin', if she presd much harder. Presently I hearn her a tremblin', and then she loosend her holt an' rolled over on her side. I laid still 'twill I got to my usual size, and then riz up to look for Boss. I was willin' to quit. Thar was Boss, one of the bisiest dogs you ever seed, a findin' what she was made outen—he naterally had his head clene in the hole I had made in her with "old bowie." The bar was dead, and me and Boss had licked her!

I was a skinin' of her when the boys kum up, an' such a nuther spree we had arter we got to the Squire's I never spects to have again. I'm off to-morrow for up the drink.

Yours 'twill bym-by,

Ruff Sam.

—*N. O. Picayune.*

Little Neck Tom[1]

In still earlier times so immense were the flocks of teal, the best water fowl known when roasted by Phillis, not excepting the boasted, wild, celery-fed canvas-back of the Chesapeake, that it used to be told when I was young, that Thomas E. Hazard, of Little Neck Farm, and hence called Little Neck Tom, the father of the late Sylvester R. and Dr. R. R. Hazard, of Newport, once shot with a single sweep of his long duck gun in the North Narragansett Pier pond fifty-one teal that he got, and then followed the remainder of the flock to the south pond, where he again raised them, and with another sweeping shot of his gun brought down forty-nine more, making just one hundred teal at the two shots.

John Bass[2]

After walking thirty miles from Seboomook to Caucomgomoc in the morning, John Bass and I sighted two deer some distance apart. John had only one bullet left, but he said he'd get both those deer anyway. He went up to a tree about half way between them and stuck his jack-knife in it. Then he came back to where I was, took aim at his knife and fired at it. I'll be a son of a sliver from a piece of liver if that bullet didn't split clean in two on the handle of the knife and each half bounce off and kill a deer.

---

[1] From Thomas Robinson Hazard: *The Jonny-Cake Papers of "Shepherd Tom"* (Boston: Printed for the Subscribers; 1915), pp. 76–7.

[2] By Richard M. Dorson in *Southern Folklore Quarterly*, December 1944, p. 280

Mr. L.[1]

When he resided in Mississippi, Mr. L., (we will thus designate him,) had a great desire to kill a bear; and with this view, he visited a great swamp lying between the Yazoo and Mississippi river; and, by previous invitation, took up his quarters at the house of his friend, Mr. Bookout, who resided on the Sunflower river, a tributary of the Yazoo. Here bears were said to be so plenty, that they might have been hunted as Abram Defiance was wont to hunt them on the Bayou Pierre—[another episode]—Abram figured some thirty years ago in Port Gibson, then one of the most flourishing towns in this State. He fell in one evening, at his own tavern, with a credulous Yankee, to whom he told some wonderful stories about matters and things in this country, and wound up by stating the enormous number of bears there were in the cane-brakes on the Bayou Pierre, "and," added he, "I have found out a new way of hunting the rascals, without the loss of powder or shot."

"Ah!" said the Yankee, "now *do tell!* how is that?"

"Why," replied Defiance, "we get half a dozen long poles, and, after hardening the ends in the fire, as Ulysses did when he was about to bore out the eye of Polyphemus, we make them very sharp, and give each one to a stout negro man, and with these we go along the roads which have been cut through the cane-brake and punch violently into all the thickest places."

"And," asked the Yankee, "do you kill many in that way?"

"Oh, no," replied Defiance, "d—n the one!"

Ab Yancey's squirrel-hunt[2]

Wal, gentlemen, when I was a young-un powder an' ball was high an' hard t' git, so we allus had t' make ever' shot count. I recollect one time I was a-tryin' t' git two red squirrels lined up so's I could kill both of 'em with one bullet. Thar was four of 'em a-runnin' 'round in a chinkapin tree, an' I reckon I must have sot thar twenty minutes afore I got 'em set to suit me. When I pulled trigger I seen

---

[1] From Porter's *Spirit of the Times,* November 11, 1848.

[2] Reprinted from *Ozark Mountain Folks* by Vance Randolph (New York: Vanguard Press; 1932), pp. 143–5. Copyright, 1932, by Vanguard Press, Inc.

both of 'em fall, but jest then I heerd turkeys a-yoikin', an' it warn't but a leetle ways off I seen seven hens an' a gobbler a-settin' in a tree. Seems like that 'ar bullet done skittered over thar some way, an' split the limb they was a-settin' on, an' ketched their feet in th' crack.

"Wal, sir, I clumb up t' git them turkeys an' wring their necks afore they could bust loose on me, but just as I was a-comin' down I lost my holt an' fell slap-dab into a bresh-pile. Thar I was a-scramblin' an' a-rollin', an' afore I could git out I'd smothered a hull gang o' quails an' two big swamp-rabbits! I jest tied them eight turkeys an' them forty-one quails an' them two swamp-rabbits all t'gether with pawpaw bark, an' back I went a-packin' 'em t' whar my squirrels was at. One o' them squirrels had fell in th' creek, so I waded in atter him. Hit was deeper'n I figgered on, an' th' water was kinder riled up an' dingy like. . . . When I got out on th' bank ag'in, danged if my pockets an' boot-tops wasn't jest chuck full o' fish—mostly perch an' goggle-eye!

"Whilst I was a-stringin' them fish I retch back t' scratch a chigger-bite, an' my ol' shirt was too dang-tight anyhow, so one o' th' buttons popped off'n it. I seen th' dang thing go a-whistlin' off into a bunch o' hazel bresh, an' I aimed for t' hunt it up soon as I got my fish strung t' suit me. D'rectly I heered a turrible scufflin' round an' gaspin' an' gurglin' in them bresh, so I drapped th' fish an' snuck over whar I could peek in. Thar was a big buck a-rollin' round, an' he was a-dyin', too, but danged if I could see what kilt him. Hit kinder skeerd me. . . . But I just cut his throat anyhow, t' let him bleed right good, an' thar was my ol' button stuck in his wind-pipe! he must of opened up his mouth for t' belch, I reckon, an' that 'ar button jest flipped in thar an' shut his wind plumb off! Hit shore was th' biggest one-bullet huntin' I ever done, seen, or hearn tell of. . . . Thar was one deer, eight turkeys, two swamp-rabbits, forty-one quails an' maybe fifty pounds o' fish, an' Pappy shore was proud when he seen me draggin' of it all home.

"Hit was a sad day at our place, though, on account of Uncle Hen. Uncle Hen was a purty good feller, but he didn't have no sense, an' whut did he do but up an' call me a liar when I was a-tellin' how I got that 'ar buck. 'Liar' allus was a fightin' word in th' Yancey family, so I just naturally had t' kill him. Pap hisself said he couldn't make out t' blame me none, but it shore did gravel him t' see his own brother a-layin' thar all butchered up an' gutted that-a-way. . . . I done it with my ol' huntin'-knife, gentlemen,—same one you-uns see a-stickin' out o' my boot-top right now!"

❦

Mrs. May Lamberton Becker's note on "How Rubinstein played the pianner" gives an admirable account of the genre to which this originally literary production became attached. I have used a title that I saw on an old-fashioned elocutionist's manuscript.

The other sample of the elocutionist's repertoire given below is merely an expansion of the Irish dialect type of story that flourished, especially in the East, for half a century after the great immigration that followed the potato famine of 1846. The Irishman's ingenuous wonder at an unfamiliar land, its flora, fauna, and customs, was the mainspring of the all too simple plots of these stories. The one here selected is typical except for its greater than usual length, its kindly tone, and the gratifying circumstance that it says nothing of "Pat and Mike."

How Rubinstein played the pianner [1]

Jed Browning's Account of Rubinstein's Playing, by George William Bagby

(NOTE BY MAY LAMBERTON BECKER: Anyone who can remember the days when the elocutionist was a feature of the program at church sociables and parlor entertainments may recall a piece usually set down as "How Ruby Played," to which it is more than likely that he has listened. No doubt he listened to it more than once; it was a good old war-horse and local talent rode it freely, while visiting artists were quite likely to use it for galloping in. He will be somewhat astonished, however, to learn that it was written by an editor of the *Southern Literary Messenger* who was in later years the State Librarian of Virginia. He may even be a trifle taken aback to find that it was really written at all, it has been for so long one of those compositions that slip away from authorship and indeed altogether from print, to live on the lips and in the ears a disembodied existence.)

J ud, they say you heard Rubinstein play when you were in New York?"

"I did, in the cool."

---

[1] From *Golden Tales of the Old South,* selected, with an Introduction, by May Lamberton Becker (New York: Dodd, Mead & Co.; 1934), pp. 137, 141–5.

"Well, tell us about it."

"What? me? I might's well tell you about the creation of the world."

"Come, now; no mock modesty. Go ahead."

"Well, sir, he had the blamedest, biggest, cattycornedest pianner you ever laid eyes on; somethin' like a distractid billiard table on three legs. The lid was heisted, and mighty well it was. If it hadn't been, he'd tore the intire insides clean out, and scattered 'em to the four winds of heaven."

"Played well, did he?"

"You bet he did; but don't interrup' me. When he first sat down he 'peared to keer mighty little 'bout playin', and wished he hadn't come. He tweedle-leedled a little on the trible; and twoodle-oodle-oodled some on the bass—just foolin' and boxin' the thing's jaws for bein' in his way. And I says to a man settin' next to me, s'I, 'What sort of fool playin' is that?' And he says, 'Heish!' But presently his hands commenced chasin' one 'nother up and down the keys, like a passel of rats scamperin' through a garret very swift. Parts of it was sweet, though, and reminded me of a sugar squirrel turnin' the wheel of a candy cage. 'Now,' I says to my neighbor, 'he's showin' off. He thinks he's a-doin' of it; but he ain't got no idee, no plan of nothin'. If he'd play me up a tune of some kind or other, I'd—'

"But my neighbor says, 'Heish!' very impatient.

"I was just about to git up and go home, bein' tired of that fool-ishness, when I heard a little bird wakin' up way off in the woods, and callin' sleepy-like to his mate, and I looked up and I see that Ruben was beginnin' to take interest in his business, and I set down agin. It was the peep of day. The light come faint from the east, the breeze blowed gentle and fresh, some more birds waked up in the or-chard, then some more in the trees near the house, and all begun singin', together. People begun to stir, and the gal opened the shutters. Just then the first beam of the sun fell upon the blossoms; a leetle more and it teched the roses on the bushes, and the next thing it was broad day; the sun fairly blazed; the birds sang like they'd split their little throats; all the leaves was movin', and flashin' diamonds of dew, and the whole wide world was bright and happy as a king. Seemed to me like there was a good breakfast in every house in the land, and not a sick child or woman anywhere. It was a fine mornin'.

"And I says to my neighbor, 'That's music, that is.'

"But he glared at me like he'd like to cut my throat.

"Presently the wind turned; it begun to thicken up, and a kind of gray mist come over things; I got low-spirited, d'rectly. Then a silver rain begun to fall; I could see the drops touch the ground; some flashed up like long pearl earrings; and the rest rolled away like round rubies. It was pretty, but melancholy. Then the pearls gathered themselves into long strands and necklaces, and then they melted into thin silver streams running between golden gravels, and then the streams joined each other at the bottom of the hill, and made a brook that flowed silent except that you could kinder see the music specially when the bushes on the banks moved as the music went along down the valley. I could smell the flowers in the meadows. But the sun didn't shine, nor the birds sing; it was a foggy day, but not cold. Then the sun went down, it got dark, the wind moaned and wept like a lost child for its dead mother, and I could a-got up then and there and preached a better sermon than any I ever listened to. There wasn't a thing in the world left to live for, not a blame thing, and yet I didn't want the music to stop one bit. It was happier to be miserable than to be happy without being miserable. I couldn't understand it. . . . Then, all of a sudden, old Ruben changed his tune. He ripped and he rar'd, he tipped and he tar'd, he pranced and he charged like the grand entry at a circus. 'Peared to me like all the gas in the house was turned on at once, things got so bright, and I hilt up my head, ready to look any man in the face, and not afeard of nothin'. It was a circus, and a brass band, and a big ball, all goin' on at the same time. He lit into them keys like a thousand of brick, he gave 'em no rest, day or night; he set every livin' joint in me a-goin', and not bein' able to stand it no longer, I jumpt spang onto my seat, and jest hollered, '*Go it, my Rube!*'

"Every blamed man, woman, and child in the house riz on me, and shouted, 'Put him out! Put him out!'

"With that some several p'licemen run up, and I had to simmer down. But I would a-fit any fool that laid hands on me, for I was bound to hear Ruby out or die.

"He had changed his tune again. He hopt-light ladies and tiptoed fine from eend to eend of the keyboard. He played soft, and low, and solemn. I heard the church bells over the hills. The candles in heaven was lit, one by one. I saw the stars rise. The great organ of eternity began to play from the world's end to the world's end, and all the angels went to prayers. Then the music changed to water, full of feeling that couldn't be thought, and began to drop—drip, drop, drip, drop —clear and sweet, like tears of joy fallin' into a lake of glory.

"He stopt a minute or two, to fetch breath. Then he got mad. He run his fingers through his hair, he shoved up his sleeves, he opened his coat-tails a leetle further, he drug up his stool, he leaned over, and, sir, he just went for that old pianner. He slapt her face, he boxed her jaws, he pulled her nose, he pinched her ears, and he scratched her cheeks, till she fairly yelled. He knockt her down and he stompt on her shameful. She bellowed like a bull, she bleated like a calf, she howled like a hound, she squealed like a pig, she shrieked like a rat, and then he wouldn't let her up. He run a quarter-stretch down the low grounds of the bass, till he got clean into the bowels of the earth, and you heard thunder galloping after thunder, through the hollows and caves of perdition; and then he fox-chased his right hand with his left till he got away out of the trible into the clouds, whar the notes was finer than the pints of cambric needles, and you couldn't hear nothin' but the shadders of 'em. And then he wouldn't let the old pianner go. He fetched up his right wing, he fetched up his left wing, he fetched up his center, he fetched up his reserves. He fired by file, he fired by platoons, by company, by regiments, by brigades. He opened his cannon, siege-guns down there, Napoleons here, twelve-pounders yonder, big guns, little guns, middle-sized guns, round shot, shell, shrapnel, grape, canister, mortars, mines and magazines, every livin' battery and bomb a-goin' at the same time. The house trembled, the lights danced, the walls shuk, the floor come up, the ceilin' come down, the sky split, the ground rockt—BANG!

"With that *bang!* he lifted hisself bodily into the ar', and he come down with his knees, his ten fingers, his ten toes, his elbows, and his nose, strikin' every single solitary key on that pianner at the same time. The thing busted and went off into seventeen hundred and fifty-seven thousand five hundred and forty-two hemi-demi-semi-quivers, and I know'd no mo'."

Jimmy Butler and the owl[1]

(An impersonation. "Who! Whoo! Whooo!" should be given with high pitch, descending slides, and tremulous stress on "whooo!")

T was in the summer of '46 that I landed at Hamilton, fresh as a new pratie just dug from the "ould sod," and wid a light heart and a heavy bundle I sot off for the township of Buford, tiding a taste of a song, as merry a young fellow as iver took the road. Well, I trudged on and on, past many a plisint place, pleasin' myself wid the thought that some day I might have a place of my own, wid a world of chickens and ducks and pigs and childer about the door; and along in the afternoon of the sicond day I got to Buford village. A cousin of me mother's, one Dennis O'Dowd, lived about sivin miles from there, and I wanted to make his place that night, so I inquired the way at the tavern, and was lucky to find a man who was goin' part of

---

[1] From Frank H. Fenno: *The Science and Art of Elocution* (Philadelphia: John E. Potter & Co.; copyright Frank H. Fenno, 1878), pp. 160-4.

the way an' would show me the way to find Dennis. Sure he was very kind indade, an' when I got out of his wagon he pointed me through the wood and tould me to go straight south a mile an' a half, and the first house would be Dennis's.

"An' you've no time to lose now," said he, "for the sun is low, and mind you don't get lost in the woods."

"Is it lost now," said I, "that I'd be gittin, an' me uncle as great a navigator as iver steered a ship across the thrackless say! Not a bit of it, though I'm obleeged to ye for your kind advice, and thank yiz for the ride."

An' wid that he drove off an' left me alone. I shouldered me bundle bravely, an' whistlin' a bit of time for company like, I pushed into the bush. Well, I went a long way over bogs, and turnin' round among the bush an' trees till I began to think I must be well nigh to Dennis's. But, bad cess to it! all of a sudden I came out of the woods at the very identical spot where I started in, which I knew by an old crotched tree that seemed to be standin' on its head and kickin' up its heels to make divarsion of me. By this time it was growin' dark, and as there was no time to lose, I started in a second time, determined to keep straight south this time, and no mistake. I got on bravely for a while, but och hone! och hone! it got so dark I couldn't see the trees, and I bumped me nose and barked me shins, while the miskaties bit me hands and face to a blister; an' after tumblin' and stumblin' around till I was fairly bamfoozled, I sat down on a log all of a trimble, to think that I was lost intirely, an' that maybe a lion or some other wild craythur would devour me before morning.

Just then I heard somebody a long way off say, "Whip poor Will! Whip poor Will!" "Bedad," sez I, "I'm glad it isn't Jamie that's got to take it, though it's more in sorrow than in anger they are doin' it, or why should they say, 'poor Will?' an' sure they can't be Injin, haythin, or naygur, for it's plain English they're afther spakin'. Maybe they might help me out o' this," so I shouted at the top of my voice, "A lost man!" Thin I listened. Prisently an answer came.

"Who? Whoo? Whooo?"

"Jamie Butler, the waiver!" sez I, as loud as I could roar, an' snatchin' up me bundle an' stick, I started in the direction of the voice. Whin I thought I had got near the place I stopped and shouted again, "A lost man!"

"Who! Whoo! Whooo!" said a voice right over my head.

"Sure," thinks I, "it's a mighty quare place for a man to be at this time of night; maybe it's some settler scrapin' sugar off a sugar-bush for the children's breakfast in the mornin'. But where's Will and the rest of them?" All this wint through me head like a flash, an' thin I answered his inquiry.

638

"Jamie Butler, the waiver," sez I; "and if it wouldn't inconvanience yer honor, would yez be kind enough to step down and show me the way to the house of Dennis O'Dowd?"

"Who! Whoo! Whooo!" sez he.

"Dennis O'Dowd," sez I, civil enough, "and a dacent man he is, and first cousin to me own mother."

"Who! Whoo! Whooo!" sez he again.

"Me mother!" sez I, "and as fine a woman as iver peeled a biled pratie wid her thumb nail, and her maiden name was Molly McFiggin."

"Who! Whoo! Whooo!"

"Paddy McFiggin! bad luck to yer deaf ould head, Paddy McFiggin, I say—do you hear that? An' he was the tallest man in all the county Tipperary, excipt Jim Doyle, the blacksmith."

"Who! Whoo! Whooo!"

"Jim Doyle the blacksmith," sez I, "ye good for nothin' blaggurd baygur, and if yiz don't come down and show me the way this min't, I'll climb up there and break every bone in your skin, ye spalpeen, so sure as me name is Jimmy Butler!"

"Who! Whoo! Whooo!" sez he, as impident as iver.

I said never a word, but lavin' down me bundle, and takin' me stick in me teeth, I began to climb the tree. Whin I got among the branches I looked quietly around till I saw a pair of big eyes just forninst me.

"Whist," sez I, "and I'll let him have a taste of an Irish stick," and wid that I let drive and lost me balance an' came tumblin' to the ground, nearly breakin' me neck wid the fall. When I came to me sinsis I had a very sore head wid a lump on it like a goose egg, and half of me Sunday coat-tail torn off intirely. I spoke to the chap in the tree but could git niver an answer, at all, at all.

Sure, thinks I, he must have gone home to rowl up his head, for by the powers I didn't throw me stick for nothin'.

Well, by this time the moon was up and I could see a little, and I detarmined to make one more effort to reach Dennis's.

I wint on cautiously for awhile, an' thin I heard a bell. "Sure," sez I, "I'm comin' to a settlement now, for I hear the church bell." I kept on toward the sound till I came to an ould cow wid a bell on. She started to run, but I was too quick for her, and got her by the tail and hung on, thinkin' that maybe she would take me out of the woods. On we wint, like an ould country steeple-chase, till, sure enough, we came out to a clearin' and a house in sight wid a light in it. So, leavin' the ould cow puffin' and blowin' in a shed; I went to the house, and as luck would have it, whose should it be but Dennis's.

He gave me a raal Irish welcome, and introduced me to his two daughters—as purty a pair of gurls as iver ye clapped an eye on. But

639

whin I tould him me adventure in the woods, and about the fellow who made fun of me, they all laughed and roared, and Dennis said it was an owl.

"An ould what?" sez I.

"Why, an owl, a bird," sez he.

"Do ye tell me now?" sez I. "Sure it's a quare country and a quare burd."

And thin they all laughed again, till at last I laughed myself, that hearty like, and dropped right into a chair betwen the two purty girls, and the ould chap winked at me and roared again.

Dennis is me father-in-law now, and he often yet delights to tell our children about their daddy's adventure wid the owl.

The American publicity man is uniquely cynical. Unlike other advertising men, he hardly makes a bow in the direction of sober truth. He can get away with everything but murder, and he knows it, and knows that the customers like it. When preceding a circus or ballyhooing a forthcoming Hollywood production, he lets himself go. The late Harry Reichenbach was a richly inventive example; two of his more moderately preposterous fancies are set forth here.

The American newspaper's circulation gag (as reporters call it in their more formal moments) is akin to circus ballyhoo, but cannot be carried out without the assumption of a serious mask. One of the best of these, in its own curious way, is still affectionately remembered in Boston and Maine and probably elsewhere; Joe Knowles was but the puppet, his manipulators impersonated the Great American Comic Spirit itself.

Frauds are one step down from exaggerated advertisements, but inventive frauds are often cherished by the American public. Prince Mike Romanoff is well known, Prince Zerdecheno (described below) much less so. Their ideas are similar.

American promotion in England[1]

E. W. Fredman, editor of "The Film Renter," decided to give me a luncheon which was attended by a number of British theatrical and motion picture producers. After the dessert there was a general discussion of American versus British films and their respective methods of exploitation. A young man arose and said, "Mr. Reichenbach, I have just completed a picture and I'd like to engage you to handle the publicity for its opening in London. It is frankly an experiment to see how American promotion tactics would work out in England." The speaker was Guy Newall, a progressive young producer and actor, and the picture he referred to was later called "The Bigamist."

Sir Charles Higham, British publisher, and one of the leading adver-

[1] Reprinted from *Phantom Fame,* by permission of Simon and Schuster, Inc. Copyright, 1931, by Harry Reichenbach. Pp. 189–95.

641

tising men of England, got up and told the guests that it would be a waste of time and money to engage me as he could not conceive that a typically American publicist would accomplish anything in England for the English people were unaccustomed to the rather crude American tastes and methods. I began to smoke around the collar. I flatly disagreed with the honorable Sir Charles and said that while my methods might be strange, it was because they were new, and if Newall would be willing to pay the salary I commanded I'd undertake to interest the English a little. Newall gamely accepted the offer, fixing my salary at 250 pounds a week and the use of a Daimler automobile, which meant an extra 50 pounds weekly.

By this time all the guests were eager for the experiment and Bob Lawson, a well-known London publicity man, asked me to tell them what the American would try to show dear old England.

"If you'll consider what I say confidential," I observed, bending over to the gathering in an intimate fashion, "and promise not to mention it to anyone outside this room, I'll be glad to outline my plans."

All pledged themselves to the strictest secrecy and I continued. "First, I'll get a stereopticon machine and project an ad on the walls of Buckingham Palace. The next day all London will be talking about it!" This was a bombshell.

"What! Advertise on the walls of the King's Palace!" Was the American press agent mad? Nobody waited to hear any more details of my plan for fear they would be accused of treason. The following day, the *Daily Express* carried a complete description of my demented plan as did the film journal, "Cinema"; and the editor of the *Daily Mail* sent a reporter to get further details from me on my proposed sacrilege. Not one of these clever English publicists thought for a moment that I might be spoofing them. I hadn't the remotest idea of going through with such a scheme, but I did find out that a pledge to secrecy was as sacred in England as in America.

The first step in my publicity campaign was entirely different and designed to worry Sir Charles Higham in particular and his skeptical friends in general. Three hundred of the most prominent theatrical and motion picture men in London received letters in a feminine hand, which said:

Dearest:

During our long and intimate acquaintance I have never asked a favor of you, but now the time has come when I must. I am in a desperate position and I need your help. Enclosed you will find a key. If you do not hear from me again before next Tuesday you will on that day receive a package which holds the thing most dear to both of us. Unlock it and act like a man.

I. D.

It was, of course, similar to the letter I had sent to picture exhibitors in America and with similar results. Sir Charles Higham, one hour after receipt of this mysterious epistle, called on his solicitor and turned the letter over to him. I can't say whether in America or in England more of these letters were turned over to lawyers, but men proved to be men in both countries. They spent a week of worry waiting for the package which consisted of a copy of "The Film Renter" containing a double-spread ad of "The Bigamist." The English exhibitors resented this idea of publicity and talked about it so incessantly that for a time there was no other subject in the film world. The initials I. D. of the letter were those of Newall's co-star, Miss Ivy Duke.

The next step was to post several thousand six-sheets with the printed matter inverted. We received hundreds of letters telling us of the grave error committed and members of the bill-posters' union came around to apologize for their colleagues. Friends hinted that I was being discriminated against. Again the picture was the center of discussion.

A few mornings afterwards, I covered London with small "snipe" posters:

WANTED

Herbert Arnott, who poses as an English gentleman, known in France as "The Bigamist." A reward of 500 pounds sterling will be paid for his arrest and conviction.

DESCRIPTION

Height—5 ft. 10 inch.
Weight—182 lbs.
Eyes—Mixed gray and brown.
Hair—Mixed gray and brown.
Beard—Full grown, gray and brown.
Complexion—Light.
Nose—Straight.
Age—About fifty.
Affects blue serge clothes.
In the event that you apprehend Arnott, or discover his whereabouts, notify the nearest police station.

On the poster was a picture of Guy Newall in the role of "The Bigamist," with a beard in full bloom. No man with a beard was safe on the London streets. Two days later a representative of Scotland Yard ordered us to take the posters down. "You are liable to have plenty of lawsuits," he assured us, "for everybody in London is dragging old men into the police stations and claiming the reward. Besides, you'll be fined five shillings per poster because the printer's name does not appear."

The next obstacle to overcome was the press. The ads I designed were refused by the *Daily Mail* because they would attract too much attention. After the type and design had been altered and the ad couldn't be distinguished from the rest of the page, it was printed. The same thing happened to our electric sign. We were told it couldn't be put up because it would be noticed.

A Cinematographers' Convention was to be held and I tried to rent banner space in the hotel lobby. They wanted more for that space than the convention paid for the hall. An English publicity man on the other hand acquired the concession at a nominal fee. There was a quiet, bullheaded determination to frustrate me at every step.

I found out that the two-day convention was to wind up with a dinner. A few hours before the dinner, a young man approached the maître d'hôtel and said, "You needn't include rolls in your provisions for tonight. The committee will furnish its own rolls. They'll be delivered to you at six o'clock." The maître d'hôtel eagerly welcomed the saving.

That night when eight hundred British film men sat down to dinner, grace was said by the Rt. Rev. Henry Russell Wakefield, Bishop of Birmingham, and the band played "God Save the King."

Then eight hundred guests reached out and picked up eight hundred rolls. Most of them, hungry and impatient did not wait to break the bread and bit into it, catching a piece of paper between their teeth. The others, who opened their rolls more leisurely found in them a strip of printed advertising matter reading,

"THE BIGAMIST WHICH OPENS AT THE ALHAMBRA NEXT MONDAY WILL BE BREAD AND BUTTER AT YOUR BOX OFFICE."

Either because of the excitement or because he was unusually hungry, the Bishop of Birmingham swallowed half of the advertisement and later started suit against me for 150,000 pounds which spread "The Bigamist" all over the front pages of England. The *Daily Graphic* editorially complimented the enterprise of the publicity man who had literally turned advertising into food. And the English who had refused the American high pressure publicity method finally wound up by eating it.

The result of it all was that "The Bigamist" opened to a packed house and was a sell-out during its three-week engagement at the Alhambra. It scored a new record and set a first mark in the history of British screen productions where an all-English film played to a profit in what was considered a "legitimate" engagement. Yet it required an American press agent to show them how to sell their own product to their own people.

A NOTE ON JOE KNOWLES, THE NATURE MAN

Knowles died on October 22, 1942, in Seaview, Washington, at the age of seventy-three, but I have retained Mr. Boyer's account of his later years, as the nature man never wholly lost his own peculiar brand of grandeur. The Boston Post signalized his passing by a front-page story, with a picture of Knowles wearing a bearskin and carrying a bow and arrow. The headline stated that Knowles "lived for sixty days by his own efforts in [the] wilds of Maine," and the accompanying story asserted that he "convinced all" that "modern man with native intelligence and courage can triumph." This phrasing seems rather guarded.

In 1913 the Boston firm of Small, Maynard and Co. published a book, now rare,[1] with the following title: *"Alone in the Wilderness,* by Joseph Knowles. Illustrated from drawings on birch bark, made by the author in the woods with burnt sticks from his fires, together with photographs taken before and after his experiences." This seems to have been the nature man's own work. Its philosophy, of which there is a great deal, is expressed in a style that some would think a bit lush, but, as Joe says (p. 61.), "A primitive man can be sentimental if he wishes to."

The nature man[2]

W hen Joe Knowles emerged from the Maine wilderness on October 4, 1913, two months after entering it with nothing but his ingenuity and a breechcloth, his presence was so powerful that it seemed doubtful if it would ever fade. Wearing a half-tanned bearskin whose stench was later the subject of affidavits, occasionally thumping his chest like an exuberant gorilla, he began his triumphant return to a civilization which had feverishly followed in the press the account of his bare-knuckle fight against nature.

A crowd of two hundred thousand welcomed him to his Boston home. Women fought to find his lips. Editorial writers apostrophized his triumph as that of "a naked man against the tooth and claw of nature," and as "a noble piece of poetry." Preachers likened him to John the Baptist, who had preceded Joe into the wilderness. Five hundred young women demanded and received the privilege of caressing the muscles of his back. It seemed incredible then that the nature man would go the way of city flesh and vanish into the obscurity that has hidden him for twenty years.

Joe entered the wilderness at King and Bartlett Lake in the Dead River region of northwest Maine on August 4, 1913. The public first heard about it in the Boston *Post* of Sunday, August 10th. Purporting

---

[1] Mr. Boyer does not seem ever to have encountered this opus. The loss is his.
[2] By Richard O. Boyer in *The New Yorker,* June 18, 1938, pp. 21–5. Permission The New Yorker, Copyright 1938, The F-R. Publishing Corporation.

to have been written before Joe entered the woods, the announcement quoted him as saying, "I am not interested in money and my
purpose is entirely scientific. I shall enter naked and take with me
absolutely nothing. I shall see absolutely no one. I shall keep a birch-
bark record with charcoal of my progress and place it each week under
a stump where a trapper will get it and send it to the Sunday *Post.*"

The response to Joe's announcement was overwhelming. Two hundred letters were received by the *Post* the next day. A man in Portland
said he held himself and his bloodhounds in instant readiness to
plunge into the woods if nothing was heard the following Sunday.
When that day arrived, a five-column head across the front page of the
Post informed the world that the first birch-bark bulletin had turned
up and there was no necessity for the bloodhounds. Knowles was
alive. He was eating fish caught by the swift cunning of his hands. He
had made a fire by rubbing two sticks together. He was sheltered by a
rude lean-to. On succeeding Sundays the public learned that Joe had
run down a deer and strangled it with his bare hands and had slain
a bear with a club. He had made himself a bearskin coat.

Knowles had also made an increase of 31,210 in circulation for the
Post and thousands of converts for Mother Nature. Some twenty newspapers in all parts of the country were buying the syndicated story of
his adventures. A mass atavistic nostalgia seized the populace that
summer, if letters to newspapers are any indication. Scores approved
the suggestion of one Carl Norzinsky of Boston, who wrote, "Why
cannot Knowles found a colony of those who would like to do as he
is doing if they only knew how? Knowles has discovered something
big."

Knowles' thoughts, as reported in the papers, turned often to
motherhood and our little fellow-creatures of the wood and stream.
"Today is my birthday," said one entry on the purported birch-bark
record. "It is a holiday for me. I hear the voices of my woodland
neighbors and feel the presence of my mother." In a later communication Joe's admirers read, "I don't even have to mention liquor to a
Boy Scout for he well knows its evils. God's fresh air is the greatest
stimulant in the world." Another time they read, "My God is the
wilderness; my church is the church of the forest." Joe's character
shone through his dispatches as that of one possessing the strength of
the eternal hills, the purity of the stars.

The idea for the nature man was born one humid afternoon of the
summer before all this, amid the fumes of a Washington Street saloon
in Boston. One of its parents was Joe himself, a large, hairy man with
a huge beak of a nose, who seemed to alternate between fits of verbal
vigor and a melancholy lassitude. When the vigor was upon him, he
had a monomania for boasting that he could enter the woods un-

clothed and weaponless and maintain himself endlessly through his extraordinary woodlore. When the melancholy had seized him, one could shout and he would not seem to hear, push him and he would not seem to feel. But a short time later he would be roaring of his wilderness skill again and edging about the bar permitting patrons to feel his muscle. He was proud of his strength and pleased when vital statistics were demanded. He was forty-four years old, five feet nine and two-tenths inches tall, his upper right arm measured 14.4 inches, and his weight would have been less than 191 pounds had it not been for a slight bulge at his middle. With an engaging smile revealing a flash of toothy gold, he'd explain that his strength and cunning derived from a youth spent as a trapper and wild-animal painter in his native Maine. He was then a part-time artist on the Boston *Post*.

If it had not been for a man named Michael McKeogh, Joe might still be standing before a bar telling what he would do to the wilderness if he ever caught it out alone. McKeogh was thirty years old, a free-lance newspaperman, and it was his will that pushed Joe away from his nice warm bar into cold reality. It was McKeogh who sold the idea to the newspapers.

McKeogh says now it all began when he read "Robinson Crusoe." He had been much impressed by the fact that the book was written in 1719 and was still selling well. He believes he was thinking about this when Joe's booming voice in the smoke-filled saloon suddenly leaped to meaning in his mind.

"We'll make a million," he told Joe, and they began to talk it over. Knowles was delighted not only at the prospect of money but at having an auditor who didn't care how often he repeated himself. Knowles talked and talked. He had an answer for everything. On a barroom table, with pencil and pad, McKeogh made a day-by-day schedule of Joe's two months in the wilderness, labelling it "A Modern Robinson Crusoe." It was to be the basis of a book which would make them rich. He'd make a notation, "Tuesday: kills bear," then ask, "But are you sure you can do it, Joe?" Joe would take a drink and enumerate five or six ways of killing a bear without a rifle. Gradually, with the utmost caution, McKeogh eased Joe into a state of action.

A bit bewildered but not yet fully resentful, Joe found himself in Maine on August 4th, thirty miles from a railroad. It was raining. He seemed despondent as he slowly bared his soft whiteness to a group of vacationists at the foot of Bear Mountain, beside King and Bartlett Lake. While Joe was leaving the world behind, McKeogh was busy at a typewriter in a cabin two miles away on Kempshall Point, at the other side of Bear Mountain. He had bid Knowles farewell the day before. With McKeogh was Fred Allen, a Maine guide who was to do the cooking and retrieve Joe's weekly messages from an already chosen stump and mail them, when McKeogh had expanded them into a suitable number of words. A few hours after Joe took leave of civilization, McKeogh was tapping out the nature man's final statement, "I shall see no living soul for two months," when Joe walked in in his G-string.

He said no word. He merely sat down and made no move toward the woods. Further, he made no answer to McKeogh's exclamations, no reply when his friend pleaded, "Be a man, Joe, be a man" and in an impassioned address pointed out that the whole world was watching him. Even twenty-four years later McKeogh can scarcely bring himself to discuss it. "I tell you it was hell," he says. At any rate, three weeks later Joe was famous and was still in the cabin, or close to it. He became as thrilled as the rest of the world by McKeogh's stories about his single-handed fight against "the tooth and claw of nature." He agreed to let his beard grow, and to lie naked in the sun and get tanned up. Often the nature man, after a meal in the cabin, actually went for walks in the woods, and once or twice he slept in deserted camps instead of McKeogh's headquarters.

McKeogh's creative spirit withered under the strain. The fine specificity with which he had documented Joe's first accounts of his terrific struggle gradually vanished. Once, while McKeogh was suffering over his typewriter, Joe was sprawled in the sun before the cabin when he heard footsteps that his trained instinct told him were not those of a friend. He loped into the cabin, streaked by the typing McKeogh, and scrambled under the bed. When McKeogh opened the door, a foot prevented him from closing it. The foot belonged to Allie Deming, a trapper who had been reading the newspapers.

"Where's Joe?" he asked, his expression indicating that the question was rhetorical.

"What do you mean, 'Where's Joe?' "

"I been watching around here for three days."

Before McKeogh could answer, Joe surrendered.

"Let him in, Mac," he said. "Maybe we can come to an understanding."

Deming was employed at $2.50 a day. He later suggested that his pay be doubled, and it was. Still later he hinted that he be given an automobile. He was put off from day to day and the motor never materialized. Deming's employment led to the discharge of Allen, the guide who stood ready to retrieve Joe's messages if there ever had been any. Allen suggested that this was not a wise move. It was decided that he was right. His pay was continued, although he retired to his home in Farmington, Maine. The additional expense was borne by the *Post,* one of whose editors wrote McKeogh, "wouldn't it be fine if Joe fought a wildcat?"

648

Joe gave hardly a thought to the suggestion. He spent his days squatting in the woods, for Allie's visit had convinced him that his spot in the sun before the cabin was not safe. McKeogh was encouraged, visiting Joe daily with his lunch and advice. He'd shout, "You'll make a million, Joe, if you get going!" but the hunched figure would not reply. McKeogh says it suddenly dawned on him that Knowles had no money sense. McKeogh then changed his strategy. What purported to be Joe's birch-bark record for September 16th said casually, "A yearling bear fell victim to my pitfall last night." A day or two later, Joe moved and seemed to hear when McKeogh told him that the citizens of Boston so admired his pluck that they were building a statue of him on the Common. "In a bearskin, Joe, in a bearskin!" McKeogh shouted. This canard profoundly impressed Joe. He began digging a pit designed to snare a bear and give validity to the statue on Boston Common. He went for a walk in the woods and actually found a deer. It had been dead some time, but Joe skinned it anyway and tacked the hide to the cabin door. The hide was so fragrant that McKeogh ripped it down and threw it into the woods. This incident destroyed Joe's newly gained morale. He plunged once more into motionless melancholy, and McKeogh's impassioned apologies could not quicken him.

By this time McKeogh was pretty disheartened himself. For weeks a craving for apple pie had tortured him. He dreamed of pie one night and on the following day set out for Eustis, twelve miles away, and bought one for his dinner. When he returned he was too tired to eat, so he placed it on a window sill to keep for next day. In the early morning he heard a step and whirled in time to see his pie vanishing into the wilderness in the hands of his pal, the nature man.

Now the breach was too wide to heal. Knowles and McKeogh never spoke as friends again. McKeogh kept on because he had got himself into it and couldn't get out. Ten days before the nightmare ended, he was visited by five Maine game wardens. One of them had copies of the *Post* in which Joe had been represented as killing the bear. Knowles had neglected to take out a hunting permit. While the wardens were still there, McKeogh had another visitor. He was Bert Ford, reporter for Mr. Hearst's Boston *American*, who said he was out to expose Joe as a fake. The wardens and reporter left in a group to find Knowles, and McKeogh loped into the wilderness and sought out the melancholy Joe in his customary retreat. The news made no impression on the recumbent nature man. "You'll be put in prison, Joe, you'll be put in prison!" McKeogh shouted, but he could not pierce Joe's trance. It was not until the sound of footsteps was heard that the nature man condescended to act. He crashed off through the woods with the game wardens in pursuit.

649

Dodging behind trees, lying prone in concealing bushes, he led the life of a fugitive for ten days, and later declared, "I was like a wild animal at bay." He had been forced to live on food found in trappers' cabins.

Joe sneaked back to McKeogh's shack finally and was persuaded to change his running territory from Kempshall Point and environs to a base twelve miles away, near Eustis. This was on October 1st, and although Joe was somewhat safer from arrest his troubles were not over. He was to emerge October 4th, and in the meantime, somewhere, somehow, a bear had to be found, killed, and skinned. Joe had repeatedly been described in the public prints as the wearer of a bearskin cloak. He had fashioned a sort of skirt from the deerskin which had offended McKeogh, and it was imperative that he make good on the rest of his costume.

When defeat seemed certain, Bill Hall, a friend of the trapper, Allie Deming, shot a bear. Allie bought the hide for $12. It was draped over Joe's shoulders despite his complaints that he could not stand the smell. He also protested the decision that, to avoid arrest, he should emerge from the wilderness across the Canadian boundary at Megantic, sixty miles away. He said he was afraid he'd get lost in the woods trying to find Megantic. McKeogh hired an Indian to guide the nature man through the wilderness. Low in mind but high in odor, he trudged off behind his chaperon.

McKeogh made his way to Megantic by canoe and buckboard. He found it an up-and-coming village. Some of its go-getters, on hearing of Joe's approaching arrival, decided to arrest and hold him, on the premise that his detention would draw large and profitable crowds. McKeogh met a Canadian game warden with a warrant charging Joe with building a fire without a permit. He engaged a room in the local hotel, bought a half-dozen bottles of whiskey, and invited the Canadian game warden to his room. At about four in the afternoon McKeogh walked unsteadily from the room, alone. About the same time, the Indian deserted Knowles ten miles from Megantic, believing that the nature man could find the rest of the way by himself. Knowles walked three miles and got lost. He was trying to hire a horse and buggy at a settlement near the railway when he heard a train approaching. He flagged it, borrowed fifty cents for fare from the conductor, and rode into 'Megantic on cushions. He found McKeogh, and together they started for Boston.

Joe's spirits rose as the train bore him back to a world which seemed composed exclusively of frantic crowds who loved and admired him. The only flaw in his happiness was his bearskin. Uninterested passengers complained. The conductor tactfully suggested that Joe ride in the baggage car. Joe was indignant. A compromise was arrived at.

The bearskin would stay in the baggage car and Joe would remain in the passenger coach. A gray flannel shirt and trousers were purchased at a way stop. Joe changed back into his bearskin before each subsequent stop and each speech before cheering crowds. Between trains at Augusta he paid, with funds provided by the *Post,* $205 in fines for infractions of the game laws.

There were banquets and receptions at the larger towns. It took Joe five days to reach Boston. When he arrived there, the North Station was packed. A messenger who had to get to the train gates was passed hand over hand above the heads of the crowds. A woman at the edge of the throng butted frantically against the human wall and cried, "Let me touch him! Let me touch him!" until she fell unconscious and was carted off to a hospital.

An impromptu parade formed and, as Joe stepped into his car at the head of it, McKeogh said, "I suppose you don't need me now."

"No, I don't," said Joe, and McKeogh went home. He never saw Knowles again.

"Thousands upon thousands shouted themselves hoarse as the fur-clad man passed through the city streets," said the *Post,* and added, "It was the largest crowd since Bryan." At Boston Common, Joe was greeted by city and state officials and made a brief speech. Then the triumphal procession moved to Harvard University.

Here Dr. Dudley Allen Sargent, director of physical education at the University, who had examined Joe before he entered the wilderness, said that Knowles had grown a tenth of an inch and that his "physical condition proves the scientific worth of this remarkable experiment." He added, "He has not suffered from lack of salt." Dr. Sargent invited Joe to his school, the Sargent Physical Training School for Women. As Joe entered, five hundred students sang a song especially written to commemorate his triumph. While Dr. Sargent lectured, Joe exhibited his muscle. He bared his torso so the girls could see better.

This was on October ninth. Knowles remained a happy man until December 2nd. On that day, Mr. Hearst's Boston *American* began its threatened exposé, in which it called Joe "The Dr. Cook of the Maine woods," and declared unequivocally that he was a fake. Each day for two weeks it printed a first-page box in which it dared Joe to sue for libel. Although Ford, who wrote the stories, attempted to prove categorically that Joe had done none of the things he claimed to have done, public interest centred on the bearskin. Ford said he had examined it, that he had found in it two bullet holes, indicating that Joe had not killed the bear with a club, and that the skin had been professionally tanned and cured. In the public mind the crucial question became, after a day or two, "Does Joe's bearskin stink?" If it did, it proved that it had not been tanned by an expert, that the job might have been done by Joe himself. All other points were somehow ignored. The *Post* accepted the challenge. Its entire front page of December 8, 1913, was devoted to affidavits, most of whose signers solemnly swore that Joe's bearskin smelled to high heaven.

When this failed to convince skeptics, Joe bought a bear. He shipped it to the Dead River region, tied it up with a clothes-line, and dragged it over the rocky ground five miles to his pit. He shoved it into the pit and beat it to death with a club, before witnesses.

For this act, Joe was threatened with arrest by the Society for Prevention of Cruelty to Animals. Clearly events were closing in on him and he decided to seek a virgin field for his talents as far from Boston as possible. He had made about three thousand dollars out of vaudeville appearances, and with this he set out for San Francisco. Upon his arrival there he was profoundly pleased by an extraordinary manifestation of the Hearst journalistic genius. In Boston the Hearst paper had exposed Joe as a fake. In San Francisco, the Hearst papers considered Joe the epitome of integrity. The *Examiner* hired him to repeat his Maine exploit in the Siskiyou Mountains.

Eight days after Joe stripped to his G-string in California, the World War broke out and the nature man moved progressively back into the inside pages of the paper. Little added circulation resulted from the stunt, and when Joe came out six weeks later he was quoted as asking rather bitterly, "What does the public care about a naked man in the wilderness when Belgian babies are having their hands cut off?" He appeared at a few banquets and at Boy Scout jamborees, but soon people stopped paying attention to him. In the summer of 1916 he was among the unemployed when an executive of Hearst's New York *Journal* had what seemed to be a stroke of genius. "How about bringing Knowles East and sending a woman into the woods with him?" he asked. Joe was shipped East. Once more he stripped to his G-string and edged into the greenery of Essex County, New York, with the slim loveliness of Elaine Hammerstein and numerous chaperons. After a few days Miss Hammerstein, a granddaughter of Oscar Hammerstein, quit the wilderness declaring that mosquitoes had convinced her that the experiment was impractical. Joe followed her out. Thus he passed finally from the news, still a fairly romantic figure in his G-string.

Joe is sixty-eight years old now and says that at last he has found the perfect life. He was married shortly after his return from Essex County to an old sweetheart, Miss Marion Louise Humphrey, of Dedham, Massachusetts. He lives now with her near Cape Disappointment on the coast of the State of Washington in a house built of driftwood. He is very mellow these days, and his crazily angled home has a sign near the door which reads "Welcome Stranger, Pause a While."

The land it is set on is lapped on three sides by the Pacific, and when June and December tides rise to their height, Joe's house is on an island and his sign is somewhat meaningless. Yet when the June tides are gone and summer days are fine, he has many visitors, for his home is not far from Seaview, Washington, near the Oregon line. Then little boys are led by their mothers to a point near Joe and are told, "There's the nature man." Joe beams at them, for he still likes attention.

He has been permanently marked, it seems, by the grandiose periods that described his exploits of the past. As he speaks of "Mother Ocean" he has a fine proprietary air. His style is reminiscent of a McKeogh dispatch. "Mother Ocean," he said recently, "supplies all my wants. All I have to do is sit and wait, and she throws up what I need at my door. She gave me driftwood for my house. The other day she gave me a can of kerosene for light. She gives me clams and fish and crabs. The pancakes I had for breakfast this morning were made out of flour from a wrecked ship. And one time last summer Mother Ocean brought me in some of the finest etching paper I have ever used."

Joe, however, augments the inflow from Mother Ocean by painting. (Remember, he was a part-time artist on the Boston *Post* before he became the nature man.) His paintings are vigorous, the draftsmanship accurate, the color bold. He frequently turns out designs for the covers of outdoor magazines, and some years ago he did a series of murals in the Hotel Monticello at Longview, Washington. They are filled with Indians and cowboys, and one local critic said they had "plenty of giddyap."

He expresses no curiosity concerning his colleagues of the woods, who are scattered far and wide. The lovely Miss Hammerstein, middle-aged now, is married to a Los Angeles insurance broker. Allie Deming, the Maine trapper who trapped Joe, is nearly fifty and is still in the woods. McKeogh, in his sixties, is an investigator in the Department of Internal Revenue at Boston. He sometimes shakes his gray head sadly and says, "We could have made a million if Joe had only acted right."

Joe is perhaps the most cheerful of the lot.

"I can get along without money," he says, "but I can't get along without nature."

The virgin of Stamboul[1]

In 1919, Universal produced "The Virgin of Stamboul," a costume
picture starring Priscilla Dean. It was the entirely original story
of a Turkish maiden abducted by a villain, Wallace Beery, and rescued
by a hero, Wheeler Oakman, who off the screen was Miss Dean's husband. Costume pictures at the time had become as serious a menace to
the box-office as theme songs today, and Universal feared that this
latest and most expensive of their dress parades would never bring
back even the cost of the celluloid.

Preparations for the stunt were almost as elaborate as the production of the picture. I took a trip to Little Turkey east of Chatham
Square and found that in the war of the tea-houses all the Turks had
been routed by Greeks and Armenians. I befriended an Assyrian,
Khalie Ossmun, who promised to dig up eight Turks and he did.
They looked as if he had dug them out of sewers. Two of them were
ex-dishwashers, one was a pastry cook, another a porter and two sold
home-made lemonade out of huge brass tureens strapped to their backs
like papooses. The seventh was a fierce-looking Musselman with an
ugly scar that almost cut his face in two, and the eighth was a white-
haired old Turk with a pedigree who kept mumbling all the time that
his brother was a "pasha." I found out later that a "pasha" was a
rubber in a bath.

My Assyrian friend Khalie being the most intelligent and persona-
ble, I appointed him chief Sheik Ali Ben Mohamed, ruler of this
motley band. The knife-scarred Turk whom we called "Goom" became lord high aide-de-camp and the white-haired old mumbler I
turned into the Grand Caliph Shafkrat. The pastry cook became his
lordship, the Effendi Houssein, the two ex-dishwashers acquired the
titles of Generals Hamedan and Rafkhat respectively and the lemonade
pedlars became the grand eunuchs of the Sheik's harem, Jamil and
Abdul Halsh.

After freely distributing these high ranks and titles, I let them spend
a night at the Turkish bath which was something new to the Turks
and then transformed my mob of eight into a high diplomatic body on
a secret mission from the Levant. A theatrical costumer dressed them
in lavish splendor from pompons to aigrets and from sea-green trousers
to gold-crescented turbans. The next thing was to teach the Turks the
manners and customs of their native land. I persuaded a friend of
mine, Alexander Brown, who had spent many years in Constantinople,

---

[1] Reprinted from *Phantom Fame*, by permission of Simon and Schuster, Inc.
Copyright, 1931, by Harry Reichenbach. Pp. 106–13.

as general representative of the American Licorice Company, to show them how to act with true Turkish elegance. For an entire week he drilled them in handling table service. He taught them how to wear their decorations, how to salaam, and how the eunuchs were to taste all food before their masters would take the chance.

Another week passed rehearsing the Sheik on the story he would have to tell newspapermen, while all the other members of this august body were warned to keep their mouths shut. For many hours I would sit around with my Turks in a rehearsal hall and hurl questions at them which I thought reporters might ask and to all inquiries they were to give but a single answer, "We cannot talk. You must ask the master." The master knew his speech by heart and would say nothing he hadn't memorized.

We were ready to make our arrival into New York from Turkey. I had my secretary telephone the Hotel Majestic and say, "Montreal is calling." I spoke to the hotel manager, Jack Heath, in a tortured dialect explaining very dimly that, "We are the Turkish mission which comes to your country on a very secret importance. Please reserve for us the best rooms of the suite and protect us please from the newspaper reporting!" Two days later our royal party arrived at the Majestic. O. O. McIntyre, then the hotel's press agent, told me later that "the gang not only looked like Turks but they smelled like Turks."

At four o'clock that afternoon the Grandees of the Porte made their first public appearance in full regalia, going to the hotel tea-room in state according to all the rules of Turkish royalty as laid down by the American Licorice Company's manager. Ossmun and Sheik acted as if cameras were turning in all corners. As I passed through the lobby, John McMahon, New York dramatic critic confided to me, "I understand this is a Turkish war mission."

McIntyre tipped off the newspapers reticently as if they were being let into a secret of international significance. That night the royal suite was a reporters' convention. The next morning the newspapers throughout the country and throughout the world gave many thousands of columns detailing the story of Sheik Ali Ben Mohamed's strange and mysterious mission in America. The hired costumes received the most minute and painstaking descriptions in the press. The New York "Tribune" pictured my Chatham Square Assyrian as follows:

"There was the Sheik Ben Mohamed of Hedjaz, which all students of the League of Nations know to be a newly formed kingdom of Arabia, the subjects of which bear no love for the Turkish Empire, from which it was dismembered.

"A burnous of maroon, margined with a wide band of yellow silk and piped with pea-green, partially hid more gorgeous garments of the

Arab nobleman. His fez lent shape to the white folds of linen that draped over it and swathed about his neck. The linen was bound closely about his head by a turban of orange pattern that revealed the Sheik as a holy man."

Even the Prince of Wales's latest clothes were never more faithfully reported than these gaudy remnants of a Shubert flop. Then Khalie Ossmun recited with a marvelous memory the little speech we had rehearsed in the hall on Sixth Avenue:

"Gentlemen, I come to this country, which to my desert-trained eyes is like the heaven promised in the Koran, to seek the betrothed of my younger brother. She is Sari, so beautiful that in all Turkey there was none like her. She was known as the Virgin of Stamboul."

Then he proceeded to give a complete summary of the nine-reel thriller starring Priscilla Dean, but the reporters swallowed every word avidly as news of the first magnitude.

"Her father was very rich," murmured the Sheik, raising a weary hand to shield his piercing black eyes; "her mother too was of royal blood. Sari had an English governess. The American soldiers came to Stamboul. They saw Sari. One of them she saw. They spoke together, she proud of her few words of English. Then she disappeared. That same day the American transport sailed for this country. For three months we searched Turkey. Sari's mother died of grief. Then her father. We had established that she was not dead. We knew all too surely that it was a love affair that had caused the Virgin of Stamboul to disappear."

All this the reporters copied verbatim. Then the Sheik told them that the Burns and Val O'Farrell Detective Agencies had been retained to aid in the world-wide search. He made them print an offer of ten thousand dollars reward for information leading to Sari's discovery. He told them that she was heiress to about a hundred million. He didn't even forget the detail that her English governess, after weeping many days, had drowned herself in the Bosporus. By killing off the entire household in Turkey we eliminated the possibility of any one cabling there for confirmation.

As soon as the Sheik had completed his tale the reporters again fell to describing his garments. Even that lynx-eyed newspaperman, Boyden Sparkes, devoted half a column to the costume. He reported the silver-mounted scimitar with ebony hilt and the maroon burnous that only partially concealed a robin-egg blue tunic braided with lavender. He noted the baldric of raspberry cord and the purple jacket lined with vermilion silk and striped with many bands of gold braid. But he also detected what he told me later was the first scintilla of suspicion, that beneath all this majesty of attire peeped out the starched cuffs of a shirt, a bit soiled, that might have been made in Troy, New York!

656

Up to this point the Sheik had been doing splendidly. But the starched cuffs bothered Sparkes. He asked the Turkish lord whether he knew any Americans and Ossmun promptly answered, "I know your Mr. Henry Morgenthau very well. I am to have dinner with him." I had anticipated the question and the day before I learned from Morgenthau's secretary that he would be away for the week-end. It was therefore safe to use his name.

When the interview ended none of the reporters questioned the Sheik's story in the slightest. They ran out into the hall, hugged each other with delight, and dashed to the nearest telephones to report the greatest romantic news scoop in years. Only Boyden Sparkes seemed worried. He hesitated, then went into the manager's office and we heard him call up Morgenthau. To my amazement Morgenthau was in. I vanished. So did McIntyre.

The next day Sparkes wrote just as elaborate and full an account of the story as all the others, but near the end he added, "Mr. Morgenthau said Sheik Ben Mohamed was a blasted liar. Mr. Morgenthau said more. He said the Sheik's costume was too good to be true. He made a solemn statement that he wasn't going to have the Sheik dine with him, and was unkind enough to call him a fake. But that won't interfere with the early release of that thrilling picture, 'The Virgin of Stamboul.'"

In view of Morgenthau's statement it seemed that the publicity stunt was killed. But it wasn't. There was that quality of fascination about the incident that made it almost better than truth. It had become romance, illusion. It was one of those episodes which gave public and press the feeling that if it didn't happen, it should have happened! Besides getting its quota of one to two columns in every daily, the Fox News Weekly, Kintograms and Pathé Weekly each paid the Sheik fifty dollars to go to Central Park and pose for the news reels. The Hippodrome Theatre gave a box party to the royal visitors and even spread a carpet from the curb to the lobby that the holy feet of the dishwashers and lemonade pedlars should not touch unhallowed ground. Many night clubs invited the Sheik and his party and undoubtedly recognized among them some of their former help.

A few days later when Sari was found by Val O'Farrell in a rooming-house on Kenmare Street, the newspapers again covered the story. The reporters swarmed into the royal suite at the Majestic and were treated to a stirring Oriental scene. Thru an open door they saw a young hysterical girl tossing in a bed surrounded by the Sheik and five kneeling Turks, while a physician stood near her constantly jabbing hypodermics into the mattress as a nurse anxiously made notes on a chart. The Sheik, deeply touched and distracted, found time however to come out and tell the reporters that Sari had been saved and that the party would sail Saturday on the White Star Line. In everybody's presence he handed ten one-thousand-dollar bills to Val O'Farrell who returned them later on when nobody was around. The Sheik thanked the American press for its cooperation and said that it was no wonder, judging by its press, that the American people were the most enlightened in the world. An agent of the White Star Line entered with nine first-class cabin tickets. Not a single cue went wrong.

The girl who played Sari for me was an accomplished actress, but as she could speak neither Turkish nor French, we did not allow the reporters to interview her. We told them she was delirious, but we made her sit up quietly in bed to get her picture taken. The press reported every detail faithfully to the end and "The Virgin of Stamboul" scored a record at the box-office.

Prince Zerdecheno [1]

I have not quite the same feeling toward Lord Beaverbrook that I have for Prince Zerdecheno. Perhaps that is because I had the inestimable privilege of acquaintance with the Prince, and knew Lord Beaverbrook simply as a name out of the newspapers. But I think my prejudice lies deeper than that. For Lord Beaverbrook, if you remember the recent stories, employed his assumed nobility as a device for defrauding gullible ladies. With his charming Mayfair manner, he induced some fifty maids and matrons to believe that they were being positively careless with their money or jewels unless such things were given into his hands for safekeeping. Of course, he did this with a becoming air. And his undeniable talent for the strange profession which he followed is plainly apparent if you scan the list of names he successively bore: Baron Beaverbrook, Karl Edwards, John V. Wiedemeier, Arthur Brooks, Sigmund Engel, Sigmund Runne, Sidney Renne, Wallace Siegfried, and Karl von Edwards.

But it cannot be denied, even after observing such evidence of praiseworthy resourcefulness and a real feeling for romance, that my Lord gave a deplorably commercial taint to his practice of the earnest art of imposture.

Now Prince Zerdecheno was moved by no such material principles. Of course I do not presume to say that he did not manage a neat living out of his elegant attitude. But I am positive that he pursued no cash-in-hand profits. He wanted, most of all, to receive the deference due to a Crown Prince.

---

[1] Reprinted from *That's New York!* by Morris Markey and John Bull (New York: Macy-Masius; 1927), pp. 101–6. Copyright, 1927, by Macy-Masius.

Zerdecheno was married. His wife was a pretty Kentucky girl, and wise. But I never knew certainly whether she believed in her husband's royalty or not. Together they lived in a furnished apartment in the fashionable East Sixties, and they paid their rent promptly. But the only suit of clothes the Prince owned was a London cutaway. He could afford, too, a fresh gardenia for his lapel every morning. But generally when he accepted invitations to fashionable teas he went alone. The Princess, it seems, had great difficulties in the delivery of her gowns. They never came on time.

He made no secret of his genteel shabbiness. Indeed, he usually introduced the subject himself, diffidently and in a manner that bestowed resounding praise upon his wife—and upon the custom of marrying for love. The last time he explained this situation (the versions rarely agreed) was at a gathering in a rather fashionable lady's house. There was quite a crowd, but when his drawling voice turned to his affairs, nearly everybody stopped to listen.

"I am going home before long"—invariably he introduced the story in that fashion. "I am going home before long. My father"—nodding here, ceremonially, and pausing in his speech. "My father is growing old, and I think perhaps that he will forgive me as he realizes that he must die soon, and some one must take over the government.

"You see, he never forgave me for marrying an American. He had placed seven hundred women in my private palace—and from these I was to select as many wives as necessary. The notion of marrying just one woman, and by the Christian ceremony, staggered him. Coming to America staggered him, too—giving up all the magnificence in which I lived, to dwell in a little apartment with only one valet.

"Are you bored? —Well, well, well—" His eyes became reflective, and he put the tips of his long fingers together. "Perhaps you would like to know what I gave up for this American Princess of mine, and to live in America?

"You see, the blood of Egypt's Pharaohs runs in my veins. My lineage extends back four thousand years. And all my fathers lived only for the luxury they could gather about them. In my private palace, for example— Remember, it was built for me when I was a baby, or I never would have allowed it. Well, it was all of white marble. Three hundred and fifty rooms and a courtyard of twenty acres. In the stables were six hundred camels and six hundred horses, and my servants numbered four hundred, all seasoned soldiers.

"In my early days I never dressed in any cloth but white satin. My favorite robe, I remember, was made of twenty yards. Thirty men were killed in a battle as they brought it in a caravan over the hills from Paris, where it had been made especially for me. In my hat was a ring of diamonds supporting six ostrich plumes. And the hilt of my sword was one huge emerald. I will not tell you of the seven hundred wives. It would bore you. It bores me. I—I am in love!

"And all that magnificence is gone. For my father refuses to send me money. Yet I am a philosopher; a philosopher in love. And what could be more delightful?"

I did not blame Prince Zerdecheno, that day, for quietly slipping into his pocket the $100 bill which a deeply impressed spinster lady gave him. Why not? She had been amused and thrilled. It was at least a hundred times better than the movies. And the movies cost a dollar.

As it fell out, however, some earthbound tailor or other complained to the courts about his bill, which Prince Zerdecheno seemed determined to forget. The tabloid papers spied a story. And pretty soon there were dispatches from Europe saying that the territory known as Turkestan had no local government, had no king, and certainly had no Crown Prince. The palace, too, seemed hard to locate.

So they came down heavily upon Zerdecheno's head. And finally even the government got interested. Some disposition, they felt, must be made of such a fellow. They could discover no crime that he had committed in this country, and for a little while it appeared astonishingly as if nothing could be done about him after all. But then somebody remembered that he stole an overcoat in London one time. He was deported.

The next few weeks were rather tragic for the poor fellow. When his ship reached England the authorities would not let him land. He threatened, of course, hinting at the power of his arm and even threatening to call out a troop of camels. But the Britishers were stern, and back he came to America. But America, officially, was rid of him, and would not hear of his putting foot on our sacred soil again. And so, for a time, he simply traveled back and forth between the two continents. At last France took him and made, so I hear, a good pants presser of him.

But I don't believe he will stick to his job long. The sense of kingship has gotten into his blood. Almost certainly he has an actual belief in his royal prerogative. And some day—who knows?—he may march proudly into St. James' Palace, his Kentucky Princess on his arm, offering brotherly respects to his Majesty the King of England. I shall certainly continue to expect that much of him.

Jesse James Benton has but an innocent and uncomplicated practical joke to describe; in fact, he did not even plan a hoax. But his delight in the discomfiture of his victims is so wholehearted that it is communicated to the reader.

"The Awl" is rather a parlor game than a story. I encountered it some thirty years ago in southern New England, but the present version comes from New York State. Internal evidence suggests that it is an old-timer; in fact, the story may fall flat today because many an American audience could be found in which nobody could define an awl or a last—or, perhaps, even a cobbler!

The story of the magic turtle has its setting in Paris, and I hesitated about including it, for that reason. I am grateful for the moral support of Mr. Samuel Hopkins Adams, who quite independently suggested its inclusion.

Timeworthy proved himself phony adman Keating.

Mr. Adams calls the story of the Staples sisters "the most elaborate and skilful fake in radio annals," and no reader is likely to think this an overstatement.

The milkmaid[1]

I ate at the boarding house run by Mrs. Lemons. She were feeding about one hundred miners at a meal, and they were howling for milk, each and every meal. If there were condensed milk in them days I never saw any.

After a couple of days of listening to them, I said to Mrs. Lemons, "If I can manage it to furnish you with milk, ma'am, what will you give me a gallon, and how much will you contract for each day?"

She figured awhile and said, "I'll pay you fifty cents a gallon and take from fifty to seventy-five gallons a day."

"If I start this dairy to furnish you with milk, how long will you contract for?"

"One year, young man," she said.

---

[1] From Jesse James Benton: *Cow by the Tail* (Boston: Houghton Mifflin Co.; 1943), pp. 189–92.

"Fine. I'll leave to get the cows in the morning." That night we signed the contract.

There was no place, in a way, to buy milk stock in Arizona, no big dairies of any sort or milk herds. I'd have to ride around to the small Mormon villages and buy cows and calves here and there from the small Mormon farmers. I pulled out for the San Pedro River settlements of Mormons, about fifty mile to the west, and returned some time later with twenty-seven cows and their calves. I started building corrals and sheds and bought milk pails and were soon ready to begin. I do believe I owned the first real dairy, run as a dairy, in the Territory of Arizona.

I took over where the calves left off, for they had done my milking on the drive. Them cows were sure bad actors. Some would give a pint, some a quart, and I'd get kicked into the fence and over the fence. The buckets got so dented up that I had to send over to Willcox and Tombstone for another lot of them, as the first were now past holding milk. I think I got about two gallons that first morning, and that was half dirt.

"Well," I says to myself, "them scurvy Mormon farmers sure told me some of the damndest lies about these cows being milk cows. They are range-bred or I'm a horse's Adam's apple."

I was plumb disgusted and telling about it down town when an old Mormon miner come up to me and said, "Say, pardner, them cows you bought bin milked by wimmin folks. Don't you know a Mormon man never milks? Tonight you put on a dress when you go down to milk and you won't have no trouble."

That were a new wrinkle on my horns about cattle.

He says, "See my lip? That is a kick I got from a cow one night after my wife left me." He sure did have a funny-looking lip, all gouged out and crooked.

Well, I thought it over and went to my landlady and said, "I want to hire some of your girls to work for me."

"Lord," she said, "These girls can't milk. I got 'em here from Kansas City to wait on table, and that's all they know."

When I told her about what the Mormon had said, she offered to loan me a dress to wear.

"All right, ma'am," says I, "you and me is about the same size, I reckon." I said that to please her as she weighed over two hundred and me only one hundred and sixty-five.

She brung me out a red calico dress and I done it up in papers and went down to the corral where I put it on. Perfect fit!—after I tucked it in and tied a string around the waist. She had given me a sunbonnet too, which I tied under my chin, to fool them cows. Also I had shaved clean that day, moustache and all, as I didn't aim to have another failure when milking time come round. I fooled more than the cows.

I was getting my pails ready and patting one of the cows, which were acting calm and agreeable, when along come a bunch of miners just off the shift. Ho! What a surprise—a new dairy started in town and a fine young lady for milkmaid. Every old miner passing close to the fence had to get a better look at them cows and milkmaid, and would say, "Howdy, lady." I'd bow and smile, but never say a word. They finally would go on.

Pretty soon they begun to come back for milk and would say, "Lady, have you any milk to sell?"

"Yes, sir, plenty," I said in a falsetto voice that I tried to make sweet and ladylike.

So everything went fine, cows behaved like lambs, and I had three dates for that night. All three men come to the house about eight o'clock and asked for the new milkmaid. I had posted the boy working for me in front to tell each one that I had went to town. They all three come into town looking for me, each one separate, not knowing about the others. Some of the boys and I was watching, and it sure looked funny to see them three old fellers looking up and down the streets and waiting around on the corners for me to show up, and there I was within fifty feet of them.

They hung around till near midnight, and it got just too good to keep. The boys and me were near busting with it. We told it around, and by next day everybody knew it. Say, those three miners had to leave town the hazing got so bad!

The awl[1]

There was going to be a hanging in the Schoharie jail yard, and Zadig Lape and his boy Sam counted on going. Zadig's woman wanted to go too, but Zadig told her that it was no kind of a thing for a woman to see. Then she said it couldn't be decent for a boy to see, and Sam couldn't go. Zadig didn't care if he couldn't. But Sam, who was kinda simple anyway, wanted to go because he had never seen a hanging. So he just let out an awful beller and hollered and bawled until his ma told him he could go to the hanging if he'd tell her when he got back just how it was. He give his word he would, and away he and his pa went in the big bobsleigh, for it was wintertime,

---

[1] From Emelyn Elizabeth Gardner: *Folklore from the Schoharie Hills, New York* (Ann Arbor: University of Michigan Press; 1937), pp. 182–4.

behind Zadig's spanking team of sorrels. Horses was Zadig's "specialty" when there wan't no hanging to take his attention.

Well, the hanging went off all right, and Zadig and Sam started for home. When they got there, Zadig went to the barn to fodder the stock, and Sam went into the house to tell his maw how things had gone. He told her all about the way the prisoner was led out, the praying for him and all. Then when it come time to show how the job was done, Sam went and got a rope and fastened one end of it to a big iron hook in the ceiling and made a slipnoose in the other end. When he got the noose all fixed about ten foot from the floor, he told his ma that, if she would stand on a chair that he set for her and let him slip the noose over her head, he'd show her just how the hanging was done.

She was so simple that she done just as Sam told her, and when he got everything fixed just right, he said: "And now they kicked the block out from in under the feller like this." And with that he kicked the chair right out from in under his ma's feet. He never thought to kill his ma, because she'd been awful good to him. But he was that simple he didn't realize what he was a-doing. No more did his ma, because she was simple, too.

When he saw his ma a-hanging there looking so kinda strange with her eyes a-popping out of her head, he was scared and shoved the chair back in under her feet. But of course it didn't do no good because her neck was busted plum in two. Sam got the butcher knife and cut the rope, and when he seen how his ma just fell outa the chair onto the floor in a heap, he lost all the few wits he'd ever owned. But he had sense enough to know he'd killed his ma and would likely be hung for murder like the feller he'd seen hung at Schoharie. Not knowing what to do but hoping to save his hide, he drug his ma over to her rocking chair by the windy and somehow propped her up in the chair with her knitting in her hands naturaler than life.

When Zadig come from the barn, he seen her a-setting there as he'd seen her hundreds of times before—only not noticing him—and he thought to have a little fun with her. He was great on jokes, surprising folks when they wa'n't expecting nothing and the like of that. So he made a snowball—what he thought was a soft one—and trun it agin the windy. But by Jocks, it went right through the glass and hit his woman on the temple, or at least so it appeared. Sam hadn't fixed her to stand snowballing, so she just toppled out of her chair onto the floor. Zadig felt awful because he hadn't counted on scaring her into a fainting fit. He rushed into the house, threw snow into her face, and done everything he'd ever hearn tell of and made up some, to bring folks out of a fainting spell. But nothing worked. He called to Sam, but Sam was out of hearing. After a spell he made up his mind that his woman was dead and that he had killed her. He knew that when the neighbors found out, he would be tried for murder and most likely hung like that feller at Schoharie. Yet in a way he was innercent. He had liked his woman and been good to her.

All at once he thought of a plan to save himself from being hung. He went and got Sarah's bunnit and blanket shawl and wrapped her up for a ride. Then he went to the barn and hitched the horses to a sleigh that was loaded with straw that he had pitched down from the mow for bedding the stock when it come chore time. He druv up to the back door that nobody could see from the road and somehow got Sarah a-top of the load. Her body sagged over so she 'peared to be half laying down. But she looked quite natural and Zadig didn't lose no time in jumping onto the seat and driving off like the Old Boy hisself was after him. Up hill, down dale he went, lickety-split, plying the gad at every jump until he come to a steep pitch with a sharp turn at the foot. As the horses came near the turn, he lashed them to top speed, the sleigh slewed as he had calculated, and over she went into a gully. The horses was so scared that they tore themselves loose and legged for home and left Sarah and Zadig with the hull load of straw a-top of them.

I forgot to say that at the foot of the hill, where the upset was, stood a cobbler's shop. In the shop was the cobbler working away at the— at the—at the—

(At this point, anyone listening to the story is supposed to supply the word "awl" or "last," whichever comes to his mind. Thereupon the storyteller smiles and remains silent. The listener usually says: "Well, what did the cobbler do?" Thereupon the storyteller replies: "You have said it. That's all" or "That's the last," according to the word supplied. "I wasn't there to see.")

The magic turtle[1]

At the time of which I was speaking, there was an architectural student who lived with another American on a little street running into the rue de l'Université. His rooms were on the third floor, and under him the proprietress of the first-floor shop had on her window sill a goldfish tank in which she kept several fish and a very small turtle. These were the delights of her leisure moments, sharing her affections with her old husband and her cat. My friend, leaning out of

[1] From Hans Zinsser: *As I Remember Him: the Biography of R. S.* (Boston: Little, Brown & Company; Atlantic Monthly Press; 1940), pp. 178–9.

his window on mellow evenings, smoking his pipe, could look down directly into the tank, and he often watched her as she broke bread crumbs for her pets, muttering terms of endearment. On such an evening he suddenly conceived a brilliant idea. The next day he went to the fish market and bought a series of six turtles, ranging in size from one like a five-franc silver piece to one about six inches across. At the same time he bought wire, a bit of cheesecloth, and a bamboo fishing pole, which he smuggled into his rooms after dark and from which he fashioned himself a very small scoop net. Each day, after that, very early in the morning, he would lean out of his window, fish out the old lady's turtle, and put in a bigger one. The first exchange she didn't notice. When the second one went in, this time about three inches across, she looked surprised, but only said, *"Tiens! Tiens!"* When the third one appeared, she began to show signs of excitement. First she called her husband; then the neighbor's wife; gradually the other neighbors. There were animated discussions. The facteur offered advice; said she was feeding too heavily. The fourth turtle changed the place into a public sensation. The old lady began to tell people her system. The fifth one, about five inches across the top, started a riot—not without some tragedy, for this turtle began to chew the fish. The old man bought a separate small tank for the sole surviving goldfish. A reporter from the *Paris-Midi* came in and wrote a story. It was a headliner. Madame Perrier became famous. She was interviewed, and it was said that her husband would be decorated.

The architect never put in the sixth turtle—the tank wasn't quite large enough. But he had a still more brilliant idea. He now began to make the turtles small again. He skipped the fourth one—took it out and let it loose in the Seine. He put in the third, which diminished the animal to half-size in a single night. Now the excitement really began. An official from the Jardin des Plantes paid a visit. He pulled at his beard, wagged his head, and, being from Rouen, said: "C'est *vraiment* cocasse." The shop did an enormous business. All the children of the neighborhood came in for sucres d'orge and had a look without extra charge. My friend skipped to the original beast and destroyed the evidence in his wash-basin, putting the remaining turtles into his pocket and carrying them out to the Bois. When he came home that night, he stopped in to see the turtle. Madame Perrier had become a national heroine. She had given her magic turtle to the man from the Jardin des Plantes for observation.

Byron Keating[1]

Three months ago, advertising trade papers carried stories that Byron Keating had opened an advertising agency. When he landed his first account—the Little Tot Food Products Co.—such trade papers as *Broadcasting* carried the news. Then *Advertising Age* bulletined that Byron Keating Co. ("Cincinnati's fastest growing agency") was planning a new campaign for Soyscuits, a soybean biscuit mix.

But Keating made his biggest splash in the report of his talk before the Cincinnati Businessmen's League. Said Keating: "Agencies are doomed unless they establish totalitarian principles . . . with clients. Businessmen should keep their fingers out of advertising. Many agencies are producing inferior advertising, against their better judgment, for fear of losing lucrative accounts and because account executives 'butter-up' the client."

From frustrated copywriters all over the country, this speech brought Keating high praise, along with requests for jobs. Commented *Advertising Age*: "It's things like this that reaffirm our occasionally wavering faith that it's fun to be in the advertising business." Worldly-wise *Variety* headlined the talk "Just Let 'em Pay the Tab—Keating."

A month ago, advertising trade papers carried news of the death of "Byron Keating, 59, after a heart attack attributed to overwork." Actually, Byron Keating was killed by his own parents—the two Cincinnati copywriters from whose lively imaginations he had sprung to hoax the advertising world.

Keating's creators were small, witty James B. Hill and big, sandy-haired John L. Eckels, advertising-agency copywriters. They dreamed up Keating to win an argument that political bigwigs are built by publicity, that they could create a tycoon in their own business out of thin air. They spent $4 on letterheads, sent publicity releases to newspapers and magazines, invented companies and clubs for Keating to address. When the American Newspaper Publishers Association and Dun & Bradstreet Inc. requested financial statements, Authors Hill and Eckels decided the hoax had gone far enough.

Last week the remains of Byron Keating—piles of news clips—were decently interred in Keating's "office," the middle drawer of Hill's desk. Hill and Eckels have only one regret: "We had a corker planned. We were going to phony up a foundation-garment account

---

[1] From *Time*, December 25, 1944, p. 80. Courtesy of *Time*, Copyright Time Inc. 1944.

667

for Byron Keating. We were going to have the phony company pick a Miss Uplift from clerks behind brassière counters."

Minnie and Susan [1]

Breakfast and fan mail came together for the Town Crier, and were attacked with equal avidity of appetite. Much of the correspondence was winnowed out in the studio, but it was understood that all appeals and requests were to be delivered to the principal for disposition. One such message, reaching him late in February, 1935, stirred him to the depths by its simplicity and sincerity, and no less because of that element of mystery which never failed to excite him.

On the evidence of this and later records, Minnie and Susan, sisters and far along in years, eked out a miserable existence in a single tenement room somewhere north of Troy, N. Y. Only their sewing machine stood between them and destitution. Their environment was a slum, bordering a disused canal. Fuel they grubbed from refuse heaps. All their water must be carried by hand up the long, dark flights of stairs. Their light was from an electric fixture of the public-utility system which obligingly shone it at their window. While one sewed on piecework for a local shirt factory, the other recited passages from the Bible, in which they were well versed by childhood training. They had but one wish: to stay together until the end. After all these years of sisterly association, a sundering of the tie would be intolerable. Minnie was eighty-six; Susan, ten years younger. Both were ill and crippled with rheumatism.

Ninety-nine times out of one hundred that sort of letter ends in importunity, brazen or covert, for a small donation. This was the shining exception. Since no identification was possible, neither last name nor address being given, almsgiving was out of the question. The sisters wanted something quite different. Desperate as was their condition, one luxury remained to them, their radio, "a great blessing" since it brought to them the inspiration and comfort of the Town Crier broadcasts.

"Life is a little hard," the letter went on, "and this winter we have been so lonely and cold and were hungry at times. . . . Old age is so frightening when one is sick and alone. But we have each other. And we have real pleasant times in the evenings. I prop Minnie up in bed and, oh, Mr. Woollcott, I wish you could see her face when she hears

---

[1] Reprinted from *A. Woollcott: His Life and His World*, by Samuel Hopkins Adams, Reynal & Hitchcock, Inc., N. Y., 1945; pp. 237–43.

668

your voice. You see, you make it seem as though one of our own had come back to us through the long-ago years. . . . We are glad that you are young and strong and famous and have so many friends."

Would Mr. Woollcott read the Twenty-third Psalm to them over the air? "It would mean so much to Minnie. Perhaps your people would not like it. Young folks want to be gay. But we are so near the Valley of the Shadow. If you can ever do it we will whisper it with you, word for word. The Lord is my Shepherd."

The writer, signing merely "Susan," apologized for not giving their full names. They feared that it would be thought "very rude, but we are fearsome that the charities will find out about us. They might put us in a home—separate us. We shall be separated soon enough."

The whole letter breathed a spirit of fortitude and resignation. Against such an appeal the always impressionable Woollcott heart had no defense. Read them the Twenty-third Psalm? He would do it, though it cost him his contract. The Cream of Wheat officials made no objections; indeed, they were heartily sympathetic.

Accordingly their star artist appended to his message of the evening the following passage, a notable example of his special talent for sentimental stimulus:

There is something I must read because I have been asked to do so by one whom no one could refuse. The next two minutes of this program are addressed solely to her. I do not know her name nor where she lives, and would not tell you if I knew. She is eighty-six years old and will not see again the childhood home toward which all her thoughts run on these long, cold winter nights. I wish I had some magic carpet on which she could be transported to that hilltop farm on the coast of Maine—near Belfast, it was—where she used to stand with the wind whipping the skirts of her checkered pinafore (the anachronism is Woollcott's, not the sisters') and her hand shading her eyes while she looked out across the waters of Penobscot Bay, watching for the first glimpse of her father's sailing vessel coming down from Boston. I can almost see the shower of apple blossoms from the twisted trees behind the farm house. I can almost see the little girl herself, a shy forgotten Rebecca of some unchronicled Sunnybrook Farm. She asks me to read something tonight to her and promises that, lying in the frightening darkness, she will say the words with me as they leap the miles and miles which lie between us. Man and boy, I have worked ever since I was a kid and have, in my time, been given many and varied jobs to do, but none—I think you cannot doubt this—none in all my life I have been more earnestly anxious to do well. I can only try. I will try now.

From all accounts he was never more effective. He read with fervor, simplicity, and such authentic emotion that it communicated itself to his hearers. The response was impressive. Radio addicts flooded the CBS mail with offers of aid, with peremptory demands, some of them, that they be allowed to help.

The sisters kept silence for a month. Then came a second letter, this one signed "Susan Lovice Staples," which might have indicated abandonment of anonymity had there been any address. Again there was an apology for secrecy, explaining ". . . dear Mr. Woollcott, we wouldn't let you see us, so bent and twisted and soiled." The letter began: "Dear Friend and Gentle Heart," and went on:

> You can never know the help and comfort you have been to us. . . . Oh, if you could only have been in our little room that February evening when your kind voice spoke The Lord is my Shepherd. . . . It seemed as though you had taken our feeble old hands in your strong young ones and were showing us the way home to Mother, Father, and the boys. Dear Mr. Wooll-cott, you brought a little bit of heaven to us that winter night. . . . We could hardly believe you were talking to us. For of course we realize you know so many accomplished, scholarly ladies and gentlemen.

The sustaining message had come barely in time. Minnie was dead of weakness and privation.

Further family details in the letter developed the background, though not definitely. There was a deep-sea father, lost in a gale with his two older sons. A third brother, "dear little Justin" had gone wrong, though the loyal sisters were persuaded that he never meant any harm. Grief and shame had killed their mother. The old house on the hill must be sold, together with the Indian shawls, the gold breast-pins, the family silver, etc. ("sea captains' daughters always had nice things.") The impoverished spinsters drifted to New York State, to live their starveling life on the meager wage of the shirt factory. The Town Crier carried copies of the letters in his pocket and read them emotionally to his friends.

"The finest tribute ever paid me," he declared.

He did not take it out in emotion. His philanthropic and his detective instincts both clamored for action. Inquiry in the collar-and-shirt districts, set afoot after the earlier letter, had been fruitless. Maine might yield a better return. Woollcott sent an emissary to Belfast who scrutinized tombstones, investigated records, and interviewed Oldest Living Inhabitants. No such names as Staples or Lovice came to light. There was neither record nor memory of a lost sea captain who left children named Minnie, Susan, and Justin.

It was bewildering, infuriating. The tenderhearted broadcaster could not rid himself of an intolerably affecting picture: the aged spinster alone in the tenement room, too proud for charity, certainly in dire want, quite possibly starving, and so waiting for death. There had been a hint of finality, of farewell, at the close of the Staples letter, with its assurance that the two sisters would be loving him in heaven, "just as we loved you on this earth. God bless you, my dear boy—my dear boy."

With the Cream of Wheat officials warmly concurring and only waiting to dig generously into their own private pockets, an appeal over the radio was formulated. The Town Crier called upon Susan to reveal herself. Let her look upon him as her lost brother, eager to help her. Her secrecy would be respected. All that he asked—and with him many friends unknown to her—was to give her comfort and security, put her beyond the fear of want for the rest of her life. Minnie was dead; there was no longer the question of separating them: would she not write him on his promise that her privacy should be respected?

No reply. Susan, as a baffled studio official remarked, had crawled into obscurity and pulled the obscurity in after her.

The final chapter was written several months later. Susan, too, was dead: had died happily in the very act of listening to the Town Crier. One who signed herself "Nurse Obrien," otherwise unidentified, wrote in very bad typescript:

"When it got time for you to talk she asked me to raise her up in bed and put her sister's Bible in her hand. I turned the dial and Mother of God pretty soon if you didn't begin to talk to her. I wish you could have seen her little wasted face when you called her your sister. It looked like a light had been lit and was shining through her eyes and skin. She stretched out both of her arms like she was taking hold of your hands. . . . Once she called your name and blessed you and once said something about some still water. She died at just eleven o'clock."

There was a reference to Father O'Reily and an inclosure: an old-fashioned gold-mounted locket, enclosing a strand of Susan's mother's hair.

For most people this would have ended the matter. Not for Alexander Woollcott. His sleuthing instincts were rampant. Furthermore, he was not convinced by the "Obrien" letter. It seemed to him quite possible that Susan, having learned of the efforts to trace her, had taken fright and, with her delicacy up in arms at the impending threat of charity, had promulgated the mortuary letter with a view to checking the investigation. He sent his business manager and general factotum, Joseph Hennessey, to Troy with instructions to stay there until he had uncovered something definite.

Clues were not lacking. The three postmarks were all in the Troy region, one being Watervliet, the other two Albany. The epistolary styles of the sisters was convincing; the paper cheap and ruled; the spelling not impeccable; the handwriting of the rounded type taught in the sixties and seventies. The locket, too, was authentically in period.

The local indications, carefully indefinite though the writers had been, offered some help. The tenement, as described, stood beside the old canal bed. It was without modern heating, illumination, or plumbing. The electric light bulb outside might be identifiable. It was not much to go on, but it was something. Hennessey proved himself a patient and careful investigator. He skirted both banks of the abandoned waterway throughout the region. The scope of his inquiry was conveniently limited by the fact that very few tenements in the district were so ancient as to be wholly devoid of conveniences. None of them had a public-utility light shining into an upper room. Nobody in any of the rookeries could identify two aged spinsters as tenants. The name Susan Lovice Staples drew a blank.

Next, the investigator took up the death of Susan. All was equally dark here. No Nurse Obrien was registered in the district. No Father O'Reily was known in the diocese. Mortuary records failed to show the death of Susan Lovice Staples or any other seventy-six-year-old spinster, on or about November 24, nor did an exhaustive canvass of local undertakers yield any results.

Now, all deaths in New York State are reportable. Bodies must be duly certified for burial. The inference was inevitable. Susan had not been buried. Presumptively, then, she had not died.

Neither had Minnie! Parallel inquiry into the matter of her decease drew another blank. No person who could by any stretch be made to fit the measure of an eighty-six-year-old maiden lady from a canalbank tenement appeared in the vital statistics at the time of her supposed demise.

On the strength of this impressive array of negations, Hennessey suggested fraud and chicanery to his principal. Woollcott was indignant. He would not listen to such heresy. The letters were indubitably genuine. Look at the handwriting. The locket was authentic beyond doubt. Was it conceivable that anyone would perpetrate so laborious a hoax for no ascertainable reason? If hoax it were, the practical joker would be sure to reveal himself presently to reap the enjoyment of his coup. He, Woollcott, would gladly lay a heavy bet that no such revelation would be made. He would have won the bet.

Once and once only, as far as the record shows, did he admit to a doubt. It was obvious that if malign inventiveness had been at work, it must have been fathered by some person or persons with (1) a grudge against Woollcott, (2) literary ability of no mean order, (3) a sense of "period," (4) a habitat in the Albany-Troy region. The radio-author-critic had plenty of enemies, well or ill earned, but none of them, so far as he knew, lived in that region. The other three requirements were fulfilled by Harold W. Thompson, who had been a freshman when Woollcott was a senior at Hamilton. Dr. Thompson was a scholar, an antiquarian, the author of several books, and a resident of Albany, being on the faculty of the N. Y. State College. No grudge existed, to the best of Woollcott's knowledge; still, you never can tell.

He could not be expected to keep in mind all the people who imagined themselves injured by him.

To nobody else did he confide his suspicions. But at Thompson's quarter-century reunion, the former senior detached himself from a group of his friends, crossed to the class of 1912, and addressed Thompson with the classic freedom of the campus.

"Well, you plushy pedant, your little jest has cost me just about a thousand dollars."

Quite genuinely astonished, Thompson replied, "I haven't a notion what you're talking about."

"You did it," growled Woollcott, "Nobody else could have done it. A low, Slimer trick." ("Slimer" is the opprobrious Hamilton epithet applied by an upperclassman to a freshman.)

The accused repeated his denial and mildly suggested that maybe the 1909 man might like to buy him a drink and elucidate. Woollcott snorted and withdrew. Some months later he brought up the matter after a trustee meeting, and told Thompson the whole story. Thompson replied with some feeling that if he were concocting a joke on Woollcott, it would not be at the expense of his best quality, but of some less admirable characteristic. Whether his denial was accepted, he never knew, though the pair parted on good terms.

One feature of this, the most elaborate and skilful fake in radio annals, which eluded Sleuth Woollcott but would undoubtedly have been noted by his detective idol, Sherlock Holmes (though Dr. Watson would, of course, obligingly have missed it), was the date of the Minnie and Susan letter displaying the family picture in all its detailed and archaic perfectionism.

It was April 1.

There is little to choose between Nate Arnold and Satchel-Eye Dyer. The American proverbial phrase "dumb like a fox" might apply, in part, to either; both know themselves to be a bit eccentric; they don't mind, and even accentuate their oddities deliberately, not grudging the neighbors such pleasure as this will surely afford them. Dyer's hinged house is a migrant; that is to say, the story of a man who builds a boat in his cellar and tears down a wall to get it out is one that appears sporadically in different parts of America. Nate Arnold's piano that had to stay out in the yard (too big), and be played on out there, is vaguely reminiscent of the Peterkin family's famous piano. In that case, of course, it was the player who remained outdoors.

Easy go [1]

But now I'm going to tell you about the greatest pocket miner we ever had here in Columbia, and that's Nate Arnold. Nate, he had worked the placers in the early days, and when they give out he climbed like other hopeful miners from the gulches into the hills, and went to prospecting around, and him and his partner, Jim Carey, located a couple of pretty good mines over by Yankee Hill that they called the Rifle and the Smooth Bore. But it was always easy go with Nate, whether it was easy come or not. Whatever money he got out of the mines, he spent it high, wide, and handsome. Nate's purse, it was open at both ends, you see, and as soon as these mines petered out and they was no more money coming in, that purse was flat empty.

One day Carey says to him, "Nate," he says, "we're out of grub." So they took stock of their assets, and it turned out that Nate had nothing and Carey had six bits. Carey says, "Nate," he says, "you take this six bits and go down to town and buy us a loaf of bread and lay out the rest in beans, and we can get along for a couple of days more anyway."

So Nate, he started down the Yankee Hill road towards town, and in about half an hour he come back up the road again, with a sack.

---

[1] Reprinted from *Ghost Town* by G. Ezra Dane, in collaboration with Beatrice J. Dane (New York: Alfred A. Knopf; 1941), pp. 76–82, by permission of Alfred A. Knopf, Inc. Copyright 1941 by G. Ezra Dane.

When Carey saw him coming he thought Nate had made a quick trip and must of had a lift, but he was so hungry he begun getting the pot ready right away to cook the beans. Well, Nate come into the cabin, and he set the sack down on the table. But when Carey went to open it, that sack started moving and flopping around and a hissing noise came out of it. So Carey jumped back and he asked Nate, "What in the name of Jehoshaphat have you got in there, Nate?" he says.

"That's an owl," Nate says, and he reached in the sack and, sure enough, he brought out a big, old, blinking old owl, rustling his feathers and hissing.

"He's got spunk, that owl has," says Nate, "he'll make short work of the mice around this cabin."

"Mice, hell!" says Carey, "they've all died of starvation. That's what we'll be doing, too, if we don't get some grub," he says, "and here you come back with an owl! You can make yourself some owl soup if you want to. I'm going down to get that bread and beans myself. Give me the six bits," he says.

"What six bits?" says Nate.

"*What* six bits? The *only* six bits," says Carey. "I give it to you to get the grub with."

"Oh, *that* six bits?" says Nate. "Why, I give that to an Indian boy I met on the road, for this owl," he says.

Well, that was too much for Carey. He called it quits and went off to prospect for better diggings; but Nate, he kept on hunting around and digging around there by Yankee Hill and running up bills at the different stores and talking big to keep his hopes up. "Boys," he'd say, "I ain't going to go on forever perching out here on this rock pile. I'm going off where I can see somp'm, and have somp'm. They's three things I'm going to have when I make a strike, boys," he'd say, "and that's a fast horse, a fast woman, and a fighting dog!"

But finally it got where Nate was eight hundred dollars in debt to the different storekeepers, and his credit had run out everywhere except at Knapp's. One day he was in there and ordered some beans and bacon, and Sewell Knapp give him the grub, but he says to him: "I don't like to say it, Nate, but this will have to be the last time," he says, "I can't carry you any longer."

So that meant Nate was at the end of his rope. On the way up the hill he got to feeling so tired and discouraged that he set down on a rock to rest a while and to think where he could get another grub stake. Well, while he sat there, he had his prospector's pick in his hand and he was tapping away between his knees on this rock, in an absent-minded way. The more he thought, the worse he felt, of course, and all the time he was working his feelings off on the rock.

Finally he says: "Damn it!" he says, "I'll show 'em! I've still got

675

hope!" and with that he raised his pick up and swung it down with all his might against that rock. But instead of cracking the rock or bouncing off, the pick stuck there, like an ax will stick in a log.

That took Nate by surprise. He looked down and, lo and b'God, he saw the pick was stuck in a chunk of gold.

So right then and there Nate staked out his claim. He set up his four stakes and he got out his pencil and on the back of an old bill he wrote: *Hope Mine, staked out by Nate A. Arnold,* and under that he put the date.

So that's where Nate Arnold made the fortune that he spent so free. He paid up his debts, and then the gold pieces begun pouring through his purse, in again and out again faster than ever. I told you how he handled the six bits. Well, he got rid of a hundred thousand dollars the same way. The only difference was, he didn't have the hundred thousand all at once, so he couldn't spend it all at once.

He got a couple of honest fellows to work in his mine for wages while he done what he could handle best—the spending of the money. And as if he couldn't spend it fast enough himself, he married a Mexican woman with two daughters and he hung jewelry on them like you'd hang tinsel on a Christmas tree. His wife had rings down to the tips of her fingers almost, and a gold chain that hung down to her waist, with gold tassels on it; and he had a watch-chain to match, so heavy it wore out his vests. He bought his fast horse for six hundred dollars, and a jump-seat buggy for four hundred. He had it made to order to fit the family. And my! people would look up to you then, you know, if you drove around in a thousand-dollar outfit. Yes, and he even had his fighting dog, to run along behind.

Gee, I remember once when that dog—it was one of them bull terriers and it was named Benicia Boy, after the prize fighter—I remember when he fought with old man Day's big mastiff, Music, that was supposed to be the best fighter in the diggins.

Nate was telling us about it afterwards—how Benicia Boy had, in about two minutes, sent old Music ki-yi-ing up the gulch.

"When Benicia Boy come back," Nate says, "he was so proud of himself that he curled his tail up over his back till it lifted his hind legs clean off the ground."

Well, then, Nate, after he had the family outfitted, he had to take them out to see the world, and for the world to see, so they went on a trip to San Francisco. And when they come up from down below, he was telling what good service they had at the Palace Hotel, where they had stopped. "We was there a week," he says, "and the accommodations was good. They sent bellboys around with anything you wanted, whenever you wanted it. Me and the wife and girls was there a whole week," he says, "and they only charged us seven hundred dollars. I thought that was very reasonable for such an accommodating place."

After they got back from this trip they fixed up their cabin at Yankee Hill. They bought a two-thousand-dollar piano that was too big to go through the door, so they kept it out in the yard. They'd give parties where the whole town would be invited and Nate would hire the full brass band to furnish the music. Oh, Nate was a big man in town—as long as his money lasted.

Why, when he'd drive down the street in his fancy rig and would draw up in front of his favorite saloon, the saloon-keeper would run out with a chair, and he'd set the chair beside the buggy for Nate and his wife to step down on. And this saloon-keeper's wife, she'd run out and she'd throw her arms around Mrs. Arnold and kiss her, there in the street, and then she'd take her into the parlor and entertain her while Nate was treating the boys in the bar-room, "throwing his pearls amongst the swine," as Aaron Morgan says. That's pretty good, too, you know, coming from Aaron, because I happen to know that more than once—Well, we'll let that pass.

One afternoon Senator Steve Wing, the tinsmith, was in there with Nate and he says to him, he says, "Nate, don't do as I do, but do as I say," and he went on to advise him. "Put some money in the bank or invest it in something safe, and then you can have your sprees and your good times and never have to worry, and when your mine gives out you'll still have an income." But Nate, he just reached in his pocket and pulled out a twenty-dollar piece, and he says: "Steve," he says, "where that come from they's plenty more. Let's have a drink." So he slapped this double-eagle onto the bar, and the saloon-keeper give them their drinks. Well, they had the drinks and then the saloon-keeper, rubbing his hands in the way he had, and sort of hesitating, he says: "Anything more, gentlemen?"

"Oh, no," says Nate. "Put that twenty out of sight," he says. "Put it in the till, and never mind the change."

That's what the saloon-keeper was waiting for, you know; he knew what was coming. That wasn't the first twenty he'd had out of Nate for one round of drinks.

But afterwards, and it wasn't long afterwards, the Hope Mine give out just like the Rifle and Smooth Bore had done, and Nate was broke again. He went to this same saloon-keeper then and wanted to borrow five dollars; but the saloon-keeper says to him: "Nate," he says, "I'm sorry, but I haven't got it on hand. The whiskey drummer's just been through and I give him all I had." And his wife, that had loved Mrs. Arnold so when Nate was flush, after that, when Mrs. Arnold come walking into town and she'd see her coming down the street, she'd go inside and slam the door.

Well, he was a great old Nate. So far as I know, it's no sin to spend your own money, and Nate sure had a lot of fun slinging his around as long as there was any to sling. Yes, he got what he wanted while he could enjoy it. And suppose he had saved fifty thousand dollars; it would of done him little good that night a few years later when his heart give out while he was climbing alone up the trail to Yankee Hill.

Satchel-Eye Dyer [1]

I'd always felt humanity needlessly ignored his history. Satchel-Eye lived eighty-six years with only one paragraph in the local paper to preserve his memory. The Caesars, Lincolns, Pitts, Nelsons and Edisons are all right in their limited ways, but Satchel-Eye Dyer deserves more than the back seat historians would give him.

Take, for instance, his views on bringing up children. Once Satchel-Eye and his two sons were sawing cord-wood by the side of the road. When Marvin Foster, the mailman, drove up one of the boys was sleeping in the weeds near by, and the old man and the other boy were working as if a thundershower were on the way. Marvin inquired, as anyone would, and learned that the old man and the sleeping boy had had an argument. To establish his supreme position as head of the family, Satchel-Eye had punctuated his final remark by whanging the son across one ear with a length of cord-wood. Impressed by the sheer weight of the old man's argument, the boy had temporarily withdrawn to think things over. While Marvin was learning the details, the boy suddenly came to, and, realizing the error of his convictions, he jumped up and began sawing wood like a good one. Some years later this boy studied medicine, and when people around here last heard of him he had found a new way to cure burns which was considered very helpful.

One other time Satchel-Eye felt the need of instructing the younger boy on some minor point, so he jounced him up and down in the tub on the end of the well sweep until the point was made. On this occasion the boy detected some minor *non sequitur* in the reasoning, however, because he subsequently locked the old man in the icehouse until he should cool off. The father, unperturbed by this dissension, carefully considered the intellectual aspects of child training, and

[1] From *Farmer Takes a Wife* by John Gould (New York: William Morrow & Co.; 1945), pp. 133–42. Copyright 1945 by John Gould. By permission of William Morrow & Co., Inc.

678

when he got out he chased the boy across the town, practically cutting his legs off at every jump with a horsewhip.

A lifetime composed of thousands of similar instructive activities should not go unnoticed—but it has. Outside the narrow limits of his own community, Satchel-Eye remains unknown; whereas nearly everyone has heard of Napoleon. The first recorded incident in the life of this remarkable man was prophetic, but unheeded by chroniclers. Some years before Satchel-Eye was born the western section of the town burned off, and although the trees had since grown in again people still referred to the area as "the burnt woods." Young Dyer, about four, got lost in there and a posse located him after two days of search.

He was sitting on a stump, contemplating the ground in abject despair, and as the searchers came up behind him they heard him say, "Hello, God—my name is 'Delbert Dyer; I got lost in the burnt woods. My mother has lost a fine boy!" Thus the fine boy was saved for a lifetime of useful works, and he ultimately proved in many ways the accuracy of his own estimate.

The formative years of his life are obscure. He married Nellie Overton and brought her home one afternoon to share his weal and woe. That evening he pulled a chair up to the table and began picking over beans while the lovely bride deployed herself in a rocker by the window and watched the gathering twilight steal across the verdant brightness of her wedding day. She folded her hands in her lap and sighed.

Satchel-Eye looked up and said, " 'Hain't you got su'thin' you can be doing, some mending or knitting?"

The next day the barn burned. He saved the stock, and had to turn the dining room into a tie-up. Satchel-Eye began at once to get out the timbers for a new barn, but it took three years to build it and in the meantime the animals were replenishing the earth. They eventually occupied three rooms downstairs, a bedroom up, and the sheep were in the back open chamber.

In addition to this, Satchel-Eye used the parlor for a carpenter's shop and occasionally shod a horse or two in the kitchen. When Dr. Dowd arrived to assist in Nellie's first accouchement, he found the woman comfortable enough in bed with a yearling heifer tied to a doorknob, and he said afterwards he might just as well have driven his mare and buggy right upstairs. He peeled off his coat and sent Satchel-Eye down for some hot water. After a grinding of gears and scraping of hinges below, Satchel-Eye appeared almost at once with the hottest water the doctor had ever used. It appeared that Satchel-Eye had rigged a bellows on the kitchen range, to assist in shaping horseshoes, and by giving a few pumps on the handle he had made water boil in a matter of seconds. Thus Sylvanus was born, and Dr. Dowd was given his choice of cash (his bill was ten dollars) or two hundredweight of yellow-eye beans. Being to the manner trained, Dr. Dowd took one bag of beans and five dollars, and jokingly said, "When I come back next year, I hope you'll have either a barn for your stock or a house for your family."

When he came back the next year, to witness the arrival of Rufus, the barn had indeed been built in the meantime, but now the house had burned, and Nellie was awaiting her time on a brass bed in the grain room, while Satchel-Eye spoke reassuring words to her and rocked little Sylvanus in his cradle with one foot. To improve his time he mended a bridle, which Nellie was steadying for him with one hand. This time Dr. Dowd took one bag of beans and abated the five dollars, telling Satchel-Eye to put it towards the saw-bill for a new house. Dr. Dowd was a good man.

After the new house was built, Satchel-Eye continued to confuse his two buildings, which is scarce to be wondered at, and he always did some living in the barn and some work in the house. He always maintained a repair shop in the parlor, and Uncle Timothy once heard him tell his boy, "Go in the parlor and get the monkey-wrench —it's on the joiner's bench behind the keg of shingle nails." One winter they made twenty-five beehives in the parlor, accumulating some good shavings for poultry litter. So the next spring Satchel-Eye started raising ducks. It seemed unnecessary to move the shavings, so they put the ducks in the parlor. They built a runway so the ducks could come and go by a window, and they fenced off the front lawn for a range. The feed hoppers were on the front piazza.

Nellie, who hadn't been brought up to just this kind of a program, accepted it with good spirit. To show that she participated they tell the story of the goose. Satchel-Eye had a goose about two-thirds the size of a young bull, and one day Nellie was home alone and she tipped a wooden washtub off a bench onto the goose. Considerably mangled, the goose set up a great cry. Nellie knew the goose was, now, fit only for dinner, and she knew it was essential to dress her out at once. To chop off her head, Nellie needed an axe—but after a frantic search she realized the axes were all up in the woods. Nellie combed the parlor, pantry and barn for a substitute instrument. Soon she located a handsaw, and she held the goose down with one knee and sawed off her head.

One winter Nellie had the pip and took to her bed. The men did the housework and brought her food. In her illness she had lost interest in nearly everything, and to the comings and goings of the world she was so-so. It must have struck her, as time went on, that continuous but mainly similar conditions prevailed. Things happened, but she knew they would, and they always did, and it was tiring to care one way or the other. So when Sylvanus brought up her breakfast and reported, "Maw, the old hoss has fell down dead," Nellie did her best.

She asked, "Which way did he fall, Sylvanus?"

It was about that time Satchel-Eye built a boat. Being thirty-five miles from the ocean, on a hill where brooks ran only in the spring, he had hardly any need of a boat. All the lumber was cut on the place, shaped in the parlor, and fitted in the front bedroom. They made a steam box (for steaming the ribs) and connected it by a hose to a five-gallon can on the kitchen range. The hose burst and turned Rufus's face blue. While it was healing he grew a beard, whereupon the others grew beards and they looked like three ancient mariners when they came out front one day and took the house down to move the boat.

They hoisted the boat up, backed a hayrack under it, and took it down beneath the barn. Then they slung cables around it and brought it up under the floor—where it was still hanging fairly recently. Someone asked Satchel-Eye one time why he built it, and he said it was a handy thing to keep beans in. Then they rebuilt the front of the house, and hung it on hinges in case they should ever build another boat. This was handy, of course, and they made a practice of keeping things in there under cover. They'd come out and prop up the front of the house, yelling and hollering at a great rate, back in the horses, and come out with a set of logging sleds or a manure spreader.

Satchel-Eye's boat was full of dry beans most of the time. When he was a youngster he had been impressed with his father's good fortune when the price of beans sky-rocketed during the Civil War. Soldiers, presumably, lived on beans, and anyone who happened to have a good supply when war was declared made out all right. Satchel-Eye noticed, too, that after the cessation of hostilities beans were again reasonable in price. He was therefore able, when the battleship *Maine* figured in the news, to place his hands on the accumulated beans from many years hopeful hoarding.

He went up to the city and visited a storekeeper. After the usual conversational preludes he inquired about the price of beans. The storekeeper told him, and it was the best figure since Grant took Richmond. Satchel-Eye asked, "How many'll you take at that price?"

"All you've got-bring 'em in."

So the next morning when the storekeeper came down to open up he found Satchel-Eye sitting on the curbstone out front with an ox-goad between his knees. Standing before him was a handsome yoke of Herefords hooked to an old-time high-wheeled cart. The cart was piled sky-high with bags of beans. "Great Scott," said the storekeeper, "I didn't suppose you'd have that many!"

So Satchel-Eye pointed up the street with his goadstick, and heaving into sight were Sylvanus and Rufus, each teaming their own Hereford steers, and each yoke drawing a sky-high load of beans. The storekeeper mortgaged his place at the bank to pay for the three loads—but of course he made money on the deal. People around here, knowing how hard and dry those beans had become as they awaited a price in Satchel-Eye's barn, have always felt specially sorry for the boys who marched away to lick Spain.

Beans were naturally a plentiful commodity on Satchel-Eye's own table, and they relate that he had a method of frustrating any objections from his fed-up family. At times Nellie served beans morning, noon and night—day in and day out. They had to wait for pigs to fatten or potatoes to grow, but beans were always plentiful and (fortunately) nourishing. At these times, when they came to table, Satchel-Eye would draw in his chair, reach for the tureen, lift the cover, and with exquisitely simulated joy would cry, "Ah-h-h! Baked beans!"

One time a new minister called on them and took dinner during a bean period. Satchel-Eye was just about to cry, "Ah-h-h! Baked beans!" when Nellie said, "I'm sorry, Reverend, not to have nothing better for tonight than baked beans."

Satchel-Eye was equal to it. He lifted the cover and said, "Plenty good enough for me, and good enough for me good enough for anybody, pass your plate." The minister had three helpings, and said they were the best beans he ever ate. Then they sat around and talked, and when the minister went Satchel-Eye gave him some money for the church and a bag of beans for himself. Then one Saturday night the Dyers got all dressed up and went to town to take supper with the minister, where they had a good time. The minister was much astonished, but he made out all right, and he never called on Satchel-Eye again.

When the boys were in school one of them said the teacher spanked him. Satchel-Eye was indignant. He grabbed up a club and went right over to see the teacher. "Don't you never spank my boy again," he shouted. "You use this club on him!" Of course, with anyone like Satchel-Eye around it was natural to saddle stray stories on him— some of which are worth believing. But on the whole it is unnecessary to improve on him; he went his own independent way and left aplenty without improvisation by others.

Some of his reactions to the world outside were memorable. He didn't leave the farm often, but he went abroad with his eyes open and came home wiser and always richer. Once he went to State Fair and brought Nellie home five dollars' worth of spun sugar, the pink kind. He never saw any before, and he knew Nellie hadn't, and he wanted her to taste it. It filled the whole back of the wagon, and she piled it up in the pantry and said, "Thanks, 'Delbert, I'll try some after supper."

Another time he was up to the city and he saw a box kite in a store window. He bought one, and he and the boys studied it out. Then they made a big one, with improvements, and they flew it with five balls of binder twine. It hung off over the village for weeks, unless the wind shifted, and then they had a windlass they'd made with a grindstone crank to bring it home with. They'd play round with boats and kites a while, and then they'd fall to and work like beavers. The old man didn't stand any foolishness when they were working. People said they'd trot the horses down the field when they were loading hay, tossing up bunches as the rack went by and getting in seven or eight loads an afternoon. They'd cut wood for two weeks and have enough for two years, and in another week they'd get out lumber enough for a set of buildings. Then they'd quit work all at once and maybe go fishing for two or three days at a time. They always brought back some trout, alive, in a bucket of water, and dumped them in the well. People going by would see Satchel-Eye sitting on the well curb with a fish pole and think Simple Simon had moved in. But Nellie usually had trout to fry if she wanted them, and they said the fish didn't hurt the well a bit—kept the water pure.

The boys left home after a while. Rufus married a city girl and afterwards kept store in Portland. He used to come home once in a while—Nellie said to get a square meal as it's well known you can't bake a decent bean in the city. The other boy went back to school when he was a man grown, and kept at it until he got a medical degree. He grew famous and lost touch. Nellie lasted only a few weeks after Satchel-Eye died. Just long enough to sell the stock and wind things up.

Satchel-Eye said he'd had a good life. He knew everybody thought him queer and he didn't mind a bit. He said, "I always did just what I'd a mind to, the best way I had of doing it. I figure things different, that's all. People are so afraid of being laughed at that nobody has any fun." Nellie said, "Well, 'Delbert, if you've had fun, then it's all right."

He came in from milking one night, said he felt tired, and he didn't wake up the next morning. Harry Dustin came up and helped Nellie get ready for the funeral. He wheeled out shavings all morning, and then they set the casket on the carpenter's bench in the front windows.

After the services they propped up the front of the house and the hearse backed right in.

The undertaker said it was the slickest rig he ever saw.

683

The collector of oral tales, like the collector of any other sort of folklore, must be on his guard against products of an author's study that have escaped and found themselves a new and sometimes exhilarating life among the word-of-mouth story-tellers. Not that there is any harm in such migrations—they sometimes produce very delightful results—but it is just as well to keep the types separate. Otherwise the critic may fall into some strange illusions as to the nature of the myth-maker.

It would be difficult, perhaps, to find any English prose further from folklore than the starched and stilted writing of Joseph Addison. Yet there are two yarns told by him, one in the *Tatler* in 1710, and another in the *Spectator* in 1714, which are likely to have been the actual parents of our next two stories—here entitled "Frozen Words" and "Bundle of Troubles." It is true that the notion of frozen words is found in Antiphanes, and in Rabelais (IV,55,56), and in Baron Munchausen, and that the idea that each man prefers his own misfortunes to another's is to be found in Horace; but it is also to be remembered that Addison's essays were disseminated for generations in volumes of extracts, and especially in school "readers." In the American versions of these tales the stilted language ("Methought there was a proclamation made by Jupiter that every mortal should bring in his griefs and calamities," etc.) has disappeared, and the locale has become American and prosaic. The troubles, for instance, are not brought to "a large plain appointed for the purpose," but to "the depot check-room," a significant improvement; and the frozen words are transferred from vague Arctic wastes to "Blairstown, New Jersey"; they even turn into frozen locomotive whistles—on "the Chesapeake and Ohio"!

Frozen words [1]

N o, I do not love you," she said coldly. And just how coldly things can be said is illustrated by a tall story from the boys at Camp No-Be-Bo-Sco, near Blairstown, New Jersey. The boys at No-Be-Bo-

---

[1] From Lowell Thomas: *Tall Stories* (New York: Funk & Wagnalls Co.; 1931), pp. 199–201.

Escaped Literature

Sco tell us how cold it was out their way. On the morning of February 7, of this year, several of them were standing out in the open. They started to talk, but the conversation froze as it came out of their mouths. The congealed and solidified words fell clattering on the icy ground. The boys got a basket. They gathered the frozen words and took them to their camp-fire. They had to thaw out those words to find out what they were talking about.

I told this story over the radio in honor of Washington's birthday, and I'm sorry I did so, because there appears to be an element of inaccuracy in the yarn of the boys of Camp No-Be-Bo-Sco. In fact, they were telling a lie, which George Washington never did. The Tall Story Club loves to tell the truth, especially on Washington's birthday.

G. W. Bateman, of New Brunswick, New Jersey, severely points out the inaccuracy in the boys' story. He says they couldn't have picked up all the frozen words they let fall, because Mr. Bateman, while driving around Blairstown at about the same time, cut three of his tires to ribbons, driving over those confounded frozen words. The boys must have been using hard words from the way those tires were ripped to pieces.

Moreover, they were not so hard but that Mr. Bateman's tires smashed several of them, and therefore those pulverized frozen words could not have thawed out and be heard as real words any more. They could only have been incoherent mumbling sounds.

Mr. Bateman thinks the boys might have collected the frozen words and stored them away somewhere instead of letting them lie around on the public highway to rip up people's automobile tires.

The incident cost Mr. Bateman the price of a couple of new tires, but at the same time it didn't immediately discommode him. After his tires were cut to pieces he just kept on going, because it was so cold that the air in the tires was frozen solid. The rubber was completely slashed away, but the frozen ozone made a reasonably good tire, altho slightly bumpy.

[1] The dangers incurred by the railroads during cold weather are brought forward by Fred L. Wise, of Bedford, Pennsylvania, who recalls a happening down in the mountains of West Virginia. A train was rumbling along, and it was bitterly cold. The engineer pulled the whistle but, to his astonishment, there was no sound. He pulled that whistle three times in all, but still there was not a peep. Then he realized that it was so cold the sound had been congealed. The toot of the whistle had frozen in mid-air.

Several months later, when it was spring in the Blue Ridge Mountains on the trail of the lonesome pine, that same train was bumping

---

[1] Ibid., pp. 197-9.

along. The engineer heard a whistle, then another, and then a third. It was a warm spring day, and he realized that what he heard were the same three whistles that he had blown several months before. They had just thawed out.

Some of the less intellectual members of the Tall Story Club seemed to doubt the factual truth of that one. And so a countrywide inquiry was made for witnesses who had been present at the remarkable occurrence. C. B. Zinn, of St. Albans, West Virginia, came forward and stated that he was on that same train when the whistle froze. His testimony, duly attested by a notary public, states that the train was on the Coal River Division of the Chesapeake & Ohio Railroad. In the train crew were Engineer Stern and Conductor Holstead.

Mr. Zinn further deposes and says that because of the frozen whistle, the only way that the train crew could get their signals from the engineer was by the pieces of frozen whistle blast which fell as chunks of ice on the cars behind. If two large pieces and two small ones dropped on the roof, that was the signal for a crossing. And when one extra large piece fell, the brakeman knew the train was approaching a station. This seems to clear up all possible doubt or misunderstanding.

J. C. Graham, of Amherst, Massachusetts, observed a peculiar phenomenon, at Oshkosh, Wisconsin, a number of years ago. There was a spell of extremely cold weather followed by a sudden thaw. A terrific shrill noise was heard all over the country. The people couldn't hear themselves think. Several became deaf from the intensity of the noise and are still hard of hearing. Scientists were consulted and explained that the weird noise was caused by the freezing of the whistles during the cold spell and then the abrupt rise in the temperature which caused all of those whistles to thaw at the same time in one terrific blast.

[1] Back in the late "nineties," at **Railroad, Pennsylvania**, they had a memorable blizzard. It was so cold in the boiler-room of a factory that the flames in the firebox froze solid. E. N. Reichard, of the town of Railroad was there, and he saw the firemen slashing at the frozen blaze with a slashbar, trying to loosen the fire. It was of no use. After two days of diligent but futile work, they had to thaw out the flames with blow torches. Mr. Reichard concludes his narration with the following salutation: "Yours in fraternity of the Mystic Knights of Tall Stories."

A warning against the dangers of frozen flames comes from Jack Fisher, of Muncie, Indiana, who tells of a Michigan farmer who was burning brush one winter day. It was so cold that the flames leaping

[1] Ibid., pp. 195–7.

up from the brush piles were frozen. The farmer broke them off and piled them up in his barn like cordwood. In the spring the flames thawed out, and turned into ordinary fire once more. They set fire to the barn, which set fire to the house, which set fire to the village, which started a forest fire, which burned up half of the State.

In New Brunswick, Canada, it gets so cold that the electric lights freeze, which causes them to give a very peculiar cold light. C. I. Tompkins, of East Florenceville, New Brunswick, tells us that at times the natives have tried to thaw out the electric lights with a blow torch. But the blow torch freezes. Many of the local New Brunswickers, therefore, have given up in despair and are merely expecting relief from the cold in the next world.

Michigan, of course, is a State where you might expect to find the coldest kind of cold weather. J. E. Barnhard, of Fremont, Michigan, informs the Tall Story Club that it got so cold up his way one day that the sunbeams froze and the natives cut them into lengths and used them for flashlights.

In a town about fifty miles north of Kenosha, Wisconsin, it gets so cold that the people don't use any artificial lighting for street illumination at night. During the day the sunlight freezes on the ground. And, as a result, the people have sunlight all night. This remarkable incident is related by A. P. Kubec, of Kenosha.

[1] An incident of a frozen flame with a singular aftermath comes from a Tall Story Club member of Tarpon Springs, Florida. He embellishes the lore of the Great American Whopper with an account of how he was lost while hunting squirrels one bitterly cold night in the Everglades of Florida. Of course the Everglades are supposed to be a trifle warm, but any tall-story teller knows of far more remarkable things than forty below zero in the Everglades in August.

In any case, the man from Tarpon Springs, after wandering about in the bitter gale, came upon a log cabin where an old man lived in the company of a few hens. A roaring blaze in the fireplace, and the weary wayfarer was soon thawed out. Then he and his host went to bed, leaving the fire burning. The next morning they found that the flames had frozen stiff. The old man got an axe and chopped the yellow icicles of frostbitten fire into pieces and threw them out of the window.

Later in the day he went to the hen house to get some eggs to cook for dinner. The hens had been eating the chunks of frozen flame. The heat of their bodies had thawed out the congealed bits of fire. Then the hens had gone ahead and laid their eggs. The two men were greatly astonished to find that the eggs were hardboiled.

---

[1] Ibid., pp. 193–5.

Sergeant Wooten, of Selfridge Field, Mt. Clemens, Michigan, relates a similar incident that happened in Georgia. In this case we have an old gentleman who was a confirmed bookworm. He sat reading while the norther was blowing in the window, and that norther was so cold that it froze the flame in the lamp. In order to put out the light, the bookworm had to break the flame off and throw it outside. An old hen ate it. That frozen flame must have been very hot, because for the next three weeks she laid hardboiled eggs.

F. E. Hotchkin, of Glen Gardner, New Jersey, was at Middletown, New York, in 1936, and stopped at a place where they left the lamp burning in the bedroom all winter, because the flame was frozen and they couldn't put it out. They had to wait for warm weather. It never occurred to them to break the flame off and throw it away, because the family is Scotch and they never throw away anything.

Bundle of troubles[1]

One night Mose went to bed 'bout bowed down with his troubles. Seem like all of 'em was a-hoppin' on him at oncet. He turned and twisted, but by'n by he went to sleep and then he had the dream.

Seem like, in the dream, ever'body had all a-sudden started miratin' and fussin' 'bout their troubles. Seem like they couldn't talk 'bout nothin' else. Fin'ly, the debbil, he got tard of all this loose talk 'bout troubles, caze most of 'em was blamed on him. Then one Sadday, 'thouht nobody 'spectin' him, he 'peared uptown, jes as the streets was most crowded, and he rung a bell to call all they 'tensions to him.

When ever'body gathered 'round, he say like this:

"I bin hearin' a powerful lot 'bout all you folkses troubles. Yo'all thinks you is got more troubles as anybody. And I's a-gittin' mighty tard a-hearin' 'bout nothin' else. Yo'all nussin' your troubles so hard you ain't got no time for no real sinnin'.

"I tell you what I's a-gonna do. I's a-gonna take up all of you troubles. Ever'body what has got troubles, jes wrop 'em up in a bun'le and bring 'em down to the depot check-room right away and I'll take 'em up and rid each and ever'body of you troubles. Now go home and wrop them troubles up and hurry down to the depot with 'em."

[1] From W. C. Hendricks (editor): *Bundle of Troubles, and Other Tarheel Tales* (Durham: Duke University Press; 1943), pp. 3–7.

"Told to W. E. Hennessee by Harry Hobson of Cleveland, N. C., who heard the story from one of his Negro farmhands, Jonathan Hobson." (Note by W. C. Hendricks.)

Well, it didn't take Mose more'n a minit to git home. He say he warn't runnin' 'zactly, but he was a-passin' a lot of folks what was.

He got the biggest thing he could find to hold all of his troubles, which was a big paper box with "Saunders Tripe" printed on the outside. Mose didn't think it would begin to hold all his troubles, but he started in a-packin' anyway.

First went in his old rhumatiz, and then his cawns.

"Yo'all bin hurtin' me for many the year," he say, "and I's sho glad to part company with you."

Then went in the lan'lord, and the sto'keeper what Mose owe for his fertilize. Then there was his back church dues what he hadn't paid, and that yeller gal over at Marse John Simmons' place. I don't know why he put her in, but he did. Then he throwed in his sore tooth, and his boy what got drunk all the time, and the old plow what never would foller a straight furrow. Then went in his old black skin, all his gray hair, and his wife's naggin', and the hatchet what would fly offen the handle. He throwed in his old mule, Bess, what kicked the daylights outen him ever time she got a chancet, and that sportin' nigger what was a-slippin' 'round his youngest gal.

He throwed in a heap more tribalashuns, and it seem like the box jes' wouldn't hold all of 'em, but there was allus a lil room at the top.

By'n by he had 'em all in, and then he took a big breaf and a piece of old plow line and tie them troubles up hard and fast in the box. He made a nice bun'le and throwed it on his wheelbar and started for the depot.

It took him a long time to git there, caze the streets was packed with folks all loaded down with bun'les. There was old Sis Thompkins what didn't anybody know ever had a trouble in her life, and what was allus a-laffin', and a-jokin', and a-goin' on. She was loaded down with such a big bun'le that she had three of her lil gran'chillun a-helpin' her tote it. There was the preacher with a good-size load. There was even white folks, and Mose was surprise at that, but they seem to have the biggest bun'les of all. There was old Cunnel LeRoy, the biggest man in the town; even he had a bun'le. It warn't a very big bun'le, 'bout the size of a dozen eggs wropped up, but it was a bun'le just the same.

When Mose got to the depot, the check-room was piled up to the ceilin' with bun'les, and the debbil had three-four of his imps a-helping him with the checkin'. Mose put down his bun'le, and a perlite lil imp put a check on it and handed Mose a stub.

"What fo' you gimme this check?" say Mose. "I don't want the bun'le back—no time atall."

" 'Tain't you check," say the perlite lil imp. "It's somebody else's check. You see it's like this: Next Chusday all yo'all what's checked

689

a bun'le of troubles comes back here with these checks and you gets somebody else's bun'le of troubles. Ever'one of you has been a-sayin' that you troubles was worser yit, so the Old Man he gonna let each'n of you trade and git somebody else's troubles."

"Well," say Mose. "I sho won't mind that. Maybe I git some nice easy troubles like dander, or a good-lookin' wife, or too much money." And then he put out for home.

Long 'bout cain't-see time, when Mose was a-settin' on his porch, he got to thinkin' 'bout the propersition, and the more he think 'bout it the lessen he likes it. He 'members somethin' 'bout ole Cunnel LeRoy, and some of the other folks, too. Seem like it jes warn't workin' out like he had thunk. By'n by he got down his hat and his walkin' stick and he went down to the depot to see how things was a-comin'. When he got there, first thing he heerd was somebody laffin', and he looked 'round the corner of the pile of bun'les and there was the debbil and the imps a-laffin' fit to kill. Seem like they had jes heered the bestest joke anybody ever told.

"Now look here," say Mose to hisself, "When the debbil gits to laffin' somebody bound to git the worst of it. I ain't never heerd of the Old Boy a-doin' anybody a favor yit lessen he gits the best of the deal."

So he went up to the debbil, perlite-like, and he say, "Mister Debbil, mebbe I make a mistook today I left a big bunch of troubles with you, but I ain't so sure now that I wants to part with 'em. They bin with me so long I thinks that I's growed kinda fond of 'em. Wonder could I get 'em back 'thouht nobody axin' me no questions?"

The debbil he open his mouf wide and laff. And when he laff it was worser as when he frowns. His eyes didn't have no whites in 'em and was all shiny like they bin polished. His funny skin was a-twitchin' and his tail was a-lashin' back'rds and for'rds.

"Br'r Mose," he say, 'tween laffs, "I's powerful sorry to tell you, but the check for you bun'le is in somebody else's hands now, and I don't see how you can git it back."

"Well, then," say Mose, "I won'er iffen you can show me what kinda lookin' bun'le this here check of mine calls for?"

"To be sho," say the Old Boy, and he looked at the check, and went 'round comparin' it with the checks on the bun'les.

"Here it is," he fin'ly say, and he holds up the lil bun'le of troubles of Cunnel LeRoy. "Looks like a mighty nice lil bun'le of troubles you gonna git Chusday, Br'r Mose. I congratulates you. Jes a lil bun'le of white folks troubles. That ought'n worry a old darkey like you."

When Mose see that bun'le he scairt most to death.

"Please, suh, Mister Debbil," he say, "please, suh, gimme my old bun'le of troubles back. That's it right over there by that lil green imp, in the box marked with the tripe. I bin a-thinkin' it over and my troubles ain't so bad. I kinda miss the ole cawns and the rhumatiz, and the game tooth. By rights I owes the lan'lord, and the sto'keeper, and it wouldn't be right not to pay 'em. That yeller gal ain't gonna bother me no more, caze she's gittin' crazy 'bout somebody else. I kin take a firmer hand with the chillun, and I don't mind being mule-kicked, or throwed by the plow, and I kinda misses the old woman's naggin' already. To tell the truf, I don't believe they was troubles after all— jes lil worries, and I misses 'em tubble. Won't you please to give 'em back, suh?"

The debbil he laff agin, and he laff and laff. And Mose begin to back off a lil way. Then the debbil look mad, and he say: "Take you bun'le of troubles, Br'r Mose," he say, "but don't you ever let me hear you fussin' 'bout 'em agin, or I'll give you some sho-nuff troubles."

Mose grab up his troubles and toss 'em up on his shoulder like they was no more'n a box of feathers. It didn't take no wheelbar to git 'em away from that depot.

Why didn't Mose take old Cunnel LeRoy's troubles when he had a chancet? I axes him that.

Mose say he see a coffin in that bun'le, and he 'members jes in time that the Cunnel's trouble was a lil old cancer of the stummick.

Hitch-hiker stories came to America not with the automobile, but with the much later phenomenon of "thumbing a ride." Their variety is considerable, but most of them are sinister; there is the old woman who is seen (just in time) to be wearing hob-nailed boots and packing a gun; there is the gypsy who foretells Hitler's death to the people who give her a lift; little has been heard from her since Hitler's passing. There is, in lighter vein, the hitch-hiker who asks the driver the time; subsequently the driver, realizing that his watch is gone, pulls a revolver and says: "Give me that watch and chain!" The hitch-hiker submits, is put out, flees; when the driver gets home he finds his own watch; he has robbed the stranger. (This one is always told as true, with names and places.)

The stories that follow are also usually told (and best told) as true. The Emily stories are localized, by Russell Maloney's telling, in New York, but they are told elsewhere as true. I have told one of them as an incident occurring in Providence, and gullibly thought I was narrating a fact. (I even knew the heroine—I thought!) The necklace story is a common migrant, though it has a slight flavor of Maupassant. The legend of the storekeeper who can't be bothered with sales is only an anecdote, yet it is crammed with character. (Vermont is probably the most apposite of its habitats.) But the tale of the vanishing hotel-room has almost infinite forms and a complicated appeal; it has mystery, pathos, and even terror. Whoever invented it was presenting to other narrators a framework on which they could stretch a varicolored tapestry indeed.

The last story has in a double sense passed into history; one variant form represented the obnoxious victim as saying: "I hope this war [that was World War II] lasts forever." Had she existed, she would have deserved what she supposedly got.

Emily's adventures in New York[1]

There are three apparently indestructible anecdotes, which have been coming in at least once a week ever since I can remember. They are always garnished with what scholars call a wealth of corroborative detail: the incident in question happened last Tuesday to the contributor's Cousin Emily in Pelham Manor, and the editors have permission to check with her if they don't believe it.

1. Last Tuesday Cousin Emily's cat died. After puzzling for a long time about what to do with the tiny corpse, Emily wrapped it up in a shoe-box and took it in to New York, planning to drop the box into the first refuse basket she came upon. Before she found one, however, a man snatched her parcel and ran.

2. Emily wore her new hat to luncheon at a smart restaurant. Seated across the room was a woman wearing an exact duplicate of the hat. Being a good sport about the whole thing, Emily caught her eye, pointed to her own head, and made a rueful face. The woman merely looked alarmed, finished her meal hastily, and left. Later, in the powder room, Emily looked in the mirror and discovered she *hadn't* worn the new hat that day, after all.

3. Emily had to go to a funeral at one of the big Fifth Avenue churches. Arriving in town a little early, she went shopping at Saks and bought a small, flowered hat. At the door of the church a man offers to take her parcel, and Emily, supposing this to be the custom at this particular church, gives it to him. Later, as the casket is carried out, she sees on top of it, in the company of several small floral pieces, her flowered hat.

The pearl necklace[2]

This "pearl necklace" story has been told at one time or other about every big department store in the country, although most narrators insist angrily that it happened "to their own cousin."

[1] Reprinted from *It's Still Maloney, or Ten Years in the Big City*, by Russell Maloney, p. 44, by permission of The Dial Press, Inc. Copyright 1946 by The Dial Press, Inc.

[2] Reprinted from *Try and Stop Me*, p. 185, by permission of Simon and Schuster, Inc. Copyright, 1944, by Bennett Cerf.

A lady and her daughter are sauntering down Fifth Avenue. In front of Tiffany's the young girl's "pearl necklace" breaks, and the pearls roll all over the street. She reclaims them, and suggests giving them to Tiffany's for stringing.

"We can't ask Tiffany's to restring things like that," protests the mother. "After all, the whole necklace cost only $12.98 at Blank's." Anyhow, they enter Tiffany's. The man at the repair desk takes one look at the loose pearls, asks to be excused for a moment, and returns with the general manager, who offers the startled lady fifty thousand dollars for the lot.

The explanation? The president of Blank's has smuggled in the strand of pearls for his wife by hiding them with a shipment of cheap imitations addressed to the store's bargain jewelry department. The special marking on the real pearls has been lost, and the strand mixed up with all the others. The honest lady brings them back to Blank's just in time to clear the saleswoman, who has been accused by the president of stealing the pearls for her own purposes.

Of course, a story like this *could* have happened in real life. Reasonable odds against it: 4000 to 1.

Don't keep 'em [1]

If it was inconvenient for him to find anything for which a customer asked, Mr. Burchard was not above saying he did not have the article. Almost always, however, the customers turned away were strangers or summer people, for whom he had little use. They were, he thought, ruining the town. Once a summer visitor wanted to buy a cleat of a certain size.

"Haven't got 'em," said Mr. Burchard, shortly.

"Oh, but you must have. All I want is a plain galvanized iron cleat, about so big."

"Nope, don't keep 'em," said Mr. Burchard.

"I'm sure you do," said the visitor.

Mr. Burchard shook his head.

After the visitor was out of sight, Mr. Burchard remarked, "I got 'em all right, but I wouldn't sell 'em to him."

When I first knew of this it seemed to me that there was a perverse quality in Mr. Burchard's attitude; but later, in the light of longer observation and experience, I could see that he was making a gesture of independence, of an independence that meant much to him, and

---

[1] From: *Country Editor*, by Henry Beetle Hough, copyright 1940, reprinted by permission of Doubleday & Company, Inc., pp. 49–50.

694

to me, and to all of us, although we are too blind to see. This was one of the shadows of the old order. After all, why should store-keeping be on a dead level, with cash its only aim and only regulator? Under certain circumstances, purchasing may even be a privilege instead of a favor, and friendship may be as much the life of trade as competition. I would not recommend Mr. Burchard's treatment of customers, but I would recommend his point of view.

The vanishing hotel-room

The story of the vanishing hotel-room has its setting in Paris, but the two leading characters are American, it may very possibly—who knows?—have been invented in America, and certainly it has been told here for many years. Many years?—forty-odd at the very least, for when I first heard it (more than a score of years ago, in Vermont), the narrator definitely dated it at the time of "the" Paris exposition—that is, the exposition of 1900. But it has been told of the exposition of 1925; I must confess to having told it myself of the colonial exposition of 1931.

Two ladies, Americans, speaking little French, arrived one evening in Paris. They were mother and daughter; they had been on a Mediterranean cruise, and came via Marseilles from Cairo (or Constantinople, or Beirut). They were weary, and the elder lady seemed ill. At the hotel (the Continental, the Crillon, a small hotel without a name) her condition became alarming. The anxious daughter saw her installed in a comfortable-appearing room (but the crimson wall-paper was ugly), and having obtained from the hotel clerk a physician's address (no telephone?—we must remember that the story dates back at least to 1900), set out in a cab, for she wished to make a personal appeal, having sensed that the city was crowded and services of all sorts hard to obtain.

The cab was shabby, the horse slow, and the driver stupid; moreover, there seemed to be some confusion about the address—and when it was reached, no one answered the bell. Frantically the young woman besought the driver to find any physician—anyone at all, for much time had been lost.

But now there was further delay. The cabby appeared at a loss, but finally drove to an obviously obscure neighborhood and routed out his "own" doctor. They returned to the hotel.

Here the tale becomes nightmare, for the hotel clerk, asked about the elder lady's condition, appeared baffled, and said:

"But Mademoiselle arrived alone."

Nothing could shake this strange story, and the frightened girl went up to the room; she had kept her key. The doctor trotted along beside her, and when the door was opened, he was forced to hold her up as she cried:

"This is not the room!"

And, indeed, the wallpaper was gray, the furniture, which had been dark, was now white and gold, and the position of bed, table, and fireplace seemed altered. Yet the number on door and key was unchanged. The clerk was summoned, and protested that this was the room the young lady had engaged.

"But my mother! Where is my mother?"

The question was never answered. Nobody in the hotel had ever seen (or so they said) an elder lady. The cab (in later versions, the taxi) that had brought them to the hotel never reappeared. The police, called in, were polite and sought to be helpful. No clue. The girl collapsed; after a long illness she recovered to find the mystery deeper than ever. But she was persistent, and was able finally to establish that her room—was it No. 13?—had been hastily repapered and refurnished, all within a couple of hours. She had been lied to, systematically, at every turn. Her mother was dead and buried—but how, and where?

And at this point the teller allows his listeners to hazard a guess; if they seem obtuse, he is likely to remind them that the ladies had come to Paris from the East—

Of course it was bubonic plague; of course it was discovered while the girl was seeking the doctor; of course the victim was hustled away, since a panic in the exposition-crowded city was unthinkable, and of course the room was redecorated in record time. Everything else depends on the taste and fancy of the narrator, and variations are very numerous. Nowadays the cab is a taxi, and there may even be some telephoning. The hotel moves about Paris. Sometimes there is a strange odor—a mingling of disinfectant and perfume?—in the room when the girl enters it for the second time. Sometimes the secret is unraveled by an American diplomat, sometimes by the girl's suitor; sometimes somebody confesses.

Well, there is the story. The late Alexander Woollcott, who told it [1] much according to traditional lines, had heard that it appeared in the London *Daily Mail* in 1911, and in the *Detroit Free Press* in 1889. Whatever its origin, it is now, in its oral form, a tall tale of America.

---

[1] *While Rome Burns* (New York: Viking Press; 1934).

The vanishing lemon-pie[1]

C hief," I wired, "there definitely *is* a lemon-pie lady. But we positively won't find her. Shall I come in? Or do you want me to make this a career?"

The assignment was ending—just as it began—by shaming me. I don't like being put in the position of one of those movie reporters. You know, the Front Page hokum.

Newspapering is a business with me, not an adventure, so you can figure my feelings when Mr. Kemp handed me this job, phonier than anything you ever read in a book on reporting.

Kemp is the publisher. I hadn't talked to him, except to say "Good evening," or "Good night," twice in my seven years on the Metropolitan. I was certainly flattered when he called me in as his personal choice for a job, but irritated when it turned out to be a lone-wolf, movie-style assignment.

"Bob," he said, "people are pretty fed up with war, war, war. What we need is color. What the text-books call 'human interest.' But on a big scale. Deep and sharp. 'Color' so compelling we can lead with it from time to time, shoving the war out of the headlines."

I just tried to look intelligent and let him get to something I could sink my teeth in. It turned out to be meringue.

"The Lemon-pie Lady is exactly our dish," he said. "You've read all the stories about her, I suppose?"

"Yes," I replied. "The one about the soldiers giving a homeward-bound reporter $8-and -cents to give to an anonymous dame who's supposed to have slapped a juicy pie in the puss of another anonymous dame griping about the war in an anonymous bakery in at least six big cities of the U. S. A."

"I see you don't believe the pie incident happened or the lady exists," Mr. Kemp remarked.

"No, Chief, I don't," I agreed.

"Well, that's too bad," he said slowly. He struck the Big Man in Journalism pose and let me have it: "It's just your hard luck, because you're the man who's going to have to find her!"

I reeled out of his office with instructions to spend what I needed— on the Metropolitan you can spend it but then you have to sue the accounting department to get it back—and bring in the story. I was to start in Kansas City.

---

[1] By George Marion. From *Newspaperman*, January 1946. Mr. Marion writes for the Sunday section of the New York *Mirror*. The newspaper-style paragraphing is retained here.

On my way West, on an upper suitcase in a coach aisle between two sailors and under two Marines with passengers tramping over us all night to get a drink or because they had too many, I made up my mind. But fully.

I dedicated myself to supplying Kemp with the biggest, best-written, juiciest, prize-winningest, phoniest fake any editor ever got. And boy, I said to myself, does he deserve it. Boy, did he ask for it.

But habit is a funny thing. Even when faking, I can't help doing the routine checks. Just to provide local color for my yarn, I toured all the bakeries in Kansas City.

Well, you guessed it. I walked right smack into the bakery where it happened. No mistake, no doubt, no question.

The baker gave me a circumstantial account. The lady on the receiving end was a regular customer of his and confirmed it. At least two other patrons who saw it, corroborated the baker's story.

Mrs. Pie-Face didn't want to talk about it but admitted that her face was the one that launched the lemon-pie. The baker and the two eye-witnesses agreed Pie-Face was moaning about some home-front "hardship", when, without a word of warning, the Lemon-Pie Lady let fly for a bull's eye.

I wrote a good story, if I do say so myself. It was almost as good a yarn as the fake I had planned, though a little harder to believe. Kemp held the story for a couple of days and then found the right break in the news to give him a chance to spill it all over page one. My expense account was okayed without my even seeing my lawyer. It was all just too beautiful.

What was especially "too" about it was that Kemp wanted more, more, more, and there wasn't any more. In desperation, I checked other towns where the same incidents had been reported.

Well, in Salt Lake City I did it again! Or rather, she did it again! I don't blame you. I didn't believe it either. But as you know, the wire services picked up my story in the Metropolitan and checked it down to the bottom crust. The baker backed me up and Mrs. Salt Lake Pie-Face was too funny in the newsreels to be phony.

Now I was in trouble. The whole affair became a national romance. "Find Lemon-Pie Lady," screamed Kemp's wires. Wearily and warily, I hit the meringue trail again.

In three months of war-time railroading, I confirmed the Lady in about one out of every three major cities I struck. But the more I learned, the less I understood. Until one day an idea hit me like a cold shower.

I retraced my route, asking certain questions all the way. When I was through, I sent in my last story. But final. Then I typed out a wire to the Boss.

"Chief," I said, "there definitely *is* a lemon-pie lady. But we positively won't find her.

"I've checked from Kansas City to the Golden Gate, from Seattle to Miami, from New Orleans to St. Paul, from Portland, Maine to Portland, Oregon.

"She's been there and gone—but she never was. She threw lemon-pies aplenty. Lemon cream pies. But she didn't buy them in the bakery where she threw them because they don't make them.

"Nobody makes those pies since Pearl Harbor, Chief. They're not allowed to use the sugar.

"You can see what I'm getting at, Chief. I don't want to make myself eligible for the Fog Island Mental Rest and Nerve Resort, so I won't say what I mean. But we won't find the Lemon-Pie Lady any more than we can find Paul Bunyan.

"Shall I come in, Chief, or do you want my resignation?"

Standard works of reference are not listed.

In addition to the indispensable *Journal of American Folklore* and to the *Southern Folklore Quarterly* (Gainesville, Florida), the following periodicals have been helpful:

American Literature (quarterly, Duke University Press).

Arizona Quarterly (Tucson, Arizona).

The Southwest Review (Dallas, Texas).

The following books contain useful discussions of American narrative art:

BLAIR, WALTER: *Horse Sense in American Humor from Benjamin Franklin to Ogden Nash.* The University of Chicago Press. Chicago, 1942.

——: *Native American Humor.* American Book Co. New York, 1937.

MASTERSON, JAMES R.: *Tall Tales of Arkansaw.* Chapman and Grimes. Boston, 1942.

MEINE, FRANKLIN J.: *Tall Tales of the Southwest, 1830–1860.* Alfred A. Knopf. New York, 1930.

ROURKE, CONSTANCE: *American Humor, a study of the national character.* Harcourt, Brace & Co. New York, 1931.

DORSON, RICHARD M.: "Jonathan Draws the Long Bow," Harvard University Press. Cambridge, 1946.

Stories told by the editor or taken from unpublished sources are not included in the following listing. The titles have been regularized as follows: author (or editor), title of book or periodical, publisher, place, date.

ADAMS, CHARLES FRANCIS: *Three Episodes of Massachusetts History.* Houghton Mifflin. Boston, 1893. Two volumes. Vol. I.

ADAMS, SAMUEL HOPKINS: *A. Woollcott, His Life and His World.* Reynal & Hitchcock. New York, 1945.

ALEXANDER, T. H.: in the *Reader's Digest,* December 1937, condensed from the *Saturday Evening Post* for October 23, 1937.

ALLEN, ETHAN: *A Narrative of Col. Ethan Allen's Captivity* (etc.). Thomas and Thomas. Walpole, New Hampshire, 1807.

ALLEN, JOSEPH CHASE: in the *Vineyard Gazette,* November 9, 1945, January 12, 1945.

——: in *The Narrow Land,* by Elizabeth Reynard.

ALLOUEZ, PÈRE CLAUDE: *Early Narratives of the Northwest, 1634–1689.* Louise Phelps Kellogg, editor. Charles Scribner's Sons. New York, 1917.

ANON.: in *Harper's New Monthly Magazine,* Vol. XI, June to November 1855 (October issue).

ANON.: *Life of General Marion.* Lindsay & Blackiston. Philadelphia, 1847.

ANON.: in *Time*, December 25, 1944.

ANON. (Mate of ship *Niagara*): in *There Goes Flukes*. W. H. Tripp, editor. Reynolds Printing. New Bedford.

ANTHONY, IRVIN: *Revolt at Sea*. Putnam's. New York, 1937.

ASWELL, JAMES R.: *God Bless the Devil*. Tennessee Writers Project. University of North Carolina Press. Chapel Hill, 1940.

AUDUBON, JOHN JAMES: *Ornithological Biography*, Vol. I. Judah Dobson, Philadelphia, 1831.

AUSTIN, WILLIAM: *A Book of New England Legends* by Samuel Adams Drake. Roberts Brothers. Boston, 1884.

BACON, EDWIN M.: *Historical Pilgrimages in New England*. Silver, Burdett & Company. New York, Boston, Chicago, 1898.

BAGBY, GEORGE WILLIAM: *Golden Tales of the Old South*. Selected, with an introduction, by May Lamberton Becker. Dodd, Mead & Company. New York, 1934.

BARBER, JOHN WARNER: *Connecticut Historical Collections*. New Haven, 1836. P. 432.

——: *Historical Collections: Massachusetts*. Dorr, Howland & Co. Worcester, 1839.

——: *The History and Antiquities of New England, New York, New Jersey, and Pennsylvania*. William C. Lord. Portland, 1848.

BARNARD, JOHN: *Ashton's Memorial: or an authentick account of the strange adventures and signal deliverances of Mr. Philip Ashton* . . . Richard Ford and Samuel Chandler. London, 1726.

BARTRAM, WILLIAM: *The Travels of William Bartram*. Philadelphia, 1791. Macy-Masius, New York, 1928.

BECK, HENRY CHARLTON: *Jersey Genesis: the story of the Mullica River*. Rutgers University Press. New Brunswick, 1945.

BECKER, MAY LAMBERTON: *Golden Tales of the Old South*, selected, with an introduction, by May Lam-

berton Becker. Dodd, Mead & Company. New York, 1934.

BELL, MAJOR HORACE: *On the Old West Coast*. William Morrow & Co. New York, 1930.

BENÉT, STEPHEN VINCENT: *Thirteen O'clock*. Farrar & Rinehart. New York, Toronto, 1937.

BENTON, JESSE JAMES: *Cow by the Tail*. Houghton Mifflin Company. Boston, 1943.

BENTON, THOMAS HART: *An Artist in America*. Robert M. McBride & Co. New York, 1937.

BERRY, ROBERT ELTON: *Yankee Stargazer, the life of Nathaniel Bowditch*. Whittlesey House. McGraw-Hill Book Co. New York, 1941.

BICKEL, KARL A.: *The Mangrove Coast*. Coward-McCann. New York, 1942.

BLAIR, WALTER: *Tall Tale America*. Coward-McCann. New York, 1944.

——: *Native American Humor*. American Book Company. Boston, 1937.

BOATRIGHT, MODY C.: *Tall Tales from Texas*. The Southwest Press. Dallas, 1934.

BOTKIN, B. A.: *A Treasury of American Folklore*. Crown Publishers. New York, 1944.

BOYER, RICHARD O.: in the *New Yorker*, June 18, 1938.

BRYAN, GEORGE S.: *Mystery Ship*. J. B. Lippincott Co. Philadelphia, New York, 1942. Abstracted by G. S. Bryan from the *Strand Magazine*, July 1913.

BURNETT, WHIT, editor: *Two Bottles of Relish*. Dial Press. New York, 1943.

BURNS, WALTER NOBLE: *Tombstone*. Doubleday, Page & Co. Garden City, N. Y., 1927.

BYRD, WILLIAM: *A Journey to the Land of Eden and other papers*. 1841. Macy-Masius, The Vanguard Press, New York, 1928.

CALMER, EDGAR: in *Story*. Vol. IV, No 19, February 1934.

CARMER, CARL: *The Hudson*. Farrar & Rinehart. New York, 1939.

CAPE CODDER, A: *Traits of American Humour*, edited and adapted by the author of *Sam Slick, The Old Judge*,

The English in America, etc. (i.e., Thomas C. Haliburton). In three volumes. Colburn & Co. London, 1852. (See also HALIBURTON.)

CARVER, JONATHAN: *Captain Jonathan Carver's Narrative of his capture and subsequent escape from the Indians at the bloody massacre committed by them when Fort William Henry fell into the hands of the French under Gen. Montcalm in the year 1757.* Written by himself. Reprinted by S. G. Drake: *Tragedies of the Wilderness.* Boston, 1846.

CAWLEY, TOM: in *Newspaperman.* Hyde Park, Mass. July 1944.

CERF, BENNETT: *Try and Stop Me.* Simon & Schuster. New York, 1944.

(CHAMBERLAYNE, RICHARD): *Lithobolia or the stone-throwing devil,* etc. by R. C. esq. London, 1698.

CHAMBERS, E. P.: in the *Vineyard Gazette.* December 1, 1944.

CHASE, RICHARD: *The Jack Tales. Folk Tales from the Southern Appalachians,* collected and re-told by Richard Chase. Houghton Mifflin. Boston, 1943.

CLARKE, IDA CLYDE: *Men Who Wouldn't Stay Dead.* Bernard Ackerman. New York, 1945.

COFFIN, ROLAND F.: *An Old Sailor's Yarns.* (*Note:* I have not been able to see a copy of *An Old Sailor's Yarns.* I give the story as quoted in *The Story of the New England Whalers,* by John R. Spears.)

COOLIDGE, DANE: *Old California Cowboys.* E. P. Dutton & Co. New York, 1939.

CRANE, CHARLES EDWARD: *Winter in Vermont.* Alfred A. Knopf. New York, 1941.

CROCKETT, DAVID: *The Adventures of Davy Crockett,* told mostly by himself (a reprint of *The Autobiography of David Crockett,* 1834) Charles Scribner's Sons. New York, 1934.

——: *Colonel Crockett's Exploits and Adventures in Texas.* T. K. and P. G. Collins. Philadelphia, 1837.

CRONYN, GEORGE: in *Two Bottles of Relish,* edited by Whit Burnett. Dial Press. New York, 1943.

CULLEN, MOLLIE: in *Newspaperman.* July 1944.

CUTTING, EDITH E.: *Lore of an Adirondack County.* Cornell University Press. Ithaca, New York, 1944.

D., H. L.: *The Rocky Mountain Herald.* May 12, 1945. (i.e., H. L. Davis).

DANE, G. EZRA, in collaboration with BEATRICE J. DANE: *Ghost Town.* Alfred A. Knopf. New York, 1941.

DAVIDSON, SGT. BULL, editor: *Tall Tales They Tell in the Services.* Thomas Y. Crowell Co. New York, 1943.

DEVOTO, BERNARD, editor: *Mark Twain in Eruption.* Harper & Brothers. New York, 1940.

DICK, EVERETT: from *The Sod-House Frontier,* condensed in the *Reader's Digest,* November 1937.

DOBIE, J. FRANK: in *Tall Tales from Texas,* by Mody C. Boatright.

——: *In the Shadow of History.* Texas Folk-lore Society Publications, No. XV. Austin, 1939.

DORSON, RICHARD M.: in *Southern Folklore Quarterly.* June 1944 and December 1944.

DUNTON, JOHN: *Letters Written from New England A.D. 1686.* Prince Society. Boston, 1867.

DURIVAGE, FRANCIS A., and BURNHAM, GEORGE P.: *Stray Subjects Arrested and Bound Over.* Carey and Hart. Philadelphia, 1848.

DUVAL, JOHN C.: in *Southwest Review.* Vol. XXIV.

EARLY, ELEANOR: *An Island Patchwork.* Houghton Mifflin Co. Boston, 1941.

ESPINOSA, AURELIO M.: in *Journal of American Folklore.* January-March 1943.

FENNO, FRANK H.: *The Science and Art of Elocution.* John E. Potter & Co. Philadelphia, 1878.

FISHER, VARDIS: in *Idaho Lore.* Federal Writers' Project. The Caxton Printers. Caldwell, Idaho, 1939.

FLINT, TIMOTHY: *Recollections of the Last Ten Years.* Cummings, Hilliard & Co. Boston, 1826.

GARDNER, EMELYN ELIZABETH: *Folklore from the Schoharie Hills, New York.* University of Michigan Press. Ann Arbor, 1937.

GAUVREAU, EMILE: *My Last Million Readers.* E. P. Dutton & Co. New York, 1941.

Ghost Town News. Buena Park, California. December 1943.

GOULD, JOHN: *Farmer Takes a Wife.* William Morrow & Co. New York, 1945.

GRAHAM, FREDERICK: in the *New York Times.* May 17, 1945.

GYLES, JOHN: *Memoirs of Odd Adventures, Strange Deliverances, etc., etc., in the Captivity of John Gyles Esq., Commander of the Garrison on St. George's River.* Written by himself. Boston in New England. Printed and Sold by S. Kneeland and T. Green in Queen-street, over against the Prison. MDCCXXXVI.

HADFIELD, ROBERT L.: *Mutiny at Sea.* E. P. Dutton & Co. New York, 1938.

HALIBURTON, THOMAS C.: *The Attaché, or Sam Slick in England.* Stringer and Townsend. New York, 1856.

——: *Traits of American Humour.* London, 1852.

HALPERT, HERBERT: in *Southern Folklore Quarterly,* June 1944.

HARRIS, JOEL CHANDLER: *Uncle Remus, His Songs and His Sayings.* D. Appleton & Co. New York, 1888.

HATCHER, HARLAN: *The Buckeye Country.* H. C. Kinsey & Co. New York, 1940.

HAZARD, THOMAS ROBINSON: *The Jonny-Cake Papers of "Shepherd Tom," together with reminiscences of Narragansett schools of former days.* D. B. Updike, The Merrymount Press. Boston, printed for the subscribers, 1915.

HERSEY, JOHN: in the *New Yorker,* June 17, 1944.

HOLBROOK, STEWART H.: *Ethan Allen.* The Macmillan Co. New York, 1940.

——: "The Wildest Man of the West," in *American* Mercury, December 1943.

——: *Murder Out Yonder.* The Macmillan Co. New York, 1944.

HOUGH, HENRY BEETLE: *Country Editor.* Doubleday, Doran & Co. New York, 1940.

HURSTON, ZORA NEALE: *Mules and Men.* J. B. Lippincott Co. Philadelphia, 1935.

HENDRICKS, W. C., editor: *Bundle of Troubles, and Other Tarheel Tales.* Duke University Press. Durham, North Carolina, 1943.

INGERSOLL, RALPH: *The Battle is the Pay-off.* Harcourt, Brace and Co., Inc., 1943.

IRVING, PIERRE M.: *Life and Letters of Washington Irving.* G. P. Putnam and Son. New York, 1867.

IRVING, WASHINGTON: *The Sketchbook of Geoffrey Crayon, Gent.* G. P. Putnam & Son. New York, 1868.

JOHNSON, CAPTAIN EDWARD: *Wonder-working Providence of Sion's Savior in New England.* London, 1654. Reprinted, edited by J. F. Jameson; Charles Scribner's Sons, New York, 1910.

JOHNSON, ROBERT UNDERWOOD: *Remembered Yesterdays.* Little, Brown & Co. Boston, 1923.

JONES, LEALON N. (editor): *Eve's Stepchildren.* The Caxton Printers. Caldwell, Idaho, 1942.

JONES, N. E.: *The Squirrel Hunters of Ohio or Glimpses of Pioneer Life.* The Robert Clarke Co. Cincinnati, 1898.

KANE, HARNETT T.: *Deep Delta Country.* Duell, Sloan & Pearce. New York, 1944.

KELLY, JOHN: *Of the Captivity of Frances Noble who was, among others, taken by the Indians from Swan Island in Maine, about the year 1755.* Compiled by John Kelly Esq. of Concord New Hampshire, from the Minutes and Memoranda of Phinehas Merrill, Esq. of Stratham, in the same state; and by the former Gentleman communicated for publication to the Editors of the *Historical Collections of N. H.* Reprinted by S. G. Drake: *Tragedies of the Wilderness.* Boston, 1846.

KELSEY, D. M.: *Our Pioneer Heroes*

and Their Daring Deeds. Scammell & Co. Philadelphia, St. Louis, 1885.

KENNEDY, STETSON: *Palmetto Country.* Duell, Sloan & Pearce. New York, 1942.

KERMAN, KEITH: in *Eve's Stepchildren.* Selected and edited by Lealon N. Jones. The Caxton Printers. Caldwell, Idaho, 1942.

LAUGHEAD, W. B.: *Paul Bunyan.* Red River Lumber Co. Westwood, California, 1940.

LEHR, ELIZABETH DREXEL: *"King Lehr" and the Gilded Age.* J. B. Lippincott Co. Philadelphia, 1935.

LOMAX, JOHN A.: in *Southwest Review,* Vol. XXIX.

LOVERIDGE, G. Y.: the *Providence Sunday Journal,* April 2, 1944.

MALONEY, RUSSELL: *It's Still Maloney.* Dial Press. New York, 1945.

MARION, GEORGE: in *Newspaperman,* January 1946.

MARKEY, MORRIS, and BULL, JOHN: *That's New York.* Macy-Masius. New York, 1927.

MASTERSON, JAMES R.: *Tall Tales of Arkansaw.* Chapman & Grimes. Boston, 1942.

MATHER, COTTON: *Magnalia Christi Americana.* Vol. I. Silas Andrus & Son. Hartford, 1855 (copyright 1852).

——: *Magnalia Christi Americana, or the Ecclesiastical History of New England.* Vol. II. Silas Andrus & Son. Hartford, 1853.

——: *The Wonders of the Invisible World, being an account of the tryals of several witches lately executed in New England.* John Russell Smith. London, 1862.

MATHER, INCREASE: *A Brief History of the War with the Indians.* London, 1676. Quoted from G. L. KITTREDGE: *The Old Farmer and His Almanack.* W. Wace & Co. Boston, 1904.

——: *Remarkable Providences.* 1684. John Russell Smith. London, 1856. Reprinted, London, 1890.

MENCKEN, H. L.: *Heathen Days.* Alfred A. Knopf. New York, 1943.

MERSHAM, WILLIAM B.: in *Field and Stream,* April 1926.

MOODY, W. R.: *Noted Witnesses for Psychic Occurrences.* Boston Society for Psychic Research. Boston, 1928. Compiled by the Research Officer of the Society.

MORISON, SAMUEL ELIOT: *Harvard College in the Seventeenth Century.* Harvard University Press. Cambridge, 1936.

MURDOCK, KENNETH B.: "William Hubbard and the Providential Interpretation of History." In *Proceedings of the American Antiquarian Society,* Vol. LII.

NEVINS, ALLAN: *The Gateway to History.* D. Appleton-Century Co. New York, 1938.

NEWELL, WILLIAM WELLS: in the *Journal of American Folk-Lore,* Vol. V. Published for the American Folk-Lore Society by Houghton Mifflin Co. Boston, 1892.

OLSEN, J. E. and BOURNE, E. G., editors: *The Northmen, Columbus and Cabot. Original Narratives of Early American History.* Charles Scribner's Sons. New York, 1906.

P., C. A.: in *Ring-tailed Roarers. Tall Tales of the American frontier, 1830–1860.* Edited, with an introduction, by V. O. Chittick. The Caxton Printers. Caldwell, Idaho, 1941.

PELL, JOHN: *Ethan Allen.* Houghton Mifflin Co. Boston, 1929.

PERRY, CLAY: *Underground New England.* Stephen Daye Press. Brattleboro, 1939.

PETERS, REV. SAMUEL: *General History of Connecticut.* London, 1871. Reprinted, D. Appleton & Co. New York, 1877.

PLENN, J. H.: *Saddle in the Sky.* Bobbs-Merrill Co. Indianapolis, 1940.

PORTER, WILLIAM T.: in *Spirit of the Times,* October 21, 1848, February 26, 1848, April 22, 1848, March 22, 1851, August 5, 1846, June 10, 1848, March 4, 1848, April 22, 1848, April 29, 1848.

RANDOLPH, VANCE: *Ozark Mountain Folks*. The Vanguard Press. New York, 1932.

RATCHFORD, FANNIE E.: in *Coyote Wisdom*. *Texas Folk-lore Publications*, No. XLV. Austin Texas Folk-Lore Society. Austin, 1938.

REICHENBACH, HARRY, as told to FREEDMAN, DAVID: *Phantom Fame*. Simon & Schuster. New York, 1931.

ROBINSON, ROWLAND E.: *Uncle Lisha's Shop*. Forest and Stream Publishing Co. New York, 1887.

ROGERS, STANLEY: *Ships and Sailors*. Little, Brown & Co. Boston, 1928.

ROURKE, CONSTANCE: *American Humor*. Harcourt, Brace & Co. New York, 1931.

RUSSELL, CHARLES EDWARD: *From Sandy Hook to 62°*. The Century Co. New York, 1929.

SANDBURG, CARL: *The People, Yes*. Harcourt, Brace & Co. New York, 1936.

S., W. T. (SCOTT, WINFIELD T.): in "In Perspective," the *Providence Journal*, September 9, 1941.

SKINNER, CHARLES M.: *Myths and Legends of Our Own Land*. Vol. II. J. B. Lippincott Co. Philadelphia, London, 1896.

SMITH, CAPTAIN JOHN: *Generall Historie*.

——: *The General Historie of Virginia, New England and the Summer Isles*. London, 1624. Reprinted, Glasgow, J.: MacLehose & Sons, 1907.

SNOW, EDWARD ROWE: *Pirates and Buccaneers of the Atlantic Coast*. Yankee Publishing Co. Boston [1944].

SONNICHSEN, C. L.: *Roy Bean. Law West of the Pecos*. The Macmillan Co. New York, 1943.

SPEARS, JOHN R.: *The Story of the New England Whalers*. The Macmillan Co. New York, 1908.

SPERRY, WILLIAM L.: *Summer Yesterdays in Maine*. Harper & Brothers. New York, London, 1941.

STEVENS, JAMES: *Paul Bunyan*. Alfred A. Knopf. New York, 1925.

STOCKTON, FRANK R.: *A Story-teller's Pack*. Charles Scribner's Sons. New York, 1897.

TEALE, EDWIN WAY: *Dune Boy, the early years of a naturalist*. Dodd, Mead & Co. New York, 1943.

THOMAS, LOWELL: *Tall Stories*. Funk & Wagnalls Co. New York, 1931.

THOMPSON, HAROLD W.: *Body, Boots & Britches*. J. B. Lippincott Co. Philadelphia, 1940.

THOMPSON, MORTON: *Joe, the Wounded Tennis Player*. Doubleday, Doran & Co. Garden City, N. Y., 1945.

THURBER, JAMES: in the *Saturday Evening Post*, April 5, 1941.

TRAIN, ARTHUR: *Puritan's Progress*. Charles Scribner's Sons. New York, 1931.

TWAIN, MARK: *How to Tell a Story, and Other Essays*. Author's National Edition. Harper & Brothers. New York, 1899.

——: *A Tramp Abroad*. Author's National Edition. Harper & Brothers. New York, 1907.

VESTAL, STANLEY: *Short Grass Country*. Duell, Sloan & Pearce. New York, 1941.

VORSE, MARY HEATON: *Time and the Town*. The Dial Press. New York, 1942.

WASHINGTON, GEORGE: *Writings of George Washington*. Bicentennial Commission Edition. U. S. Government Printing Office. Washington, 1937.

WASSON, GEORGE S.: *Captain Simeon's Store*. Houghton Mifflin Co. Boston, 1903.

WEYGANDT, CORNELIUS: *New Hampshire Neighbors*. Henry Holt & Co. New York, 1937.

WHALON, MARK: *Rural Free Delivery, recollections of a rural mailman*. Stephen Daye Press. Brattleboro, 1942.

WHITE, WILLIAM C.: "Pecos Bill and the Willful Coyote," in *Two Bottles of Relish*, edited by Whit Burnett. Dial Press. New York, 1943.

WILDES, HARRY EMERSON: *The Delaware*. Farrar & Rinehart. New York, 1940.

WISTER, OWEN: *The Virginian*. The Macmillan Co. New York, 1902.

Bibliography

——: *Red Men and White.* Harper & Brothers. New York, 1895.

WITHERSPOON, HALLIDAY (WILL NUTTER) : *Liverpool Jarge.* Square Rigger Co. Boston, 1933.

WOOLLCOTT, ALEXANDER: in the *New Yorker*, March 15, 1930.

WPA (Workers of the Writers' Program of the WPA in the State of Montana), WILLIAM A. BURKE, editor: *Copper Camp.* Hastings House. New York, 1943.

ZINSSER, HANS: *As I Remember Him, the biography of R. S.* Little, Brown & Co. Boston, 1940.

A NOTE ON THE TYPE

The text of this book has been set on the Linotype in a type-face called "Baskerville." The face is a facsimile reproduction of type cast from molds made for John Baskerville *(1706–1775) from his designs. The punches for the revived Linotype Baskerville were cut under the supervision of the English printer George W. Jones.*

John Baskerville's original face was one of the forerunners of the type-style known as "modern face" to printers: a "modern" of the period A.D. *1800.*

The typographic scheme and the binding design are by Warren Chappell, *who also drew the decorative illustrations that appear on the title and book-title pages. The book was set up in type, printed, and bound by* Kingsport Press, Inc., *Kingsport, Tenn.*

A NOTE ON THE TYPE

The text of this book has been set on the Linotype in a type face called "Baskerville." The face is an intimate reproduction of type first from molds made for John Baskerville (1706-1775) from his designs. The punches for the revised Linotype Baskerville were cut under the supervision of the English printer George W. Jones.

John Baskerville's original face was one of the forerunners of the type to be known as "modern face" to printers a "modern" of the hundred years.

The typography, book and the binding design are by Warren Chappell, and also here the decorative illustrations that appear on the title and back title pages. The book was set up in type, printed, and bound by Kingsport Press, Inc., Kingsport, Tenn.